SAFER SHIPS, CLEANER SEAS

REPORT OF LORD DONALDSON'S INQUIRY INTO THE PREVENTION OF POLLUTION FROM MERCHANT SHIPPING

Presented to Parliament by the Secretary of State for Transport
by Command of Her Majesty
May 1994

Cm 2560   LONDON: HMSO   £38 net

LORD DONALDSON'S INQUIRY

Chairman: The Rt Hon The Lord Donaldson of Lymington

Room 018
Lambeth Bridge House
LONDON SE1 7SB

8 April 1994

The Rt Hon John MacGregor OBE MP
Secretary of State for Transport
2 Marsham Street
London SW1P 3EB

Dear Secretary of State,

In January 1993 you appointed me Chairman of an Inquiry

"To advise on whether any further measures are appropriate and feasible to protect the United Kingdom coastline from pollution from merchant shipping. Due consideration should be given to the international and economic implications of any new measures."

You also appointed Mr John Rendle CBE and Professor Alasdair McIntyre as assessors.

Although the term "assessors" is no doubt appropriate in the light of the outstanding technical expertise which Mr Rendle and Professor McIntyre respectively brought to bear on the subject matter of the Inquiry, I should like to make it abundantly clear that we all played an equal part in our deliberations and that the Report which I attach hereto is the Report of all three of us. The term "Donaldson Inquiry" was used solely in the interests of brevity.

In making our recommendations we have not only sought to give due consideration to the international and economic implications of any new measures, but have borne in mind the constraints on public expenditure which exist at the present time and may be expected to continue for some time to come.

No Inquiry of this nature and scope could be undertaken without high quality supporting staff. May I express my gratitude and that of Mr Rendle and Professor McIntyre to you for having seconded so special a team which, under the leadership of Angela Moss, has displayed such skill, dedication and enthusiasm for the task. Whilst the responsibility for the Report is ours alone, the contribution of the team has been invaluable.

Yours Sincerely,

DONALDSON OF LYMINGTON

To advise on whether any further measures are appropriate and feasible to protect the UK coastline from pollution from merchant shipping. Due consideration should be given to the international and economic implications of any new measures.

CONTENTS

CHAPTER 3

CHAPTER 4

CHAPTER 5

CHAPTER 6

CHAPTER 7

SHIP DESIGN, CONSTRUCTION, MAINTENANCE, EQUIPMENT AND
RELIABILITY   69

CHAPTER 8

SHIP OPERATION AND CREWING   91

CHAPTER 9

CHAPTER 10

CHAPTER 11

CHAPTER 14

(All diagrams prepared by the Hydrographer of the Navy)

CHAPTER 15

CHAPTER 16

CHAPTER 20

DEALING WITH EMERGENCIES – EMERGENCY TOWING AND SALVAGE

CHAPTER 21

CHAPTER 22

CHAPTER 23

PRINCIPAL CONCLUSIONS AND RECOMMENDATIONS   363

COLOUR PLATES

ABBREVIATIONS AND ACRONYMS

AAIB	Air Accidents Investigation Branch
ACTRAM	Advisory Committee on the Transport of Radioactive Materials
ADS Pack	Aerial Dispersant Spraying Package
AMSA	Australian Maritime Safety Authority
ATBA	Area To Be Avoided
BP	British Petroleum Company plc
BT	British Telecommunications plc
C130	Hercules aircraft
CAA	Civil Aviation Authority
CAAM	Centre Administratif des Affaires Maritimes
CHA	Competent Harbour Authority
CHIRP	Confidential Human-factors Incident Reporting Scheme
CIF	Cost, Insurance and Freight (contract)
CNIS	Channel Navigation Information Service
COASTGUARD	The Coastguard Agency
COW	crude oil washing
CRISTAL	Contract Regarding a Supplement to Tanker Liability for Oil Pollution
DANI	Department of Agriculture for Northern Ireland
DC3	Dakota aircraft
DGPS	Differential Global Positioning System
DMEO	Director of Marine Emergency Operations
DoENI	Department of the Environment for Northern Ireland
DSC	Digital Selective Calling
DWR	Deep Water Route
dwt	deadweight tonnage
EC	European Community
ECDIS	Electronic Chart Display and Information System
EEA	European Economic Area
EEZ	Exclusive Economic Zone
EPIRB	Emergency Position-Indicating RadioBeacon
ESGOSS	Ecological Steering Group on the Oil Spill in Shetland
EURET	European Research on Transport
EUROREP	European Reporting (Zone)
FOBAS	Lloyd's Register Fuel Oil Bunker Analysis and Advisory Service
FSA	Formal Safety Assessment
GAFT	Government Assistance For Training
GESAMP	Group of Experts on Scientific Aspects of Marine Pollution
GLA	General Lighthouse Authority
GMDSS	Global Maritime Distress and Safety System
GPS	Global Positioning System
grt	gross registered tonnage
HMCG	Her Majesty's Coastguard
HNS	Hazardous or noxious substances
HTS	High tensile steel
IACS	International Association of Classification Societies
IAEA	International Atomic Energy Agency

IAPH	International Association of Ports and Harbours
IBC Code	International Code for the Construction and Equipment of Ships carrying Dangerous Chemicals in Bulk
ICS	International Chamber of Shipping
IEC	International Electrotechnical Commission
IGC Code	International Code for the Construction and Equipment of Ships carrying Liquified Gases in Bulk
ILO	International Labour Organisation
ILU	Institute of London Underwriters
IMDG	International Maritime Dangerous Goods (Code)
IMM	Intermediate Ministerial Meeting
IMO	International Maritime Organization
INLS	International Pollution Prevention Certificate for the Carriage of Noxious Liquid Substances in Bulk
INTERTANKO	International Association of Independent Tanker Owners
IOPC	International Oil Pollution Compensation (Fund)
IOPP	International Oil Pollution Prevention (Certificate)
ISM	International Management Code for the Safe Operation of Ships and for Pollution Prevention
ISU	International Salvage Union
ITF	International Transport Workers Federation
ITOPF	International Tanker Owners Pollution Federation Ltd
ITZ	Inshore Traffic Zone
JRC	Joint Response Centre
LNG	Liquified natural gas
LOF	Lloyd's Open Form
LPG	Liquified petroleum gas
MAFF	Ministry of Agriculture, Fisheries and Food
MAIB	Marine Accidents Investigation Branch
MAREP	Marine reporting
MARPOL	International Convention for the Prevention of Pollution from Ships
MARS	International Marine Accident Reporting Scheme
MEHRA	Marine Environmental High Risk Area
MEO	Marine Emergencies Organisation
MEPC	Marine Environment Protection Committee (of IMO)
MMSI	Maritime Mobile Service Identity
MOR	Mandatory Occurrence Reporting (Scheme)
MOT	Ministry of Transport
MOU	(Paris) Memorandum of Understanding
MPCU	Marine Pollution Control Unit
MRCC	Marine Rescue Control Centre
MRSC	Marine Rescue Sub Centre
MSA	Marine Safety Agency
NRA	National Rivers Authority
NRPB	National Radiological Protection Board
NSC	North Sea Conference
NUMAST	National Union of Marine, Aviation and Shipping Transport Officers
NVQ/SVQ	National Vocational Qualification/Scottish Vocational Qualification

OCIMF	Oil Companies International Marine Forum
OECD	Organisation for Economic Cooperation and Development
OMBO	One Man Bridge Operation
OPA 90	United States Oil Pollution Act 1990
OPRC	International Convention on Oil Pollution Preparedness, Response and Cooperation
OSPAR	Convention for the Protection of the Marine Environment of the North East Atlantic
P & I Club	Protection and Indemnity Association
ppm	Parts per million
PCB	Polychlorinated biphenyl
QSCS	Quality System Certification Scheme
RNLI	Royal National Lifeboat Institution
RSPB	Royal Society for the Protection of Birds
RSS	Register of Shipping and Seamen
RYA	Royal Yachting Association
SAR	Search and rescue
SASEMA	Sociedad Estatal de Salvamento y Seguridad Marítima
SBT	Segregated Ballast Tanker
SDR	Special Drawing Rights
SGO	Surveyor General's Organisation
SI	Statutory Instrument
SIAS	Ship Inspections And Survey
SIRE	Ship Inspection Report Exchange
SIRENAC	Système d'Information Relatif aux Navires Contrôlés
SOAFD	Scottish Office Agriculture and Fisheries Department
SOLAS	International Convention for the Safety of Life at Sea
SOTNAV	Guidelines on Safer Oil Tanker Navigation
STCW	International Convention on Standards of Training, Certification and Watchkeeping for Seafarers
TBT	Tributyl tin
THORP	Thermal oxide reprocessing plant (at Sellafield)
TOVALOP	Tanker Owners Voluntary Agreement concerning Liability for Oil Pollution
TSS	Traffic Separation Scheme
UKAEA	United Kingdom Atomic Energy Authority
UNCLOS	United Nations Convention on the Law of the Sea
VLCC	Very Large Crude Carrier
VTS	Vessel Traffic Service
WSL	Warren Spring Laboratory

Overview

1   The task of the Inquiry has been to identify what more can reasonably be done to protect the UK coastline from pollution from merchant shipping. Our conclusion is that, whilst much is already being done, there is a pressing need for the United Kingdom to take new initiatives internationally, regionally and nationally.

2   The pollution we are concerned with can take many forms, but all involve the escape from ships of substances which should not be in the sea or on our shores. They may be oil, they may be hazardous or noxious substances, such as chemicals or explosives, they may be garbage, they may be micro organisms carried in ballast water or they may take other less familiar forms.

3   The escape may occur as a result of the deliberate action of ships' crews or it may be accidental. Some discharges of polluting material are permitted under conditions prescribed by internationally agreed regulations. These regulations are continually revised and tightened, but we have encountered at least one case in which they are clearly inadequate, namely, the apparently legal discharge of an additive for lubricating oil which killed hundreds of seabirds (paragraph 9.30). Illegal discharges are also a major problem. However they are widely spread, and in any particular area the greatest problem is likely to be that of an accidental discharge.

4   Why does this happen? High standards of ship design, maintenance and operation, which would reduce pollution to largely acceptable levels, cost money. This is a reason, not an excuse. The shipping industry worldwide is fiercely competitive. It has to be, because there is vast overcapacity. This produces low or negative profit margins and a strong temptation to cut corners, resisted to their credit by some, but far too few, shipowners. In one way or another we have to make it unprofitable to cut corners.

5   The root cause of virtually all the pollution with which we are concerned is human failing. This is not to say that it will always be the immediate cause. Disaster may overtake the finest of crews, if there are defects in the design of their ship. On the other hand the finest ship can be wrecked by a negligent crew. It is always idle to seek to change human nature. The answer to the problem lies in working with it and seeking to provide incentives and encouragement for the adoption of the highest standards at every level, coupled with disincentives, including harsh sanctions for those who persistently ignore their responsibilities towards the environment.

6   Maritime transport, like aerial transport, is essentially international in character. The United Kingdom is as much threatened by passing traffic as by ships destined for our ports. The threat is all the greater because our islands have a coastline which is the third

longest[1], and at least as vulnerable as any other, in Europe. The measures which we recommend therefore need, in the main, to be adopted in cooperation with our regional neighbours and preferably on a worldwide basis. The primary role of the United Kingdom Government must be to take the lead, but there are some measures which can and should be taken, if necessary, unilaterally.

7   Primary responsibility for the safety and operation of ships lies with the States whose flags they fly and with the classification societies which they sometimes employ. If these responsibilities were effectively discharged by all States and classification societies, the problem of maritime pollution would be substantially reduced. Unfortunately they are not. This difficulty is high on the agenda of the International Maritime Organization (IMO).

8   Ideally Flag States which failed to live up to their internationally agreed obligations would face severe sanctions, including withdrawal of recognition of their authority. The consequence of this would be that ships would have to reflag with more responsible States. This may come and we recommend in Chapter 6 that the United Kingdom Government gives strong support to any measure designed to improve Flag State Control. However we should deceive ourselves if we imagined that any major improvement will occur in the short or even medium term and cooperative self-defence by Port and Coastal States in our region is the only practicable alternative. Although the tonnage of UK registered merchant ships is now only 1.35 per cent of the world total, the United Kingdom is one of the major Port and Coastal States in terms of the tonnage of shipping calling at and passing our ports. As such it must bear a heavy responsibility for exercising leadership in this endeavour.

9   We already have in place, under the Paris Memorandum of Understanding (Paris MOU), a cooperative regional system whereby, on average, one in four ships calling at North West European ports are inspected with a view to confirming that they comply with internationally agreed standards of design, maintenance and operation. Notwithstanding the very considerable obstacles to effective inspection imposed by international Conventions which give *prima facie* credence to Flag State certificates of compliance and by the need to avoid undue interference with commercial operations, the gravity of the threat to our coastline from substandard ships and operators is clear. In 1992 nearly half the 15,000 inspections undertaken revealed deficiencies which should not have existed and in nearly 600 cases the deficiencies constituted so great a threat to the safety of the ship's crews, other vessels and the environment, that the ships had to be detained until they had been repaired. If instead of ships the inspections had been of aircraft, there would have been a public outcry. The situation should be no more acceptable in the maritime field.

10   In Chapter 11 we examine this system and make recommendations designed to build upon and improve it. At present the inspections constitute the maritime equivalent of

---

[1] Norway 16,093 km: Greece 13,676 km: United Kingdom 12,429 km. The next longest are Turkey 7,200 km and Spain 4,964 km. Source: *Mangon's Marine Almanac* (Taylor and Frances) 1991 ISBN 0 8448 1674 4.

roadside checks of heavy goods vehicles, albeit targeted at certain categories of vessels which have been shown to be more likely to be substandard than others or where the consequences of any deficiency are likely to be particularly serious. The essence of our proposals is that these inspections should take on more the character of the Ministry of Transport (MOT) Test enforced for vehicles registered in the United Kingdom. No doubt similar tests apply in other European countries.

11   Consistent with this, ships would be required to target themselves for inspection. Those visiting Paris MOU ports for the first time and thereafter at least annually (more frequently in the case of tankers) would be required to give advance notice of their arrival in order that an inspection might be arranged. If significant deficiencies were found, they would be required to target themselves for inspection at the next Paris MOU port which they visited. If deficiencies were such that vessels had to be detained they would be required to target themselves for inspection at every Paris MOU port which they visited for the next 12 months.

12   At present an irresponsible shipowner may well take the view that his economic interests are best served by ignoring safety standards and taking the chance that his ship will not be inspected and (which does not necessarily follow) that if inspected the deficiencies will not be detected. Self-targeting will not only increase these chances, but bring them sharply to his attention. Our recommendations include a provision for severe sanctions for substandard ships involving obligatory delays before they are allowed to load or discharge or even a denial of that right. Furthermore in recognition of the facts that, regardless of the effectiveness or ineffectiveness of Flag State controls, shipowners and managers have a primary responsibility for safety at sea, and that they are unlikely to neglect only one ship in a fleet, our recommendations contemplate the possibility of self-targeting and sanctions being applied to all ships in the same ownership or management.

13   It is not only Port State authorities which can bring pressure to bear on shipowners and managers to improve standards. Shipowners need to find charters. Charterers and their brokers need to weigh lower freight rates against the risk that the cargoes will not arrive or will arrive damaged. Underwriters compete for risks, but not for claims. Once shipowners find that they are being discriminated against in the marketplace because of their safety records, they are likely to change their attitude towards standards. With this in mind, we recommend that steps be taken to improve the dissemination of information as to the standards maintained by different ships and fleets.

14   A striking feature of ships, as contrasted with aircraft, is their relative anonymity whilst *en route*. This is a positive incentive to wrongdoing, whether in the form of deliberate discharges or negligent operation. We discuss the merits and future prospects for radio and radar transponders on ships which would remove this anonymity. This is being studied by IMO, but some time must elapse before standards are agreed and even longer before most ships are equipped. Meanwhile we have no doubt that this anonymity should not be allowed to continue and recommend that all merchant ships should display simple identification signs painted in large characters on their decks and sides.

15   But the removal, or at least a reduction in the measure, of anonymity is not enough. For much of their voyages ships are out of sight of land, although not necessarily beyond a range within which they are capable of polluting the coastline. Some ship Masters undoubtedly take the view that "out of sight is out of mind". We accordingly attach importance to a degree of aerial and other surveillance and make recommendations for achieving this with minimum cost. Even more important we wish to establish a climate in which ship Masters never know when they are being, or are likely to be, observed and will act accordingly.

16   Our recommendations are by no means confined to deterring and detecting wrong-doing. Even good shipowners and ship Masters need help in the form of information when planning their voyages. We make a number of recommendations designed to assist them. Two deserve particular mention. The first is the publication of a *Seaway Code* designed to remind them of practical steps which can be taken to reduce the risk of pollution and of the regulations, including UK requirements, which will affect any voyage to or from the United Kingdom. In addition it would afford them a ready means of identifying sources of more detailed information.

17   The second is the establishment of MEHRAs – Marine Environmentally High Risk Areas. We have been struck by the fact that the average ship Master neither knows, nor has the means of knowing, that the nature of the shoreline is such that if his ship grounded, for whatever reason, there could be a risk of exceptional damage which might expose his owners and insurers to substantial liabilities. We recommend that this be remedied. MEHRAs, which would be limited in number in order to underline their significance, would be established where there was **both** a significant concentration of shipping and a high risk of environmental damage. They would feature not only in the *Seaway Code*, but would also be marked on Admiralty Charts. This is only one of several recommendations we make on routeing.

18   However successful efforts may be to improve standards, the fact has to be faced that the sea is a dangerous place. Incidents with a potential for polluting the coastline and coastal waters will still occur. If such incidents cannot be prevented, their consequences can be minimised. In this context it is a mistake to regard oil tankers as the only source of danger. Bunker fuel is a very serious pollutant and many large dry cargo vessels carry as much bunker fuel as the cargo of a small coastal tanker. Furthermore relatively small oil spills can have serious consequences. Vessels which are in distress, or which have lost power and are in danger of grounding or being in a collision, need immediate assistance in the interests not only of the environment, but also of saving life and property.

19   This is the traditional role of the salvage tug. But it is becoming an endangered species. Ironically this is due in part to the fact that there are fewer casualties than previously, although, with the development of larger ships, when they do occur the consequences can be more serious. We recommend that urgent steps be taken to restore this salvage capability. What is needed is a cooperative scheme, in partnership with neighbouring States wherever practicable, to establish franchises for a few high-powered salvage

vessels and a larger number of less powerful vessels with other duties which can nevertheless administer salvage first aid pending the arrival of more specialised and powerful assistance.

20 The availability of such assistance will, of course, be of no avail if ship Masters cannot be induced to inform the coastal authorities the moment that even the possibility of the need for such assistance arises. Due to personal pride and misplaced optimism, at present this often does not happen. We therefore recommend that the existing duty to report is strengthened and that Coastal States should be more ready to intervene where necessary.

21 Whilst we have no doubt that "prevention [of pollution] is better than cure", the fact has to be faced that "cure" may not always be possible. We have accordingly examined with care the United Kingdom's facilities for cleaning up oil spills. They are impressive. Criticism has been directed at the United Kingdom's unique and expensive capacity to spray dispersant from the air, but we have come to the conclusion that the special character of our coastline justifies its retention. We make recommendations designed to improve still further the United Kingdom's facilities for dealing with pollution once it occurs.

22 We were bidden by our terms of reference to take account not only of the international, but also the economic, implications of any new measures and we have done so. We have no doubt that giving effect to our recommendations will involve an expansion of resources and increased costs. However if, as we contemplate, they are taken in cooperation with our regional neighbours, there will be no change in our relative competitive position. Insofar as the playing field is level, it will remain so. Nor do we think that the expenditure contemplated is of an order which can have any perceptible effect on the United Kingdom's economy. There remains, however, the question of who should foot the bill in the first instance. This is considered in Chapter 22. Suffice it to say that we have no doubt that the principle to be applied is that the polluter and potential polluter should pay.

23 This overview contains but a bird's eye view of the main thrust of our recommendations, which are set out in detail in Chapter 23. Our detailed findings and the full reasons for those recommendations are in the body of the Report.

Chapter 1

Introduction

The *BRAER* and the Shetland Islands

1.1   On 5 January 1993 one of the Shetland Islanders' worst nightmares became a reality. The MV *BRAER* went onto the rocks at Garths Ness. She was fully laden with 84,700 tonnes of Norwegian Gullfaks crude oil and some 1,600 tonnes of heavy fuel oil bunkers. The weather was atrocious – storm force winds and mountainous seas. There were all the makings of a major economic and ecological disaster for the local community.

1.2   In the event the consequences were serious but miraculously less catastrophic than might have been expected. The reason was that Gullfaks is a relatively "volatile" crude which the high winds and exceptional seas were largely able to disperse. Nobody could anticipate a recurrence of such a combination and the Shetland Islanders' fears for the future were reinforced.

1.3   The Marine Accident Investigation Branch of the Department of Transport at once began to inquire into the circumstances which led to the wreck of the *BRAER*. Its report was published on 20 January 1994[1]. It concluded that the immediate cause was a failure of the vessel's engines. This could have happened anywhere. In different circumstances or a different place, she might well have been saved. Equally she might have been wrecked on a quite different part of the United Kingdom or some other coastline.

1.4   This is important because it demonstrates that it is not only the Shetland Islands which are at risk from pollution from merchant shipping. Those islands have special characteristics which make them vulnerable. The weather is at times exceptionally hostile. The islanders are largely dependent upon the sea for their livelihood. But the same can be said of the Western Isles. Other coastal dwellers can and do make similar claims for the importance of their particular coastline based upon such factors as dependence upon tourism and the importance of the flora and fauna to be found there. The seriousness of the consequences of pollution will vary from place to place, but so will the risk of pollution occurring. The inhabitants of some areas can point to a greater degree of risk than in the case of the Shetland Islands because of the greater density of shipping.

This Inquiry

1.5   It was against this background that the Inquiry was set up. Our task has been to consider the risk of pollution from merchant shipping to the United Kingdom coastline as a whole. This has not meant that we have forgotten the *BRAER* and the Shetland Islands.

---

[1] Report of the Chief Inspector of Marine Accidents into the engine failure and subsequent grounding of the Motor Tanker Braer at Garths Ness, Shetland on 5 January 1993—ISBN 0 11 551210 1.

Far from it. We have sought to learn from this experience and that of earlier polluting incidents and to apply those lessons on a wider scale. In addition, throughout the Inquiry we have been kept informed of relevant shipping casualties[2] and, in some cases, of "near misses", as they have occurred. Indeed, we attach almost as much importance to "near misses" as to actual casualties, since very small differences in circumstances can convert one into the other with its attendant risk of pollution. A brief description of some of these incidents, including "near misses" as well as actual collisions, strandings and groundings, is at Appendix L. The sites of the incidents recorded are generally shown on the map at Appendix R.

Scope – "the coastline"

1.6   We have taken a broad, and in our view sensible, view of the meaning of the phrase as extending to seaward of the low water mark to include areas of sea where fish farms are situated and to landward of the high water mark to the extent that it can be reached by waves or spray in storm conditions. In the context of river estuaries, it is difficult to define precisely where the river banks end and the coastline begins, but for our purposes we regard such precision as unnecessary.

1.7   The United Kingdom coastline is nearly 12,500 km or 8,000 miles long[3] and our territorial waters amount to 125,000 square miles (about one third of a million square km)[4] – far more in relation to land mass than most of our European partners. The coastline encompasses a diversity of geological structures and natural habitats, ranging from cliffs and exposed rocky shores through sandy and muddy beaches to sheltered bays and lagoons. The unpolluted coastline provides recreation and enjoyment for the public, habitats for a great variety of wildlife, and commercial resources for fishermen.

Scope – pollution

1.8   There is a natural tendency to think of coastal pollution in terms of oil. You can see it, taste it and smell it. It has very distressing visible consequences for birds and sea mammals. However, we have also had to consider the risk of other kinds of pollution, such as from chemicals and other hazardous and noxious substances, including nuclear cargoes. In addition, pollution can occur from biocides used on the hulls of ships to prevent marine growths and from garbage and dunnage[5]. Even rats escaping from vessels can be a problem, as the case of the *DARIUS* shows (see paragraph 17.12). Pollution can also occur as a result of organisms being transferred in ballast water from one part of the world to another, thus introducing alien and potentially damaging species of life into United Kingdom waters.

1.9   "Pollution of the marine environment" is defined in the United Nations Convention on the Law of the Sea 1982[6] as:

---

[2] A "casualty" in this context means an incident which involves actual damage to a ship through mishap, or a ship which has suffered such damage.

[3] Source: *Mangon's Marine Almanac* (Taylor and Frances) 1991—ISBN 0 8448 1674 4.

[4] House of Commons Environment Committee Report session 1991–92—*Coastal Zone Protection and Planning*.

[5] "Dunnage" is wooden or other cheap material used to protect cargoes from damage which is often thrown overboard after use.

[6] Part I Article 1(4).

"The introduction by man, directly or indirectly, of substances or energy into the marine environment, including estuaries, which results or is likely to result in such deleterious effects as harm to living resources and marine life, hazards to human health, hinderance to marine activities, including fishing and other legitimate uses of the sea, the impairment of quality for use of sea water and reduction of amenities."

1.10   For our purposes we have confined our attention to waterborne pollutants even though airborne pollutants, such as smoke and fumes from loading oil, come within this definition. We have not considered pollution by sewage from ships: while this is a potential problem it does not appear to be an actual one.

1.11   We have found that pollution control and safety are very closely linked, because the best way to maintain safety and to prevent pollution is to preserve the integrity of the ship. Much of this report is thus as relevant to safety as it is to pollution.

Scope – merchant shipping

1.12   We have taken "merchant" to mean broadly "commercial" and accordingly have included freight and passenger vessels including air cushion vehicles (hovercraft) when used at sea, although these do not in fact pose any special problem. We have, however, excluded oil rigs and platforms whether or not they are floating structures.

1.13   Warships and fleet auxiliaries are clearly outside our terms of reference and in any event are likely to constitute less of a pollution risk because of the high standards of seamanship and discipline which are to be expected. This exclusion is however important in the context of international rights of passage and of our recommendations concerning identification, reporting and routeing all of which are made in a context which excludes any application to warships whether British or foreign.

International implications

1.14   Shipping is an international business, operated and regulated internationally. We have no doubt that in this context international action is generally more effective than national action. However there are grades of internationalism. There is the International Maritime Organization (IMO) which embraces many nations. There is the European Community (EC)[7]. There are the "clubs" of European States which are signatories to the Bonn Agreement and to the Paris Memorandum of Understanding on Port State Control. Some action needs to be taken by all nations, some is more appropriate for clubs of nations, and some can be taken unilaterally: but it is always necessary to bear in mind the legitimate interests of other States, and that unilateral action by other States could harm UK interests to an unacceptable degree.

---

[7] We continue to refer to the European Community (EC) despite the formation of the European Union on 1 November 1993. Only the European Community has any legal personality, though it is now buttressed by two inter-Governmental bodies, one dealing with common foreign and security policy, the other dealing with home affairs and justice policy. The three together form the European Union.

The polluter pays principle and the user pays principle

1.15   Throughout our study we have borne in mind the polluter pays principle and the user pays principle. The first, that the polluter should pay for the cost of his pollution, including the cost of measures needed to limit pollution or deal with its effects, has been a cornerstone of Government policy for many years. So has the similar user pays principle, which in the marine context means that those who use facilities such as harbours and navigational aids should pay for them through dues rather than be subsidised by the general taxpayer. Neither principle is universally applied. For instance, most inspections of foreign flagged vessels visiting United Kingdom ports are paid for by the United Kingdom taxpayer, and light dues, which fund navigational aids, are not charged on small pleasure craft.

The precautionary principle

1.16   We were also aware of the precautionary principle, which has been accepted by the United Kingdom Government for some years. The 1992 North East Atlantic Convention (which has been signed but not yet ratified by the United Kingdom) defines this as:

> "The precautionary principle, by virtue of which preventative measures are to be taken when there are reasonable grounds for concern that substances or energy introduced, directly or indirectly, into the marine environment may bring about hazards to human health, harm living resources and marine ecosystems, damage amenities or interfere with other legitimate uses of the sea, even when there is no conclusive evidence of a causal relationship between the inputs and the effects."

1.17   This approach does not and cannot mean that no activity can be carried out unless it has been proved to be completely harmless. Many essential activities, including shipping, can never be made completely harmless.

1.18   These three principles – the polluter pays principle, the user pays principle and the precautionary principle – are important and highly relevant to our study. They are particularly pertinent to our recommendations on emergency assistance in Chapter 20 and on new funding arrangements in Chapter 22.

Our approach

1.19   From the outset we made it clear that the Inquiry was not concerned to reinvestigate or apportion blame for past incidents of pollution. Our task, as we saw it, was to look to the future and, with a view to making recommendations designed to protect our coastline, to enlist assistance from all possible sources. In this, at least, we have been very successful. We have received a large number and variety of submissions which have been of inestimable value, as have our hearings and our visits. It would be inappropriate to single out any contributors for special mention, but a full list is set out at Appendix B. To all of them we extend our grateful thanks.

1.20   The range of subjects within our terms of reference is very wide indeed. In order to keep our study within a reasonable timescale, and our Report within reasonable bounds, we have broadly confined ourselves to issues which have been raised in evidence or otherwise drawn to our attention. This self-denying ordinance means that there are actual and potential problems which we have not been able to cover. One such is when potentially dangerous or polluting goods, carried in standard containers as part of a normal cargo, are washed overboard and break out of those containers: one recent case involving the *SHERBRO* is mentioned in Appendix L. Another is possible spills from transfers of oil from off-shore installations to ships. These transfers are already tightly regulated, not least for safety reasons, and in general are so far off-shore that any oil spilled is unlikely to hazard our coasts.

1.21 Because of fast-changing circumstances, we found at a late stage in our deliberations that we required further information, the need for which had not earlier been apparent. Equally we found that in the light of the changing scene we were contemplating different or additional recommendations, the validity of which needed to be tested. This led to a series of dialogues with those concerned. If it was suggested that our ideas were mistaken, we weighed the objections, but were not deflected unless convinced of the validity of those objections.

Extending the Inquiry

1.22 In November 1993 two fish factory ships, the Latvian *LUNOHODS-1* and the Russian *BORODINSKOYE POLYE*, were wrecked near Lerwick in Shetland. At our suggestion, the Shetland Islands Council announced on 18 November 1993 that we would consider further written representations on the problems posed by these ships. Four representations were received as a result, and are taken into account in Chapter 17.

Value for money

1.23 We have borne in mind the need to cost our recommendations where practicable, and to ensure that those recommendations represent good value for money. This is not easy. As we explain in Chapter 4, the economic evaluation of the benefits of marine safety and pollution measures is in its infancy. It is extraordinarily difficult to assess the likelihood of a catastrophe and the chances of averting it. Both the cost and the effectiveness of many of our recommendations depend on the outcome of negotiations and cannot be accurately assessed in advance.

1.24 We have therefore made the best assessments of costs that we could, in those areas where it is practicable to make any assessment. We asked the Department of Transport to consider our assessments, and the figures quoted in the Report take account of the Department's advice. This inevitably meant that the Department of Transport had foreknowledge of what some of our recommendations might be. We listened to, but did not always accept, their views on what we had in mind. The only alternative would have been to make tentative recommendations, ask the Government to assess the costs and benefits and then reconsider our recommendations in the light of knowledge of costs. The demerits of this would have outweighed the merits.

The form of our Report

1.25 We begin our Report with a description of the complexity of the problem and the reasons why pollution and its prevention are so important. We move on to deal with two of the major issues underlying the whole Report: the need to judge the effectiveness of proposed measures and international law. The next group of chapters deals with the first line of defence against pollution: the construction, operation, maintenance and inspection of ships. After that come the secondary defences: navigation, the routes ships take and surveillance from shore, together with the largely self-contained problem of fish factory ships followed by insurance and compensation issues which indirectly affect behaviour. Then the tertiary defences: what is done, and what needs to be done, to prevent ships in difficulties from becoming casualties, followed by the fourth level, of response to pollution which cannot be prevented.

1.26 This Report covers a wide range, and we hope that it will be read by an equally wide range of people. They include those to whom the sea is an everyday working environment and those who see it largely as a wildlife habitat, an amenity or a pleasure ground. They also include shipowners and agents; insurers; inspectors, from both Government and classification societies; lawyers; Government negotiators; Coastguards; salvors; harbour and local authority staff; and many more – including taxpayers, and manufacturers and consumers of goods which travel by sea, who will indirectly pay any increased costs.

1.27 All these people have a legitimate interest in the prevention of pollution of our coasts: and none has an exclusive interest. Compromises are essential, and our aim is to find the most satisfactory – or perhaps the least unsatisfactory – ones. We have tried to include in this Report sufficient background information and explanation to make it clear to all readers why we have reached our conclusions. This necessarily means that on each subject we have gone into more detail than an expert will require.

Other studies and developments

1.28 The prevention of pollution from merchant shipping, and the closely linked question of the safety of merchant shipping, are hardly new areas for study. We have read and been influenced by many reports: several are mentioned in these pages. We have been particularly influenced by the Eighth Report of the Royal Commission on Environmental Pollution on *Oil Pollution of the Sea*[8], by the Report by the Select Committee on Science and Technology of the House of Lords, chaired by Lord Carver, on *Safety Aspects of Ship Design and Technology*[9], and by the report *Ships of Shame*[10] by the Australian House of Representatives Standing Committee on Transport, Communications and Infrastructure, and the relevant responses by the UK[11] and Australian Governments.

---

[8] Cmnd 8358: ISBN 0 10 183580 9*.
[9] HL Paper 30-I Session 1991–92: ISBN 0 10 482192 2.
[10] ISBN 0 644 25859 4.
[11] *The Government Response to the House of Lords Select Committee on Science and Technology Report on Safety Aspects of Ship Design and Technology*—Cm 2121—ISBN 0 10 121212 7.

Studies following the BRAER incident

1.29   Other parallel inquiries have been carried out into the *BRAER* accident and its aftermath:

(a)   the Marine Accident Investigation Branch (MAIB) of the Department of Transport has investigated the causes of the accident. We are grateful to the Chief Inspector for showing us a copy of his draft findings on the causes of the accident at the same time as he circulated it to interested parties for comment. While there is, not surprisingly, some overlap between the Chief Inspector's recommendations and our own, we must stress that the recommendations in this Report are ours alone, reached quite independently of MAIB. The Chief Inspector's recommendations are reproduced in Appendix Q;

(b)   because the *BRAER* was registered in Liberia, the Liberian Bureau of Maritime Affairs also carried out an investigation into the causes of the accident, in close cooperation with MAIB[12]. The recommendations of the Liberian Investigator, Captain A R Goddard, are also reproduced in Appendix Q;

(c)   the then Director of Marine Emergency Operations of the Department of Transport reported, with recommendations, on the emergency response to the accident. His report was submitted to the Inquiry in evidence and some – but not all – of his recommendations are taken up here. His report was published at the same time as the MAIB and Liberian reports into the causes of the accident on 20 January 1994[13];

(d)   the ecological effects are the subject of a report by the Ecological Steering Group on the Oil Spill in Shetland (ESGOSS) appointed by the Secretary of State for Scotland[14], whose interim report[15] we have studied with great interest. We understand that ESGOSS plans to report again in late June 1994; and

(e)   in April 1993 the Minister of Agriculture, Fisheries and Food announced a review of the testing and approval system for oil dispersants and the circumstances in which chemical dispersants are likely to be the most effective clean-up technique[16]. The review will take into account the findings of ESGOSS and of this Inquiry. We understand that MAFF intend making the results of the review available for public consultation when draft recommendations have been drawn up.

1.30   We have not been inhibited in our investigation or our findings by this multiplicity of inquiries, but we have tried, through informal contact, to avoid unnecessary duplication of effort. More importantly, we have also tried to ensure that all relevant questions have been covered by one body or another.

---

[12] *Report of Investigation into the Matter of the Loss by Grounding of the Motor Tanker BRAER on the South Coast of Shetland Island 5 January 1993:* published by the Bureau of Maritime Affairs, PO Box 10-9042, Monrovia, Liberia, available from International Registries Inc., Northumbrian House, 14 Devonshire Square, London EC2M 4TE.

[13] *The Braer Incident*—ISBN 0 11 55 1208 X.

[14] Hansard 11 January 1993 col 626.

[15] *An interim report on surveying and monitoring*, May 1993, published by the Scottish Office—ISBN 0 7480 0767 9.

[16] Hansard 1 April 1993 col 329.

International developments

1.31 It must not be forgotten that on 3 December 1992, only a month before the *BRAER* was wrecked off Shetland, the tanker *AEGEAN SEA* was wrecked off La Coruña in northern Spain. The European Community felt that common action to protect Member States was essential. Following a joint meeting of the Environment Council and the Transport Council of Ministers on 25 January 1993, the European Commission Communication *A Common Policy on Safe Seas*[17] was published on 24 February 1993 and approved by the Councils of Ministers, with some amendments, in June 1993.

1.32 The United Kingdom Government also believed that further restrictions on the routeing of vessels were needed as fast as they could be put into place. New measures were submitted to and agreed by a sub-committee of the International Maritime Organization in May 1993 and approved by the full IMO Assembly in November 1993. With one exception, where further work was needed, they came into force on 28 November 1993. Details of routeing measures, including the new ones, are in Chapter 14. We commend both the United Kingdom Government and international bodies for moving so fast to take the action they believed necessary.

Interim recommendations

1.33 On 27 May 1993, following our hearings in Shetland, we asked the Secretary of State to arrange for a study of traffic in the Fair Isle Channel. Our letter is reproduced at Appendix O, and the conclusions of the study are to be found in Chapter 14. We are grateful for this assistance.

1.34 On 10 June 1993 we wrote to the Secretary of State to inform him that we believed that the Salvage Convention 1989 and the 1992 Protocols to the 1969 Civil Liability Convention and to the 1971 Fund Convention should be ratified and brought into effect quickly, and that we hoped that primary legislation to that effect would be introduced. Our letter is reproduced at Appendix P.

Implementation of our recommendations

1.35 We were delighted that the Merchant Shipping (Salvage and Pollution) Bill was introduced to Parliament by Mr David Harris MP, with support from Opposition parties and assistance from the Government, in January 1994. This Bill provides for the ratifications we sought, and clarifies and amends other pollution prevention measures as discussed in our hearings. It anticipates some of the recommendations we had intended making. We very much welcome this advance implementation of a small but important part of our recommendations, and look forward to the speedy implementation of the remainder which will, overall, have a considerably greater effect.

1.36 We note that the *Report of the Enquiry into River Safety* by Mr John Hayes[18] recommended that the Government should review and publish annually an account of the

---

[17] Commission of the European Communities COM(93)66 final—ISBN 92 77 53341 2.
[18] Cm 1991, HMSO 1992—ISBN 0 10 119912 0.

progress made on the implementation of recommendations made after all major disasters. The Government accepted this in relation to transport disasters. Although this report does not deal with a particular disaster it does deal with a potentially disastrous situation, and we recommend that **an annual report on its implementation should be made to Parliament**.

Chapter 2

The Complexity of the Problem

Human error

2.1 In the last analysis it is individuals whose conduct leads directly or indirectly to pollution. It is generally accepted that human error is the cause of about four fifths of marine accidents. We are surprised that the figure is so low: we believe that human error, at some stage in a chain of events which could start with the design of a vessel, is the root cause of virtually all accidents. The only exception that we can see is the highly unusual case of unforeseeable forces overwhelming a vessel or her crew.

2.2 Any recommendations for further measures to safeguard our coastline have to take the fullest account of the likelihood of error by individuals. They must take account of human nature rather than seek to change it and must work within a framework of practical incentives and sanctions.

Commercial pressures

2.3 Another major constraint, which no recommendations of ours can change, is the commercial pressures which all shipowners face. These unavoidably influence the behaviour of the major players in the industry. The effects of market forces are illustrated in the recent history of the oil tanker trade.

2.4 In the late 1960s and early 1970s the worldwide tanker industry enjoyed a period of prosperity fuelled by an unprecedented growth in seaborne oil trade. Tanker capacity trebled between 1968 and 1976. The oil price "shocks" of 1973 and 1979 left the industry heavily oversupplied with tonnage and led to far-reaching structural changes. At about the same time, newly industrialised economies in the Far East began to build up large, modern, competitive fleets as their international trade increased, at the expense of the UK and other western European national flag fleets. Many owners flagged out in order to remain competitive. Major technological changes led to larger units, higher speeds, more automation and smaller crews, mainly from countries with low wage economies. The decline in the numbers of western European seafarers has been dramatic. There is now serious concern whether essential maritime services, including Government functions, can continue to be provided by citizens of the countries concerned.

2.5 Most of the shipping industry has suffered a period of deep depression since the mid-1980s with falling freight rates and substantial overcapacity. The potential consequences for safety and pollution avoidance include:

(a) overcapacity in the bulk trades, leading to cut-throat competition with insufficient revenue to finance operations and replacements properly;

11

(b) the departure of many established shipowners from the industry and their replacement by others, some of whom seek profit with little regard for standards;

(c) the fragmentation of shipowning and management with the traditional, integrated shipping company replaced by contractors providing management and labour, often under short-term arrangements. Cargo interests, charterers, owners, managers, Masters and crews may all be separated to the extent that lack of understanding and poor motivation may become serious problems in times of emergency; and

(d) the emergence of some open registries offering lax facilities under which bad practice is able to flourish.

2.6 There are still good companies endeavouring to meet good shipping practice under difficult financial conditions. There is also some evidence of an increasing awareness within the industry of the problems with which it is beset and an increasing desire to put these right. Ranged against and overshadowing this beneficial desire for change are deep-seated bad habits, entrenched attitudes and a shortage of revenue for training and reinvestment.

International law

2.7 The sea constitutes the world's greatest highway. Its use is enjoyed by all nations and the continuance and safeguarding of that use is essential to an island nation such as the United Kingdom. By far the greater part of it – the High Seas – is outside the territory or control of any individual nation, although the ships which use it are floating and mobile parts of the territory of the nation whose flag they fly. Other parts – and they are the parts with which we are principally concerned – lie within the territory or varying degrees of control of individual nations, but subject always to the rights of other nations under international law.

2.8 Both respect for international law and enlightened self-interest dictate that in formulating recommendations we should avoid infringing the rights of other nations and should test their reasonableness in terms of other nations seeking to apply a similar approach to United Kingdom shipping bound for their ports or seeking to pass through their waters. In particular we have been concerned to uphold the international right of "innocent passage". This is of particular relevance to our Inquiry because much of the shipping which passes close to our shores flies the flags of other nations and has neither sailed from nor is destined for a United Kingdom port. We discuss international law in Chapter 5.

The international approach

2.9 In the year between the start of our hearings and the submission of our Report, international discussions and agreements have moved on. There have been many meetings of the numerous committees and sub-committees of IMO. The European Commission has produced its policy document *A Common Policy on Safe Seas*, and the Council of Ministers has endorsed it. Many other formal and informal discussions between Ministers, Government officials and shipping and environmental interests have driven forward policy, regulation and cooperation. We welcome this progress, and in this Report we suggest some new directions in which policy, regulation and cooperation might move.

2.10   But there are difficulties in such activity. One is the need to sustain a coherent policy, for which clear and agreed objectives are required. Another is the need to concentrate on those measures which will achieve the objective most effectively in relation to the resources used. A third is the need for close cooperation between many different bodies in different countries – and cooperation on a global scale is not easy to achieve.

2.11   It is because of these difficulties that the international community has recognised the primacy of IMO in all matters related to the safety and cleanliness of the sea. We too recognise that it is essential that nothing is done to **conflict** with IMO or with any of the international Conventions and agreements. Nevertheless, the fact remains that international organisations, including IMO, normally work through consensus. While this has great merit when a unified approach towards problems is agreed and carried out, finding a consensus can lead to frustrating delays. A balance is sometimes needed between consensus and speed, and there may sometimes be good reasons for a single country or group of countries to move faster than the remainder of IMO.

2.12   This option is always subject to a Government's obligations in international law and to practical considerations, but we note that the UK has already considered going it alone. Following failure to reach agreement through IMO on the implementation of higher damage stability standards for roll-on, roll-off passenger ferries, Ministers stated in December 1992 that if international agreement was not forthcoming the UK would consider taking national action to ensure that vessels visiting UK ports met those standards. Agreement on a European level was subsequently achieved.

The key players

Flag States

2.13   As we have said, ships form a floating and mobile part of the nation whose flag they fly – hence the expression "Flag State". It follows from this that that nation and that nation alone has an unfettered right to make rules and regulations governing the design, construction, maintenance, manning and operation of that ship. But Flag States have duties as well as rights. They have a duty to ensure that their ships comply with the standards accepted by the Flag State under international law and Conventions. Regrettably Flag States are not uniform in their determination or ability to discharge this duty. We discuss Flag State Control of vessels in Chapter 6.

Coastal States

2.14   These are States whose coastline is passed by shipping coming from and destined for ports outside that State. They have limited rights to take action in the event of a real and imminent threat of damage to their coastline. These are explained in Chapter 20.

Port States

2.15 These are the States at whose ports or anchorages ships call. Given the absence of a uniformly high standard of regulation and enforcement of their obligations by Flag States, Port States have of necessity to exercise such powers as they have to detect substandard ships entering their waters and to take precautionary or remedial action. The United Kingdom, in cooperation with other nations which are parties to the Paris Memorandum of Understanding (see paragraph 2.19), plays a leading part in this process. Nevertheless, we consider that more needs to be done unless and until Flag States can be induced to apply and enforce uniformly high standards on their ships. We discuss Port State Control in Chapter 11.

2.16 The Marine Safety Agency (MSA), an executive agency within the Department of Transport, carries out inspections on UK registered vessels under Flag State Control and on other vessels under Port State Control. Until 1 April 1994 it was the Surveyor General's Organisation (SGO). Its role, which is largely unchanged, is explained in Appendix C.

International Maritime Organization (IMO)

2.17 IMO is a permanent specialised agency of the United Nations dealing with maritime affairs and consists of all 137 Member States. It coordinates and promotes international agreements on maritime safety and the prevention of maritime pollution. Once ratified by member Governments, Conventions agreed through IMO have the status of international law. Codes and recommendations adopted by the IMO Assembly are not binding on Governments but are usually implemented by Governments through domestic legislation.

2.18 Like many such organisations, IMO has a complex structure of committees and sub-committees, whose meetings are arranged a long time in advance. This makes for slow progress. We have been much heartened by recent signs that IMO can act quickly: in particular, we were impressed by the speed with which new routeing measures submitted by the UK Government were approved during 1993.

European clubs of nations

2.19 *Port State Control:* fifteen European States (Belgium, Denmark, Finland, France, Germany, Greece, the Republic of Ireland, Italy, the Netherlands, Norway, Poland, Portugal, Spain, Sweden and the United Kingdom) are parties to the Paris Memorandum of Understanding on Port State Control. Canada is expected to join in May 1994.

2.20 *North East Atlantic:* the same States, minus Greece, Italy and Poland, but with the addition of Iceland and the European Community, are signatories to the "OSPAR" Convention for the Protection of the Marine Environment of the North East Atlantic, and, with a couple of exceptions, to the Oslo and Paris Conventions that it will replace. At present, the main relevance of these Conventions to the Inquiry's work is in dumping from ships, but the machinery exists in the Conventions to take initiatives over a wider field.

2.21 *Pollution response arrangements:* eight European States (Belgium, Denmark, France, Germany, the Netherlands, Norway, Sweden and the United Kingdom), with the European Community, are parties to the 1983 Bonn Agreement which deals with precautions against, and response to, spills of oil and other harmful substances in the North Sea and English Channel. The similar Lisbon Agreement (between France, Morocco, Portugal and Spain, with the European Community) provides similar cover further south. Similar bilateral arrangements also exist between the Republic of Ireland and the United Kingdom.

2.22 *North Sea States:* the eight Bonn Agreement States, with Luxembourg and Switzerland, meet in North Sea Conferences, which consider a wide range of questions, including various aspects of shipping such as port reception facilities and jurisdiction to enforce anti-pollution regulations.

2.23 *European Community:* the EC's approach has been centred on trying to achieve enforcement of IMO regulations and resolutions to an agreed consistent standard. The European Commission is active in the various organisations described. In addition, the European Community is considering a wide range of initiatives on the basis of the Commission's paper *A Common Policy on Safe Seas.*

2.24 *European Economic Area:* the EEA Agreement brings into many of the aspects of the EC's work (but with different procedural arrangements) a further range of States: Austria, Finland, Iceland, Liechtenstein, Norway and Sweden. It remains to be seen how EC activities affecting shipping and the marine environment will be developed in this forum.

Shipowners

2.25 The primary responsibility for the standard of design, construction, maintenance, manning and operation of the ship lies with the shipowner. To say that shipowners' attitudes towards this responsibility vary is a masterpiece of understatement. All are concerned with their financial survival and some hope to trade profitably. But whilst at one end of the scale there are shipowners who from pride, a long tradition of shipowning or an enlightened long-term self-interest insist upon the highest standards, at the other end of the scale there are fly-by-night owners whose sole concern is for the "fast buck" at whatever price in terms of the safety and welfare of officers and crew. The latter kind of shipowner will ensure that his vessels fly the flag of whatever nation seems the most likely to tolerate the lowest and cheapest standards.

2.26 Unfortunately, there is a strong temptation to go for the cheapest rates compatible with basic performance requirements. We suspect that, with a few exceptions for dangerous cargoes such as liquified natural gas (LNG), liquified petroleum gas (LPG), bulk chemicals and nuclear materials, too many people succumb to this temptation. The overall picture is gloomy. Traditional values of good management, competence, operational practice and ship maintenance have to some extent slipped away. In the current climate of ingrained bad habits, an inadequate supply of good seafarers and depressed economic conditions, the prospects for improvement without prompt and vigorous corrective measures are not good.

Charterers

2.27 Charterers fall into three broad categories:

(a) *charterers by demise* who take over the whole manning and operation of the vessel for a long period of time. They are only distinguishable from shipowners in that they are not the legal owners of the vessel;

(b) *time charterers* who hire the vessel and her crew for a period of time and are entitled to direct where and when she shall go during that time. Bunkers[1], which are potentially a major source of pollution, are their property; and

(c) *voyage charterers* who hire the vessel for a specified voyage but have no direct control over the vessel.

2.28 Demise charterers have virtually the same power to prevent pollution or the risk of pollution as owners. Time charterers have such power by exercising discretion in their choice of vessel and also by the exercise of a power to give the Master directions as to the employment of the vessel. Voyage charterers could no doubt insist upon special "anti-pollution" clauses in their charterparties, but in practical terms their power to reduce the risk of pollution is limited to the exercise of a discretion as to what ships to charter. Both time and voyage charterers are faced with uncomfortable choices between safer but more expensive ships, or ones that are less safe but cheaper.

Cargo owners

2.29 Cargo owners may also fill the role of shipowners or charterers. For example oil companies usually ship their products in vessels owned or chartered by them. However, in the dry cargo trades this will often not be the case. Whether they have any discretion in the choice of vessel which carries their cargo will depend upon a number of factors, notably how and when they became owners of the cargo. Thus at one end of the spectrum, the purchaser of a cargo which is already afloat has no choice other than to decide not to buy the cargo. At the other end the cargo owner who is the shipper under a Cost, Insurance and Freight (CIF) contract will usually be able to choose.

2.30 Owners of oil cargoes have a strong incentive to be selective because they have a potential liability if their oil creates pollution. In the case of other cargo owners, such incentive as exists stems from the need to ensure that the cargo arrives safely, and there would be an incentive only if receipt of insurance monies is not an adequate compensation in the event of non-arrival or arrival damaged, or because of a desire to avoid adverse publicity.

Shipbrokers

2.31 Shipbrokers form the link between shipowners looking for commercial opportunities for their vessels and cargo owners (or charterers) who need suitable ships to carry their goods. The shipbroker matches cargoes to ships and negotiates and structures the deal

---

[1] Oils that are used to fuel and run the vessel.

(fixture) between the various parties. The London shipbroking market is the largest in the world so the various brokers involved have access to at least some information on a significant proportion of the world's merchant shipping fleet. The shipbroker usually has a detailed knowledge of the quality of the ships and owners with which he is dealing and is an important link in the commercial chain.

Underwriters

2.32 Marine insurance is a sophisticated and complex industry. There are hull underwriters, cargo underwriters, liability underwriters and Protection and Indemnity (mutual insurance) "Clubs". In addition there are reinsurers who insure the primary underwriters wholly or, more usually, partially. In varying degrees underwriters can and do influence standards of safety in the shipping industry by the imposition of higher rates of premium, higher excesses, special warranties or a refusal to accept the risk. However, marine insurance, like shipowning, is a highly competitive business and for an individual underwriter to take a tough line may result not in safer shipping, but only in his losing business to a competitor. Insurance is discussed in Chapter 18.

Classification societies

2.33 These are organisations staffed by marine surveyors who act for Flag States, shipowners and underwriters in developing and enforcing standards of design, construction and maintenance. They vary greatly in their quality, capacity and dedication and all are faced, like underwriters, with competitive pressures. However they are, or should be, in the front line when it comes to insisting upon high standards of ship construction, maintenance and repair. Their role is discussed in more detail in Chapter 7.

The maritime assistance organisations

2.34 Although our concern is generally limited to organisations which may be involved when an incident is threatened or has occurred which could lead to pollution of the United Kingdom coastline, we include for completeness all search and rescue organisations.

HM Coastguard (HMCG)

2.35 HM Coastguard is a Search And Rescue (SAR) organisation whose primary role is the saving of life at sea. Nevertheless it has an important role in the United Kingdom's defences against coastal pollution, because it is likely to be the first to hear of an accident or incident which creates the threat of pollution.

Search and rescue helicopters

2.36 HM Coastguard operates three SAR helicopters – based at Sumburgh (Shetland), Stornoway (Western Isles) and Solent (southern England). These are funded by the Department of Transport. HM Coastguard can also call on three Royal Navy SAR helicopters (for which the Department is charged only in respect of out of hours operations) and on eight Royal Air Force SAR helicopters, which are not charged to the Department at all.

The Royal National Lifeboat Institution

2.37   The UK is unique in that lifeboats are provided, equipped and operated not by the State but by a charity, the Royal National Lifeboat Institution. The RNLI spends over £40 million a year on lifeboat services[2], none of it contributed by the State. The UK is lucky to have such an organisation which so willingly provides an excellent service.

The Marine Pollution Control Unit (MPCU)

2.38   This is a Governmental organisation which has the ability to arrange for assistance to vessels in distress and which, in some circumstances, can require the vessel to accept such assistance. It also has the main responsibility for cleaning up pollution.

2.39   HM Coastguard and MPCU together form the Coastguard Agency (or COAST-GUARD), an executive agency within the Department of Transport. On 1 April 1994 COASTGUARD replaced the Marine Emergencies Organisation (MEO). Its role, which is largely unchanged, is described in Appendix I. The Chief Coastguard and the Director, MPCU both report to the Chief Executive of the Coastguard Agency.

The National Environmental Technology Centre

2.40   Warren Spring Laboratory (WSL) has, for many years, been the Government's centre of expertise in environmental technology. As an agency of the Department of Trade and Industry, WSL has offered impartial expert advice based on over 30 years of research, development and technical services in spill technology. WSL staff have also assisted MPCU operationally during major spill incidents. On 1 April 1994 WSL combined with the long-established environmental capability and expertise of AEA Technology to form the National Environmental Technology Centre based at Culham in Oxfordshire.

Salvage and towage organisations

2.41   These private sector companies have a vital role to play when vessels get into difficulties and the services which they provide can make all the difference between a pollution-free incident and one which causes extensive pollution. The Royal Navy also has salvage capacity which is generally used only for naval vessels. Salvage and emergency towing are discussed in Chapter 20.

The General Lighthouse Authorities (GLAs)

2.42   Three General Lighthouse Authorities – Trinity House, the Northern Lighthouse Board and the Commissioners for Irish Lights – are responsible for providing and maintaining aids to general navigation in UK waters. The cost is funded through light dues paid by or on behalf of ships calling at UK and Irish ports.

---

[2] RNLI Annual Report 1992.

Local and harbour authorities

2.43   If polluting matter escapes from a ship there are organisations which have the power and duty to seek to prevent or limit the damage. Which organisation is involved depends upon the location and size of the escape, but the principal agencies are the harbour authority, if the escape occurs there, and the Marine Pollution Control Unit if it occurs outside the limits of a port or is on a scale which the harbour authority cannot handle. The National Rivers Authority also has a role in England and Wales, described in paragraphs 21.110 – 21.111. Local authorities have accepted responsibility for cleaning the shoreline.

Fisheries Departments and statutory conservation bodies

2.44   The Ministry of Agriculture, Fisheries and Food (MAFF), the Scottish Office Agriculture and Fisheries Department (SOAFD) and the Department of Agriculture for Northern Ireland (DANI), as appropriate, advise on reactions to spills. So do the three statutory nature conservation bodies: English Nature, Scottish Natural Heritage and the Countryside Council for Wales. The Department of the Environment for Northern Ireland provides similar advice.

Chapter 3

The Sources and Effects of Pollution

Sources of pollution

3.1   Since pollution arises from human activities, most of the contaminants entering the sea come from the continental land masses and can be traced back particularly to centres of population and to industrial and agricultural operations. The proportions from different sources have been estimated as follows[1]:

Waterborne land-source pollution	44%
Airborne land-source pollution	33%
Marine transportation	12%
Marine dumping (of mainly land-source waste)	10%
Off-shore oil production	1%

3.2   Although the contribution from shipping is a relatively small proportion of the total, it can cause significant environmental effects when it occurs in coastal waters or enclosed sea areas.

Oil pollution

3.3   The most common contaminant from ships is oil, which also has the highest public profile. The word "oil" refers to a wide range of materials including petroleum (crude oil), bunker fuels, petrol and lubricants. Crude oil is a natural substance, produced over geological time from the remains of plants and animals, so it can serve as food for bacteria, which break it down eventually to its basic components, mainly hydrogen and carbon. Crude oil in bulk coats and smothers organisms. It is toxic when fresh but after weathering in the sea only the most refractory components remain, forming floating tar balls which are widely dispersed by wind and tide, and although chemically inert, reduce beach amenity when washed up on the coast. Highly refined products of petroleum such as petrol are particularly toxic but are also extremely volatile and quickly evaporate from the sea surface.

3.4   It was estimated in 1981 that 3.2 million tonnes of oil reached the sea annually, and that about 46 per cent of this was derived from marine transportation, including tanker operations, other shipping activities and accidental spills from ships. The estimates[2] below indicate that the total amount from marine transportation has reduced substantially.

---

[1] Data from 1990 UN Report *The State of the Marine Environment*—UNEP Regional Seas Reports and Studies No. 115.
[2] Group of Experts on Scientific Aspects of Marine Pollution (GESAMP), Reports and Studies No. 50 *Impact of Oil and Related Chemicals and Wastes in the Marine Environment*.

	(all figures in million tonnes):	
	1981	1989
Tanker operations	0.700	0.159
Dry docking	0.030	0.004
Marine terminals (including bunkering operations)	0.022	0.030
Bilge and fuel oil discharges	0.300	0.253
Tanker accidents	0.400	0.114
Non-tanker accidents	0.020	0.007
Scrapping of ships	[–]	0.003
Total	1.472	0.570

3.5   Oil from tanker operations appears to have reduced dramatically: this is probably at least in part because of the increasing use of segregated ballast tankers (discussed in Chapter 7) and generally tighter regulation. But although the reduction is welcome, over 150,000 tonnes is still a very large quantity of oil to be released in a year, and these figures should not lead to complacency. Such oil will be released in harbours, and at sea along the main traffic lanes. When discharged in the open ocean it initially forms slicks which can damage seabirds, but it degrades naturally leaving only flakes and tar balls.

3.6   Although a comparatively small proportion of the total comes from single accidents such as the *AMOCO CADIZ*, the *EXXON VALDEZ* and the *BRAER*, large spills of oil in small areas can inflict serious damage and attract public interest. Therefore most public attention is focused on accidents.

3.7   While these large incidents involving many thousands of tonnes of oil are the most dramatic, it is important to appreciate that the threshold for damage in an enclosed area can be very low and that damaging amounts of pollutants can come from small vessels of all types. The loss of 630 tonnes of No 2 fuel oil from the barge *FLORIDA* in Buzzards Bay, Massachusetts in 1969, for example, caused severe environmental pollution. In addition, the transfer of oil always involves the risk of spillage, whether during loading at off-shore installations, discharging or loading at terminals on-shore, or simply in routine bunkering operations. Hundreds of small spills are reported every year and many must go unreported. They are often treated immediately with dispersant if appropriate or left to disperse naturally.

3.8   It should also be appreciated that although cargoes make up the overwhelming bulk of oil transportation at sea, it would be wrong to consider cargoes as the only threat from accidents. All types of vessels carry oil as fuel, and bunkers from a wrecked vessel can do great environmental damage. The spill of about 1,160 tonnes of Bunker "C" from the *ESSO BERNICIA* at Sullom Voe in 1978 resulted in a clean-up operation which lasted six months.

Chemicals and radioactive materials

3.9   Oil may be the major contaminant in terms of total bulk, but it is not the only hazardous substance transported at sea. Others include sulphur and fertilisers in dry-bulk carriers, and petrochemicals (including liquified petroleum gas), caustic soda solutions and sulphuric acid in liquid bulk carriers. About 25 million tonnes of such chemicals were so transported in 1985. These are regulated (as is the prevention of pollution by oil) through the International Convention for the Prevention of Pollution from Ships 1973, as modified by the Protocol of 1978, generally known as MARPOL. The most toxic chemicals, such as biocides and tetraethyl lead, are carried by container vessels and as packaged cargoes in dry-cargo vessels or passenger ships in accordance with the International Maritime Dangerous Goods (IMDG) Code.

3.10   Chemicals which are both toxic and persistent are of special concern, particularly synthetic organic compounds – insecticides, herbicides, fungicides and antifouling agents such as tributyl tin (TBT) (discussed in Chapter 9) as well as industrial chemicals such as polychlorinated biphenyls (PCBs). Since these are entirely man-made they are not easily degraded by bacteria and so persist for long periods in the environment and can build up to dangerous levels in food chains. Drums containing toxic substances can be a potential threat to the public if washed up on shores. Other chemicals transported by sea, acids, alkalis and fertilisers, are less persistent but are often carried in bulk and may be hazardous at the high concentrations which may be found in the immediate vicinity of a spill.

3.11   Special attention is given to radioactive material transported by sea. It is carefully packaged and marked so that it can be retrieved intact in the event of an accident. Control of toxic and radioactive substances is discussed in Chapter 10.

Garbage

3.12   Even apparently innocuous discards such as garbage can cause problems. In particular, synthetic materials such as plastic straps and sheeting and synthetic nets and ropes will persist for years in the sea. They entangle or kill wildlife and by damaging ships could lead indirectly to a major pollution incident. In addition, they accumulate on beaches and are visually offensive. Control of garbage under MARPOL is discussed in Chapter 9.

The effects of pollution

3.13   Pollution in the sea can affect public health, kill marine plants and animals, damage fisheries and reduce amenities. The precise effects of substances spilled or released into the sea from ships depend on the composition, the toxicity and the quantity of the substances, and also on the environmental conditions.

Concentration and extent of pollution

3.14   An important factor in determining the effect of a contaminant is its concentration. This will be highest at the site of an incident, but will progressively decrease with distance and time by dispersion and dilution. Dispersion will be least in still, enclosed waters, as was the case with the barge *FLORIDA* quoted in paragraph 3.7 above, where the effects of the oil persisted for more than 10 years, and greatest in areas exposed to the open sea, and when currents, tide and wind are strong. Bad weather can be favourable to rapid dispersal especially with off-shore winds, but adverse when sea conditions impede treatment operations.

3.15 A very large spill over an extended period will have maximum impact. In the *IXTOC* incident (a wellhead blow-out in 1979) oil travelled across almost the whole width of the Gulf of Mexico and reached the shores of south Texas, but for most off-shore spills, there is a good chance of the oil being dispersed and reduced to tar balls before it reaches the coast. Oil from the *ARGO MERCHANT* which ran aground on the Nantucket Shoals off the east coast of the USA in 1976, for example, was carried away and lost in the Atlantic. On the other hand, a spill close to the coast can have maximum impact, especially with on-shore winds. The *AMOCO CADIZ* grounding off Brittany in 1978 released 230,000 tonnes of oil which contaminated a wide range of coastal systems, including rocky shores, sandy pocket beaches, saltmarshes and estuarine tidal rivers. But even less than a hundred tonnes of oil can inflict lasting damage if it reaches sensitive areas.

The nature of the coastline

3.16 Indeed, once pollutants have come ashore, the degree of damage will depend on the nature of the coastline. Rocky shores, which are usually populated by seaweeds and attached animals such as limpets and mussels, tend to be exposed to waves, and the movement of the seas has a cleansing action. Sandy beaches are also usually subjected to at least moderate wave action, but in this case waves may be able to bury the pollutant deep into the sand. Oil and other pollutants can become trapped in coastal wetlands or buried in beach sediments and may leach out for up to a decade.

3.17 Considerable efforts are made to treat a spill at sea and prevent it reaching the coast, but local geography can cause problems. The configuration of the coast may make it difficult to set up protective booms, and clean-up after pollution may be impeded by the remoteness or inaccessibility of the site.

The consequences of pollution

Seabirds

3.18 Seabirds are the species most generally vulnerable, particularly to floating oil and other viscous substances. Birds which land on or dive through slicks become coated with oil, which clogs the fine structure of the feathers responsible for maintaining water repellance and heat insulation. This causes birds to lose their natural buoyancy and their thermal protection. In the struggle to stay afloat and keep warm they quickly become exhausted. In addition, they attempt to clean their plumage by preening and so ingest toxic oil.

3.19 It is difficult to estimate accurately the number of seabird casualties from oil pollution. Counts of oiled birds on the shore may not give the true picture because of inaccessibility of beaches, inadequacy of the search, corpses washed out to sea and also because some of the corpses may have been oiled after death. After the *TORREY CANYON* incident just over 7,800 dead birds were counted but the actual number killed was estimated to be nearly 30,000. There is not necessarily a clear correlation between the volume of the spill and the number of bird deaths, and much will depend on the distribution of bird flocks at the time. During the *BRAER* incident for example most of the birds were out at sea well clear of the wreck and mortalities were much less than would have occurred during the breeding season.

3.20   Quite apart from those killed by a spill, many oiled birds are washed up on beaches throughout the year. It is suspected that these are contaminated by bilge and ballast water, and such chronic pollution is thought[3] to cause the deaths of at least as many birds as are killed by the spectacular incidents. In spite of the large number of casualties the impact on the total population of a given species may not be significant, although if a species is already declining or if its major breeding ground is badly hit the effect can be more serious. The sight of oiled birds struggling to survive is highly distressing but their cleaning and rehabilitation is difficult, and only a very small proportion can be saved.

Fish and fisheries

3.21   Wild fish, living beneath the sea surface, are able to detect and avoid oil which contaminates the water column and are thus seldom directly affected by pollution. Fishing operations such as the shooting and hauling of nets and creels could be impeded, since gear operated through a slick would be contaminated. Most commercial species of invertebrates are not very mobile, especially those living on the seabed, and shellfish beds are at risk from oil sinking onto the bottom.

3.22   Contamination of farmed fish is a major concern, as the fish are confined in cages and cannot avoid the oil. This is well demonstrated by the £14 million so far paid in compensation to Shetland salmon farmers following the *BRAER* incident, when fish, although not killed, were tainted. Unfortunately, even the public perception that fish may have been taken from an affected area can make them unsaleable.

Other wildlife

3.23   Other marine life – plant and animal plankton in the water column – are likely to be affected only immediately beneath heavy slicks. The major damage occurs when oil comes ashore and coats the beaches, smothering living organisms and causing toxic effects when fresh.

3.24   Marine mammals, particularly seals and otters, can also be damaged. After the *ESSO BERNICIA* spill at Sullom Voe, 14 otters were killed and many others were known to be affected by oil. However, the Interim Report from ESGOSS[4] found that no seal or otter deaths could be attributed to the *BRAER* oil spill, though at about the time of the spill two otters were killed by road vehicles, one allegedly driven by a television crew.

---

[3] *Oil in the Sea* 1985. National Academy Press, Washington, D.C.—ISBN 0 309 03479 5.
[4] ISBN 0 7480 0767 9.

Local communities and economic damage

3.25 Damage to fish and fisheries can have a substantial effect on local communities dependent on them. In addition to the direct losses, loss of an area's good name may have a damaging effect. It is claimed that this happened in Shetland following the *BRAER* incident.

3.26 Oil spills and other pollution can also result in considerable harm to local communities when beaches and beauty spots are contaminated. Amenity is reduced and tourism is discouraged, perhaps with considerable financial loss to the area. Beaches which are oiled or covered with plastic debris and oiled seabirds lose their attraction and holidays are cancelled. Again, the loss of an area's reputation, however undeserved, can cause more damage than pollution itself.

Public health

3.27 Public health is usually at risk only in special circumstances, for example when drums of toxic or explosive substances are washed onto beaches. A very unusual feature of the *BRAER* incident was that both oil and small amounts of dispersant were blown onto the land, affecting local people and their livestock. The effects appear to have been short-lived but are being monitored by ESGOSS.

Taxpayers

3.28 Some other sufferers from pollution are less obvious. First comes the national taxpayer and council tax payer. The marginal costs of clearing up an oil pollution incident are likely to be largely met from the International Oil Pollution Compensation Fund (described in Chapter 19), but the staff costs of preparing to deal with an incident are substantial and are not refunded. Nor are the costs, also substantial, of prevention. In cases of non-oil pollution, the taxpayer may have to bear the whole cost of cleaning up.

The shipping industry

3.29 Finally, incidents can also harm the shipping and related industries. The crew of the vessel concerned may lose their possessions, their jobs, their health and even their lives. The vessel owner, the charterer and the cargo owner suffer commercial losses, though these are normally covered by insurance. They may also gain an unenviable reputation – Exxon cannot enjoy the close association of the company name with the *EXXON VALDEZ* incident. The insurers obviously lose. The classification society and Flag State concerned may be criticised. It must be in the interest of all these bodies to work together to prevent such incidents happening.

Prevention or cure?

3.30 This is a false antithesis in the context of marine pollution, since total prevention of pollution will always prove an unattainable goal, and a capacity to cure, or at least ameliorate, will always be required. Complete cure is, unfortunately, rarely possible, as once substances have been released into the environment they can never be recalled, but most habitats are able to recover in time.

3.31   Nevertheless this is an important and relevant question in terms of the allocation of resources. In some countries there is concentration upon limitation of damage. **We have no doubt that in so far as choices have to be made in a United Kingdom context, the concentration should be upon preventing incidents which have the potential for leading to pollution and, insofar as that fails, in preventing the escape of pollutants from the ship.**

The nature of pollution incidents

3.32   The prevention of accidental pollution in the sea is very closely linked to safety, as the crew is likely to be endangered by any incident which involves a breach in the integrity of a vessel sufficient to cause pollution. Prevention of pollution is thus best achieved by preventing accidents. Conversely, measures to prevent pollution are likely to improve safety.

3.33   Although there are special problems with oil tankers, because of the large quantity of potential pollutant on board, **we think that it is important to consider the causes of maritime accidents generally and put measures in place designed to reduce the risk across the board.** We reach this conclusion not only because maritime accidents to whatever type of craft can, and often do, put lives at risk, but because all but the smallest ships carry persistent oil[5] in bunkers which is a serious pollutant. Indeed large container ships or bulk carriers (an example of which is shown at Plate 6) may carry a quantity of bunkers which is as large as the cargo of a small oil tanker. It is also important to remember that even the best vessels can be put at risk by worse ones.

3.34   Two accidents investigated by MAIB illustrate this. In one, a large loaded tanker, the *ROSEBAY*, was struck by a fishing vessel, the *DIONNE MARIE*. The main cause of the collision was a grossly inadequate lookout in the *DIONNE MARIE*. The fishing vessel rammed the tanker and despite the great discrepancy in size, it was the tanker which suffered the greater damage, her hull being breached and some 1,000 tonnes of oil cargo spilled into the sea. The clean-up operation is described in Chapter 21.

3.35   In the other, the competitors in the Cowes Classic powerboat race ran into fog. In spite of this some of them continued at very high speed, and one struck a loaded tanker lying at anchor. Fortunately, the collision was only a glancing blow and no harm was done, but if the angle of impact had been only slightly different, the tanker's hull might have been ruptured and the powerboat so damaged that her highly volatile fuel escaped: the

---

[5] Broadly speaking "persistent oils" are residual hydrocarbons which are not amenable to rapid disappearance due to natural forces. However, because of the wide range of types, names and mixtures of products it is more difficult to give a precise definition which makes clear the dividing line between "persistent oil" and "non-persistent oil". The International Oil Pollution Compensation Fund booklet *A Non-technical Guide to the Nature and Definition of Persistent Oil* concludes that it is possible to define "persistent oil" and "non-persistent oil" by testing the properties of a particular product: "All oils which are not within the category of 'non-persistent oil' as defined shall be regarded as 'persistent oil'. 'Non-persistent oil' is oil which, at the time of shipment, consists predominantly of non-residual fractions and of which more than 50% by volume distils at a temperature of 340°C when tested by the ASTM Method D 86/78 or any subsequent revision thereof". Under this definition products such as gasoline and kerosene are "non-persistent" while marine diesel oil, lubricating oils and residual fuels are "persistent".

result could have been a catastrophic explosion, far more serious than the actual spill in the other incident.

3.36 No two accidents are ever quite the same. It is all too easy for those looking at causes to concentrate on how to prevent a particular accident from recurring – firmly shutting and securing the stable door after the horse has bolted – without considering the chances of that particular combination of circumstances happening again. It is much more instructive to look at a pattern of accidents and, just as importantly, near accidents to try to identify these patterns and underlying problems, and to establish priorities. We discuss this in Chapter 12.

Chapter 4

Effectiveness and Value for Money

4.1   Some means of disposing of pollutants are of commercial benefit to the polluter: it is, for instance, expensive for a power station to fit and run flue gas desulphurisation equipment, and there would be commercial advantages to an owner who avoided doing so. There are commercial advantages in the deliberate discharge to sea of polluting material, discussed in Chapter 9: it is quicker, easier and cheaper to throw garbage overboard than to dispose of it properly. There may be commercial advantages in poor managerial, maintenance or operational practices, though there are commercial risks attached which cannot be ignored. There are certainly commercial advantages in taking the shortest route: the problem here is that there may be risks, particularly to the environment, which the owner or Master does not appreciate. But there is no commercial advantage to anyone in the worst sorts of marine pollution: a holing or grounding with consequent loss of bunker oil or cargo. While there may be the occasional scuttled ship, generally speaking no owner or Master will deliberately endanger his ship.

The need and scope for regulation

4.2   In an ideal world everyone concerned with shipping would ensure that all ships were built, maintained and operated to publicly acceptable standards of safety. No one would adopt an attitude of "it couldn't happen to me", and controls would be irrelevant. But we do not live in such a happy world, and controls are needed for the protection of crews, passengers and the environment. There can be no question of allowing essential standards to be reduced to the lowest common denominator: the likely consequences of that in terms of human misery, loss of life and ecological destruction are too terrible to contemplate.

4.3   We must stress that, with very few exceptions, we are not seeking increases in agreed international standards on ships' construction, maintenance or operation. Most standards are adequate if they are applied properly: the problem is that application is not always adequate or consistent. If they were universally met, the risks to safety and to the environment would be substantially reduced.

4.4   The fly-by-night operator already has an unfair competitive advantage over good shipowners who meet existing standards and encourage a safety culture. Increasing standards without enforcement by all Flag States to the same high level would only make things worse, increasing the risks of pollution by driving the good operators out of business, and encouraging shipowners to flag out. We therefore concentrate in this Report, so far as ships' construction, maintenance and operation are concerned, on finding means to improve compliance with existing standards on the maintenance and operation of vessels rather than seeking to raise those levels. We are very pleased to note that IMO is adopting a similar approach.

4.5   Improving compliance will in many cases require a greater attention to enforcement of existing rules. It may even require concerted action by the international community to deal with persistent problems of poor or non-existent enforcement by a small handful of States. But it will also involve a change of emphasis, from establishing new rules and guidance to ensuring that existing rules and guidance are properly respected, and, above all, to ensuring that the shipping community understands and accepts the reasons for them.

4.6   We recognise that this will not be easy, despite our firm belief that many shipowners, charterers, Masters and crews, and those who support them such as insurers and classification society surveyors, are sensible and reasonable people who share the very widespread concern for the environment which has been evident during this Inquiry. They are busy people, often preoccupied with the need to earn a living in a precarious and highly competitive industry. They do not intend putting ships, lives and the environment at risk – who would? – but they may not appreciate the possible consequences of their actions. We are convinced that such people are amenable to explanation and persuasion, and that explanation and persuasion should feature prominently in the enforcement – in the broadest sense – of existing standards. But rogues most certainly exist, at all levels up to and including Flag States. Firm action needs to be taken against them.

Value for money

4.7   Our recommendations will inevitably lead to some increases in costs. We have considered the best information we could get on the likely costs and are convinced that our recommendations represent good value for money, but we have not been able to quantify them precisely. Although it is technically not within our terms of reference, we have also considered carefully whether there are any existing arrangements and practices which do not represent good value for money and could be scaled down or even abandoned to make way for proposals which represent better value.

4.8   In principle, we believe that any additional costs associated with safety and pollution avoidance must be carefully assessed, to ensure that resources are used as effectively as possible. Ideally, there should be an objective evaluation and quantification of the direct and indirect costs and benefits of all pollution and safety measures. This is often not practicable for the reasons we discuss later in this chapter. While costs and benefits should be assessed as impartially and analytically as possible, the value attributed to many of the benefits of safety regulation will have to rely on informed judgement. This Report incorporates our judgements, and it will be clear where we believe the balance of advantage lies.

The effects on the United Kingdom fleet

4.9   In considering costs and benefits, it is important to examine the effects of our recommendations on the viability of the United Kingdom fleet. We believe strongly that the United Kingdom registered fleet and its operators are generally among the best in the world, with sensible safety standards, good morale and an intelligent appreciation of routeing advice and the reasons for it – though, as we point out in paragraph 6.31, there is room for improvement. These high standards, while excellent in themselves, increase the costs of the fleet in relation to dubious operators who cut corners. High standards thus damage the United Kingdom fleet's ability to compete on price. Measures to bring other fleets up to the standards of the best can only improve the cost competitiveness of responsible owners such as our own.

4.10 Fiscal or other encouragement causing shipowners to remain with or flag into States insisting upon the highest standards, such as the United Kingdom, would without doubt make a major contribution to producing safer and thus cleaner seas. Evidence submitted to the Inquiry about tax incentives for shipping suggested that such incentives could prove financially and economically advantageous within the decade. Intuitively there seems no reason to disagree with that view, though the financial and economic advantages of such a policy are outside the scope of this Inquiry.

The effects on United Kingdom trade

4.11 The United Kingdom, as an island nation, imports and exports a high proportion of its goods by sea. In 1992 seaborne trade represented 91 per cent and 77 per cent of imports by weight and value respectively and 97 per cent by weight and 74 per cent by value of exports[1]. Increases in costs to shippers could increase the costs of import and export. We therefore need to consider how our recommendations might affect the costs of transport through United Kingdom ports.

4.12 An increase in these costs could make it more difficult for United Kingdom ports to compete with continental ports for transshipment. It could have a disproportionate effect on the profitability of those shipping companies whose services are almost entirely in and out of United Kingdom ports, relative to those which operate mostly elsewhere. It could have a discouraging effect on United Kingdom trade through increasing transport costs, and thus increasing the total costs of raw materials and other imports and exports to and from the United Kingdom. It could have an effect on the industries such as marine insurance which support shipping. These are crucially important considerations for an economy as dependent on trade as ours, and we must be convinced that the imposition of costly controls is justified by the expected benefits.

4.13 Dubious operators have, as we have pointed out, lower costs than good ones and can thus charge lower freight rates. This is best described as cheating. It cheats good operators, it often cheats an exploited crew, and it cheats us all by unnecessarily increasing the risks of pollution around our coasts. Despite all the best endeavours of our Port State Control inspectors, it is clear that some goods imported to or exported from the United Kingdom are carried on very poor ships: one such is described in Appendix E. Given that these cheats go to considerable pains to conceal their true character, there is no sure way of assessing how many there are: all we can say is that the risks to our coasts – and to the

---

[1] Figures taken from *Transport Statistics Great Britain* 1993 Edition—ISBN 0 11 551173 3.

safety of the crew and of those who may have to risk their lives to save them – are unnecessary and unacceptable.

4.14   It is our **intention** that our recommendations will force the operators of such ships to improve their standards or go out of business. That may increase freight rates slightly. That may in turn increase very slightly indeed the cost of trade to and from the United Kingdom, and thus lead to a minuscule increase in prices. But one cannot have it both ways. If freight rates are lower than those which a reputable shipper can afford to charge, then a small increase is an unavoidable and necessary part of bringing ships trading to our ports, and to those of like-minded States, up to an acceptable standard. The possible cost of not doing so, in terms of pollution and perhaps loss of life, is far greater.

4.15   We cannot estimate the absolute increase in freight rates that might result from successful implementation of our recommendations. For the reasons we discuss in Chapter 22, we believe it will be so small as to be imperceptible. But it needs to be stressed that we hope and intend that action should be taken internationally, by clubs of European States, on virtually all of those of our recommendations which are designed to raise actual standards of ships and shipping to the levels agreed internationally. Assuming that other countries also pursue our recommendations actively, as we trust they will through enlightened self-interest, any small absolute rise in freight rates will affect the shippers of all those States equally. We recognise, however, that any across-the-board increase in freight rates will still affect most those countries which depend most on sea transport for their trade, notably island States like the United Kingdom.

The value of pollution prevention

4.16   It is important not to overestimate the benefits of pollution prevention, especially in the wake of a major pollution incident. Pollution prevention measures which are poor value for money may also divert scarce resources from measures to protect human life. Happily such an antithesis is rare, since improved safety measures are likely both to preserve human life and to prevent pollution.

4.17   Putting a value on the benefits of pollution prevention is difficult. There are four main elements to be taken into account. The first three, clean-up, repair costs and economic losses, are generally easily measured after the event. They are however difficult to predict because they can vary hugely from incident to incident.

4.18   Valuing the fourth element, damage to wildlife and amenity, presents real problems of both logic and practicality. Some attempts have been made, but there are as yet no satisfactory measures, and it is not clear that there ever will be. But if only the costs of economic loss and clean-up and repair are used, an important dimension is left out of account. In the absence of a convincing method of determining the intrinsic value of the natural heritage, a judgement will be required.

Value for the taxpayer

4.19   We need to consider not only costs to the shipping and related industries but also the cost of any new measures to the State – which means in practice to taxpayers. Ideally, all Government expenditure should be assessed carefully to ensure that the benefits outweigh the costs. We have already mentioned that this is difficult in practice. Accurate costing of many of our proposals depends on negotiations with other Governments and with the private sector, as well as on details yet to be worked up. It is also notoriously difficult to establish the probability of a particular type or location of a catastrophe, and thus what the specific benefits of our proposals will be in terms of catastrophes averted.

4.20   We are seeking to change behaviour to encourage better practice in all circumstances, and above all to alter the chains of small events which can lead to disaster. No one knows how many near disasters there are: though we were surprised to discover how many near misses there are in United Kingdom waters which never reach the headlines. Despite advances in Quantified Risk Assessment[2], it remains very difficult to predict the form, time or place of disaster, and precision is impossible. The effects of a collision or grounding are equally difficult to predict. We discuss in Chapter 12 (paragraphs 12.52 – 12.55) the work being done on Formal Safety Assessment which looks at the totality of a ship's performance, adopting a similar approach.

4.21   All this means that however accurate the calculation of costs of a particular measure may be, assessment of whether that measure will be effective in preventing disaster will be complex and may be inconclusive. Much could be done to inform judgements, but this would almost certainly fall short of a full monetary valuation of the relative benefits of different measures.

4.22   Despite the difficulties, work is going ahead. The Marine Pollution Control Unit (MPCU) of the Department of Transport has commissioned a three-year study to quantify the risks of oil tanker cargo spills in UK waters. The aim is to produce estimates of the geographical distribution of the risk and its breakdown by accident type, spill size, oil type and prevailing weather conditions. The results will allow MPCU to identify, for any area of UK waters, the likelihood of oil spills of different sizes and types and to carry out tests to help get the best out of its response capability.

Comparing the costs of prevention with the costs of cleaning up

4.23   The cost of cleaning up after a pollution incident is obviously unavoidable. The cost of prevention is not so obviously necessary, because its effectiveness is difficult to demonstrate. We would like to see a proper comparative evaluation carried out, though this would inevitably take a long time and could not be done within the lifetime of this Inquiry. But it is worth noting that Port State Control – described in Chapter 11 – which is an invaluable first line defence against both pollution and safety risks, costs the UK less than a third of the amount spent on maintaining an aerial spraying capacity to deal with

---

[2] Quantified Risk Assessment is used extensively in many fields to estimate the probability of events including those which have never occurred.

actual spills – the fourth line of defence. As we explain in Chapter 21, we believe that the latter cannot be dispensed with: but the comparison is instructive.

Assessing proposals for regulation

4.24 We have already commented (paragraphs 2.9 – 2.12) that international discussions and agreements are continually driving forward policy, regulation and cooperation. It should be obvious, but perhaps it needs to be pointed out that regulation, whether national or international, should never be an end in itself but always a means to an end. If it does not achieve that end, or if that end would be better served in a different way, the regulation is probably useless – and may be worse than useless if it discourages or prevents effective action. That means it is essential to consider **before** agreeing to proposals how they will be implemented and enforced, how much their implementation and enforcement will cost both the regulators and the regulated, whether the benefits justify the costs and whether there are any better ways of achieving the same ends.

4.25 It must however be recognised that some measures cannot practicably be enforced. It is impossible without quite disproportionate expenditure to monitor what happens on board a ship at sea and, outside fairly small areas, precisely what route she takes. To do so would in any case risk reducing the authority of the Master to an unacceptable degree. It must also be recognised that compromises may have to be made between a proper consideration of detail and the speed of setting up new agreements.

Assessing international agreements

4.26 This is a particularly important point to remember in considering international agreements, many of which are inevitably compromises reached between those who believe they do not go far enough and those who believe they go too far. There is a danger in reaching such agreements that not enough thought may be given to enforcement and the encouragement of compliance, or to the necessary backchecks to establish first, whether the new agreement concerned is complied with, and second, whether it has the intended effect.

Assessing Government policies

4.27 This danger is reduced so far as internal regulation and agreements within the UK are concerned, but it still exists. The two new Agencies, MSA and COASTGUARD, share some responsibilities: in particular, in several areas MSA is responsible for formulating policy and COASTGUARD for carrying it out. Clearly the closest cooperation is needed. Inevitably, the two Agencies have yet to settle down and to establish procedures to ensure this: we hope they will do so quickly.

4.28 **We recommend that the UK Government sets up mechanisms to ensure that, so far as practicable, proper consideration is given to the full costs, including the costs to third parties, of any new measures it agrees, either with other**

Governments or domestically, before they are finalised. Similar consideration needs to be given to compliance, enforcement and backchecks.

Assessing our proposals

4.29   We have applied these precepts to our own work so far as they are relevant and practicable. Given all the disadvantages of increasing costs, we have tried to estimate the costs of our proposals and, as explained in paragraphs 1.23 – 1.24 above, we have sought the help of the Department of Transport in doing so. Neither we nor our Secretariat have the specialised knowledge, the resources or the time to undertake the necessary complex and lengthy studies to assess the benefits of our proposals in monetary terms. We have nevertheless kept in mind the need to be confident that the expected benefits are worth the costs. We have also kept in mind the precautionary principle (paragraph 1.16) accepted by the Government, and the general desirability of erring on the side of caution.

Chapter 5

International Law and Agreements and National Law

5.1   The sea occupies 70 per cent of the earth's surface. Many nations, particularly island nations such as the United Kingdom, are dependent upon it for the maintenance of their standards of living and even their continued existence in a form which their present inhabitants would recognise. The freedom and safety of the seas are vital to their national interests. These interests include:

(a)   national defence – the movement of warships;

(b)   trade – the carriage of goods or people by ships;

(c)   protecting the environment and flora and fauna;

(d)   fishing and the winning of living resources from the sea;

(e)   off-shore oil and gas;

(f)   cables and pipelines;

(g)   marine scientific research; and possibly, in the future

(h)   exploiting certain minerals from the deep seabed.

5.2   Small wonder therefore that international law recognises and seeks to uphold the rights of all to use the sea for the carriage of goods and passengers. Small wonder that the so-called "right of innocent passage" has played a large part in our deliberations, as has international law itself.

International law

5.3   The concept of international law is familiar to lawyers and those whose work is transnational in character. However, if only for the benefit of others, it deserves a word of explanation. It is different from national law. In the United Kingdom the law is to be found in our statutes and the common law. These statutes can in general be repealed, amended or added to at any time by our national Parliament at Westminster. The common law, as declared by the courts, is in a continual process of evolution as an instrument for adjusting the rights and obligations of all who inhabit our shores, insofar as such rights and obligations are not regulated by statute. Two features are paramount, neither of which is to be found in international law. The first is that the terms of our national law are, in theory at least, capable of precise ascertainment at any particular time. The second is that the rights and obligations arising under our national law are enforced by the courts and the executive power of the State.

5.4   International law consists of agreements between two or more nations, taking the form of treaties or international Conventions and "customary international law" which might perhaps be described as the international equivalent of the common law. It is brought together in UNCLOS, the United Nations Convention on the Law Of the Sea, which we describe in paragraphs 5.15 – 5.20 below. The whole constitutes a code of conduct more or less generally accepted as constituting an appropriate degree of comity between nations based upon more or less enlightened self-interest.

5.5   Customary international law, like the common law, is in a continual state of evolution, but unlike the common law its terms at any particular time may in some respects be difficult to ascertain. Treaties and Conventions place obligations upon their signatories and, like ordinary contracts, can be honoured in the breach or in the observance. Disputes between States as to whether there has been a breach of international law, whether based upon customary law, treaties or Conventions, can be and often are resolved by the International Court of Justice at The Hague or by arbitration. Submission to such a jurisdiction cannot be directly enforced, nor can compliance with a judgement or award, although if a State submits to the jurisdiction it will usually voluntarily honour the decision.

5.6   Despite what might appear to be its inherent weaknesses, international law does establish a duty on all States to cooperate in establishing international rules and standards to prevent, reduce and control pollution of the marine environment. An important part of that duty is an obligation to promote the adoption of routeing systems designed to minimise the threat of accidents which might cause pollution of the marine environment.

5.7   The need to achieve international consensus on changes in the rules constrains what is possible in the development of the regulatory framework for merchant shipping. We wholly accept that our recommendations must be consistent with the United Kingdom's rights and obligations under international law. That does not preclude any unilateral action not in conflict with international law, which the sovereign status and powers of the United Kingdom clearly allow. It is merely that unilateral action will often be unwise or futile, either because it will prevent the achievement of consensus or because a consensus is necessary in order to make it effective. It also needs to be borne in mind that unilateral action by the United Kingdom may encourage unilateral action by other countries on perhaps less good grounds. This might severely damage the legitimate interests of many States including the United Kingdom.

The law of the sea

5.8   International law tries to regulate all the potentially conflicting uses of the sea, and to deal with its ever increasing uses in terms of both number and scale. Each nation's territorial sea extends in principle for a set distance to seaward of the low water mark. This distance used to be 3 nautical miles but is now more usually 12 miles. However there are obvious inconveniences in the territorial sea having a highly irregular invisible seaward boundary reflecting the profile of the low water line where there are indentations, headlands and islands. Accordingly international law has evolved to meet this difficulty and in some circumstances it is permissible to use a straighter baseline than the low water mark. Thus, for example, it is sometimes permissible to draw a straight baseline between two headlands. From this it follows that there will be parts of the sea on the landward side of parts of the baselines. These waters are known as "internal waters".

Modern divisions of the seas

5.9   The United Kingdom's baselines were declared by Order in Council in 1964, thus defining its internal waters as well as its territorial sea. These internal waters include most of the major estuaries and firths such as the Humber, the Wash, the Thames Estuary, the Bristol Channel, the Solent, the Solway Firth, the Firth of Forth, and Belfast Lough, and the entire sea area between the main chain of the Outer Hebrides and the Inner Hebrides, and between the Inner Hebrides and the Scottish mainland. In 1987, following the lead of many other Coastal States, the United Kingdom extended its territorial sea from 3 to 12 nautical miles to seaward of the baselines[1]. The United Kingdom's internal waters and territorial sea are shown on the map at Appendix R.

5.10   Both the Channel Islands and the Isle of Man have their own territorial seas extending 3 miles from the coast in the case of the Channel Islands and 12 miles in the case of the Isle of Man. These are shown in Appendix R.

5.11   In addition to internal waters and the territorial seas there are now "contiguous zones" extending to a maximum of 24 nautical miles from the baseline. These can be ignored for our purposes, since no steps have been taken to define a United Kingdom contiguous zone. There are "Exclusive Economic Zones" (EEZs) extending up to a maximum of 200 nautical miles from the baseline. The United Kingdom has not so far claimed an EEZ, but exercises various aspects of an EEZ jurisdiction, for example over fisheries[2]. And there is the Continental Shelf[3] which can be more extensive than the EEZ. It is relevant to the winning of seabed minerals but not to the subject matter of this Inquiry.

5.12   That leaves only "the High Seas" where all nations enjoy equal rights and freedoms. In earlier times this term was clearly defined as the world's seas lying outside the various territorial seas. The advent of Continental Shelves and EEZs has complicated the concept in that in those areas the traditional freedoms are in some respects curtailed, but most of the world's sea still forms "the High Seas" in the traditional sense.

5.13   Where the distance between two or more Coastal States is not wide enough to accommodate the maximum extent of these areas as so defined, jurisdictional boundaries

---

[1] The Territorial Sea Act 1987.
[2] Fisheries Limits Act 1976.
[3] Continental Shelf Act 1964.

can be agreed. The United Kingdom has agreed boundaries covering the English Channel and the whole of the North Sea. In addition it has an agreement with the Republic of Ireland in respect of the boundaries of areas of the Continental Shelf in the Irish Sea and west of Scotland.

5.14   The powers and duties of States under international law are different in relation to the various zones. Thus there are duties which apply in an EEZ which do not apply in a territorial sea and duties which apply in a territorial sea which do not apply in internal waters. Conversely there are powers which are exercisable in internal waters which are not exercisable in a territorial sea and powers which are exercisable in a territorial sea, but not in an EEZ.

The United Nations Convention on the Law of the Sea, 1982 (UNCLOS 1982)

5.15   The United Kingdom is a party to the four Geneva Conventions on the Law of the Sea of 1958 which first codified much of the traditional law of the sea.

5.16   Although the 1958 Conventions remain in force, they have been overtaken in some respects by UNCLOS 1982, which was negotiated through the United Nations and which codified, confirmed and clarified the earlier agreements and also made some modifications and introduced new concepts. The United Kingdom took a major part in the drafting of this Convention, but it has neither signed nor ratified it because the Government has found certain elements of Part XI (dealing with the exploitation of the seabed of the High Seas) to be unacceptable. We understand that industrialised States involved in its preparation have not ratified or acceded for similar reasons.

5.17   UNCLOS 1982 required ratification by 60 States. It will come into force on 16 November 1994, 12 months after ratification by the 60th State (Guyana).

5.18   Notwithstanding its decision not to sign and ratify the Convention, the United Kingdom, like most other Governments, accepts UNCLOS 1982 in many ways as accurately representing the state of that part of international law which is relevant to our Inquiry. Many Governments, including the United Kingdom, have enacted domestic legislation to give effect to some of the powers and duties envisaged by the Convention, such as the 12 mile territorial sea. Because the text was the result of very detailed negotiations which went on for nearly a decade, and mostly represents a consensus view of all nations after all interests had been considered, the International Court of Justice has taken UNCLOS 1982 into account when considering relevant cases.

5.19   Whatever its actual or perceived shortcomings, UNCLOS 1982 has had a marked and beneficial effect in harmonising the practice of States, reducing the number of disputes between them and encouraging them to submit to the International Maritime Organization (IMO) proposals for traffic schemes and other measures designed to improve safety at sea.

It is obviously in the best interests of all States to follow the generally acceptable parts of UNCLOS 1982, and we hope that the problems in relation to Part XI will soon be overcome.

5.20   So the most probable future for those parts of the international law of the sea which concern us is gradual evolution, involving the implementation by national legislation of the various options and possibilities contained in UNCLOS 1982. This evolutionary process can, and we hope will, be accelerated by initiatives taken by individual nations or groups of nations, including the United Kingdom, where further measures can be demonstrated to be for the common benefit of the international community.

Innocent passage

5.21   The vitally important right of innocent passage within the territorial sea was confirmed by Article 17 of UNCLOS 1982, which declares that, subject to the terms of the Convention, ships of all States enjoy the right of innocent passage through the territorial sea. This right also exists in relation to those parts of the internal waters of a State which had been considered to be part of the territorial sea or the High Seas before the drawing of straight baselines[4]. Outside territorial waters it is subsumed in the freedom of navigation enjoyed by all ships on the High Seas and, subject to certain restrictions, within EEZs.

5.22   "Internal waters" can include areas of sea which have been used by international shipping for centuries. Both the 1958 and 1982 Conventions make it clear that a right of innocent passage exists in such cases. We return to this point in Chapter 14 where we discuss the specific problem of the Minch.

5.23   Innocent passage is defined in Articles 18 and 19. "Innocent" excludes warlike activities, acts that breach the fiscal or immigration law of the Coastal State, acts of wilful and serious pollution, and activities of fishing, research and surveying. "Passage" covers journeys through the territorial sea which may or may not involve entering the internal sea or a port.

5.24   Under Article 21(1) Coastal States can legislate to impose restrictions for certain limited purposes. Furthermore, Coastal States can attach conditions (which must be reasonable and non-discriminatory) to entry to internal waters or to a port (Article 25(2)).

5.25   Foreign ships exercising the right of innocent passage are required to comply with all such laws and regulations and all generally accepted international regulations relating to the prevention of collisions at sea (Article 21(4)).

---

[4] Article 8 (2).

Transit passage

5.26   Articles 37 - 44 of UNCLOS 1982 set out the right of ships to pass through straits which are used for international navigation between one part of the High Seas or an EEZ and another part of the High Seas or an EEZ. This is known as the right of "transit passage". In some respects it differs from the right of "innocent passage". It should be noted that in accordance with Article 38 the right of transit passage does not apply "if the strait is formed by an island of a State bordering its mainland" and "there exists seaward of the island a route through the High Seas or through an Exclusive Economic Zone of similar convenience with regard to navigational and hydrographic characteristics".

5.27   The United Kingdom recognises a right of transit passage through several straits forming part of the territorial seas: the Dover Strait, the Fair Isle Channel (between Orkney and Shetland) and the North Channel (between Northern Ireland and Scotland). The United Kingdom has also specifically recognised a right of innocent passage through the Pentland Firth (between Orkney and the Scottish mainland), and the passage between the Isles of Scilly and Cornwall[5].

Ships not on passage

5.28   Article 18(2) is an important part of the definition:

> "Passage shall be continuous and expeditious. However, passage includes stopping and anchoring, but only in so far as the same are incidental to ordinary navigation or are rendered necessary by *force majeure* or distress or for the purpose of rendering assistance to persons, ships or aircraft in danger or distress."

5.29   Accordingly the right of innocent passage does not entitle ships to "park" in territorial waters for purely commercial reasons – for instance, as a floating store or factory. It must follow that the Coastal State can instruct the Masters of such vessels to move if they do anchor for long periods without a valid reason related to passage. When oil tankers "parked" in Lyme Bay, the United Kingdom Government did just this, and the tankers left. A similar problem has arisen recently in Scottish waters. This is discussed in Chapter 17.

5.30   There is no doubt as to the United Kingdom Government's power in international law to instruct the Masters of such vessels to move or to impose conditions which must be met if they are to remain. There do not however appear to be any satisfactory powers in domestic law under which they can be ordered to move on, apart from Section 12 of the Prevention of Pollution Act 1971 which applies only in the special case where the ship has had an accident and serious pollution is threatened. **We recommend that suitable powers should be taken.**

---

[5] In the debate on the Territorial Sea Bill, House of Lords, 5 February 1987. Hansard col 382.

The rights of States within internal waters and the territorial sea

5.31 Coastal States have an unrestricted right to control shipping in internal waters, except where the right of innocent passage exists in accordance with international law.

5.32 In the case of territorial waters Coastal States can, subject to general rules of international law, use national legislation to impose rules on ships exercising the right of innocent passage. For our purposes the main justifications for such rules[6] are:

(a) the safety of navigation and the regulation of maritime traffic;

(b) the conservation of the living resources of the sea; and

(c) the preservation of the environment of the Coastal State and the prevention, reduction and control of pollution thereof.

5.33 These powers are more restricted in international straits, where international agreement is needed for traffic management schemes and pollution control rules. Any rules relating to such straits must not hamper transit passage[7].

5.34 There is no power to levy charges for passage through the territorial sea or international straits[8].

5.35 States can also issue advice to shipping. Advice takes two forms: that endorsed by IMO and published in the regularly updated *Ships' Routeing*[9], and advice issued locally in publications or Notices to Mariners. *Ships' Routeing* contains details, with chartlets, of all measures – Traffic Separation Schemes, Deep Water Routes, Areas To Be Avoided, other routeing measures and associated rules and recommendations on navigation – endorsed by IMO.

The rights of States within the EEZ

5.36 Part XII of UNCLOS 1982 deals with the protection and preservation of the marine environment. Its detailed rules, which have been implemented by few States, allow for limited action to protect the environment in the entire EEZ, the territorial sea and internal waters.

5.37 A small but, we believe, potentially significant article in Part XII, Article 211(6)(a), entitles Coastal States to impose special and additional mandatory measures for the prevention of pollution from vessels in an area where there is a particularly strong case for this in relation to its oceanographical and ecological conditions and the particular character of its traffic. The exercise of this power is subject to IMO determining that the preconditions

---

[6] Listed in Article 21 of UNCLOS.
[7] UNCLOS Article 24.
[8] UNCLOS Article 26.
[9] Published by the International Maritime Organization—ISBN 92 801 1266 X.

to its exercise are met. The Australian Great Barrier Reef is subject to such a measure, although we understand it to be regarded by international lawyers as an *ad hoc* decision rather than an example of the application of Article 211(6)(a).

5.38 All States in the North Sea Conference (see paragraph 2.22), including the United Kingdom, declared in 1992 that they would coordinate their extension of jurisdiction in the North Sea and harmonise enforcement practice in relation to pollution from vessels in conformity with Part XII of the 1982 Convention. The Merchant Shipping (Salvage and Pollution) Bill will give the UK Government the necessary domestic powers.

Other Conventions

The five main Conventions

5.39 The importance of the 1958 and 1982 Conventions is that they codified the generally accepted rights and duties of nations. However there are five other major international Conventions to which the United Kingdom is a party and which are very relevant to this Inquiry.

The Convention on the International Regulations for Preventing Collisions at Sea 1972

5.40 This lays down requirements for collision avoidance and amongst other things prescribes the conduct of vessels in Traffic Separation Schemes which have been adopted by IMO. An example of such a scheme is that in the Dover Strait, instituted in 1967, which was the first of its kind in the world. The Convention is incorporated into United Kingdom law by the Collision Regulations or COLREGS[10]. Routeing measures are discussed in Chapter 14.

The International Convention for the Prevention of Pollution from Ships 1973 (MARPOL)

5.41 MARPOL, as amended by the 1978 Protocol, contains five separate Annexes: Annex I deals with pollution by oil; Annex II with pollution by noxious liquids in bulk; Annex III with dangerous substances in package form; Annex IV with sewage; and Annex V with garbage. Annexes I and II are compulsory for all contracting parties. Annexes III and V are optional[11] in the sense that States which are parties to the Convention may opt out of either or both of these Annexes in respect of their own waters or ships flying their flags. Ships flying the flags of States which have opted out may nevertheless be subject to the rules in Annexes III and V when in the waters of States which have accepted them. Annex IV is also optional but insufficient parties have so far ratified it for it to enter into force internationally.

5.42 Only those Flag States (the majority) which are parties to MARPOL 73/78 are obliged to take steps to implement its rules in respect of ships on their registers. Ships of States not party to it may be subject to the rules when in the waters of States which are

---

[10] SI No. 1798 of 1989, amended by SI No. 638 of 1991.
[11] Article 14 (1).

parties to the Convention, to the extent that this may be necessary to ensure that no more favourable treatment is given to such ships[12]. MARPOL 73/78 is chiefly discussed in Chapter 9.

The International Convention for the Safety of Life at Sea 1974 (SOLAS)

5.43   SOLAS, together with the Protocol of 1978 and subsequent amendments, sets out detailed agreements on the construction and equipment of vessels, particularly of oil tankers and other bulk carriers, which we discuss in Chapter 7, and of the principles of navigation, which we discuss in Chapter 13.

The International Convention on Standards of Training, Certification and Watchkeeping for Seafarers 1978 (STCW)

5.44   This provides standards for deck, radio and engineering activities, laying down principles for watchkeeping and minimum requirements for certification. It is discussed in Chapter 8.

The International Convention on Load Lines 1966 and its Protocol of 1988

5.45   The Load Line Convention sets limits on the draught to which a ship may be safely loaded according to specified circumstances. The basis of the Convention is that by assigning freeboards[13] a measure of safety is applied to the ship. Factors taken into account in determining the freeboard include the structural strength, stability and compartmentation of the ship, and the means to ensure the prevention of entry of water through exposed parts of the hull, such as hatches. The visible manifestation of this Convention is the historic "Plimsoll Mark" on the sides of merchant vessels.

5.46   The contracting parties to these five Conventions are bound to ensure the application of these rules to ships flying their flags, although some of the rules are in sufficiently general terms as to leave Flag States, and classification societies acting on their behalf, considerable scope for varying interpretation.

5.47   The other important Conventions and agreements are listed in the following paragraphs.

Non-discrimination

The Barcelona Convention 1923

5.48   This Convention provides for the openness of ports and non-discrimination against ships of parties to the Convention on **commercial grounds**. There are only a small number of parties to this Convention, but they include the UK.

---

[12] Article 5 (4).
[13] That is, the height a ship's outer deck edge must be above the water level.

Vessels and crewing

The Merchant Shipping (Minimum Standards) Convention 1976 – the International Labour Organisation Convention No 147

5.49   This Convention, which has been ratified by the UK, includes a requirement to have laws or regulations laying down hours of work at sea. It is discussed in Chapter 8.

The (Paris) Memorandum of Understanding on Port State Control 1982

5.50   Fourteen European States (see paragraph 2.19) agreed in 1982 to cooperate within the limits of enforcement action permitted by international law, in order to harmonise practice on checking that ships and their crews are covered by valid certificates under the relevant international Conventions. A fifteenth State (Poland) joined in 1991 and the first non-European State, Canada, is expected to join in May 1994.

Pollution prevention

The Oslo Convention 1972

The Convention on the Protection of the Marine Environment of the North East Atlantic (the OSPAR Convention) 1992

5.51   The Oslo Convention provides for controls over the dumping of waste and other materials from ships in the North East Atlantic. Decisions under it have progressively eliminated the dumping and incineration at sea which may be permitted, and only restricted categories (such as dredged material) remain. The Oslo Convention will be replaced by the OSPAR Convention when the latter comes into force. The Oslo Convention was implemented in the areas designated under the Continental Shelf Act 1964 by legislation now in the Food and Environmental Protection Act 1985 as amended by the Environmental Protection Act 1990.

The London Convention 1972

5.52   Similar provisions on a global scale are contained in the London Convention 1972 (formerly known as the London Dumping Convention). The legislation implementing this is also the Food and Environmental Protection Act 1985 as amended.

The Declaration on Coordinated Extension of Jurisdiction in the North Sea (the Paris Declaration) of 1992

5.53   Eight States agreed in September 1992 to joint action to extend their enforcement of international rules against pollution by discharges and emissions from shipping beyond their territorial waters and, if appropriate, out to the 200 nautical mile limit of the EEZ. They also agreed to extend the scope of inspection. The Merchant Shipping (Salvage and Pollution) Bill (see paragraphs 1.35 and 5.66) includes provision for the United Kingdom to extend jurisdiction to enforce such rules up to 200 miles.

Liability and compensation

The International Convention on Civil Liability for Oil Pollution Damage 1969

The International Convention on the Establishment of an International Fund for Compensation for Oil Pollution Damage 1971

5.54   These two Conventions make provision for compensating those who suffer loss as a result of pollution caused by laden tankers carrying persistent oil in bulk. The first imposes a liability on the shipowner, up to relatively high monetary limits, to pay compensation regardless of whether the pollution was caused by his fault. The second establishes an international compensation fund. These are supplemented by two international schemes devised by the trade. Substantial revisions to these Conventions were adopted in November 1992 which will be implemented in the UK under the Merchant Shipping (Salvage and Pollution) Bill: full implementation will require enough ratifications to bring the Protocols into force. The Conventions are described more fully in Chapter 19.

5.55   No similar arrangements exist in relation to pollution from non-persistent oils or other hazardous or noxious cargoes. The United Kingdom has supported the call in the AGENDA-21 of the United Nations Conference on the Environment and Development for the development of similar arrangements for other hazardous cargoes, and the North Sea States have committed themselves to considering separate action if there is not adequate progress on this in the International Maritime Organization.

Convention on Limitation of Liability for Maritime Claims 1976

5.56   The 1976 Limitation Convention provides rules on liability for damage from most pollution not covered by the Civil Liability Convention 1969 but does not cover damage caused by nuclear cargoes. It is described more fully in Chapter 19. The limits of liability set in the Convention are widely seen as inadequate and efforts are being made to increase them.

The Paris Convention on Third Party Liability in the Field of Nuclear Energy 1960

The Brussels Supplementary Convention 1963

The Vienna Convention on Civil Liability for Nuclear Damage 1963

5.57   The Paris Convention, which has been ratified by Organisation for Economic Development and Cooperation (OECD) countries including the UK, makes the operator of a nuclear installation strictly liable for damage to third parties and sets limits of liability. It covers damage caused by nuclear cargoes in transit as well as site-based risks. The Brussels Convention is supplementary to it and raised the levels of liability in the Paris Convention for Contracting Parties. The Conventions and their Protocols were implemented in the UK by the Nuclear Installations Acts 1965 and 1969 and subsequent amendments. The Vienna Convention covers similar points in relation to a different group of countries. The regime for compensation for damage caused by nuclear materials in transit is described in Chapter 19.

Pollution emergencies

The International Convention relating to Intervention on the High Seas in Cases of Oil Pollution Casualties 1969

The Protocol Relating to Intervention on the High Seas in Cases of Marine Pollution by Substances Other than Oil 1973

5.58   The United Kingdom is a party to the Intervention Convention and its 1973 Protocol. They are implemented through the Prevention of Oil Pollution Act 1971, which gives the Secretary of State extensive intervention powers in relation to all ships within United Kingdom territorial waters and United Kingdom registered ships outside them. The powers are discussed in Chapter 20 and are described in Appendix J.

The Salvage Convention 1989

5.59   The Salvage Convention, discussed in Chapter 20, introduces a new regime of "special compensation" for measures taken by salvors to protect the environment. It has been signed by the UK and will be ratified when the Merchant Shipping (Salvage and Pollution) Bill is enacted.

The response to pollution incidents

The Bonn Agreement for Cooperation in dealing with Pollution of the North Sea by Oil and Other Harmful Substances 1983

5.60   The Bonn Agreement by the North Sea States and the European Community is designed to coordinate responses within the North Sea, the English Channel and the Western Approaches to problems caused by possible pollution from oil and other harmful substances, from both shipping and off-shore activities. It allocates responsibility for taking the lead in response to incidents outside territorial waters and provides for cooperation in response.

The International Convention on Oil Pollution Preparedness, Response and Cooperation (OPRC Convention) 1990

5.61   This Convention provides a framework for international cooperation for combatting major oil pollution incidents. Though it has not been signed by the United Kingdom it will be ratified once the Merchant Shipping (Salvage and Pollution) Bill has been enacted. The Bonn Agreement and the OPRC Convention are discussed in Chapter 21.

The incorporation of Conventions into UK law

5.62   International law and agreements regulate relations between States. National laws regulate the rights and duties of natural and juridical persons subject to those laws. The two come together in two ways. First, some international agreements require States which are parties to give effect to them in their national laws. Second, international law and agreements constrain the sovereign right of States to legislate to the extent that no State should make legislative provisions which are inconsistent with its international obligations.

The Merchant Shipping Acts

5.63 International Conventions and agreements bind the UK only after it has accepted them by signature and, if the Convention or Agreement so provides, by ratifying them. By the "Ponsonby Convention" (so called after the Minister who introduced it), UK ratification occurs only after the instrument has lain before Parliament for 21 sitting days, in order to give opportunity for objection to be taken. Ratification can also take place only when UK law is consistent with the requirements of the instrument: this may require legislation, either primary[14] or secondary (or subordinate)[15], between signature and ratification.

5.64 Most of the Conventions have been incorporated into UK law or otherwise implemented through a series of Merchant Shipping Acts. The key Act is the Merchant Shipping Act 1894, which has been repeatedly amended. Others include the Merchant Shipping (Oil Pollution) Act 1971, which gave effect to the 1969 Civil Liability Convention; the Merchant Shipping Act 1974, which gave effect to the 1971 Fund Convention; and the Merchant Shipping Act 1979, Sections 20 and 21 of which allow the implementation through subordinate legislation of ratified Conventions on pollution from ships and on safety and health relating to shipping.

5.65 We were pleased to learn that as part of the Government's review of the whole field of Government regulation, with the aim of relieving industry of all unnecessary burdens, the Department of Transport is putting in hand a review, to be completed within a limited timescale, of all Merchant Shipping legislation, primary and secondary.

The Merchant Shipping (Salvage and Pollution) Bill

5.66 The Merchant Shipping (Salvage and Pollution) Bill was, as we recorded in paragraph 1.35, introduced to Parliament in January 1994. It is designed to:

(a) give effect to the Salvage Convention 1989;

(b) enable the implementation of the International Convention on Oil Preparedness, Response and Cooperation 1990;

(c) facilitate the making of subordinate legislation when implementing international agreements relating to marine pollution;

(d) give effect to the Paris Declaration;

(e) provide for the implementation of the Protocols of 1992 to amend the International Convention on Civil Liability for Oil Pollution Damage 1969 and the International Convention on the Establishment of an International Fund for Compensation for Oil Pollution Damage 1971; and

(f) set out the general functions of the Secretary of State for Transport in relation tomarine pollution. No change is anticipated in the way these functions are carried out.

---

[14] That is, an Act of Parliament.
[15] That is, a Statutory Instrument made under an existing Act of Parliament.

European Community law

5.67   European Community law is in a special position in that it is superimposed upon the national laws of the Member States and, in case of inconsistency, overrides the member's national laws. The European Court of Justice also has overriding authority in areas where it has competence. As a matter of legal mechanics, this position was established in the United Kingdom by United Kingdom statute to this effect, but other Member States use different mechanisms. However the result is achieved, EC law is to be regarded as part of the national, that is the domestic, law of each Member State including the United Kingdom.

5.68   The European Community has so far had limited impact on maritime law, but following the publication of its document *A Common Policy on Safe Seas*, more activity is to be expected. In particular the EC has agreed on common application of IMO Conventions and, more controversially, the convergent implementation of IMO Resolutions – controversial because this would make mandatory Resolutions which were originally intended to be discretionary. We discuss the implementation of this policy in the context of segregated ballast tankers in Chapter 7.

The Directive on vessels carrying dangerous or polluting goods

5.69   This Directive[16] will come into effect on 13 September 1995. The operators of all ships bound for or leaving Community ports and carrying dangerous or polluting goods will be required to provide the competent authority of the State concerned with detailed information. This Directive is discussed in Chapter 15.

Draft Proposals and Directives

5.70   We are aware of draft proposals relevant to our Inquiry issued by the EC Commission on:

(a)   **classification societies.** This draft Directive[17] sets criteria to ensure that societies are competent and reliable. The Council of Ministers agreed this in principle on 29 November 1993 and it is likely to be adopted in 1994. Classification societies are discussed in Chapter 7;

(b)   **minimum training requirements** for key personnel. This draft Directive[18], which is based on the STCW Convention, was also agreed in principle by the Council of Ministers in November 1993. Training is discussed in Chapter 8;

(c)   **segregated ballast oil tankers**[19]: this proposal for joint implementation of an IMO Resolution is discussed in Chapter 7;

---

[16] Council Directive 93/75/EEC on Minimum Requirements for Vessels bound for or leaving Community Ports and Carrying Dangerous or Polluting Goods.

[17] Proposal for a Council Directive on Common Rules and Standards for Ship Inspection and Survey Organisations.

[18] Proposal for a Council Directive on the Minimum Level of Training for Maritime Occupations.

[19] Proposal for a Council Regulation on the Implementation of IMO Resolution A.747(128) on the Application of Tonnage Measurement of Ballast Spaces in Segregated Ballast Oil Tankers.

(d) **reporting by all vessels of dangerous and hazardous goods:** this[20] would extend the provisions of the agreed Directive to all ships in EC waters. We discuss it in Chapter 15; and

(e) **Port State Control**[21]: this very recent proposal is discussed in Chapter 11.

EC policy for the future

5.71   In June 1993 the Council of Ministers passed a resolution welcoming *A Common Policy on Safe Seas*, and confirming its intention to take action to improve maritime safety and prevent marine pollution. The resolution mapped out a wide-ranging work programme of legislative and other measures. The draft proposals listed in paragraph 5.70 are the first tranche of legislative initiatives in the programme.

5.72   The resolution emphasised that Community measures should apply as far as possible to ships of all flags sailing in Community waters. The key mechanisms to achieve this objective would be to strengthen inspection, to improve the safety of marine navigation, and to propose to IMO specific measures relating to environmentally sensitive areas.

5.73   Future proposals will include rules governing marine equipment, safety measures for new small passenger and cargo vessels, enforcement of certain IMO Resolutions (including the IMO Resolution on Identification Numbers for Ships), and measures to extend traffic surveillance.

5.74   In response to incidents resulting in marine pollution in European waters in the opening months of 1994, the Community's Transport and Environmental Ministers made a joint statement in March 1994. The statement was designed to give added impetus to those measures in the work programme which bear directly on reducing marine pollution.

Future developments in international law

5.75   We entirely accept that the United Kingdom must work within the confines of international law in seeking to reduce the chances of dangerous and potentially polluting incidents at sea. So must groups of nations such as the European Community and the North Sea States. We also accept that international law, treaties and Conventions do move forward. UNCLOS 1982 was itself a very major step forward and, as we have said, it is accepted in the areas with which we are concerned as being an accurate statement of current international law.

---

[20] Proposal for a Council Directive on a European vessel reporting system in the maritime zones of Member States.
[21] Proposal for a Council Directive concerning the enforcement, in respect of shipping using Community ports and sailing in the waters under the jurisdiction of the Member States, of international standards for ship safety, pollution prevention and shipboard living and working conditions.

5.76 Compromises between the often conflicting interests of different countries are unavoidable. That is why groups of countries such as the North Sea States and the European Community are in some respects moving forward in advance of IMO. While full international agreement through IMO to the measures they have undertaken would be better still, progress by groups of countries (which we refer to as "clubs") is a very great deal better than no progress at all.

5.77 Some of the recommendations in this report are "domestic" in character. Others need IMO adoption if they are to achieve anything. Yet others would be more valuable if adopted by IMO, but would achieve their objectives if adopted by the EC or by the North Sea States. However, despite the international character of shipping, it is important not to lose sight of the fact that unilateral action is sometimes an option, so long as it is consistent with international law, even if it is an option which would be adopted reluctantly and only in circumstances in which the benefits clearly outweighed the disadvantages.

The rights of Port and Coastal States

5.78 The rights of individual States and their national laws are invoked both in giving effect to international obligations and when taking unilateral action which does not conflict with those obligations. Accordingly it is to that aspect of the law which we now turn.

Port State Jurisdiction

5.79 Port State Jurisdiction is a relatively new term, but it describes an age-old concept, namely the power of a Port State to confer rights or impose duties on those using its ports. Sometimes this is achieved by the exercise of the inherent powers of the Government – what are known to United Kingdom law as "prerogative powers" – and sometimes by national legislation.

Recognition of Port State Jurisdiction in international law

5.80 Port State Jurisdiction is specifically envisaged in UNCLOS 1982 Article 25:

> "25 (1) The coastal State may take the necessary steps in its territorial sea to prevent passage which is not innocent.

> "25 (2) In the case of ships proceeding to internal waters or a call at a port facility outside internal waters, the coastal State also has the right to take the necessary steps to prevent any breach of the conditions to which admission of those ships to internal waters or such a call is subject.

> "25 (3) The coastal State may, without discrimination in form or in fact among foreign ships, suspend temporarily in specified areas of its territorial sea the innocent passage of foreign ships if such suspension is essential for the protection of its security, including weapons exercises. Such suspension shall take effect only after having been duly published."

5.81   It is also envisaged by UNCLOS 1982 Article 218, one of the Articles by reference to which the Paris Declaration of 1992 (see paragraph 5.53 above) is likely to be implemented. This reads:

> "218 (1)   When a vessel is voluntarily within a port or at an off-shore terminal of a State, that State may undertake investigations and, where the evidence so warrants, institute proceedings in respect of any discharge from that vessel outside the internal waters, territorial sea or exclusive economic zone of that State in violation of applicable international rules and standards established through the competent international organization or general diplomatic conference.

> "218 (2)   No proceedings pursuant to paragraph 1 shall be instituted in respect of a discharge violation in the internal waters, territorial sea or exclusive economic zone of another State unless requested by that State, the flag State, or a State damaged or threatened by the discharge violation, or unless the violation has caused or is likely to cause pollution in the internal waters, territorial sea or exclusive economic zone of the State instituting the proceedings.

> "218 (3)   When a vessel is voluntarily within a port or at an off-shore terminal of a State, that State shall, as far as practicable, comply with requests from any State for investigation of a discharge violation referred to in paragraph 1, believed to have occurred in, caused, or threatened damage to the internal waters, territorial sea or exclusive economic zone of the requesting State. It shall likewise, as far as practicable, comply with requests from the flag State for investigation of such a violation, irrespective of where the violation occurred.

> "218 (4)   The records of the investigation carried out by a port State pursuant to this article shall be transmitted upon request to the flag State or to the coastal State. Any proceedings instituted by the port State on the basis of such an investigation may, subject to section 7, be suspended at the request of the coastal State when the violation has occurred within its internal waters, territorial sea or exclusive economic zone. The evidence and records of the case, together with any bond or other financial security posted with the authorities of the port State, shall in that event be transmitted to the coastal State. Such transmittal shall preclude the continuation of proceedings in the port State."

5.82   The only limitations upon the power, as contrasted with the wisdom, of exercising Port State Jurisdiction are that:

(a)   it must not be exercised unreasonably;

(b)   it must not discriminate against a foreign vessel; and

(c)   its exercise must not be inconsistent with international obligations accepted by the State exercising the power.

5.83   The power has already been used by France which, by French national law, requires vessels transitting the Traffic Separation Schemes around the French coast to report to the French authorities. This requirement, not being imposed by international agreement, is effective only against French flagged vessels and vessels which visit French ports and thereby subject themselves to French jurisdiction.

5.84   It has also been used by Australia. Australian national law, enacted after consultations with IMO, requires vessels to follow specific routes through the area of the Great Barrier Reef *en route* for Australian ports. Masters can be prosecuted if they are found within Australia up to three years after the date of the alleged offence.

5.85   The EC Directive 93/75/EEC of 13 September 1993, described in paragraph 5.69, is yet another example of the use of Port State Jurisdiction: it applies only to vessels going into or out of EC ports.

5.86   In a United Kingdom context we see the most immediate and important use of Port State Jurisdiction as an instrument for use in the stricter enforcement of existing internationally agreed standards and of course new standards as they are agreed. This is mainly considered in Chapter 11.

Coastal State Jurisdiction

5.87   Coastal States have jurisdiction over internal waters, territorial waters and (for some purposes) the EEZ, but this is limited by the rights of innocent and transit passage as well as by the considerations set out in paragraph 5.82 above. Coastal State Jurisdiction is recognised in UNCLOS 1982 Article 21 (see paragraph 5.24 above). Article 211 (3), which covers both Port State Jurisdiction and Coastal State Jurisdiction, reads:

> "211 (3)   States which establish particular requirements for the prevention, reduction and control of pollution of the marine environment as a condition for the entry of foreign vessels into their ports or internal waters or for a call at their off-shore terminals shall give due publicity to such requirements and shall communicate them to the competent international organization [that is, IMO]. Whenever such requirements are established in identical form by two or more coastal States in an endeavour to harmonize policy, the communication shall indicate which States are participating in such co-operative arrangements. Every State shall require the master of a vessel flying its flag or of its registry, when navigating within the territorial sea of a State participating in such co-operative arrangements, to furnish, upon the request of that State, information as to whether it is proceeding to a State of the same region participating in such co-operative arrangements and, if so, to indicate whether it complies with the port entry requirements of that State. This article is without prejudice to the continued exercise by a vessel of its right of innocent passage or to the application of article 25, paragraph 2 [see paragraph 5.80]."

Port and Coastal State Jurisdiction and UK law

5.88   Although in terms of international law there is no doubt as to the existence and extent of the United Kingdom's right to invoke its Port (and Coastal) State Jurisdiction, it is a right which is best, and sometimes can only be, implemented by primary legislation. At present this has been done in a relatively piecemeal manner. Furthermore we were surprised to find that there was doubt as to the precise scope of existing powers in UK law. Thus on questioning by us, it appeared that no one was very sure as to the sea areas within which powers to detain ships were exercisable (see paragraphs 17.36 – 17.43). Quite apart from this the disadvantage of a piecemeal approach is that if a new need arises urgently, as has been the case with the fish factory ships (see Chapter 17), there may be no Parliamentary time available for the enactment of the necessary legislation.

5.89 We believe that the primary legislation necessary to implement our recommendations should include more general provisions:

(a) to extend UK jurisdiction to the maximum extent consistent with the UK's obligations under the Conventions, so that, for instance, the power to detain ships would be extended to the maximum area permitted by SOLAS; and

(b) to enable regulations to be made covering those aspects of Port and Coastal State Jurisdiction which are recognised by international law but which are not covered by specific Conventions or other international agreements.

5.90 Legislation on the second of these points should be strictly confined to, but cover the whole scope of, Port and Coastal State Jurisdiction recognised by international law, that is it would be directed exclusively at the objectives specified in Article 21 of UNCLOS and in particular "the safety of navigation and regulation of maritime traffic" (paragraph 1(a)), the conservation of the living resources of the sea (paragraph 1(c)) and the preservation of the environment of the UK and the prevention, reduction and control of pollution of its waters (paragraph 1(f)). It should expressly exclude power to make rules and regulations upon commercial grounds (see paragraph 5.48). It should be clear that the power could not be used in a way which would result in discrimination contrary to international law against vessels not on the United Kingdom register.

5.91 This legislation would be used to plug evident loopholes in domestic legislation, including the need for a power to require "parked" vessels to move on (paragraph 5.30). It would subsequently be available for the Secretary of State to make such rules and regulations as from time to time proved necessary and to do so within a time scale which the circumstances required.

5.92 We hope that the need for the UK to act alone, or in advance of international agreement, would not often arise: but we consider that the power to do so should be available so that when necessary the UK can act as quickly as possible without having to wait for the enactment of primary legislation. We do not envisage that this new regulation-making power would be used frequently or indiscriminately. We believe that its use should be subject to careful scrutiny, and therefore propose that it should be subject to affirmative resolution by both Houses of Parliament. It would be open to Parliament if it wished to include an additional safeguard to the effect that any rules or regulations made under this power would lapse after, say, ten years unless they had been incorporated into primary legislation.

5.93 This new regulation-making power might be achieved by an amendment to Sections 20 and 21 of the Merchant Shipping Act 1979, which already allow for the implementation by regulation of amendments to international Conventions to which the UK is a party. We do not envisage any change to the existing arrangements whereby amendments to such Conventions are implemented through regulations using the negative resolution procedure: indeed we welcome the provision in the Merchant Shipping (Salvage and Pollution) Bill whereby the procedure for implementing changes to some of the Conventions is simplified.

5.94 We recognise that Parliament may be concerned about enabling legislation which is designed to deal with problems which have not yet arisen and cannot be foreseen with precision. Such exceptional circumstances may arise with little notice and may not necessarily be permanent. It is essential that appropriate powers should be available to deal with them immediately, to protect lives and our marine and coastal environment. We believe that the use of the affirmative resolution procedure as recommended in paragraph 5.92 is enough to ensure that the powers are used with discretion.

Chapter 6

Flag State Control

Introduction

6.1   In an ideal world **Flag States**, whose flags are worn by the world's shipping, would lay down, and enforce upon their own shipowners, standards of design, maintenance and operation which would ensure a very high standard of safety at sea. **Coastal States**, along whose coasts shipping passes, and **Port States**, at whose ports or anchorages shipping calls, would have no cause to concern themselves with the maintenance of such standards.

6.2   The present system of Flag State Control falls well short of this ideal. At any one time the fleet of any Flag State will be scattered throughout the world. No Flag State has the resources to police its fleet on a continuous and all-embracing basis. The most that it can do is to insist upon periodic surveys and to undertake *ad hoc* inspection if it learns that a ship has suffered a casualty or, for some other reason such as a Port State Control inspection, it suspects that its ship no longer complies with internationally agreed standards. Good shipowners will maintain the seaworthiness of their ships regardless of whether a Flag State periodical survey is imminent. Regrettably, bad shipowners regard the imminence of such a survey as the only reason for spending money on maintenance or repairs and then only if satisfied that the survey will be thorough.

6.3   In this situation, even if Flag States were to comply to the full with their responsibilities, Coastal and Port States would still have a part to play. They would, in their own interests, be concerned to detect the few unseaworthy ships which had escaped the Flag State net. Their role would be to supplement and support Flag State Control, but not to substitute for it.

6.4   Regrettably it is beyond argument that not all Flag States live up to their responsibilities. Figures for deficiencies and detentions revealed by Port State Control inspections[1] show that, for example, of 61 Indian registered ships inspected over one in four were so seriously deficient that they had to be detained in port. Over 85 per cent of the inspections of Indian registered ships uncovered deficiencies. India, although a striking example, is by no means alone and a number of other Flag States also have a poor record. Port States, in their own vital interests, have thus been obliged to take on a much wider, more onerous and expensive task, namely picking up the pieces where Flag States have failed. Whilst we agree that Port State Control is no substitute for effective Flag State Control, we believe that there is a strong case for strengthening Port State Control, at least for the next few years, both as a means of drawing attention to the shortcomings of Flag States and of putting pressure on them to improve their performance. Our ideas on improving Port State Control are discussed in Chapter 11.

---

[1] Under the Paris Memorandum of Understanding (which we describe in Chapter 11). The figures mentioned are in the Memorandum of Understanding on Port State Control Annual Report 1992.

6.5 In 1992 6,500 different foreign flag vessels called at UK ports. Excluding short-sea ferries and fishing vessels, there were 82,600 arrivals of which 61,100, or 74 per cent, were foreign flagged. These figures demonstrate two interrelated facts of crucial importance.

6.6 First, that the proportion of the world's shipping which still flies the Red Ensign and which is thus directly or indirectly subject to UK Flag State Control has steadily declined. In 1970 the UK registered merchant fleet was the third largest in the world, amounting to over 11 per cent of the world's gross tonnage. By 1979, despite UK tonnage remaining at a similar level to that in 1970, this had fallen to under 7 per cent because of the overall increase in world tonnage. Since then the tonnage of the UK fleet has declined significantly as world tonnage has increased, to the extent that by June 1992 the tonnage of UK registered merchant vessels was less than a quarter of that in 1979 and amounted to just 1.35 per cent of the total[2].

6.7 Second, the UK, as a major trading nation wholly surrounded by sea, is heavily dependent upon foreign flagged shipping for the movement of its goods. The opening of the Channel Tunnel in 1994 will not greatly affect that dependency. If, due to inadequate Flag State Control, many of those ships are substandard, the UK is peculiarly at risk of its coastline being polluted. It follows that the UK has, of necessity, to take on the role of a major Port State Control authority. Indeed, given the decline in the size of the UK fleet, for the time being this must be its primary task (see Chapter 11).

6.8 A State which confers its nationality upon a ship, and thus authorises it to fly its flag, has an unfettered right to subject that ship to its laws. This enables it to impose and maintain standards of design, construction, equipment, maintenance and operation. Whilst there is no upper limit to these standards, there are lower limits. These stem from the various international Conventions to which Flag States are parties, such as the SOLAS, MARPOL 73/78 and Load Line Conventions, under which Flag States are required to establish that ships flying their flags comply with the provisions of those Conventions and to issue the necessary certificates of compliance. The Conventions under which certificates are issued require that these certificates should be accepted in good faith by other States party to those Conventions – for example, Regulation 17 of Chapter I of SOLAS states that:

> "Certificates issued under the authority of a Contracting Government shall be accepted by the other Contracting Governments for all purposes covered by the present Convention. They shall be regarded by the other Contracting Governments as having the same force as certificates issued by them."

The Certificates required under the main Conventions are detailed in Appendix D.

6.9 Economic and competitive considerations effectively prevent Flag States from imposing standards which are higher than those internationally agreed and any improvement in standards is thus only achievable by international agreement. The machinery for

---

[2] Figures derived from Lloyd's Register Statistical Tables June 1992—ISSN 0076 0234.

such agreement is provided by the International Maritime Organization (IMO). This is not to say that some, if all too few, shipowners do not operate to higher standards out of pride or enlightened self-interest, but they cannot be required to do so through the mechanism of Flag State Control.

6.10   Notwithstanding the fact that these international agreements already cover a wide range of matters, there is considerable room for extending their scope. This is particularly true in relation to ship management and the human aspects of seafaring. There is also a need to upgrade the existing standards. We commend the efforts made by the UK Government to persuade IMO to take steps to achieve these improvements in the scope and strictness of internationally agreed safety standards. These efforts should be continued and intensified.

6.11   States which are party to the various Conventions undertake to implement them fully by domestic legislation and all or most do so. The United Kingdom has done so by numerous regulations made under enabling statutes. This is an effective method of implementation. But legislation is one thing. Enforcement of that legislation is quite another and it is in this respect that many Flag States are wanting. Unfortunately there are at present no effective sanctions which can be deployed against them.

Enforcement of Flag State Control

6.12   It is for Flag States individually to decide how to give effect to their international obligations. In some cases the international Conventions specify precise requirements. SOLAS, for example, requires minimum pressures at fire hydrants and MARPOL includes precise formulae for the calculation of positions of ballast tanks. But in other cases, the Conventions merely specify that equipment must be "approved" by the Flag State or be "to the satisfaction of the Flag State". Sometimes such lack of precision is necessary for technical reasons or to allow for innovation. Regrettably in others it is merely designed to conceal differences of view between the members of IMO.

6.13   Methods of enforcement vary. All, at least in theory, involve initial and thereafter periodical surveys. These surveys may be undertaken by officials of the Flag State or by private organisations, such as classification societies, acting on its behalf. There is no particular merit in the adoption of one approach rather than the other or indeed in the adoption of a mixture of the two, provided always that the approach is effective. It is impossible to over-emphasise the importance of this proviso.

Flag State advantages

6.14   A Flag State has considerable advantages over Port States in controlling the safety of its vessels. It can and should maintain records of the construction details of the ship, subsequent modifications which it has had to approve and details of surveys leading to the issue or renewal of certificates. A Flag State has an unimpeded right of access to any ship on its register and can charge the shipowner for surveys and the issue of the necessary certificates.

The UK method of enforcement – the Marine Safety Agency (MSA)

6.15   Responsibility for carrying out the UK's Flag State duties falls mainly upon the Marine Safety Agency (MSA) which came into being on 1 April 1994. It is an executive agency of the Department of Transport. Until 31 March 1994 it was the Surveyor General's Organisation (SGO) which was part of the Marine Directorate of the Department of Transport.

6.16   MSA aims to develop, promote and enforce high standards of marine safety and prevention of pollution from ships. Its tasks include developing and monitoring safety and pollution prevention policies and standards; representing the Department of Transport's interests in these areas nationally and internationally; carrying out inspections of UK and foreign registered ships and enforcing standards by application of relevant sanctions; providing survey and certification services to the UK shipping industry; and setting the standards and monitoring the training of, and providing examination and certification services to UK seafarers. These tasks include not only Flag State functions but also Port State Control responsibilities which are discussed in Chapter 11 below. Individual surveyors are generally involved both in Flag State and other survey and certification work **and** in Port State Control inspections. The work and organisation of MSA are described more fully in paragraphs 6.35 – 6.46 below and in Appendix C.

6.17   It is for the Flag State to ensure that its maritime administration is capable of carrying out its responsibilities. The international standards cover a range of technical matters including design and construction, safety equipment, radio communications, safety of navigation, the carriage of dangerous goods and pollution prevention. Although the Flag State retains overall responsibility for ensuring that the international standards are properly implemented, it may delegate some or all of its functions to other organisations such as classification societies. The level of delegation differs between administrations. MSA delegates a number of functions, such as surveys of ships for the issue of Safety Construction and Load Line certificates, to five classification societies, namely Lloyd's Register of Shipping, The American Bureau of Shipping, Det Norske Veritas, Bureau Veritas and Germanischer Lloyd.

Present weaknesses of Flag State Control

6.18   When the international Conventions were originally drafted, most of the world's merchant fleet was owned by, and flew the flags of, the world's major maritime and trading powers. These States had already established survey and inspection of their ships as a matter of public policy aimed at protecting the safety of crews and passengers. While the setting of such standards was not immune from commercial pressures from shipowning interests, their enforcement was not subject to such pressures. This was presumably in reflection of the fact that in the UK, for example, there had been a long history of regulation through the Board of Trade and the fact that most UK trade was carried in UK ships which were subject to the same standards and accordingly competed fairly with one another. States had little or no direct financial interest in shipping and could apply and enforce standards in the interests of public policy without feeling any pressure to maintain or enhance their merchant fleets.

6.19   All that has changed. Today few States regard it as consistent with their national status and dignity to be without a register of national shipping of as large a size as possible. Some also regard such a register as a useful source of income. In seeking to achieve this aim, some see no need to limit eligibility to ships whose owners or operators have any connection with the State. They maintain what are called "open" registers. A few such States are landlocked and have no connection with the sea. Rather more include ships which are never likely to call at a national port. Perhaps in recognition of this fact one of the largest and, it has to be said, one of the most efficient, Liberia, maintains its register and discharges its responsibilities from an office in the USA. Relatively few Liberian ships ever call at Monrovia, their usual port of registry. Another example is Vanuatu, which has few foreign exports and whose register is run from the USA and London.

6.20   All this might be unobjectionable if, despite the very considerable difficulties in enforcing standards on ships (and shipowners) which have no real connection with the State whose flag the ships fly, agreed international standards were universally enforced. However they are not. The vice of "open" registers is twofold. First, in practice they lead to varying standards of safety. This is easily demonstrated by **Figure 6.i** (overleaf) which shows the incidence of total losses by flag. Second, the existence of "open" registers and the consequent ease with which ships can be transferred to a different register and flag has led to some shipowners shopping around for the registers which have the lowest standards of enforcement and which, in consequence, involve them in the least expense. This is positively encouraged by some of the Flag States concerned which have even been known to advertise competitive "prices" for their survey and certification work.

6.21   **Figure 6.i** is also highly significant as showing that the national fleets with the worst losses are almost all expanding.

Flags of convenience

6.22   This expression is always used in a derogatory sense, but it is not always applied to the same flags. The International Transport Workers Federation (ITF) describes any register which does not strictly limit entry to nationals of the Flag State as a flag of convenience. This may be a legitimate use of the term from the ITF's point of view, but it by no means follows that ships flying flags of convenience as so defined are substandard. Indeed in terms of that definition the whole of the Red Ensign group of flags would be characterised as flags of convenience, since the qualifications for entry, although limited, are not as limited as defined by the ITF. For example the UK register is required by EC law to be, and is, open to vessels the majority of whose 64 shares are beneficially owned by British or EC citizens or corporations. Qualifications for other Red Ensign registers are set out at Appendix G.

6.23   A more relevant definition for present purposes is that adopted by MSA as "an open register where the Flag State does not have the capability of supervising the safety of its ships".

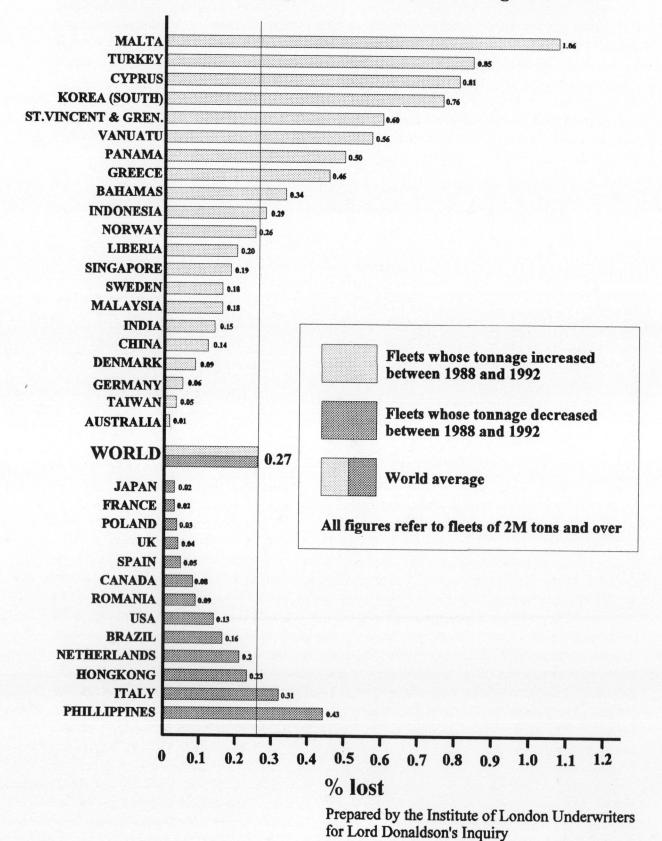

Figure 6.i

Total losses in large fleets - expanding and shrinking fleets compared. Five year average 1988-1992

	% lost
MALTA	1.06
TURKEY	0.85
CYPRUS	0.81
KOREA (SOUTH)	0.76
ST.VINCENT & GREN.	0.60
VANUATU	0.56
PANAMA	0.50
GREECE	0.46
BAHAMAS	0.34
INDONESIA	0.29
NORWAY	0.26
LIBERIA	0.20
SINGAPORE	0.19
SWEDEN	0.18
MALAYSIA	0.18
INDIA	0.15
CHINA	0.14
DENMARK	0.09
GERMANY	0.06
TAIWAN	0.05
AUSTRALIA	0.01
WORLD	0.27
JAPAN	0.02
FRANCE	0.02
POLAND	0.03
UK	0.04
SPAIN	0.05
CANADA	0.08
ROMANIA	0.09
USA	0.13
BRAZIL	0.16
NETHERLANDS	0.2
HONGKONG	0.23
ITALY	0.31
PHILLIPPINES	0.43

Fleets whose tonnage increased between 1988 and 1992

Fleets whose tonnage decreased between 1988 and 1992

World average

All figures refer to fleets of 2M tons and over

% lost

Prepared by the Institute of London Underwriters for Lord Donaldson's Inquiry

6.24 We would expand this definition to include Flag States which, whilst they may have the capability of such supervision, do not in fact exercise it for reasons of economy or a perverted desire to be competitive. We would also delete the reference to "an open register" since it is not the "openness" of the register which constitutes the vice. It is quite possible, if unusual, for a State with an open register to maintain standards which are as high or higher than is the case where a State maintains a closed register.

6.25 Accordingly we would define a flag of convenience as "a register where the State does not have the capability of supervising the safety of its ships or does not do so effectively".

Improving Flag State performance

6.26 The objective must be to eliminate flags of convenience as so defined. Progress will undoubtedly be slow because of the difficulty in undertaking international negotiations based upon the proposition that some of the participants are failing to honour their existing obligations. But a start must be made and it is to the credit of IMO that it has set up a Sub-Committee on Flag State Implementation. **We recommend that the UK Government gives the Sub-Committee its full support.**

6.27 The Sub-Committee and IMO itself are undoubtedly faced with a major problem. One of the purposes of IMO is to encourage the removal of discriminatory or unnecessary action by Governments affecting shipping engaged in international trade so as to promote the availability of shipping services to the world without discrimination. This is only achievable if all Flag States discharge their responsibilities to the full. If, as is the case at present, they do not do so, discrimination, if only in terms of Port State Control targeting, is inevitable. Furthermore, unless some major and rapid improvement can be achieved by simple persuasion, in our judgement further discrimination will have to be undertaken both in self defence by Port and Coastal States and by IMO in the general interest.

6.28 We earnestly hope that persuasion, backed by worldwide public opinion, will suffice but, if it does not, we consider that in the very near future IMO will have to consider two further initiatives. In the first IMO would publish, flag by flag, information provided by Port States on the extent to which defects are found in ships on inspection. This would bring pressure to bear not only in terms of national pride, but also commercially, because insurers, charterers and shippers could, should and, with a little urging, would take such a league table into account when considering contracting with owners of ships flying flags with a record of being substandard. In the second, which would only be necessary if the first failed to remedy the problem, Regulation 17 of Chapter I of SOLAS, and similar provisions in other Conventions, would be amended to remove the requirement to recognise certificates issued under the authority of a Contracting Government if the record of the Government concerned was held by IMO, or by a Port State without dissent by IMO, to justify such a course. **We recommend that the UK Government in cooperation with other Port States should seek to carry this process forward on these lines.**

6.29 Quite apart from a general failure to supervise the compliance of their ships with internationally agreed standards, there is evidence that some Flag States are abusing their power to grant temporary dispensations. These are not used over a wide range of aspects but primarily in relation to manning certificates, for example in the case of a shortfall in manning due to illness of a crew member. We note with satisfaction that IMO's Maritime Safety Committee is considering what can be done to prevent unscrupulous Flag States abusing the system.

UK performance as a Flag State

6.30 Whilst we have heard no criticism of the UK's performance as a Flag State, there are no grounds for complacency. Alarm bells should ring if MSA learns that a UK flag ship has been detained as a result of a Port State Control inspection. The state of the vessel which led to its detention may, of course, have resulted from a casualty or from faulty operation or maintenance by the owners, managers or crew. But the questions should always be asked – and we have no evidence that they are asked – "When was this ship last subject to a Flag State survey? Is the current state of the ship consistent with that survey having been efficient? If not, who undertook it?". This self-auditing process is all important.

6.31 We briefly mentioned in paragraph 6.4 the performance of Flag States in Port State Control inspections carried out under the Paris MOU. The statistics show that of the 246 Port State Control inspections of UK registered ships by authorities at Paris MOU ports outside the UK in 1992 over one in four (28.46 per cent) revealed deficiencies. Six out of the 189 (over 3 per cent) UK ships inspected were so seriously deficient that they had to be detained. By way of comparison, of 237 inspections of Turkish ships almost two-thirds (65.82 per cent) were deficient and 15 of the 178 ships (over 8 per cent) inspected were delayed or detained. Another example is St Vincent & Grenadines. Well over half the 375 inspections (213 or 56.8 per cent) uncovered deficiencies and almost one in six of the 247 ships inspected had to be delayed or detained.

6.32 Whilst welcoming the fact that Paris MOU figures support the view that the UK Flag State Control compares very favourably with that of most other States, we believe that the figures should still give rise to concern. While some of these deficiencies or detentions may be explicable without criticism of UK Flag State Control, it would be surprising if all are. **We recommend that the UK Government should reinforce its commitment to quality and to better Flag State implementation by monitoring its own performance even more closely.** MSA, in its capacity as the Port State Control authority, already has information derived from inspections of UK ships in UK ports, but it should also seek to ensure that it has complete and immediate information as to deficiencies in UK ships found on inspection under foreign Port State Control.

Technical assistance

6.33 We understand that some Flag States have indicated to IMO that technical assistance – money from IMO to pay for expert advice – will be required if their ability to police their fleets is to be fully effective. Clearly it is in the interests of safer shipping that such assistance should be provided, but it is not self-evident that it should be provided on terms which would involve a subsidy by efficient Flag States for the benefit of inefficient Flag States competing with them for tonnage. If, however, lack of technical assistance on subsidised terms were the only obstacle in the way of agreement to an amendment to SOLAS in order to introduce some qualification to Regulation 17 of Chapter I and to similar provisions in other Conventions, it might be a price worth paying, provided always that the obstacle to effective policing of the fleets concerned was lack of ability rather than lack of will.

The role of the classification societies

6.34   As we mentioned in paragraphs 6.13 and 6.17 most Flag States, including the UK, delegate at least some of their responsibilities to classification societies. Classification societies are international bodies staffed largely by marine surveyors. They are usually in the private sector but are not commercial profit-making organisations. Their role goes far beyond carrying out duties delegated to them by Flag States and we discuss this in more detail in Chapter 7.

Further delegation of MSA work to classification societies

Survey and certification work carried out by MSA

6.35   At present, MSA is more directly involved during the initial survey stage (when certificates are first issued) than during periodical surveys (annual and intermediate within the period of validity of a certificate) and renewal surveys (when a certificate is reissued).

Initial surveys

6.36   At the initial survey stage MSA is directly responsible for the issue of Safety Equipment Certificates, Passenger Ship Safety Certificates, International Oil Pollution Prevention Certificates, International Pollution Prevention Certificates for the Carriage of Noxious Liquid Substances in Bulk, and the various Certificates of Fitness for the carriage in bulk of dangerous chemicals and liquified gases. Despite much of the survey work relating to the Load Line Convention and Safety Construction Certificates already being delegated to classification societies, MSA continues to determine the adequacy of any equivalent arrangements and any exemptions from the requirements of the Conventions on all initial surveys.

Periodical and renewal surveys

6.37   MSA carries out all periodical and renewal surveys for passenger certificates, International Oil Pollution Prevention Certificates and Safety Equipment Certificates on ships in the UK and conducts Safety Equipment Certificate surveys on ships remote from the UK in one out of five years. MSA also usually undertakes surveys for Certificates of Fitness. Periodical and renewal certification for Load Lines and Safety Construction Certificates are delegated to the classification societies.

Surveys of ships which are not covered by the international Conventions

6.38   MSA also carries out surveys on ships that are not covered by the international Conventions – generally smaller ships such as fishing boats and ships not engaged in international trade – and on specialised ships such as pilot boats.

6.39   The MSA Business Plan for 1994-95 shows 104 man-years apportioned to survey and certification work. Of this, about 46 per cent is allocated to classed ships, 28 per cent to unclassed and specialised ships, 20 per cent to fishing vessels and 6 per cent to other surveys. Much of this work involves ships which are not covered by the international Conventions but are required to be surveyed under UK law.

The future role of MSA

6.40   In December 1992, following an earlier study which concluded that SGO should not be privatised but should become an executive agency, the Department of Transport issued a consultation document examining the options for greater private sector involvement in MSA's ship survey and certification work.

6.41   In August 1993, Ministers decided to delegate to the private sector a package of surveying and certification functions equivalent to around 25 per cent of MSA's workload in those areas. The main area of delegation concerned work on classed ships. Hull and machinery work for initial and renewal surveys of Passenger Certificates, stability approval work (except for high risk ships) under the Load Line Convention and all periodical and renewal surveys for International Oil Pollution Prevention Certificates were to be delegated to the recognised classification societies.

6.42   MSA has also to consider the scope for further delegation of work for unclassed and specialised ships, fishing vessels and others. This will involve pilot schemes to evaluate the private sector's capacity to carry out such work.

6.43   We agree that the delegation of further work in some areas makes good sense. It will certainly help to eliminate some duplication of survey work. Nevertheless we feel that the Government should proceed with caution. Whatever the long-term future of MSA, it is essential that maritime safety in the UK should not be compromised.

6.44   There are a number of points which Ministers should keep firmly in mind. As we discuss in Chapter 7, there is widespread concern at the performance of classification societies. There is evidence that registers which delegate a very large proportion of survey and certification work to classification societies have a worse safety record than registers which delegate less. The casualty experience of the Norwegian International Register which delegated all of its Flag State responsibilities clearly illustrates the dangers of total reliance on classification societies, even those of the highest international standing. The

Norwegian maritime administration has been forced to set up its own teams of inspectors to undertake worldwide spot inspections of the fleet to ensure the appropriate standards are being established and maintained. So the approach to further delegation should be a careful one.

6.45 Further delegation and the loss of fee-earning work should not of itself lead to reductions in MSA staff because of the need to maintain a proper audit of delegated work and because of the need to expand Port State Control work which we discuss in Chapter 11. MSA has already established guidelines to monitor and regulate delegated functions including a system whereby MSA can audit the societies' performance. The operation of this system will need to be assessed and developed in the light of experience of further delegation. We regard the enhanced auditing role of MSA as all important in terms of ensuring that the UK continues to be one of the best Flag States and in further improving its performance and we **recommend that the UK Government ensures that sufficient resources are available to enable this work to be carried out properly.**

6.46 To carry out this auditing function effectively and to provide technical support to the UK's negotiations within IMO and the EC it is essential that MSA retains hands-on experience of survey and certification work. The UK's role as a Flag State will be undermined if the Government's direct experience and expertise is lost. We therefore **recommend that there should be exchanges of secondees between MSA and the classification societies which carry out delegated work.** This should help to sustain direct MSA involvement in delegated functions and promote mutual best practice. Exchanges of secondments between MSA staff and oil company staff working on inspection might also be helpful. We understand that the additional costs would probably be negligible if salaries and expenses continue to be paid by the donor organisation for the period of the secondment.

Chapter 7

Ship Design, Construction, Maintenance, Equipment and Reliability

Introduction

7.1   Here and in the following chapter we suggest ways in which the reliability of ships and their crews can be improved in order to reduce the risks of accidental pollution. For convenience these chapters are split broadly between "hardware" and "software" but it is important to recognise that in operational terms "ships" are essentially a combination of both elements. We also discuss the role of the classification societies in specifying and monitoring standards of design, construction and maintenance.

7.2   In Chapter 2 we discussed the changes which have affected merchant shipping over the last 20 years or so. It is clear that many of the problems we identify have evolved as a result of the commercial pressures which developed during this period. In many ways, the culture has changed significantly. One example is the decline of the in-house design and construction teams which the major shipping companies used to employ. Design is now often left to the builders and supervision during construction assigned to classification societies. In a harsh economic climate the result has often been that ships are built down to a price with little regard to maintenance later in life. The ways in which the profile of the shipping industry has been affected by these changes is clearly illustrated by recent trends.

The age profile

7.3   According to figures compiled in June 1992, 62 per cent of the total world tonnage was over 10 years of age and 13 per cent was 20 years old or more. But for oil tanker tonnage, the proportion over 10 years old rose to 68 per cent. Although only 8 per cent of tanker tonnage was over 20 years old, 41 per cent was aged between 14 and 19 years[1]. This is a result of the "bulge" in tanker building in the mid-1970s and the downturn in the number of newbuildings and scrappings in recent years. Unless there is a significant rise in the numbers of new tankers being built and old tankers being scrapped, almost 50 per cent of the world's tanker tonnage is likely to be over 20 years old well before the end of the century.

7.4   We note that although some analysts predict a steep rise in the number of scrappings and newbuildings, others are less optimistic. A major and sustained increase in activity will be required to alter significantly the age profile of the world merchant fleet. This is particularly true of the tanker sector.

---

[1] Lloyd's Register Statistical Tables June 1992—ISSN 0076 0234.

Casualty figures

7.5 *The Institute of London Underwriters 1993 Casualty Statistics* indicate that older vessels are more vulnerable than newer ones. Only four ships out of 121 lost in 1993 were less than 10 years old. 12 out of 13 tankers lost were at least 15 years old (94 per cent of tanker tonnage lost) and all but one of these was at least 20 years old. The ILU report concludes that this may be due more to the human factor associated with older vessels than to structural condition: older ships may not necessarily be in poor repair but as they age they may be sold to operators whose standards are substantially lower. Whatever the reasons, the fact that older vessels are more likely to become casualties is worrying given that the age profile of world shipping seems likely to worsen before it improves[2].

7.6 **Figure 7.i** (opposite) shows annual total losses between 1983 and 1993. **Figure 7.i.a** shows the tonnage lost. The overall tonnage lost steadily declined between 1984 and 1989 but rose sharply in 1990 and again in 1991 to a peak of over 1,750,000 gross registered tons (grt)[3] before declining sharply in 1992 and 1993 to just over 650,000 grt. The figures for losses of different types of tonnage show wide fluctuations. Tankers totalling almost 115,000 grt were lost in 1989. This total rose in 1990 and 1991 to almost 500,000 grt before declining in 1992 and 1993 to about 190,000 grt. However, **Figure 7.i.b** shows that fluctuations in the **numbers** of tankers lost have not been so marked. Despite the fall in tanker tonnage lost between 1991 and 1993, the number of vessels concerned has remained largely unchanged: 15 were lost in 1991; 16 in 1992; and 13 reported in 1993[4]. Whilst we welcome any reduction either in the tonnage or the number of vessels lost – and we are pleased to see that bulk carrier losses have declined significantly both in terms of tonnage and numerically – some of those we spoke to expressed concern that the downward trend may not be sustained.

Vessels with serious deficiencies

7.7 In terms of major pollution accidents we have made it clear that we believe that the greatest risks are posed by oil tankers, ships such as large bulk carriers whose bunker capacities may exceed the cargo capacity of small oil tankers, chemical carriers and gas carriers. *The Paris Memorandum of Understanding on Port State Control 1992 Annual Report*[5] provides details of the Port State Control inspections carried out by the members of the Paris Memorandum of Understanding (which we describe in Chapter 11). In the report, the above types of ship are, broadly speaking, covered by four categories: tankers/combination carriers; bulk carriers; chemical tankers; and gas tankers. These categories accounted for 40.5 per cent of all the ships inspected but 47.3 per cent of all the ships detained.

---

[2] All figures taken from *The Institute of London Underwriters 1993 Casualty Statistics* issued with *The Institute of London Underwriters 1993 Annual Report*. (Institute of London Underwriters, 49, Leadenhall Street, London EC3A 2BE).

[3] Gross registered tons: capacity, in cubic feet, of the space within the hull, and of the enclosed spaces above the deck, which are available for cargo, stores, passengers and crew, with certain exceptions, divided by 100. Thus 100 cubic feet of capacity is equivalent to one gross ton.

[4] See footnote 2 above.

[5] Published by the Secretariat of the Memorandum of Understanding on Port State Control, Bordewijkstraat 4, PO Box 5817, 2280 HV RIJSWIJK, The Netherlands.

Figure 7.i
Annual total losses 1983–93

a. Tonnage

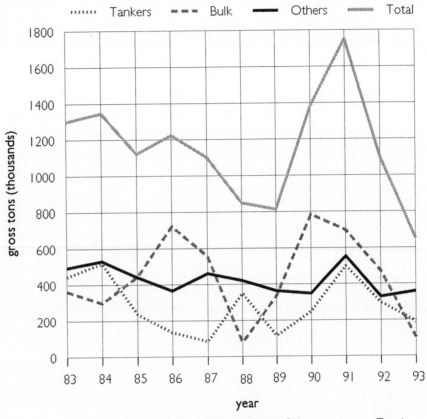

b. Number of ships

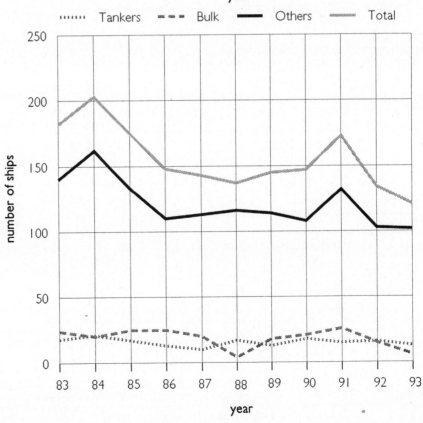

Prepared by the Institute of London Underwriters for Lord Donaldson's Inquiry

7.8 All, apart from gas tankers, showed a detention rate above the overall rate of detentions for all categories. The full details of the percentages and types of ships detained are set out in **Figure 7.ii** (below). We have not looked at the source data for these figures and various factors, such as targeting, may have affected the results. To take an unlikely example, it may be that 75 per cent of all tankers/combination carriers but only 10 per cent of gas tankers visiting Paris MOU ports were inspected. Assuming that this was the case it might be argued that if more gas tankers had been inspected the percentage with serious deficiencies might have been greater. We do not know. But whatever the actual levels of inspection, it is a fact that almost 8 per cent of tankers/combination carriers and over 6 per cent of bulk carriers and chemical tankers inspected were detained or delayed (we discuss chemical tankers further in paragraph 10.5). Whatever the type of deficiency found, this is clear cause for concern because any serious deficiency must be indicative of substandard operation, including maintenance.

The causes of accidents

7.9 Most experts agree that human error accounts for between 60 and 80 per cent of all accidents. The UK P & I Club's analysis of major claims between 1987 and 1992 supports this, with 63 per cent of major claims directly attributable to human error[6]. As a comparison, 28 per cent of major claims were caused by structural, mechanical or equipment failure, which indicates that whilst operational error is the major direct cause, "hardware" failure can also be a significant problem. Of course most accidents are caused by a combination of "hardware" and "software" factors and most equipment or structural failures will ultimately have resulted from human failure, perhaps through carelessness in design, construction or maintenance at an earlier stage.

Figure 7.ii

THE MEMORANDUM OF UNDERSTANDING ON PORT STATE CONTROL ANNUAL REPORT 1992

Delays/detentions per ship type in percentage of individual ships of respective types involved

ship types	number of inspections	number of individual ships	number of detentions	detentions in % of individual ships
general dry cargo ships	5607	3781	246	6.51
bulk carriers	3134	2302	141	6.13
tankers/combination carriers	1607	1187	94	7.92
gas tankers	284	201	8	3.98
chemical tankers	819	548	35	6.39
passenger ships/ferries	511	347	7	2.02
refrigerated cargo ships	755	548	14	2.55
roll-on, roll-off/container/vehicle ships	1753	1269	29	2.29
other ship types	313	272	14	5.15
totals	**14783**	**10455**	**588**	**5.62**

[6] The United Kingdom Mutual Steam Ship Assurance Association (Bermuda) Limited—*Analysis of Major Claims 1993.*

Regulation

7.10 The standards to which ships ought to be built and maintained are laid down in the main IMO Conventions and the Rules and Regulations of the classification society with which the ship is classed. Both are revised from time to time to take account of changing circumstances either through IMO or by the society. The revision process is often slow.

7.11 The design and construction of vessels carrying oil and other hazardous cargoes in bulk are regulated by a number of IMO Conventions. SOLAS (see paragraphs 5.43 and 7.12 – 7.21 below) applies to all vessels engaged on international voyages and includes all cargo ships of 500 grt and over. MARPOL (see paragraphs 5.41 – 5.42 and 7.22 – 7.26 below) Annex I deals with the prevention of oil pollution and applies to oil tankers of 150 grt and over and to other ships of 400 grt and over. Annex II covers the prevention of pollution by noxious liquid substances not covered by Annex I and applies to all ships regardless of size. The Load Line Convention (paragraph 5.45) which sets limits on the draught to which a ship may be safely loaded is also an important factor.

SOLAS requirements

7.12 Chapter II of SOLAS covers the design and construction of ships in general, including damage stability, machinery and electrical equipment and also fire protection, detection and extinction. The SOLAS regulations specify the requirements for items such as collision bulkheads, watertight decks, bilge pumping arrangements, stability information, machinery arrangements and also for essential pieces of equipment. SOLAS also specifies the special fire safety measures for tankers. Radiocommunications are dealt with in Chapter IV of SOLAS and are discussed in Chapter 13.

Twin screws and twin engines

7.13 SOLAS does not include specific requirements for twin screws or twin engines. The Convention states that Administrations shall give special consideration to the reliability of single, essential, propulsion components and may require a separate source of propulsion power sufficient to give the ship a navigable speed, especially in the case of unconventional arrangements. This special consideration is covered by design assessment, survey, testing and certification of propulsion machinery at the manufacturer's works, together with the evaluation of historical data of operating performance and reliability of particular engine arrangements on board ship.

7.14 The Convention requires means to be provided to allow the normal operation of propulsion machinery to be sustained or restored even though one of the essential auxiliaries becomes inoperative. This is normally achieved by designing in redundancy – a method which is also used for other systems such as electrical systems.

Designing in redundancy

7.15 This does not mean wholesale duplication of a ship's systems but duplication only of key elements, such as the duplication of electrical generating sets, essential pumps and other items, to allow normal operation if certain items become inoperative or are being maintained. Another example is an electrical system where the danger likely to result if a sensor fails can be greatly reduced by incorporating "redundant" components into the system – if one component breaks down, its "redundant" partner will automatically come into operation. We discuss duplication further in paragraphs 7.71 – 7.72 below.

Steering gear

7.16 The *AMOCO CADIZ* tanker casualty off the Brittany coast led to changes in the rules for steering gear. All new oil, chemical and gas tankers of 10,000 grt and over must have their main steering gear arranged so that loss of steering due to most likely single failures can be regained within 45 seconds. Older oil, chemical and gas tankers of 40,000 grt and over must if necessary be modified so that steering capability can be speedily regained after some types of single failure[7]. This is an example of regulation as a reaction to events as opposed to forward planning which we discuss further in Chapter 12.

Surveys during and after construction

7.17 SOLAS requires that the hull, machinery and equipment of cargo ships, including tankers, must be surveyed during construction to ensure that they comply with the requirements for the issue of a Cargo Ship Safety Construction Certificate. The initial and periodical surveys (renewal survey every five years) ensure that the arrangements, material and scantlings[8] of the structure, boilers and other pressure vessels, main and ancillary machinery including the steering gear and associated control systems, electrical installations and other equipment are in all respects satisfactory for the service for which the ship is intended. Such surveys, in the case of tankers, also include inspection of the outside of the ship's bottom, pump-rooms, cargo and bunker piping systems, vent piping, pressure vacuum valves and flame screens.

7.18 In addition to the periodical surveys, tankers of ten years of age and over must undergo a minimum of one intermediate survey (about two and a half years after each renewal survey) during the validity of the Cargo Ship Safety Construction Certificate. The intermediate survey includes inspection of the steering gear equipment and associated control systems, pump-rooms, cargo and bunker piping systems on deck and in pump-rooms, vent piping, pressure vacuum valves and flame screens, the electrical installation in dangerous zones and the outside of the ship's bottom. Such intermediate surveys are endorsed on the Cargo Ship Safety Construction Certificate. There is an obligation under SOLAS for the ship and her equipment to be maintained to ensure that the ship in all respects remains fit to proceed to sea without danger to the ship or persons on board.

Chemical tankers and liquified gas carriers

7.19 The design, construction and operation of chemical tankers and liquified gas carriers are dealt with further by Chapter VII of SOLAS. This Chapter brings into effect the International Code for the Construction and Equipment of Ships carrying Dangerous

---

[7] SOLAS Chapter II-1 Regulation 29.
[8] A set of standard dimensions for parts of a ship's structure.

Chemicals in Bulk (IBC Code) and the International Code for the Construction and Equipment of Ships carrying Liquified Gases in Bulk (IGC Code). These Codes are amended from time to time by IMO on advice from its Sub-Committee on Bulk Chemicals.

7.20   The IBC and IGC Codes contain additional requirements tailored to suit the different types of chemical and liquified gas carried. They also contain requirements for surveys to be carried out within stipulated periods so that the ship is maintained in a condition fit to carry the cargoes intended. These surveys are usually carried out concurrently with other safety surveys to avoid duplication of effort. The carriage of dangerous chemicals and gases in bulk is discussed further in paragraphs 10.3 – 10.5.

Ships carrying dangerous goods in packaged form

7.21   There are no additional design or constructional requirements above those in Chapter II of SOLAS for a ship carrying dangerous goods in packaged form. Requirements in Chapter VII of SOLAS covering such cargoes relate to packaging and labelling rather than vessel structure. Detailed requirements are contained in the International Maritime Dangerous Goods Code (IMDG Code) which is discussed further in paragraphs 10.6 – 10.12.

MARPOL requirements

7.22   Annex I of MARPOL specifies the design, construction and operation of oil tankers with the aim of ensuring protection against oil pollution in the event of collision or grounding. It also covers the control and regulation of operational pollution – which is discussed in Chapter 9. The regulations in Annex I include requirements for segregated ballast tanks, dedicated clean ballast tanks, protective location of segregated ballast spaces and requirements for minimizing oil pollution due to side and bottom damage.

Surveys of oil tankers

7.23   The structure, equipment and fittings of new oil tankers are required to be thoroughly surveyed before they enter service to ensure that they meet the requirements of Annex I for the issue of an International Oil Pollution Prevention Certificate (IOPP Certificate). Periodical surveys for the renewal of the Certificate are carried out every five years with a minimum of one intermediate survey during the validity of the Certificate which is intended to ensure that equipment and systems remain satisfactory. Administrations are also required to institute arrangements for unscheduled inspections during the validity of the IOPP Certificate unless they have established mandatory annual surveys: UK pollution prevention regulations require annual surveys.

Survey report files

7.24   We welcome the recent amendment to MARPOL[9] which requires that oil tankers over five years old shall carry a complete file of survey reports, including the results of all

---

[9] MARPOL 73/78, Annex I, Regulation 13G.

scantlings required as well as the statement of structural work carried out. This file must be accompanied by a condition evaluation report containing conclusions on the structural condition of the ship and its residual scantlings, endorsed by the ship's Flag State. The presence of this file should make it easier for Port State Control inspectors (see Chapter 11) to check the performance of Flag States (Chapter 6). **We recommend that the effectiveness of this new measure be carefully monitored by Flag States, Port States and through them IMO, and changes introduced if necessary.**

7.25   The Australian report *Ships of Shame* (paragraph 1.28) recommends that carriage of a survey history file consisting of all documents relating to a ship's structure, including a record of Port State Control inspections, structural inspections and repairs or alterations, should be a mandatory condition of port entry for all dry bulk carriers. The survey history file should be available to Port State Control and classification society surveyors. **We believe that IMO should consider extending the requirement to carry a survey history file to vessels other than oil tankers.** We recommend in Chapter 11 that ships visiting ports covered by the Paris Memorandum of Understanding should carry a log book containing details of Port State Control inspection results (paragraph 11.42).

Noxious liquids

7.26   Annex II of MARPOL covers the control of pollution by noxious liquid substances carried in bulk. Annex II relies on the IBC Code for detailed requirements for ship design and equipment. A tanker certified suitable to carry noxious liquid substances is also surveyed prior to the issue of an International Pollution Prevention Certificate for the Carriage of Noxious Liquid Substances in Bulk (INLS) and subsequently at periodical intervals with a view to ensuring that the ship remains in a condition suitable for that purpose. Noxious liquid substances are discussed further in paragraphs 9.30 – 9.36.

Classification societies

7.27   As we mentioned briefly in Chapter 6, classification societies are international commercial organisations staffed by marine surveyors. Historically they came into existence to develop and monitor standards of design, construction and maintenance for the assistance of shipowners and underwriters. Shipowners needed technical guidance to ensure that their ships were seaworthy, and underwriters needed assurance that they were. Thus an underwriter who was asked to write a policy on hull and machinery would enquire whether, and might insist that, the ship was "classed" with a classification society. Being "in class" meant, and still means, that at the last periodical survey the society was satisfied not only that the ship then complied with its Rules and Regulations, but that, barring accidents and subject to proper maintenance, it should so comply until the next such survey.

7.28   Classification society Rules and Regulations are separate from those developed by flag administrations to implement the relevant Conventions and as such they do not cover such matters as ship stability, life saving appliances and pollution prevention arrangements, as these are matters for the Flag State with which the ship is registered. However, as we saw in Chapter 6, a great many Flag States, including the UK, delegate a number of the statutory surveys for the issue of Convention certificates to the classification societies which undertake them in accordance with agreed procedures. We make a number of recommendations on this in Chapter 6.

The performance of classification societies

7.29   Ships are not necessarily, or even usually, in their home ports when the time comes for them to be subjected to a periodic survey and, between surveys, they may be damaged at any time or any place. It follows from this that if a classification society is to be able to perform its monitoring role, whether on behalf of the shipowner or of the Flag State, it needs to have the very considerable resources necessary to maintain a worldwide organisation. In recent years the number of classification societies has increased rapidly to 49. Inevitably many do not have the requisite resources or indeed expertise.

7.30   It was therefore no surprise to receive evidence of widespread dissatisfaction with the performance of some of these societies. It was in part with a view to addressing this problem that the International Association of Classification Societies (IACS) was formed. Full membership of IACS is limited to such societies as in its opinion have the necessary resources and expertise to fulfil their role. There are at present 11 such members, together with two associate members who are on the way to full membership. IACS members survey over 90 per cent of the world's merchant shipping tonnage.

7.31   Individual societies make their own classification Rules and Regulations. IACS has taken the initiative with a view to harmonising standards. It has also produced guidance for owners and operators of bulk carriers identifying potential weaknesses and remedies and has introduced enhanced surveys for bulk carriers and tankers.

7.32   IACS has developed a Quality System Certification Scheme (QSCS) which has become a mandatory requirement for members. The Scheme involves periodic auditing of members' internal quality systems to ensure that they are operating properly and that they conform with the IACS "Code of Ethics" and quality system requirements. Members whose systems pass the audit procedure are issued with a quality system certificate of conformity valid for three years. Renewal is subject to further audit. Members whose quality systems are not up to standard may have their certificates suspended if deficiencies are not rectified within a specified period.

7.33   IACS invited both IMO and underwriting organisations to participate in the QSCS. IMO agreed to take part but underwriters did not. We consider that the widest possible external involvement in monitoring and improving the Scheme is in the interests of safety and **we recommend that underwriters' organisations reconsider their position.**

7.34   As we mentioned briefly in Chapter 6 the Department of Transport also monitors the performance of the five classification societies which carry out work on its behalf. MSA has in place audit arrangements based on a Memorandum setting out the relationship between it and the societies in respect of the survey and certification of ships. Each society is subject to audit on a two yearly cycle.

7.35   The existence of IACS and the initiatives which it has taken are clearly of great benefit in terms of safety at sea. This can be demonstrated from an analysis of the level of detentions of ships by UK Port State Control inspectors. Only one foreign ship in ten visiting UK ports is classed with a non-IACS member, yet 19 per cent of ships detained are so classed. Even if the record of ships classed with IACS members is not one which would justify any degree of complacency, the contrast is glaring.

7.36   Something further needs to be done if competitive pressures are not to drive out societies with good records and favour those which provide a cheaper but worse service. This is coming to be appreciated and the new IMO Sub-Committee on Flag State Implementation has prepared a draft Assembly Resolution containing guidelines for the authorisation of organisations acting on behalf of administrations. These guidelines, which were adopted by the Eighteenth Assembly in November 1993, are based only on qualitative criteria. This work is being echoed by the European Commission draft Directive on classification societies. However, unlike the Assembly Resolution, the draft EC Directive contains both quantitative and qualitative criteria to ensure that these organisations are professionally reliable and able to maintain proper control of compliance with safety and environmental protection standards on the vessels they classify.

7.37   We support the EC's proposals and the UK Government's backing of them. We recommend that the UK Government should work through IMO to press for a review of the IMO guidelines and minimum standards for classification societies with a view to improving them as necessary and to developing, as a matter of urgency, detailed specifications on precise survey and certification functions delegated to such organisations. The UK Government should also work through IMO for swift implementation of minimum standards for all work delegated by Flag States to classification societies. Classification societies which do not meet these international standards should not be granted international recognition. A similar recommendation was made by the House of Lords Committee chaired by Lord Carver (see paragraph 1.28) and accepted by the UK Government in its response to the Committee's report.

Design and construction

Double hulls

7.38   There has been much debate about the merits of double hulled vessels, which have ballast spaces or voids around the bottom and sides of the cargo spaces, designed to reduce the chances of an outflow of pollutants in a collision or stranding. The United States Oil Pollution Act 1990 (OPA 90), using Port State Jurisdiction, requires new tankers to have double hulls and requires existing single hulled tankers to be modified or phased out by

2015. OPA 90 does not allow for any alternative designs: the United States Government remains unconvinced of the merits of alternatives to double hulls and OPA 90 would have to be amended if alternative designs were to be considered.

7.39   Similar requirements have been agreed internationally at IMO although there is some difference over modification and phase-out dates. The major difference is IMO's acceptance in principle of any alternatives to the double hull design which can offer the same level of protection against oil pollution in the event of collision or grounding.

New oil tankers

7.40   A good deal of discussion at IMO centred on the capacity of alternative designs to ensure at least the same level of protection against oil pollution in the event of collision or grounding. An IMO study compared the mid-deck concept[10] with the double hull design and concluded that a mid-deck tanker is equivalent to a double hull tanker with respect to the overall oil outflow.

7.41   The upshot was that under the new Regulation 13F of Annex I of MARPOL all new tankers over 5,000 deadweight tons (dwt)[11] must have double hulls or equivalent designs which ensure at least the same level of protection against oil pollution in the event of collision or stranding.

Existing oil tankers

7.42   Regulation 13G of MARPOL deals with existing tankers and introduces an enhanced programme of inspections during periodic, intermediate and annual surveys. It also makes provision for the phasing out or modification of existing tankers not later than 25 or 30 years after their date of delivery depending on the standard of construction at the time of build. The timetable differs in some respects from the US one.

Ships carrying noxious liquids

7.43   Similar amendments to the rules for ships carrying noxious liquid substances have not been found necessary because the IBC Code already specifies ships with double hulls or double bottoms for certain cargoes. Moreover, the safety and pollution hazards for different substances are kept under continuous review and the type of ship permitted to carry them amended as necessary.

The future of double hulls and their alternatives

7.44   Even though both IMO and the United States Government have endorsed double hulled tankers we believe that there is still scope for discussion of their merits and

---

[10] A mid-deck design tanker incorporates double sides which are used as segregated ballast tanks and a central cargo space divided horizontally by a mid-height deck. The side ballast tanks protect the cargo in the event of a collision. The division of the central cargo space provides protection in the case of a grounding because the height of the mid-deck is such that the pressure of the cargo oil at the ship bottom is less than the pressure of the surrounding water so preventing the oil escaping from the bottom of the hull if it is breached.
[11] Deadweight tonnage is the difference between the light and loaded displacements of a ship, including not only cargo but also items such as fuel and stores.

demerits. For our part, we believe that a great deal of research, into ways of limiting outflow, remains to be done before anyone is in a position to say, unequivocally, which design is the most effective. We have noted accusations that recent regulations have included an element of a "knee jerk" reaction to very damaging incidents, particularly the grounding of the EXXON VALDEZ off Alaska in March 1989, and we applaud IMO for keeping its options open by allowing equivalent designs.

7.45   It is clear that double hulled tankers can help to prevent pollution in low energy collisions or groundings, where only the outer skin is ruptured. It is equally clear that they are ineffective in high energy collisions or groundings. They also appear to have a number of significant disadvantages.

7.46   In designing a double hull, a difficult judgement is needed on the depth of the "buffer space" between the two skins. Too much buffer space reduces the cargo capacity – and therefore makes the vessel more expensive to build and operate than tankers with a lesser specification – but too little buffer space greatly reduces the level of protection in the event of a collision.

7.47   It was also put to us that whilst an accident may at first cause a breach only in the outer hull, there are circumstances where this may inevitably lead to the inner hull being breached as well. We heard, for example, that if a laden double hulled tanker grounds on a rock and the outer hull is breached, the empty ballast tanks will be flooded and buoyancy will be lost. This sinkage, in causing the ship to settle onto the rock, might result in the rupture of the inner hull. At the very least it could make salvage of the ship more difficult.

7.48   Double hulled tankers require greatly increased surface areas of steelwork, requiring high levels of maintenance and inspection to minimise the risks of dangerous corrosion. Perhaps the worst problem is the risk of explosion. Because the surfaces of water ballast spaces corrode faster than those of other areas there is a danger of small leakages of crude oil which can create explosive vapour and mixtures in the ballast spaces.

7.49   **We believe that designs must incorporate permanent and well-designed access facilities both to allow full physical inspection of the ballast spaces between the two skins and to enable repair work to be safely undertaken. We recommend that IMO, the classification societies, ship designers and others concerned with the structure and maintenance of vessels give careful consideration to these issues and introduce additional requirements as necessary.**

7.50   **We also recommend that the performance of double hulled tankers should be monitored closely by IMO in order to obtain a clearer picture of the effectiveness of the design. In the light of experience IMO may need to specify additional minimum standards for design, construction, maintenance and inspection of these vessels.**

High tensile steel (HTS)

7.51   High tensile steel has been used for many years in ship construction and its use really took off in the 1970s. It has the same fatigue properties as mild steel but has the advantage that less material is needed, so reducing the total amount of steel required for construction by as much as 15 per cent. This not only reduces building costs and fuel consumption but also increases revenue-earning deadweight. The use of HTS varies but some VLCCs[12] built in the Far East may incorporate as much as 70 per cent HTS.

The problems of HTS

7.52   While HTS corrodes at the same rate as mild steel, its scantlings are thinner than those required for mild steel so corrosion can become a problem much earlier. It has also been claimed that HTS has a shorter fatigue life than mild steel because the thinner plates are subjected to higher levels of stress. The greater flexion of HTS may also accelerate corrosion. It has been estimated that reducing the thickness of key connections in the hull structure by 10 per cent can shorten fatigue life by a quarter.

7.53   Although vessels constructed using a high proportion of HTS may be cheaper to build they are more costly to maintain and may well have a shorter life. It is vital that owners and insurers bear this in mind when weighing up the overall costs. **We recommend that IMO, the classification societies, ship designers and others concerned with the structure and maintenance of vessels give careful consideration to the survey requirements for vessels whose construction includes a significant proportion of HTS.**

Segregated ballast tankers (SBTs)

7.54   On conventional oil tankers the same tanks are used for water when in ballast and for cargo when laden. The disadvantage with this is that oily waste is discharged with ballast water thus threatening pollution. MARPOL recognises this and allows for a very small proportion of oil to be discharged with ballast water outside Special Areas: the limits and other conditions of discharge are described in Chapter 9. Tankers fitted with segregated ballast tanks, as the name suggests, have separate tanks for ballast water. These are completely separate from the cargo and fuel system and have their own lines and pumps. The double hulled tanker is one example of an SBT: the space between the cargo tanks and the outer hull is used for ballast water.

Discrimination against SBTs

7.55   SBTs have such obvious environmental benefits that one would expect States to encourage them, and possibly even discriminate in favour of them. Despite widespread enthusiasm for SBTs, this is not so.

7.56   Because the ballast tanks cannot be used for cargo an SBT must be between 15 and 20 per cent larger than a conventional tanker with the same cargo capacity. As most port

---

[12] Very Large Crude Carrier: generally taken to mean an oil or crude carrier over 150,000 dwt: an illustration of the comparative size of a typical VLCC is at Plate 8 and an actual example is shown at Plate 9.

dues are calculated according to a vessel's overall tonnage rather than her cargo capacity, an SBT of the same cargo carrying capacity will be charged more than a less environmentally-friendly conventional tanker. This is clearly unfair and gives little encouragement to owners supporting internationally agreed measures to prevent pollution.

7.57 IMO has been trying to solve this problem for many years. In November 1991 the IMO Assembly adopted a Resolution[13] which updated a measure agreed in 1977[14]. It provided a formula for calculating the tonnage of SBTs which reduced the overall tonnage upon which port dues are usually based. In November 1993, Resolution A.747(18) was adopted by the IMO Assembly. The latest Resolution replaces the 1991 Resolution but is virtually identical. We understand that the latest Resolution aims to renew momentum behind the SBT initiative after a disappointing response to earlier Resolutions. At least one European port, Rotterdam, has already taken action to implement Resolution A.747(18). Since 1 January 1994, it has offered a 10 per cent reduction in port dues for all incoming SBTs.

SBTs in UK ports

7.58 The larger ports in the UK are mostly privately owned and it is the harbour authorities and not the Government which are responsible for setting the level of port charges on a commercial basis. Ports in other countries may be publicly owned or subsidised by Government.

7.59 The British Ports Association and the UK Major Ports Group have both argued that the cost to a port of handling an SBT is no lower than that of handling a conventional tanker of similar size and that, in the UK, reducing charges for SBTs is likely to have one of two outcomes. Reducing charges for some vessels without increasing charges for others would leave ports footing the bill for encouraging environmental improvements in the tanker industry, to the possible detriment of port facilities and services. Alternatively, a compensatory rise in charges for other vessels would mean that vessels unconnected with the oil industry would be likely to pay to encourage those improvements. The ports organisations also object to a mandatory formula for reducing charges – if reductions are to be made they argue that these should be a matter for the ports acting on a commercial basis.

7.60 We believe that the UK should be, and be seen to be, in the lead in complying with IMO Resolutions. As we explained in paragraph 5.68, the European Commission envisages mandatory application of IMO Resolutions in its report *A Common Policy on Safe Seas*. Resolution A.747(18) is the first candidate for this policy: EC Ministers unanimously approved the Commission's proposal to make the Resolution mandatory within the EC and a proposal for a Council Regulation is being developed.

---

[13] Resolution A.722(17).
[14] Resolution A.388(x).

7.61 We accept that ports in the UK should generally be left to set charges without interference from Government. This is long-established Government policy. However, we believe that there are circumstances where some Government action is justified to ensure that environmentally beneficial policies are implemented for the greater good. Ministers have recognised this in supporting EC action to encourage SBTs.

7.62 We believe that the IMO Resolution should be applied in an appropriate manner at all Community ports on the basis that any increased costs should be borne by the tanker industry and not by shipping in general. This should be done by providing for differential charging between SBTs and conventional tankers at all Community ports taking into account the different charging regimes of different ports. We understand that this is the approach being adopted by the EC and welcome proposals along these lines. If the EC's efforts to make Resolution A.747(18) mandatory fail **we recommend that the UK Government should encourage IMO to reconsider and redraft the SBT Resolution so that it can be applied in practice along the lines we suggest.**

Maintenance

7.63 Proper maintenance is fundamental to ship safety. A vessel can be constructed and designed to the highest possible standards but she will soon become less safe if she is poorly maintained and operated. Corrosion control and repair of protective coatings are particularly important in hull maintenance. It was suggested to us on numerous occasions that some owners skimped on maintenance. Lack of funds, lack of trained manpower and a desire amongst some owners to keep a ship in service almost regardless of the consequences are all factors which may undermine maintenance programmes. The problems are compounded if the owner lacks a strong safety philosophy.

7.64 The reduction in manning levels on some ships may mean that although there are sufficient personnel to operate the vessel safely there is no spare capacity to carry out routine ongoing maintenance. We recognise that smaller crews, rapid turnround times and longer periods between refits are, for many operators, a matter of commercial necessity. Even so, a great deal of running maintenance can be done using travelling gangs of contractors, provided that the work is properly and safely organised. We are concerned that some owners may regard classification society and statutory surveys in the same way that some car owners see the MOT test – a need to undertake maintenance once a year when the MOT test is imminent or, in extreme cases, a chance to find out what needs to be done to reach a minimum standard before undertaking repairs.

7.65 Ongoing maintenance, in consultation with a vessel's classification society, must be the best way of reducing the risk of serious structural or mechanical failure. We welcome initiatives which alert owners to the risks of improper maintenance and operation. A good example is the International Association of Classification Societies' booklet *Bulk Carriers: Guidance and Information to Shipowners and Operators*[15] which highlights areas which may be susceptible to corrosion and bad practices which may lead to structural damage. **We**

---

[15] Issued in April 1992 by the International Association of Classification Societies, 5, Old Queen Street, London SW1H 9JA.

recommend that the UK Government should consider, with the classification societies and others engaged in the survey and inspection of ships, whether procedures can be improved to probe maintenance standards fully. It should also encourage discussion of this issue at IMO.

The age factor

7.66   As we have seen, statistics seem to indicate that older vessels are more likely to become casualties than newer ones. But age alone may not be the most significant factor. Most insurers regard a brand new ship on her maiden voyage as a potential major risk, because of the likelihood of teething problems and the inevitable unfamiliarity of the crew with the ship.

7.67   Proper maintenance will extend the safe life of any vessel, and well-maintained vessels over 20 years old are likely to be in better condition than younger vessels which have been neglected. But many vessels will not have been maintained at a consistent level throughout their lives because of changes of ownership.

Short-life ships

7.68   Some ships are specifically designed and constructed to operate for a limited period of years. Such ships comply with classification and regulatory requirements but aim for cost savings through the use of minimum scantlings and low quality components. They are not designed to operate after they become life-expired. It is up to a prospective purchaser to decide whether such a low cost, but time-limited, option suits his commercial needs. There is nothing wrong with this practice as long as such vessels are scrapped at the end of their design life and as long as proper maintenance is not discontinued as vessels near the end. Unfortunately, this is often not the case and we have heard that some short-life ships are sold at the end of their design lives instead of being scrapped. While we do not believe that arbitrary age limits are helpful – see the next paragraph – the mandatory carriage of survey history files (paragraphs 7.24 – 7.25) should help to expose such ships.

Age limits

7.69   Some have suggested that the best way to eradicate substandard ships would be to introduce an arbitrary age limit after which vessels should be scrapped. We disagree. Not only would such a measure be difficult to implement but it would discriminate against older vessels whose construction and maintenance ensured an entirely acceptable standard of safety. There would also be a danger that owners would curtail maintenance programmes as vessels neared the age limit. There is an important distinction between the arbitrary age limit described here and the provisions in OPA 90 and MARPOL which require the phasing out of oil tankers by a certain date **unless** they are modified to comply with the revised construction requirements. **The UK Government should resist any attempts to introduce arbitrary age limits.**

Reliability

7.70   It is likely that a ship which has been designed, constructed and maintained to high standards will provide consistent and reliable service. Unfortunately, negligence in one, some or all of these areas can lead to a major mechanical or structural failure.

Duplication

7.71   A number of those who wrote to us or gave oral evidence proposed radical duplication of systems such as the fitting of twin rudders, twin steering engines, twin screws and twin propulsion systems. We do not believe that this sort of across-the-board duplication is the best way forward. We believe that systems which are critical to the reliable operation of a ship should be subjected to strenuous engineering analysis with a strong emphasis on safety.

7.72   In Chapter 12 (paragraph 12.33) we emphasise the importance of learning not only from disasters but also from incidents, or "near misses", which might have ended in disaster if circumstances had been slightly different. Analysis of such data should help to establish if there are any trends in the causes of incidents. One example of a trend might be the significant number of incidents resulting from electrical failures which we have heard about during our Inquiry. We acknowledge that these failures may have been due to a variety of reasons but we believe that greater analysis of such incidents could help to establish whether there are any common features. Such analysis might confirm that current requirements are adequate but it might indicate that revision, such as further duplication of systems, is necessary.

Contaminated fuel oil

7.73   As an operational unit, a ship depends not only upon the reliability of her structure and machinery but also upon a number of other vital elements. Most importantly, the safety of a ship depends upon her crew and we discuss the "human factor" in Chapter 8. But it is easy to forget that other, seemingly minor, components such as fuel oil and lubricating oil play a vital role. A ship's engine may be well-maintained and in perfect working order but it can still fail if there is a problem with the fuel or lubricants.

7.74   A number of witnesses expressed concern about the dangers of contaminated fuel oil. It was suggested to us that if the fuel burnt in marine diesel engines became contaminated with certain additives this could lead to fuel lines and filters becoming blocked. This might result in total engine failure. It was put to us that some additives would be hard to detect.

7.75   The precise nature and effects of contamination are a matter for scientific debate, but there is no doubt that poor quality fuel oil does cause serious mechanical problems. In August 1993 there were reports that several tankers and bulk carriers had been disabled by engine failures caused by contaminated fuel oil supplied from Rotterdam and Amsterdam. This problem was first identified by the Lloyd's Register Fuel Oil Bunker Analysis and Advisory Service (FOBAS) which concluded that the high acidity of the rogue fuel oil was probably due to contamination by chemical waste. The contaminated oil caused severe damage to engine fuel pumps and injectors leading to quite rapid failure. It was estimated that more than 100 vessels could have been supplied with the contaminated oil.

7.76   Although the problem of contaminated fuel oil does not appear to be widespread, it ought to be eliminated. In the recent example, the complexity of the bunker supply market was blamed for the problem. It was argued that cross-trading between a large number of independent suppliers meant that a supplier could sell a bad product in good faith because he had bought it further up the line. If this is true, it is worrying that suppliers do not know what they are selling and it calls their quality control procedures into question.

7.77   It is obviously in the interests of both suppliers and customers that these problems should be overcome and we hope that they will cooperate with each other in seeking solutions. **We recommend that bunker oil suppliers should review their quality control systems to ensure that substandard fuel oil can be identified before it is sold.**

7.78   **We also recommend that the UK Government should encourage IMO to develop a three stage process which would apply to shipowners and bunker fuel suppliers to try to eliminate the problem of substandard fuel oil. The first stage would be that on delivering oil, all suppliers should be required to issue certificates of quality. The second stage would be on-board testing of the fuel supplied. Merchant ships, other than short-sea ferries which can be expected to make other arrangements, should be equipped with on-board testing equipment. We understand that a number of easy-to-use test kits are available to enable quick analysis of bunker oil quality.** The example which we were shown cost about £2,000. **The third stage would involve on-shore laboratory testing of a sample of the fuel oil, perhaps using the fuel quality testing services offered by the major classification societies.** If the quality of the fuel were found not to correspond with the certificate, claims should be made against the supplier. One or two successful claims would have a marked effect on standards. Shipowners should also take particular care with regard to the quality and testing of lubricants.

7.79   A failure on the part of the owner to ensure that these sensible steps were taken might constitute a failure to exercise "due diligence" to make the vessel seaworthy with consequential cargo claims if damage subsequently occurred as a result of substandard fuel oil.

Suggested improvements to equipment and fittings

7.80   Many of those who submitted evidence raised points about existing structural and design standards and we have discussed some of the issues above. But a number of others suggested that improvements to some items of vessel equipment and fittings might also help to prevent accidental pollution. We discuss a number of these suggestions below. Navigational and other electrical equipment is discussed in Chapter 13 and transponders, which enable vessels to respond automatically to interrogation by coastal authorities or by other vessels, are discussed in Chapter 15.

Stress monitoring and "black box" recorders

7.81   We have heard that there is already a wide range of equipment available to monitor the stresses placed on a ship's hull during loading or on a voyage. In some cases, this equipment can be used in conjunction with more sophisticated equipment which can record selected data relating to hull and machinery, position and course, and even bridge conversations. This latter type of equipment, which can be fitted with a "float free" capacity to enable recovery after sinking and can assist in accident investigation, is seen by some as the equivalent of an aircraft "black box" flight recorder.

7.82 Lord Carver's Committee (paragraph 1.28) recommended that all ships over 20,000 dwt should be fitted with hull stress monitoring systems and that all ships subject to the SOLAS Convention should be fitted with voyage data recorders. The UK Government agreed in principle but stressed that mandatory requirements needed to be developed through international agreement.

7.83 Early in 1993, an IMO feasibility study on possible requirements for the carriage of either stress monitoring equipment or voyage data recorders or both on bulk carriers concluded that more sophisticated voyage data recorders were not vital but that hull strength monitoring devices should be provided on new and existing bulk carriers over 20,000 dwt. The requirement should only be extended to other vessels if this proved desirable.

7.84 We support the principle that the fitting of hull stress monitoring systems and voyage data recorders to certain vessels is beneficial. Stress monitoring equipment can provide information which can help not only in targeting maintenance and improving vessel design but also in assisting Masters in handling their vessels so as to minimise unnecessary stresses. We were reassured to learn from the Chamber of Shipping that some of its members already fit their vessels with stress monitoring equipment, voyage event recorders, or both, and that these companies are assisting the Department of Transport in making their experience available to IMO. In the light of this experience there may well be a case for extending the requirement to fit such equipment. We particularly support widespread fitting of voyage data recorders covering bridge operation not only to help establish the causes of accidents but also to help concentrate the minds of those on board. **We recommend that the UK Government pursues these issues within IMO with a view to extending present international requirements.**

Anchoring systems

7.85 SOLAS includes no specific requirements for anchors and chain cables. Standards for these items of equipment are contained in classification society Rules and Regulations.

The limitations of anchoring systems

7.86 Conventional anchoring systems are extremely limited in what they can do. Indeed, it was suggested to us that anchors on most VLCCs are of little more than ornamental value. The standards specified in classification society rules are for systems which are little more than the equivalent of a car handbrake: their purpose is to secure a vessel which has been "parked" under control. Whilst they may be useful in stopping or manoeuvring a ship drifting at very slow speeds of less than one knot, they are of no use in an emergency when a ship may be drifting without power at speeds of several knots.

Improved anchoring systems

7.87   One expert[16] described an anchoring system which he estimated might be able to stop a vessel drifting at a rate of up to about four knots. Unfortunately it had proved impossible to find a shipbuilder willing to work up the design and carry out trials. We heard that it might cost as much as £280,000 to retrofit such a system to a large tanker. We also received separate evidence detailing an alternative design for the anchors themselves. It was claimed that such anchors could help to stop a vessel drifting at between two and three knots even if attached to a conventional system.

7.88   We believe that research in this area is important and some of the ideas put to us certainly appear to have potential. Unfortunately most of the systems suggested to us are largely unproven and we have not been in a position to subject them to detailed scientific evaluation. However sound the theory, the effectiveness of improved systems in stopping a disabled vessel must also depend on many variable factors such as the weather, the depth of water, the nature of the seabed, tidal drift and whether the vessel is laden or in ballast. Whilst the systems described to us might prove effective in some circumstances, there might be many other cases where conditions would greatly reduce their usefulness. In the short term we believe that it must be for shipowners to decide whether or not to invest in new equipment.

7.89   The MAIB report on the *BRAER* accident recommended that the Department of Transport should carry out research into the feasibility of anchoring systems which would enable anchors to be lowered safely from the housed position to the full extent of the anchor cables even if the ship was without power. MAIB recommended that IMO should be pressed to introduce a requirement for fitting any feasible equipment. The UK Government responded that much research had already been done into improved anchor handling equipment but agreed to evaluate existing worldwide research to establish the need for further study of this specific aspect (see Appendix Q). **We broadly agree with MAIB's recommendation, subject to an assessment of the costs and benefits of any feasible systems, and accept the UK Government's approach.**

7.90   However, we note the wider concern that present standards for anchoring systems are inadequate and **recommend that the UK Government should widen its consideration of worldwide research to include not only the specific issue raised by MAIB but also the wider issue of the adequacy of conventional anchoring systems in slowing and stopping drifting vessels.** It may be that further research is necessary. If it is, **we recommend that the UK Government should work with IMO to commission such research with a view to upgrading the present international requirements if the benefits of doing so clearly justify the costs.**

Emergency towing arrangements

7.91   In Chapter 20 we describe our proposals for improving the UK's emergency towing and salvage capability. But there is limited point in having a high level of towing capacity if

---

[16] Dr K Ridgway of the University of Sheffield.

a secure tow cannot be established on a drifting vessel. Although it is possible to get a line on board a vessel which does not have dedicated towing attachments it may be much more difficult to attach and maintain a towline, particularly if weather conditions are poor.

7.92 This has been a topic of discussion in IMO for many years. On 17 November 1983 a recommendation on emergency towing requirements for tankers was adopted as IMO Resolution A.535(13). The Resolution recommended that all tankers over 50,000 dwt built after its adoption should be fitted with emergency towing arrangements at the bow and stern and that tankers over 100,000 dwt built before adoption should also comply not later than five years after adoption.

A requirement to fit emergency towing arrangements

7.93 In May 1993, IMO's Maritime Safety Committee (MSC) approved draft amendments to Chapter V of SOLAS. The addition of a new Regulation 15-1 is expected to be adopted at the 63rd session of MSC in May 1994. The draft Regulation provides that:

> "An emergency towing arrangement shall be fitted at both ends on board all tankers of 20,000 dwt and above constructed on or after [1 January 1996]. For tankers constructed before [1 January 1996], such an arrangement shall be fitted at the first scheduled dry-docking after [1 January 1996], but not later than [1 January 1999]. The design and construction of the towing arrangement shall be approved by the Administrations, based on guidelines developed by the Organization."

We support the amendment of SOLAS and recommend that the UK Government presses IMO to ensure that this timetable is adhered to.

A specification for emergency towing arrangements

7.94 The present guidelines setting out the specification for emergency towing attachments are embodied in Resolution A.535(13). This is currently being revised as a matter of priority. The latest draft of the revised Resolution specifies towing arrangements forward and aft and requires that they can be deployed swiftly in an emergency. Pick-up gear and a towing pennant are standard for the aft towing gear but optional for the forward towing arrangement. Whilst it is true that in most cases the aft towing equipment will be accessible for the establishment of an initial tow there may be occasions, for example if the stern is on fire, when it is not. For this reason we are concerned that the specification ought to require pick-up gear and a towing pennant for the forward towing arrangements. **We broadly agree with the specification laid down in the revision to Resolution A.535(13) but recommend that the UK Government asks IMO to reconsider this aspect of the specification of the forward towing attachment.**

7.95 Both the MAIB and Liberian reports into the *BRAER* accident made recommendations about safe access to the bow from the aft superstructure of tankers to enable handling of forward towing arrangements and anchors in an emergency. Safe access is covered by the Load Line Convention. The MAIB report recommended that the revision of Resolution A.535(13) should include provisions for safe access to the anchors from the aft superstructure of tankers and that IMO should make the requirements mandatory by amending Chapter V of SOLAS. The Liberian report recommended that IMO should consider whether sufficient attention is being given to Regulation 25 (see Appendix Q). Regulations 26 and 27 of the Convention are also relevant.

7.96 The IMO working group revising Resolution A.535(13) considered the recommendation of the MAIB report and a supporting paper from the UK Government but decided not to go beyond the requirements currently set out in the Load Line Convention because the provisions for better access were not specified. IMO has however agreed to give the matter further consideration. Whatever the design of the forward towing arrangement, it is clearly important that it can be deployed rapidly. If there is no requirement for it to be remotely operated and no provision for safe access to deploy it manually we are concerned that there is no guarantee that such equipment could be deployed rapidly in an emergency. **We recommend that the UK Government should support IMO in giving this matter further consideration with a view to amending the Load Line Convention if necessary.**

Emergency valves and pipelines

7.97 We received several ingenious ideas for removing oil and other potential pollutants from tankers in the event of an accident. It was suggested to us that each tank in oil tankers and other bulk liquid carriers should be fitted with valves of a standard design to facilitate cargo removal. Pipelines, with standard connecting attachments, would be used to pump the cargo to a waiting vessel or shore-based tank. One suggestion involved the use of remotely operated vehicles to attach pipelines in hostile conditions.

7.98 There are a number of problems with this sort of idea. Firstly, a universal valve design is a prerequisite and international agreement through IMO is essential for this. Secondly, there is the concern that fitting one or more valves in each cargo tank – there are as many as fifteen tanks in a typical vessel – could bring hull stress concentrations into question and increase corrosion problems. Thirdly, there is the question of cost, both in construction and in additional maintenance. Although no estimates of cost were offered to us, construction costs would inevitably be increased and retrofitting to existing tankers would be likely to be even more expensive.

7.99 To pursue this idea, despite the uncertainties, we would need to be convinced of the inadequacy of existing equipment and techniques for removing liquid cargoes from stricken vessels. We believe that given the variety in the types of incident which occur the various stockpiles of equipment maintained by the Marine Pollution Control Unit – which takes the lead in dealing with pollution incidents such as the *BRAER* – provide an acceptable level of response. We discuss the role of MPCU in Chapters 20 and 21.

Chapter 8

Ship Operation and Crewing

8.1   There is wide agreement that about 80 per cent of maritime casualties are caused, or aggravated, by human error. Human error can never be eliminated, but reducing it must be a major priority.

8.2   The European Commission has concluded, on the basis of evidence from insurance claims, that the weight of the human element in the chain of events leading to an accident is enough to justify a high priority for measures aimed at reducing the risk of human error. As we mentioned in paragraph 5.70, the action programme set out in *A Common Policy on Safe Seas* includes measures to increase the effectiveness of the Convention on Standards of Training Certification and Watchkeeping 1978 (STCW). These are described below.

8.3   The experience of accident investigators underlines the importance of good operation as the best guard against accidents. The Chief Inspector of Marine Accidents commented in the report[1] on the collision between the *MARCHIONESS* and the *BOWBELLE* in 1989 that for many years there had been "a widespread lack of appreciation of the importance of operational matters ... a pre-occupation with the details of equipment at the expense of regard for the ship's operation as a whole." **But** he added "it is believed that the tide has turned and that the pre-eminent importance of good ship management in the broader sense is now being recognised".

8.4   While we do not doubt the Chief Inspector's conclusion, there is still a long way to go. The problem is that it is very difficult for regulators to influence the day-to-day behaviour of individuals. Individual seafarers need certificates of competence, but while certificates from all States are treated as equally valid, different States apply different standards. Once qualified, a crew's ability to work together can be tested in Flag State Control or Port State Control, for instance by a fire drill: but such tests are at best a poor approximation of a real crisis. Regulation of conduct at sea is impossible.

8.5   It is perhaps even more difficult for regulators to inculcate a safety culture. Only owners, operators, Masters and crew working together can do that. In much of this Report we suggest ways of encouraging good behaviour and a safety culture: but in the end the decisions rest with individuals.

---

[1] *Report of the Chief Inspector of Marine Accidents into the Collision between the Passenger Launch MARCHIONESS and mv BOWBELLE.* (HMSO 1991)—ISBN 0 11 551025 7.

Role of owners, charterers and managers

Separation of ownership from management

8.6   The major technical advances of the last 50 years which have led to larger ships, higher speeds and greater efficiency have brought with them greater complexity, more automation and smaller crews. At the same time, structural changes in the shipping industry have weakened some of the links which contributed to safety in ship operation. The separation of ownership and operational management has been a particular factor.

8.7   In the past, a major shipping company's design and construction team would work closely with the builder of a new ship, the classification society, the flag Administration and ship's officers. This team effort may now not apply, particularly if the owner no longer has his own team, flag work is largely delegated to the classification societies, the ship's personnel come from a crewing agent and where there is little continuity of employment in a particular ship.

8.8   Managing agents can remove some of the day-to-day concerns of running the ship but as we said earlier (paragraph 2.25) the ultimate responsibility for the standard of manning and operation of the ship lies with the shipowner. It is for owners to set the structure within which a Master can operate on the basis of his experience and to the best of his ability.

A safety culture

8.9   Good ship management depends on a culture of safety, where safety issues are given high priority in the boardroom as well as in the ship. This culture will influence the running of the company and its ships at all levels, including instructions, supervision and training. Some companies are very conscious of the need for good, well managed ships and sensitive routeing, whilst others clearly go for the cheapest options, regardless of the possible consequences. The best need encouragement and support in managing their responsibilities. Sanctions need to be applied to the worst.

8.10   Standards for the safe management of shipping are set out in IMO Resolution A.741(18) which was adopted on 4 November 1993. This Resolution contains the text of the International Management Code for the Safe Operation of Ships and for Pollution Prevention, known as the IMO International Safety Management (ISM) Code[2]. There has been a substantial UK contribution to the development of the Code. We understand that MSA will be consulting widely with industry to encourage implementation as soon as possible, giving priority to passenger ships, tankers and gas carriers. The Chief Inspector of Marine Accidents, in his report on the *BRAER*, has already recommended that the provisions of the Code should be implemented by the shore management of shipping companies as a matter of urgency before they become mandatory in 1998 (Appendix Q). **We entirely agree.**

---

[2] The text of *The International Management Code for the Safe Operation of Ships and for Pollution Prevention* is set out in guidelines on its application, published jointly by the International Chamber of Shipping and the International Shipping Federation, 2-5 Minories, London EC3N 1BJ.

8.11   We heard from both the UK Chamber of Shipping and the International Association of Independent Tanker Owners (INTERTANKO) that, despite the high demands on company resources, many of their members have introduced external audits of their company procedures to certify that they meet ISO 9002, an internationally agreed standard covering quality management systems. Such quality assurance systems do not necessarily guarantee safety but a good total quality management system will incorporate safe working practices. **We recommend that the Department of Transport should urge shipping industry representative bodies such as the International Chamber of Shipping to encourage widespread use of this standard by their members.**

8.12   **We believe that it should be made abundantly clear that it is against the long-term commercial interest of shipowners for them to ignore safety considerations, as a few evidently do.** To emphasise this, commercial sanctions and administrative deterrents need to be strengthened. This can be done in a variety of ways, from taking greater account of owners' efforts to improve standards through an adjustment of insurance premiums charged by insurers and P & I Clubs (see Chapter 18) to tightening up the policing of existing legislation through more effective Port State Control, which we describe in Chapter 11.

Charterers

8.13   Charterers would argue that shipping standards are and should remain the responsibility of the shipowner. Yet liabilities placed on charterers through developments such as oil pollution compensation schemes have enforced their involvement. In marked contrast to the oil majors, most charterers do not seem prepared to pay more for safer ships, yet there are ways in which charterers could help discourage low standards. They could exercise their discretion in the way the oil majors do, by surveying ships that are being considered for charter. They could also keep data on potential charters and insist on proper port safety procedures.

Role of Master, officers and crew

8.14   Although bad owners and managers are behind most substandard ships, the person with visible and immediate responsibility for running a ship safely and effectively is the Master. On board, decisions are taken by the Master and by senior officers, based on reasoned professional judgement, experience and training.

Erosion of the Master's responsibility

8.15   However, the rapidly increasing quality and availability of radio communications has meant that Masters are more and more likely to contact shore-based managers before reaching decisions. Increasingly, the Master is seen as one of a chain of managers in an organisation, yet his responsibility for the safety of his ship and of those on board has not in any way been reduced by the greater ease of communication.

8.16   This involvement of on-shore management in the day-to-day running of a ship has resulted in an erosion of the traditional view of the Master as sole commander. This is particularly dangerous in a crisis, where valuable time may be wasted while a Master seeks authority for a necessary action. We discuss this further in Chapter 20, where we suggest (paragraph 20.50) a means whereby Masters can be given the clearest of authority to act in a crisis. But that is not enough: Masters should not have their freedom constrained by, say, an owner insisting that a particular route or speed should be maintained despite bad weather. That could risk safety. Nor should an owner insist that a ship must arrive in port with clean ballast if there is no time to complete this operation or if there are inadequate facilities for it. **The Department of Transport should urge shipowners, charterers and insurers to consider carefully whether demands being placed upon a Master are reasonable.**

The crew

8.17   The competence and motivation of the crew, as actually demonstrated on board ship, is vital for safety, but is one of the most difficult elements in ship operation to monitor. Human factors are involved in one way or another in most shipping casualties. It is therefore particularly unfortunate that developments over the last two decades have often severed the links of loyalty between owner, ship and crew and concentrated on lowest cost. Exploitation, low morale and poor standards are the result. Indeed, there are many problems which can lead to a lack of motivation and commitment to safety, any one of which can cause or contribute to the occurrence of a serious casualty and pollution.

Training

8.18   Although the human element in incidents is very considerable, the chain of factors can be complex and remedies can be difficult to determine. P & I Club experience shows that maiden voyages are often times of high risk, presumably because of relatively untried equipment with which the operators are unfamiliar. The same is often noted after a refit. In some cases the best hope for reducing the chance of human error lies with properly designed operational procedures, good operational management and good working conditions. We believe that not enough attention is paid to familiarity with particular items of machinery and equipment and, most importantly, to instruction and practice in procedures for dealing with emergencies. Training can both reduce the risk of accident and lessen its effects by helping to ensure a successful human response to the unexpected.

8.19   Research by the Tavistock Institute of Human Relations for the Department of Transport's Marine Directorate[3] has highlighted the need for more emphasis on developing good judgement in training and on practical training at sea. Accident investigations place similar stress on these factors and on requiring all ships to observe at least the internationally recognised standards of training, operation and maintenance.

8.20   We heard evidence of inadequate training, both initially and as new equipment and methods are introduced. It was put to us that UK Masters would often find themselves

---

[3] *The Human Element in Shipping Casualties*, Marine Directorate, Department of Transport, (HMSO 1991)—ISBN 0 11 551004 4.

carrying out tasks which, with a properly trained staff, they would not have to do themselves. These unwarranted additional duties can obviously worsen the problems of fatigue and stress in a lightly-manned ship.

8.21 In some people's minds training goes little further than achieving a grade in an examination after serving for so many years at sea. This is not enough: training is available from a wide range of sources to suit individual requirements and should be seen as a constant process of refreshing and adding to knowledge and capability. Colleges in a number of countries, including the UK, train to very high standards and on-board training by experts is also available, along with courses on particular pieces of equipment provided by the manufacturer.

8.22 Of course, good seamanship also has to be learnt at sea, but it is safer to practise responses to emergencies in the classroom. An excellent means of bringing a sense of realism into that work is through simulators on which people can exercise their skills and deal with emergencies in such areas as navigation, engineering and the handling of dangerous cargoes. Generally, there is a need to ensure that all of those serving at sea have received basic craft, safety and survival training as well as the higher technical training required in order properly to carry out their job and to deal with emergencies. **We recommend that the Department of Transport should raise these points with UK owners, charterers and insurers, and seek discussions on them at IMO.**

8.23 We discuss the specific problems of training of UK crews in paragraph 8.58 onwards at the end of this chapter.

Convention on Standards of Training, Certification and Watchkeeping 1978 (STCW)

8.24 Existing international standards are set out in STCW, which was negotiated through IMO. Although conceived as a minimum requirement below which no Flag State should fall, the lack of clear definition of training standards means that STCW is often in effect the maximum level above which many States fail to rise. Due to this lack of a clearly defined standard, the quality of training abroad differs widely. These differences may well account for the wide variations in on-board technical competence which are apparent, for example, from Port State Control inspections.

8.25 In *A Common Policy on Safe Seas* the European Commission proposed a Directive that would lay down minimum training requirements within the EC for key personnel, based on the STCW Convention. Member States are urged to take action against third country crews which do not have the qualifications required by international Conventions such as STCW and press for effective application of the Safe Management Code. When the Council of Ministers met in November 1993 there was political agreement on the Directive, including its communication requirements which we return to in discussing language and cultural differences at paragraph 8.47.

8.26 The Chief Inspector of Marine Accidents, in his report on the *BRAER*, recommended that the IMO revision of STCW should stress the need for practical experience, training and thorough assessment of competence in seamanship in the widest sense of the term. The Investigating Officer, Republic of Liberia, in his report on the *BRAER*, recommended that STCW should include provision for simulated training in decision making. We entirely agree with both recommendations, which are reproduced in Appendix Q. **We recommend that the UK Government should press IMO to work towards early completion of the overhaul it has begun of STCW, taking account of requirements for modern training, audit and on-board communication: and to increase pressure on lax administrations to ensure that the standards agreed are adhered to in practice.**

International system of validation of certificates

8.27 We know that Flag States vary enormously in the extent to which they honour their commitments. Yet however much of their authority they delegate and whoever they delegate it to, including classification societies, they cannot delegate their responsibility for the standards of the officers and crews of the ships on their registers. They should not, for example, issue certificates in their own name without thorough checks on whether a person is competent and has a right to the qualification claimed. We understand that in some parts of the world it is possible to buy certificates of competence for almost any rank. The lack of any proper validation extends doubts about the issuing and value of the certificates to the training courses themselves.

8.28 The Chief Inspector of Marine Accidents, in his report on the *BRAER* (see Appendix Q), also recommended that Flag States accepting the certificates of other Administrations should take care to ensure that these matters have been properly addressed. Again, we agree. In the face of lax Flag State administration and inadequate audit arrangements **we believe not only that IMO should bring pressure to bear for general improvements but that there should be an effective backup through Port State Control checks (see Chapter 11). We also believe that there should be an international system of validation for both certificates and training courses which would involve regular inspections by someone acting on behalf of, and reporting direct to, IMO. We recommend that the UK Government pursues these points in IMO.**

Crewing

Manning levels

8.29 Undermanning, leading to an inability to perform essential jobs efficiently and to serious fatigue of those in responsible positions, can obviously lead to disaster. Cost cutting, including reduced crews, was identified in evidence to us from the National Union of Marine, Aviation and Shipping Transport Officers (NUMAST) as one of a number of common themes which they considered to be part of the complex chain of factors normally found to be the cause of accidents. We also received evidence that suggested undermanning could be a factor in lesser incidents. The Shetland Islands Council stated that operational oil-spills had occurred at Sullom Voe because of poor management systems and inadequately trained personnel who were usually present in insufficient numbers.

8.30   There are standards both for minimum crewing levels and for working hours, but they are not very effective: minima can all too easily become maxima in the eyes of less conscientious owners, and the existing international agreements include considerable latitude for Flag States which, as we have seen, can undermine their effectiveness. We have considerable sympathy with the view expressed by NUMAST that when considering safe manning scales a careful scrutiny is needed of stress on personnel and of effects on their alertness and psychology. **We recommend that the Department of Transport should raise these issues with the shipping industry.**

ILO Convention 147

8.31   This Convention[4], which has been ratified by the UK, includes a requirement to have laws or regulations laying down hours of work at sea. The Department of Transport is currently drafting regulations on hours. They will be based on a safety assessment approach (see Chapter 12) requiring a consensus to be reached on individual vessels as to what are reasonable working hours. **We believe this to be a sensible approach.**

SOLAS Protocol 1988

8.32   The Protocol[5], which requires ships of 500 grt or over to have an appropriate safe manning document, came into force on 1 February 1992. This document, voluntary in the UK for several years, forms another small step towards creating sound and universal standards of crewing. It gives minimum manning levels and takes no account of non-operational requirements such as maintenance, passenger comfort and cargo handling.

8.33   Clearly this is an area where more work is needed at IMO and elsewhere, but in the meantime the scope of Port State Control has been extended to cover the operational requirements of a vessel and the bearing that manning levels and crew competence have on those requirements.

One man bridge operation (OMBO)

8.34   Although one man bridge operation is just one example among many where undermanning can cause problems, the bridge is a particularly sensitive position for those problems to start. OMBO is now practicable through technological advances, and there are strong commercial pressures for its introduction. Many Masters are unhappy with this development: while they acknowledge that available information suggests the practice is safe, they would rather there was somebody else on the bridge to take care of the unexpected.

---

[4] International Labour Organisation Convention No. 147 Merchant Shipping (Minimum Standards) 1976.
[5] Protocol of 1988 amended Regulation 13 of Chapter V of the International Convention for the Safety of Life at Sea, 1974 (SOLAS).

8.35 We believe that in many areas around UK coasts, one man on the bridge is too few, because of traffic congestion in some areas and the particular dangers of others. During our study we came across two cases where an inadequate watch was kept. The first was the *BETTINA DANICA*, which went aground on the reef to the south west of Stroma in the Pentland Firth, a constricted area whose dangers are explained in Chapter 14. We understand that the ship's progress was monitored on shore radar but the First Mate, who was alone on the bridge, failed to pick up broadcast warnings. The second was the *HOO ROBIN* which collided with a stationary tanker outside Rotterdam after the sole watch-keeper had fallen asleep in the wheelhouse chair. These incidents are described in more detail in Appendix L.

8.36 The Department of Transport should urge extreme caution on the introduction of OMBO. It is important to take full account of human factors after properly targeted research. For example, we understand that methods are being developed, by the Department of Transport and others, to test the alertness of the officer on watch, with a failure to respond correctly triggering an alarm. This sophisticated seagoing equivalent of the railway "dead man's handle" may well solve at least some of the evident actual and potential problems of OMBO – but we need to be sure. Satisfactory solutions to the dangerous problems of undermanning and fatigue will recognise that ships are manned by human beings.

Undermanning and fatigue

8.37 Flag States can give temporary dispensations from the standards of crewing laid down in the Conventions, as we say in paragraph 6.29 and return to in paragraph 11.29. Some witnesses suggested to us that the system is abused because many of these dispensations are not reported to IMO as they should be. A further point is that dispensations sometimes run on for unreasonably long periods. A dispensation is reasonable if a replacement cannot reach the ship at the time, but it is unreasonable if the replacement is not appointed at the first opportunity.

8.38 A more fundamental problem is that international standards of manning may be too low in some cases: in particular some aspects of manning standards are open to national interpretation, leading to variations in actual levels. Consistency is extremely important. There are strong commercial pressures on manning levels; too small a crew is not only dangerous, but also represents unfair competition. If consistency is not achieved, the concept of safe manning will inevitably be weakened.

8.39 Given the possible consequences of fatigue in officers and crews, we believe firm international action is needed. **We recommend that the UK Government should press through IMO for:**

(a) **a redefinition of the circumstances in which Flag States can give dispensations on crewing levels;**

(b) **checks through Port State Control of actual dispensations, which should be reported to IMO for checking against the records held by Flag States;**

(c) **Port States to report actual dispensations to IMO for crosschecking with reports from Flag States as part of IMO's audit action,** as recommended in paragraph 8.26 above: this would not only ensure validity but would also identify those States which are overgenerous with dispensations. If some Flag States are identified as being overgenerous with dispensations, IMO as a whole will no doubt want to consider what action can be taken against them; and

(d) **a review of manning standards and reconsideration of the extent to which they should remain open to interpretation by the Flag State. It is important that this is carried out quickly and effectively, and that sensible standards are set and adhered to.**

Language and cultural differences

8.40   We believe that most owners flag out because of financial and fiscal pressures. It enables them to start again on arrangements for pay and conditions of their workforce, subject only to international agreements. Owners also acquire greater freedom to recruit Masters, officers and crew from a wide range of countries.

8.41   We do not wish to suggest that mariners of one nationality are necessarily better or worse than those of another: that would be as untrue as it would be offensive. But it is certainly true that standards of training vary between countries and that there are fundamental problems of communications within mixed crews, not just because of language differences but also because of cultural differences.

Everyday communication

8.42   On board ship the inability to converse effectively between officers, or between officers and crew, can lead directly to difficulties in operating the vessel. The ship can be put into danger if orders are not passed on properly or are misunderstood. Instructions, including manuals, which do not give enough information or are written in a language not understood by the user can compound these problems.

8.43   We have been told that poor communication can be more than just a matter of language. When ethnic groups with different cultures serve in the same ships there is evidence that some crew members will give an officer of a different nationality the answer they believe he wants – such as "Yes" to the question "Do you understand?" – whether this is true or not. There can be such wide cultural differences that the proper management of the vessel is threatened.

8.44   The need for communication ship-to-ship normally arises when vessels are in radar or visual contact and heading towards each other. As collisions usually arise from misunderstanding the intentions of the other vessel, any difficulties in identification and communication can have potentially serious consequences. We discuss in Chapter 15 some technical developments to ease the problems.

8.45 An inability to converse effectively ship-to-shore in a common language, usually English, with Port or Coastal State authorities can affect a variety of situations from getting the correct aid, speedily, in an emergency to an understanding of local dangers. We give details in Appendix L of the language difficulties that Dover Coastguards had in warning the crews of the *ETILICO* and the *SEIKO* of impending danger.

Communication in a crisis

8.46 Everyday communication is quite different from communication in a crisis. Crews which are capable of communicating with each other and others in everyday dealings may not be capable of the rapid exchanges necessary in a crisis. Everyone tends to panic in his own language: in a crisis, there could be a polyglot panic, with crews speaking only in their own languages. That is why a list of mutually comprehensible words is not enough.

EC proposals

8.47 The European Commission proposed in *A Common Policy on Safe Seas* a require-ment on Member States to ensure that officers and ratings on both Community and non-Community flag tankers could communicate directly with each other in a common work-ing language. As we mentioned in paragraph 8.25, this was followed by political agreement at the Council of Ministers in November 1993 on a Directive giving the force of Com-munity law to provisions on crew training standards agreed in IMO, and requiring enhanced standards of communication on board passenger ships and tankers[6].

Accepted practice

8.48 A common way around some of the problems of polyglot crews is for communi-cations to be channelled through the bosun or senior petty officers and their deputies. This could mean that the Master talks to the officers in one language, they talk to the petty officers in a second and the petty officers talk to the crew in a third.

Establishing the principles

8.49 It does not matter how many languages a ship may be manned in – what is vital is that no single person should provide the link. **We believe that it could be fatal to rely on a single link: the key person could be ill, asleep or otherwise unavailable in a crisis. The Master and officers must be able to communicate properly with each other and *some of them* must be able to communicate properly with the crew. The senior petty officers must always be able to communicate properly with both officers and crew. There needs to be sufficient overlap so that orders given by those in command can be understood by the crew. Any new standards should make this plain.**

8.50 The issue of communications and language is largely one for owners and managers but there is some scope for standards to be set. We note that current efforts to revise

---

[6] Hansard 6 December 1993, cols 55–56.

STCW hope to cover the issue of language. **We recommend that the UK Government should press IMO to include the general issue of communication in the revision of STCW mentioned above, taking into account the points in the last paragraph, so as to establish principles that would be useful for Port State Control inspectors.**

English as the international language of the sea

8.51   In the long term, the best solution must be for a single international language to be accepted, as is the case with aviation. In practice English (at various levels of fluency) is already widely, but not sufficiently widely, used for this purpose. **We recommend that the UK Government should press IMO to adopt English formally as the international language of the sea. Minimum standards of comprehension and ability to communicate should be set, suitable for both everyday and emergency situations.** For example, officers seeking certificates for international trading should demonstrate, by a test, sufficient proficiency in English to deal with port operations, coastal navigation and emergencies. Watchkeeping ratings should also be able to understand and respond to straightforward orders. Deficiencies in standards found by Port State Control inspectors should be notified to IMO as is, or should be, the case with manning dispensations.

8.52   Arrangements exist in the aviation field whereby the Civil Aviation Authority (CAA) runs training courses for Air Traffic Controllers from central and eastern European States. Intensive training in the English language is a significant part of this. The courses are paid for by the States concerned: there is no subsidy from the UK Government. Although there is no exact parallel, and we recognise that merchant shipping crew have a far more disparate and limited role, the UK Government might wish to consider similar arrangements whereby language training might be made available for non-native English speaking officers. However, as is the case with aviation, we can see no reason why the UK Government should pay for this.

Other problems of mixed crews

Exploitation

8.53   We were impressed by the concern expressed by those involved with welfare, notably the Missions to Seamen, at the degree of exploitation which exists. Extortion by crewing agencies and engaging seafarers from different countries to do the same job on board at grossly differing rates of pay can only lead to demoralisation. We are not in a position to form a view on this, but if the complaints from witnesses are right, it would be hardly surprising that such crews would desert a ship in time of emergency rather than use their best endeavours to prevent disaster.

8.54   Owners, demise and time charterers and P & I Clubs and other insurers all have the capacity to raise standards and to ensure that the standards that exist are properly enforced. It is also in the interests of owners and charterers to ensure that living, welfare and employment conditions do not fall below those needed to ensure good morale and motivation. **The Department of Transport should press these points upon them all.**

Pay

8.55   It is important to stress that while exploitation does undoubtedly exist and can be a major problem, it does not automatically result from flagging out. Some third world seafarers are well paid and enjoy good conditions compared with those that they might expect at home.

8.56   The recruitment of mixed crews can however lead to a problem to which we can see no solution. Crew members from, say, the Indian subcontinent, the Philippines or West Africa will all have very different cultural traditions and expectations. Their living expenses while on board are the same but the living expenses of their families at home may be quite different. If their jobs and their abilities are the same and they work on the same ship, they ought to be paid the same. Anything else is very bad for morale in the closed communities on board ship. It is not absolute levels of pay which raise the temperature so much as relative rates of pay.

8.57   The conundrum is that if their pay is the same, different standards and costs of living in their home countries ensure that one will be able to achieve a better relative standard of living for his family than the other. Pay that is reasonable to one crew member is thus generous to the other, while pay that would be reasonable to the second crew member would be unacceptably low to the first. This is, so far as we know, a problem unique to the shipping industry. The issue is not one of standard rates of pay across the industry. Differential rates for crew members working side by side doing the same job are a recipe for an extremely unhappy ship.

Training and availability of UK seafarers

Decline in number of UK seafarers and future effect on shore-based industries

8.58   In 1990, a Joint Working Party set up by Government and the British shipping industry[7] reported that the decline in the size of the fleet, the transfer of ships away from the UK register to reduce crew costs and technological developments had reduced the demand for UK seafarers. They said that in 1976 there had been 33,314 officers and 25,019 ratings whereas by 1989 these numbers had dropped to 7,892 officers and 9,946 ratings.

8.59   Since their report, fuller statistical surveys have been carried out using data not available to the Joint Working Party. The most recent figures available from the surveys show a total of 12,048 officers and 14,506 ratings. The totals include 8,580 officers and 10,570 ratings from a Chamber of Shipping survey in 1992, and an additional 3,468 officers and 3,936 ratings identified as a result of a Department of Transport survey of ships

---

[7] *British Shipping: Challenges and Opportunities,* (HMSO 1990)—ISBN 0 11 550988 7.

owned by British companies which are not federated to the Chamber of Shipping. It is estimated that another 6,000 – 7,000 British seafarers, mainly senior officers, are serving on foreign owned ships.

8.60   We heard evidence that there is a worldwide shortage of good quality trained seafarers but that it is quite possible for a flagged out owner to employ officers and crew at significantly less cost by recruiting among Asians rather than Western Europeans, without lowering standards of safety on board and without exploitation. We accept this.

8.61   We cannot accept that the employment of foreign nationals on ships which are British in all but name necessarily has a direct effect on the linked questions of safety and pollution prevention. In the last analysis, safety and pollution prevention depend upon standards and not upon nationality. It may have an eventual indirect effect if the UK finds itself in the future without enough qualified and experienced nationals to carry out the necessary task of inspection: Appendix C sets out the current position so far as MSA is concerned.

8.62   A number of other marine related occupations rely on the technical expertise of seagoing officers who come ashore at mid-career. These range from British shipping company management, through the marine insurance industry, to ports, pilots and the nautical training institutions.

Training of UK cadets

8.63   UK Merchant Navy officers usually receive training as new-entrant cadets, going on to take higher Certificates of Competency throughout their early careers. It was because of the problems foreseen on future availability of qualified mariners that the Government Assistance For Training (GAFT) scheme was set up to encourage companies to train officer cadets through a grant, which is now £55 per week per cadet. There is also support for cadets under 18 years of age through the Youth Training Scheme.

8.64   In 1988-89, the first year of the GAFT scheme, a total of 227 new recruits were supported by both schemes. This rose to a peak of 445 in 1990-91 before declining to 330 in 1992-93. This is well below the figure of 1,000 to 1,300 cadets which the Chamber of Shipping estimates are needed every year to replace the British officers now in post. Expenditure on the GAFT scheme, and on cadets supported under the Youth Training Scheme, amounted to £3.2m in 1992-93, about 15 per cent of the overall budget of the SGO (now MSA), net of fees.

8.65   It was suggested to us that pressure on shipping companies' costs in the 1970s and 1980s had not only led to redundancies amongst trained officers but also to a decline in officer cadet recruitment from about 1,400 in 1973 to 150 in 1986. We were told that the GAFT grant was a considerable help but that many companies in Britain and elsewhere were still not training because of the expense and because many filled junior officer posts with officers from developing countries – which explains the decline in takeup of the GAFT grant.

8.66 The Government has recognised that cadets who have completed their training find it difficult to get jobs with British companies at the next management level and so has decided to extend training support to British junior officers while they are studying for their higher Certificates of Competency through a NVQ/SVQ[8] route. This new scheme, announced at the end of 1993 for a trial period of three years, will target those cadets who have been through the GAFT scheme and who, therefore, hold a first certificate of competency. Junior officers employed on ships on the British register will have priority.

The way forward

8.67 The picture which we have painted in this chapter so far is coloured by deeply ingrained abuses and bad practice. These will take time to eradicate. This will only be done by an understanding and acceptance of the problems and a concerted effort to solve them by IMO, Governments and all responsible elements in shipping; they must deal with bad ships and put pressure on bad owners and managers to change their ways or get out.

8.68 The UK Government should press IMO to deal speedily and forcefully with the problems. We very much hope that other like-minded Governments will take the same approach. We expect the UK Government to show the way by continuing to develop up-to-date training and manning structures with a strong emphasis on safety, on human factors and on recent advances in technology.

Port operations

8.69 Although the best known source of accidental oil pollution is tanker collisions, groundings and strandings, there are a greater number of polluting accidents during terminal operations when oil is being loaded or discharged as a cargo, or when a vessel's fuel tanks are being bunkered.

8.70 So far we have discussed how the risk of an accident which may cause pollution may be reduced by following sensible procedures at sea. But, clearly, failure to follow the correct procedures in port can also cause pollution, or result in damage to the ship which may increase the danger of structural or mechanical failure in port or during a voyage.

The risk of pollution in ports

8.71 Pollution may occur as a result of collision with another ship or with a jetty or other fixed object. Navigational and ship handling errors are relatively frequent in ports and

---

[8] National Vocational Qualification/Scottish Vocational Qualification.

there have been cases where oil has been spilled because tankers have collided with the quayside or with tugs during berthing. In December 1978 the *ESSO BERNICIA* collided with a jetty at Sullom Voe in Shetland (see Diagram 1 on page 193) after one of the three tugs manoeuvring her had to withdraw because of a fire in her engine room. About 1,160 tons of heavy bunker oil were spilled, 600 of which escaped into Yell Sound and polluted thirty miles of coast. Such accidents may also increase the risk of fire and explosion. In addition, carelessness in loading or unloading cargo or in filling bunkers may cause tank overflows and spillages of oil or other pollutants: we discuss these in paragraphs 8.74 – 8.75 and 8.76 – 8.78 below.

8.72 Ships can also cause pollution in ports through improper disposal of garbage and the discharge of contaminated ballast water. We discuss these issues in the next chapter.

8.73 The risk of a polluting incident in port is compounded by narrow, congested waters with which the ship's crew may be unfamiliar: we discuss pilotage in Chapter 13. The fact that ships often undergo servicing and personnel changes in port can also further complicate the interface between crews and shore operators who may be unfamiliar with each other.

Cargo handling

8.74 There are two points to make here. The first concerns the immediate risk of pollution in port. Port operations are usually a team effort involving ship and shore and require joint planning. A good shipowner will ensure that his employees are familiar with the correct loading and unloading procedures for their particular ship. A conscientious port operator will ensure that incoming ships are made aware of the cargo handling arrangements for that particular port. Both can help to reduce the likelihood of accidental spillages. There are many UK ports which have very good arrangements for handling polluting substances. Two examples are Flotta and Sullom Voe, which impressed us with their organisation during our visits to Orkney and Shetland.

8.75 The second point is that improper loading can place unnecessary stresses on a ship's hull which may lead to a major structural failure in port or on a voyage and consequent pollution. The tanker *BETELGEUSE*, with 40,000 tonnes of crude oil on board, exploded in Bantry Bay off the south western coast of Ireland in January 1979 as a result of structural failure. Fifty-one people died, but oil pollution in Bantry Bay was relatively minor as much of the partly-laden vessel's cargo was burnt in the fire which followed the explosion. During our Inquiry, the *DANICA GREEN, KAPITAN DZURASHEVICH* and *VISHVA PARAG* provided examples of other problems caused by shifting cargo (see Appendix L). **All owners should ensure that their crews follow loading procedures which are appropriate to the design of their particular ship.**

Bunkering procedures

8.76 Even a small oil spill can cause major pollution in a restricted area such as a harbour. Mistakes in bunkering happen for a number of reasons. Crew members may not know how much fuel is to be loaded or may be unfamiliar with the layout of tanks and fuel-lines or the loading sequence; or equipment, such as that used for tank gauging or warning of overfill, may fail or be improperly operated. **All owners should ensure that their crews are familiar with the bunkering procedures and characteristics of their ship.**

8.77 There has been an increase in the number of bunker spills in recent years and greater environmental awareness has led to a consequent increase in the number and size of insurance claims. We support the action of at least one P & I Club in issuing advice to members detailing the checks which should be made when bunkering. More detailed advice on bunkering and oil cargo operations is available in IMO's publication *Manual on Oil Pollution Section 1 – Prevention*[9]. **All owners should ensure that their employees are made aware of such advice as a matter of course.**

8.78 The International Chamber of Shipping's *Shipping and the environment: A code of practice*[10] provides guidance to shipowners on the types of environmental standards they should develop for operations both in port and at sea. Another valuable source of guidance is the *Environmental Code of Practice*[11] by the British Ports Federation (now succeeded by the British Ports Association and the United Kingdom Major Ports Group) which high-lights members' responsibilities and the need to develop environmental policies. The UK P & I Club has produced a video, *Counting the Cost*, designed to increase awareness among Masters and officers of P & I claims which cost the shipping industry $2 billion each year. We welcome the contribution that this and other guidance can make in improving environ-mental safety in ports. **Owners should make use of this sort of general guidance to inform crews and help to prevent deliberate and accidental pollution of port areas.**

8.79 **We recommend that the Department of Transport discusses with IMO, the International Chamber of Shipping and any other bodies, such as INTERTANKO, which may be able to influence the decisions of owners, how the points in para-graphs 8.75 – 8.78 can best be taken forward.**

Transfers of oil between merchant ships

8.80 Since at least the early 1970s, it has been the practice of oil companies to transfer crude oil from large to small tankers to enable heavily laden tankers to enter northern European ports where the depth of water is limited. These operations have most com-monly taken place in Lyme Bay, (shown on Diagram 8 on page 209) where there were four transfers in the year to March 1994. We discuss the issues specific to Lyme Bay in Chapter 14.

8.81 Ship-to-ship transfers in harbour authority areas can be controlled under local har-bour legislation, but there is at present no power over transfers which take place outside

---

[9] ISBN 92 801 1152 3.
[10] Produced by ICS, 2-5 Minories, London, EC3N 1BJ.
[11] British Ports Association, Africa House, 64-78 Kingsway, London, WC2B 6AH.

prescribed harbour limits but within the UK's territorial waters. The Department of Transport is proposing to bring in regulations[12] for these areas that would prohibit ship-to-ship transfers of a range of dangerous cargoes or marine pollutants and impose strict controls on the transfers of crude oil and refined products.

8.82   Under the draft regulations, oils and refined products readily amenable to dispersants could be transferred subject to conditions, including that transfers were within certain specified areas and that the arrangements had prior written approval from the Department of Transport. Four of the specified areas are in Lyme Bay while the remaining two are off the coasts of north Wales and East Anglia. There would be more stringent requirements where oil and crude products were less amenable to dispersants. These would include a counter pollution plan for each transfer, and the presence of a suitable oil recovery vessel complete with recovery and counter pollution equipment.

8.83   Transfers of liquified gases would be prohibited, with a few exceptions[13] for gases which would have little effect on marine ecosystems. The regulations would also prohibit the transfer of bunker fuel outside port limits which has particular implications for fish factory ships (see Chapter 17).

8.84   There is a clear need to ensure that transferring cargo at sea does not create a risk of pollution, or a danger to health or to navigation, or a hazard to the environment or to natural resources. That is what the draft regulations seek to achieve. On the other hand there is also a need to avoid over-prescriptive regulations, if in their attempt to avoid all risks of pollution they simply impose too onerous a burden on good shipowners. The net effect of that may be that less conscientious shipowners take over. It must be borne in mind that regulations and activities at sea are always difficult to enforce. There is also a "salvage value" in having in this country the specialised heavy equipment and the expertise needed for the safe conduct of ship-to-ship transfers of oil.

8.85   **We recommend that consultations, which have been going on for some time, should be concluded quickly so that the draft regulations, amended as necessary to take account of our points, can be brought into force as soon as practicable.**

---

[12] Under Section 35(1) of the Merchant Shipping Act 1988.
[13] Ammonia, propylene, butane or propane or mixtures of butane and propane.

Chapter 9

Pollution from Non-accidental Discharges

MARPOL

9.1 As the figures in paragraph 3.4 show, it is estimated that in the context of shipping more oil enters the sea from discharges, both legal and illegal, than from accidents. Control of pollution of the sea by deliberate discharges from ships of waste oils and garbage is covered by Annexes I and V respectively of the International Convention for the Prevention of Pollution from Ships 1973, as modified by the Protocol of 1978, generally known as MARPOL 73/78 (see paragraphs 5.41 – 5.42). Pollution by noxious liquid substances is controlled under Annex II of MARPOL, which we discuss in paragraphs 9.30 – 9.33. MARPOL provisions are given effect by national legislation.

9.2 Different rules, which we summarise later in this chapter, apply under MARPOL in different parts of the sea. Generally:

(a) discharges cannot be made within various fixed distances from shore. The distances can be different for different types of discharge;

(b) discharges are either prohibited altogether or very strictly controlled in a Special Area designated for a particular type of discharge. Again, the Special Areas can be different for different types of discharge; and

(c) discharges of the more serious pollutants, including oils and plastics, are regulated outside as well as inside Special Areas. For example, plastic may not be discharged into the sea under any circumstances and permitted oil discharges can be made only while a vessel is on passage.

We do not deal with every aspect of MARPOL in this chapter: a more comprehensive guide is to be found in the International Chamber of Shipping's *Shipping and the environment: A code of practice*, to which we refer in paragraph 8.76.

9.3 The provision of adequate reception facilities is vital if ships are to be encouraged to land waste of all types rather than dispose of it at sea. Masters and crews are far more likely to comply with the rules if disposing of wastes is easy at all the ports at which they call. Inadequate facilities are a positive invitation to ignore the rules.

Arrangements for the development and implementation of MARPOL

9.4 IMO is responsible for the development of MARPOL, but action is needed by individual States and regional groupings to ensure its effectiveness in practice. The UK is a member of two "clubs" of States concerned with MARPOL. Their membership is listed in paragraphs 2.21 and 2.22.

9.5   The first consists of the parties to the 1983 Bonn Agreement which deals with precautions against, and response to, spills of oil and other harmful substances in the North Sea and English Channel (see paragraph 5.60). The second is the International Conference on the Protection of the North Sea (known less formally as the North Sea Conference or NSC), an informal group of Governments which has so far met three times at roughly three year intervals. The next meeting is planned for 1995, but an Intermediate Ministerial Meeting (IMM93) was held in December 1993. We discuss – and welcome – some of its conclusions later in this chapter.

9.6   Within the UK, responsibility is divided between the Department of the Environment, which takes the lead on waste management and the representation of the UK in North Sea Conference matters, and the Department of Transport which is responsible for the regulation of shipping and the representation of the UK in Bonn Agreement matters. We accept that this divided responsibility is unavoidable, but very close cooperation is required. In the past communications have not been as good as they could be, but both Departments have been making conscious efforts over the past few years to improve this situation. As always, there is room for further improvement and we hope that the efforts to cooperate fully will be sustained.

Waste oils

9.7   Estimates in 1973 and again in 1981, shown in paragraph 3.4, indicated that the largest single source of oil entering the sea from transportation activities was operational discharges from tankers, usually associated with the cleaning of cargo residues when a ship is ballasting and cleaning its tanks for the return voyage from a port of discharge. While there appears to have been a very substantial reduction in these discharges, the absolute amounts of oil entering the sea in this way remain large.

9.8   There are no Special Areas for oil discharge purposes around the UK. Designation of the North Sea was considered in 1990 at The Hague North Sea Conference[1] and in 1993 at the North Sea Intermediate Ministerial Meeting (IMM93). Ministers have decided that the issue will be considered again at the Fourth International Conference on the Protection of the North Sea (4NSC) in 1995. So far, designation has been rejected on the grounds that it might make ships more likely to increase the level of their discharges in adjoining areas, thus transferring the problem from one area to another (rather than reducing it overall) and perhaps concentrating it in equally vulnerable areas. While recent tightening of global limits might reduce any potential "boundary" effect, it also reduces the comparative advantages of Special Area status.

9.9   **Clearly, the benefits to be gained must be carefully evaluated against the likely costs involved but we would like to see the North Sea designated as a Special**

---

[1] Third International Conference on the Protection of the North Sea (3NSC), The Hague 7–8 March 1990.

Area and hope that it will prove practical to adopt this as a long-term aim. The essential first step is to ensure that there are appropriate reception facilities, not only in the UK, but in all the surrounding countries. Special Area status should be extended to include the English Channel and the Irish Sea, subject again to an assessment of costs and benefits and the essential first step of the provision of good reception facilities. The availability of reception facilities is likely to be a major factor in determining the boundaries of Special Areas. Indeed MARPOL[2] requires that reception facilities are available before designated Special Areas can become operational.

Discharges from oil tankers – ballasting

Ballasting procedures

9.10   Tankers use a variety of tanks for ballast operations, according to their age and design. The correct distribution of ballast has an important contribution to make to safety, particularly in the following circumstances:

(a)   at sea, on ballast voyages, to ensure that the ship's draught and trim achieve a proper balance between the need for fuel economy and the need to limit hull stresses and avoid damage in bad weather;

(b)   when entering and leaving port, or when in congested waters, to ensure that the ship is stable and sits deeply enough in the water to be safely manoeuvred; and

(c)   in port, to reduce the side elevation of the ship which may be exposed to high winds, with the consequent risk of damage to moorings or loading equipment.

9.11   The usual procedure for older tankers without segregated ballast tanks (see Chapter 7) is that during unloading the ship takes on harbour water as ballast. This continues until the ship is in a safe condition for unmooring and going to sea. Depending on the voyage, more ballast could be taken on once the ship has left port by pumping in directly from the sea.

9.12   On the voyage oil-contaminated ballast water will normally be discharged into the sea through a separating system with any oily residues kept in slop tanks. Ballast will be discharged nearer the loading port to achieve the right trim for berthing and to keep down the amount handled in port. The remainder is discharged during loading with reception facilities being provided for any oily residues.

Control over discharges of oily ballast water

9.13   Over the last 10 years or more there have been major changes in tanker design and operation, described in Chapter 7. Newer tankers with segregated ballast spaces have only

---

[2] Regulation 10, Annex I.

a very limited need to put ballast in their cargo tanks. But older crude oil tankers operating with crude oil washing (COW) systems (and older product tankers) do clean, decant and change their ballast. Inevitably some oil remains in the discharge. A programme of phasing out these older tankers has been introduced.

9.14 Under MARPOL rules, permitted discharges of oil and oily mixtures from oil tankers can be made only from a vessel which is outside a Special Area, proceeding *en route*, and more than 50 nautical miles from land. In July 1993 the previous permitted instantaneous discharge rate was halved to no more than 30 litres of oil per nautical mile travelled by the ship. Tankers are also required to operate an oil discharge monitoring and control system and a slop tank. Acceptable results require good operation, proper maintenance of equipment and adequate surveillance.

9.15 For older tankers on long voyages, changing ballast water should be a routine operation. Due to the risk of oil pollution, certain ballasting operations in tankers must be noted in the Oil Record Book (see paragraph 9.21), such as the ballasting of cargo tanks and dedicated clean ballast tanks, the discharge of ballast except from segregated tanks, and the discharge of water from slop tanks.

9.16 We discuss ballasting on bulk carriers in paragraphs 9.69 – 9.77.

Discharges from machinery space bilges

9.17 In 1989 it was estimated that the largest single source of oil entering the sea through shipping activities was from fuel oil sludge and machinery-space bilges. This was largely attributed to the worldwide lack of adequate reception facilities[3]. Since July 1993 all new ships and all ships fitted with new equipment must limit the oil content of any discharge to less than 15 ppm (parts per million) oil in water. New ships of 10,000 grt and above must also be fitted with automatic discharge cut-off devices. Existing ships not fitted with such devices must fit and use 15 ppm equipment by 1998. Until then discharges at the old standard of less than 100 ppm will be permitted provided the ships have approved oily-water separating equipment.

Enforcement of the regulations on waste oils

9.18 The MARPOL regulations are not easy to enforce. Certificates issued under MARPOL and other relevant documents such as the log books and record books are subject to Port State Control (see Chapter 11). A more detailed inspection can follow only if there are clear grounds to suspect a ship does not substantially meet requirements.

9.19 Equipment and operational procedures to control oil discharges are covered by the Merchant Shipping (Prevention of Oil Pollution) Regulations 1983, as amended. The

[3] Group of Experts on Scientific Aspects of Marine Pollution (GESAMP), Reports and Studies No. 50, *Impact of oil and related chemicals and wastes on the marine environment*, 1993.

Regulations provide the power to inspect, and the power to deny entry to ports or to detain, if a ship presents an unreasonable threat or does not comply with the Regulations. They also provide the power to impose penalties. Ships detained on suspicion of breaching the discharge provisions of the Regulations may be released from detention against a security[4] based on the probable value of any penalties which may be imposed.

Measurement and recording of discharges

9.20   The measurement and recording of discharges is obviously necessary to check that the limits on discharges have been complied with. In evidence we heard some scepticism on whether the records are accurate.

9.21   MARPOL[5] requires that all oil tankers of 150 grt and above, and all other ships of 400 grt and above, must keep an Oil Record Book for machinery space operations. UK regulations[6] apply this requirement to all UK registered oil tankers and to all UK registered ships over 80 grt. Tankers must also keep an Oil Record Book for cargo and ballast operations. Entries must be made for each oil-related transfer.

9.22   Automatic measurement and recording systems, which are less vulnerable to tampering, are preferable to manual ones when practicable. Automatic oil discharge monitoring and control systems are already required for some specified discharges. The systems both measure the rate of discharge of oil and stop the discharge if limits are exceeded. However, machinery space bilge pumps must at all times be available in case of flooding: such arrangements allow the discharge monitor to be bypassed because of the volumes involved. Overboard discharge monitors are required to have a recording device and a print-out of discharges.

9.23   Automatic systems may be less open to abuse but the harsh working environment can bring reliability problems. Where an immediate repair is impossible oil discharges have to be estimated by weight and a ship is allowed to proceed on only one ballast voyage before repairs have to be carried out. These monitors are considered to be the best available method but they are a weak link in the system despite the possibility of cross-checks. Surveyors would almost certainly check the Oil Record Book during Port State Control inspections but it is recognised that they would not normally carry out cross-checks against the discharge monitor print-out unless it were decided that a closer inspection was warranted.

9.24   **We recommend that there should be continuing efforts to improve the reliability of these monitors and that cross-checks between the Oil Record Books and print-outs should be a routine aspect of Port State Control inspections.**

---

[4] Merchant Shipping (Prevention of Oil Pollution) (Amendment) Regulations 1992.
[5] Regulation 20, Annex I (implemented in the UK by Merchant Shipping (Prevention of Oil Pollution) Regulations 1983, as amended).
[6] Merchant Shipping Oil in Navigable Waters (Records) Regulations 1972.

Garbage

9.25 Throwing garbage overboard may seem harmless, but it can be very damaging. Plastic, including synthetic ropes and netting, is the worst problem – it is persistent, it can kill wildlife (see Plate 19) and it can immobilise smaller vessels if it fouls their propellers. A crippled small vessel in a shipping route constitutes a collision hazard, and could be the indirect cause of a major pollution incident. Garbage is also unsightly and reduces the amenity of otherwise scenic sections of coastline.

The rules on the disposal of garbage

9.26 The North Sea and the English Channel became a MARPOL Special Area for garbage disposal purposes in February 1991. The categories of garbage and the MARPOL rules which apply to their disposal inside and outside Special Areas are:

(a) plastic: this may not be discharged into the sea in any circumstances;

(b) dunnage or packing material which floats: this can be discharged only when more than 25 nautical miles from land **and** when outside a Special Area;

(c) food wastes in particles over 25mm: these can be discharged only 12 nautical miles or more from land, both inside and outside a Special Area;

(d) food wastes in particles of 25mm or less: these can be discharged only 3 nautical miles or more from land or 12 nautical miles from land inside a Special Area;

(e) all other garbage, including paper, rags, glass, metal, bottles and crockery, in particles over 25mm: these can be discharged only when 12 nautical miles or more from land **and** outside a Special Area; and

(f) all other garbage, including paper, rags, glass, metal, bottles and crockery, in particles of 25mm or less: these can be discharged only when 3 nautical miles or more from land **and** outside a Special Area.

Enforcement of the rules on garbage

9.27 Port State Control inspectors may, if they have good reason to do so, check whether ships' personnel are aware of IMO guidelines on minimising and storing garbage, of the limits on discharging and of the Special Areas where tighter criteria apply. They may look for practical evidence of breaches such as mixing plastics with other garbage and a lack of garbage on vessels arriving from Special Areas (see paragraph 9.52).

9.28 Nevertheless, it is very difficult to detect illegal discharges and IMO recognises the problems of direct enforcement, particularly at sea. Wooden fish packing cases provide an example of the type of garbage problem that can occur in the North Sea. We understand that large numbers of these cases end up on the Skagerrak coast of Sweden and that the UK Government is attempting to identify their source and considering whether any specific measures could be practical.

9.29 In enforcing the rules, Governments are encouraged not to rely entirely on penalties, but to consider also a range of other approaches, such as the removal of disincentives, which may be more effective in increasing the use of shore-based facilities. Since the control of garbage disposal is largely a matter of "good housekeeping", programmes of education are particularly relevant. When the Merchant Shipping (Prevention of Pollution by Garbage) Regulations 1988 came into force the Department of Transport launched a campaign with the slogan *Over the side is over!* with some graphic photographs of the effects of illegal discharges. We understand that a 1992 survey for the Department of the Environment found that the campaign had had some success in making seafarers aware of the Regulations. Our recommendations on this are in paragraph 9.58.

Noxious liquid substances

9.30   Noxious liquid substances are controlled under Annex II of MARPOL 73/78, which divides them into four categories of risk, each with different limits on the amount of cargo residue that may be discharged to the sea in tank-washings. We mentioned the design requirements for ships carrying noxious liquid substances in paragraph 7.26. In early 1994 an additive for lubricating oil was discharged by the *STOLT KESTREL* in a tank-washing operation which the owners claimed met the MARPOL requirements. It polluted beaches on the north west coast of England and killed hundreds of seabirds. We understand that when MPCU followed this up, the owners agreed to pay the clean-up costs. The substance concerned is in Category D, which has the least stringent requirements. Edible oils, another Category D substance, have been known to have similar effects.

9.31   Annex II was no doubt seen as a significant advance when it was agreed in 1985[7], but it is now out of date. Category D allows up to 10 per cent of the water discharged to contain cargo residues, provided that the ship is under way and at least 12 nautical miles from land. 10,000 times more residue may be discharged than is permissible for Category C substances.

9.32   Following an initiative taken by the North Sea States as a result of the 1990 North Sea Conference, IMO is currently reviewing Annex II and we understand that a number of possible options are under consideration. One option would be to reduce the number of categories of substances from four to two, which would result in more stringent discharge requirements. Another would be to ensure that an assessment of the hazard from a substance would include the dangers to seabirds from its effect on their plumage and ability to fly. **We recommend that the UK Government should seek to ensure that revised regulations reflect the need for more stringent and effective controls on discharges.**

9.33   We were pleased to note that IMO's Marine Environment Protection Committee has issued a circular recommending that ships' Masters should ensure that cargo tanks are emptied to the fullest extent possible with the equipment on board before they are washed out to sea. If a small percentage of the cargo remains in the tanks it may be of little commercial significance, but where the cargoes are large a small percentage may still represent a significant potential for pollution.

---

[7] IMO Resolution MEPC.17(22) of 5 December 1985.

MARPOL reception facilities

9.34   As a party to MARPOL, the UK Government has a duty to ensure that ports and terminals provide waste oil and garbage reception facilities that are adequate and do not cause undue delay to ships. National regulations[8] require only that harbour authorities and terminal operators provide facilities, which must be adequate. Where facilities are inadequate or none exist, the Secretary of State for Transport has the power to issue a direction specifying the provision to be made. The need to avoid undue delay is referred to only in advisory Merchant Shipping Notices[9] although it is a prime requirement of MARPOL. **We hope that the UK Government will seek to amend this provision at a suitable opportunity, in the spirit of our recommendation in paragraph 5.89 that UK jurisdiction should be extended to the maximum extent consistent with the UK's obligations under the Conventions.**

9.35   Notice No. M.1462 gives guidance to port and terminal operators on the requirements for reception facilities for oil and noxious liquid substances and states that reception facilities **may** consist of fixed installations (such as storage tanks) or mobile facilities (such as tankers whether road, rail, ship or barge). The Government provides no advice on the standards of facilities to be provided for garbage but the IMO guidelines for implementation of MARPOL Annex V, paragraph 6.3.2.3, urge that:

> "...consideration should be given to several alternative methods available. In this regard, floating plants for collection of garbage, such as barges or self-propelled ships, might be considered more effective in a particular location than land-based facilities."

9.36   The UK has been involved in efforts made by IMO to develop a *Comprehensive Manual on Port Reception Facilities* for oil, noxious liquid substances in bulk and garbage. A draft text was approved at the 35th Session of the Marine Environment Protection Committee (MEPC 35) in March 1994. The Committee agreed that the manual should be printed as soon as possible as an IMO publication.

9.37   Given the amounts of pollutants in the seas, the temptations to add to them by the quiet, easy and free tipping of waste overboard, and given the difficulties of enforcing the regulations, it is essential that reception facilities are fully adequate for the job, both in the numbers and types of facilities available and in ease and economy of use.

Oil reception facilities

9.38   Ports are required to provide a range of different types of oil reception facilities. Large scale facilities are needed at oil loading terminals and at repair ports, providing for oily waste such as dirty ballast water, tank-washings, oily bilge water, and oily residues and sludge. Facilities at smaller ports are needed for the reception of machinery space oily bilge waters.

---

[8] The Prevention of Pollution (Reception Facilities) Order 1984, SI 1984 No. 862 and The Merchant Shipping (Reception Facilities for Garbage) Regulations 1988, SI 1988 No. 2293.
[9] No. M.1262 on garbage and No. M.1462 on oil and noxious liquid substances.

The Liverpool University study – findings on oil waste

9.39   In 1991 an informal survey, by the International Chamber of Shipping, indicated that the reception facilities provided in the United Kingdom were inadequate. The Department of Transport subsequently commissioned a research project to investigate this. The survey[10], carried out by the Liverpool University Centre for Marine and Coastal Studies, covered a relatively small number of UK ports: it is impossible to tell whether the sample chosen is representative of UK ports as a whole.

9.40   The survey concluded that with some exceptions facilities were adequate for oily wastes. It suggested ways of improving arrangements at ports through more active involvement by the harbour authorities.

Disincentives to using the facilities

9.41   Vessels need MARPOL facilities which are quick and easy to use and which do not interfere with cargo handling. Waste oil is generally discharged into contractors' road tankers and we heard evidence that ships busy loading or unloading can find it generally too much of a nuisance to have tankers alongside. It can interfere with turnround time and hoses stretched out across the quay and up over the side of the vessel can get in the way. Masters have been known to make a show of complying with their obligations by paying for a tanker to attend and remain empty rather than incur extra port dues and demurrage[11] through a delayed departure.

9.42   Even where there are some fixed berths for discharging oil waste, there can be problems of space. Masters and owners will be reluctant to move berth to discharge to reception facilities. It has been argued that dedicated barges might provide a better solution than fixed points. Barges on the seaward side of berthed vessels could take waste off without interfering with cargo handling or could meet ships at anchor out in the roadsteads (a "partly sheltered anchorage") or when they are lightening ballast off-shore.

9.43   There may be disadvantages in that waste has to be transferred twice – from ship to barge and from barge to shore – giving an extra opportunity for accidents and environmental damage. Costs are also a factor. There is an ever present need to balance greater convenience, and therefore a higher take up of facilities, against the cost of providing the service.

9.44   Another inhibiting factor raised with us is that waste oil discharged is effectively imported oil on which customs duty has not been paid and so needs to be declared. However the extent of Customs & Excise involvement seems to vary from port to port and we could not assess whether this is a serious problem. **Clearly there should be no different treatment from port to port. We recommend that the Government should consider whether the revenue raised justifies the disincentive, in terms of paperwork and the potential liability to duty, to an orderly and legal discharge of oily wastes.**

---

[10] *A Survey of UK Reception Facilities for Oil and Garbage with Reference to Marpol Annexes I and V—A Report to The Department of Transport* September 1991.
[11] A payment made in respect of the detention or delay of a vessel beyond the time agreed upon.

Garbage reception facilities

9.45   Reception facilities are required at all ports for noxious liquid substances; and for garbage including domestic and operational waste such as plastics, packing materials, paper, rags, glass, metal, bottles, crockery and similar refuse, and food and maintenance waste.

The Liverpool University study – findings on garbage

9.46   The research project mentioned above found that facilities were adequate but not good for large quantities of garbage wastes. Facilities were inadequate for small amounts of garbage, where a ship's Master might have to pay from £30 to £70 to land a few bags of domestic waste.

9.47   With few exceptions, ports kept no records which could give a reliable assessment of whether waste disposal facilities were adequate, as required by regulation. Only about 15 per cent of ships asked for waste skips and estimates from ships' agents suggested that a similar percentage of their customers wished to land oil residues.

9.48   Despite the patchy availability of facilities around the coast there have been virtually no complaints about this through the reporting system provided by Merchant Shipping Notices. However, we consider it unlikely that a Master would bother to complain unless he was a regular user of the port. It is one thing to voice complaints and quite another to put pen to paper.

9.49   The survey suggested that by following best practice, standards could be raised considerably, encouraging ships' Masters to land all accumulated waste and avoiding the temptation to discharge at sea. For example, most port operators leave arrangements for refuse collection to ships' agents and independent contractors. The survey suggested that ports could organise a more effective and cheaper service themselves.

9.50   The general conclusion of the study was that waste landed fell well short of that likely to have been generated during a voyage. There may be good reasons for this: some waste may be legally discharged or incinerated at sea. The ships concerned may have visited, or be about to visit, other nearby ports where garbage can be more conveniently landed. It is obvious that the discrepancy between waste generated and waste disposed of in port is at least partly due to illegal dumping at sea, but there is no consensus of opinion on just how much is dumped illegally.

9.51   The state of some beaches provides evidence here. The International Chamber of Shipping's Environmental Code (paragraph 9.2) suggests that most of the debris on beaches comes from land-based sources. Evidence we received from Argyll and Bute District Council suggested that most of the litter found as a result of a limited coastal survey in their area was ordinary domestic rubbish. However, marine litter surveys by the Tidy Britain Group suggest that the main source of beach litter is shipboard-generated solid wastes disposed of at sea. Further work which they carried out jointly with the Advisory Committee on Pollution of the Sea concluded that most dangerous substances or articles found on beaches were washed ashore following accidental losses and deliberate disposal or dumping at sea from ships.

9.52   The precise amounts of garbage disposed of by various means will remain a matter of speculation for as long as there is no reliable method of estimating the amount of garbage generated by particular types of ship and there is no necessity to enter details in a ship's log of amounts of garbage discharged ashore. As a first step to a more rigorous analysis of the problem than has so far been possible, and thus to long-term solutions, **we recommend that the UK Government should sponsor surveys, preferably in conjunction with IMO or with other European States, of the amounts of garbage generated on a representative sample of different types of vessel. The UK Government should also seek through IMO for a requirement that an entry should be made in the ship's log when garbage is discharged ashore, and that the entries should be subject to checking.** Taken together, these measures will enable estimates to be made of the amounts of garbage discharged at sea. **Once good estimates of average amounts of garbage generated are available, the UK Government should ask IMO to consider how a Port State Control regime (see Chapter 11) could best ensure compliance with MARPOL Annex V.**

The sorting of garbage

9.53   There is no general statutory requirement on those producing waste in the UK to sort it into different types. However, "special" (broadly, hazardous) waste must be identified so that it can be handled separately under special controls and other "controlled"[12] waste must be disposed of in accordance with the conditions in the licence of the waste disposal contractor: to do this contractors must know what they are handling. In practice, much the best way of achieving that is for the producers of waste to sort it as an integral part of the waste-producing process.

9.54   It is often not practicable for this to be done with ships' waste. Ships are not factories with production lines into which waste management can be integrated: and unlike factory managers, ships' crews have the ever-present temptation of the sea into which they could discharge waste with, often, little chance of being caught. The time available in port for waste disposal is limited, and delays are likely to lead to significant financial disadvantages.

9.55   Although ships' waste is classified as "controlled" waste, the waste management system as it affects ships' garbage does go some way towards recognising the temptations and the constraints. MARPOL requires that there should be no undue delay to ships, and waste management legislation has modifications which take account of this. Most controls under domestic legislation apply to those receiving or processing waste from ships, rather

---

[12] As defined in Section 75(4) of the Environmental Protection Act 1990 and The Controlled Waste Regulations 1992, SI 1992 No. 588.

than to the ships themselves: though IMO guidelines recognise that in some circumstances port reception may require separation on board of food wastes, cargo-associated waste and domestic and maintenance waste.

9.56   Despite the special provisions for ships, we heard evidence that some waste disposal contractors would accept only sorted waste, perhaps to make recycling easier or so that they could conform with their own waste disposal licences. The shipping companies concerned had considerable practical problems in putting garbage ashore in some ports. Complying with a range of requirements over such things as bagging up and identifying the garbage had meant a substantial additional workload. We suspect that there are many others who would not go to that amount of trouble, and that the requirement to sort waste acts as a positive incentive to illegal (or at best, undesirable) dumping of garbage at sea. This certainly ties in with the findings of the Liverpool University study.

The need for better reception facilities

9.57   The evidence submitted to us indicates that the response of some UK ports to the MARPOL requirements has been poor and that in some cases the provision of reception facilities is wholly inadequate. We are aware that the Department of Transport regards the Liverpool study as demonstrating that facilities are adequate though in need of some improvement. We consider that the study demonstrated merely that facilities for oily wastes were mainly adequate at a relatively small number of UK ports. On garbage, the study found that facilities were adequate but not good for large quantities of garbage and inadequate for small amounts. It also found that few ports kept sufficient records for a judgement on the adequacy of the facilities to be made. We cannot accept that the picture painted is satisfactory. **We are convinced that not only should there be more waste and garbage facilities but they should be easier to use. They also need to be better publicised by such means as the *Seaway Code* discussed in Chapter 13.**

9.58   Nearly a year after we began our Inquiry and after our concerns had become clearly apparent, we heard that a survey of reception facilities was being planned by MSA. We hope that this will prove the first step towards the major upgrading which is needed. **We recommend that once the level of reception facilities is established, the Department of Transport should initiate a further publicity campaign on their use and monitor its effects.**

9.59   The provision of reception facilities for waste oils and garbage is a matter for individual ports and terminals, which are obliged to ensure that they are sufficient. We are in no doubt that the spirit of this requirement has not been met. **We recommend that a statutory obligation is placed on port and terminal operators to provide reception facilities that are not only adequate but geared to ease of use and which avoid disincentives such as a requirement for ships to pre-sort waste.**

9.60   **Objective standards of levels required and ease of use are not easy to establish. As a first step, the operators of ports and terminals should consider carefully, in consultation with shipping interests and waste disposal contractors, what** level of provision is needed, how disincentives to use the facilities can be avoided and what scope there is for alternative means of waste collection, such as the use of barges rather than fixed points.

9.61 **We also recommend that facilities are certified as a means of *ensuring* that they are adequate. Two authorities would be involved: the Department of Transport as experts on what is required; and waste regulation authorities as experts on how it should be handled. Policing of the use of reception facilities must be part of such a scheme.** Clearly, there would be manpower and financial cost implications to be considered, but we believe that this will encourage the increased use of reception facilities which should have a marked effect on pollution of the seas.

9.62 We have little information on reception facilities in other countries, but we note (in paragraph 9.17) a GESAMP reference to a worldwide lack of adequate reception facilities. We were glad to learn that the North Sea Conference Intermediate Ministerial Meeting of December 1993 agreed that proposals would be put to the next North Sea Conference for systems to control and monitor the use of reception facilities. They also agreed that, where necessary, additional steps should be taken on the provision of shore reception facilities. **We recommend that the UK Government should consider actively with other North Sea and North East Atlantic States whether reception facilities need improving on a wider scale.**

Charges for the use of reception facilities

9.63 As we say in paragraph 7.61, we recognise that port and harbour dues are a commercial matter for the authorities concerned. So are charges for MARPOL facilities. However, the way in which these charges are structured can have significant implications for the environment. The Royal Society for the Protection of Birds suggested to us that falls in the proportions of oiled auks, razorbills and guillemots found in beached bird surveys on the German North Sea coast were an indication that a German experiment, involving improved oil reception facilities that were also free of charge, had been very successful in reducing oil pollution at sea. Nevertheless, we are not aware of any evidence that there is necessarily any causal link between better facilities and the reduction in oiled birds: an improved level of environmental awareness, or indeed the overall reduction in the amounts of oil in the sea from shipping which we note in paragraph 3.5, could be the cause.

9.64 We are convinced that harbour authorities should structure their charges so that reception facilities are free at the point of use but subsumed into port dues. There is no question here of attempting to disguise costs. The point is that there should be no separate, optional charge for making use of facilities. Cutting bureaucracy or paperwork is also not the issue: rather it is a means of reinforcing human psychology. When people appreciate that they are already paying for a facility, they are more likely to use it, and indeed to ensure that they make full use of it. Better use and enhanced expectations could be expected to lead to a virtuous circle – increased demand leading to increased supply.

9.65   We hope that harbour authorities will agree to new consistent arrangements whereby the cost of reception facilities is met through standard port dues rather than through additional charges, to encourage their use. We recognise that this proposal goes in some respects against the polluter pays principle, described in paragraph 1.15: but a main aim of the principle is to give incentives to reduce pollution, and in this case, where the alternative of illegal discharges is so difficult to police, we believe that the best incentive is through the system we outline. We are, however, convinced that the reception facilities element of port dues should be proportional to the size and type of vessel, reflecting the type and quantity of wastes it is likely to produce. **We recommend that the UK Government seeks the necessary changes within the UK, through voluntary agreement if possible but through legislation if a satisfactory agreement cannot be reached.**

9.66   It is important that not just UK ports but, so far as practicable, all European ports should take a similar approach, so that competition between them remains fair. The Intermediate Ministerial Meeting of North Sea States in December 1993 (paragraph 9.5) committed itself to producing "appropriate economic arrangements" for reception facilities. **We welcome this development, recognise that a North Sea agreement on this is likely to be the best way forward, and recommend that the UK Government should pursue it vigorously.**

9.67   We note that the funding of port reception facilities for oily wastes is being studied by IMO on a worldwide basis. However, their concerns seem to be focused on tankers whereas our Inquiry is much more broadly based. Engine room waste from all types of ship can cause pollution and, as we have already pointed out in paragraph 9.17, the largest single source of oil entering the sea is estimated to be from fuel oil sludge and machinery-space bilges.

Advice on the use of reception facilities other than by merchant shipping

9.68   Although this is strictly beyond our terms of reference, we note that the Royal Yachting Association (RYA) has helped with advice on garbage disposal in the past and has indicated to the Department of the Environment its willingness to do more. **We suggest that the RYA should be asked to help in further pilot studies and campaigns on garbage disposal facilities to encourage small boat users to dispose properly of garbage.**

Ballast water contamination – the import of pollutants

9.69   Bulk carriers often make one leg of a voyage in ballast so their need to take on volumes of water and the procedures involved are broadly the same as for segregated ballast tankers. Dry bulk carriers tend not to carry ballast water in tanks which are used to carry oil, and so do not normally discharge oily waste from their tanks. There is, however, the problem of the import of pollutants, pathogens and harmful alien organisms in apparently clean ballast water: this applies to all vessels, including oil tankers, taking on ballast for long journeys. In addition, some of the fine particulate material taken in with the ballast water settles out during the voyage as a sediment. A diversity of living organisms has been found in mud samples taken from the bottom of ballast tanks.

9.70   Ballast water contamination of this type arises from substances which, unlike oil, are not usually visible. If the ballast water is drawn from a polluted river, harbour or estuary, it could contain chemicals which are both toxic and persistent. These include heavy metals, industrial and agricultural chemicals and synthetic organic compounds – insecticides such as DDT, herbicides, fungicides, anti-fouling agents such as tributyl tin (TBT) and polychlorinated biphenyls (PCBs).

9.71   Such toxic substances may remain a problem whatever the length of the journey. If the ballast water is released in an open well-flushed area, the subsequent dilution may reduce the concentration of contaminants to near background levels quite quickly. However, rapid dilution is not always available, and in some circumstances of wind and tide "ponding" may occur. Ponding means that a large volume of released ballast water may float and retain its integrity for quite long periods, especially if it is less saline and therefore less dense than the receiving environment because of its river or estuarine origin. This may affect natural populations of organisms and fish farms.

9.72   Ballast water can be contaminated by imported organisms. They may cause no difficulties on short voyages because of similarities in marine communities, but on longer voyages, or on those between significantly different ecosystems, the introduction of alien species is of major concern. Hundreds of species of plants and animals have been recorded in ballast water and there are many well-documented examples of alarming alterations of marine food webs by such introductions in different parts of the world. The invasion of the Asian clam in San Francisco Bay, of the zebra mussel in the Laurentian Great Lakes, and the comb jelly fish in the Black Sea are among the most dramatic illustrations of the catastrophic impact of ballast water introductions[13].

9.73   The problem extends beyond the alteration of natural communities. Dinoflagellates, small planktonic organisms which cause unusual algal blooms, form resting cysts which can survive for long periods even in unfavourable conditions. A recent study[14] of 80 cargo vessels entering Australian ports showed that 40 per cent carried viable dinoflagellate cysts and 6 per cent contained toxic species which could damage fish and shellfish farms, posing a serious threat to aquaculture and to public health.

9.74   The UK appears so far to have been fortunate and the well-documented examples of alien species being introduced to our waters cannot be unambiguously attributed to ballast water. However, in view of the experience in other parts of the world, there is clearly no room for complacency.

9.75   Imported substances in ballast water are not easy to control. Given the volumes of water involved, fine mesh filters are not practicable, and could not remove micro organisms. Decontamination, for example by boiling, is also quite impossible with the amount of

---

[13] Carlton, J T and Geller, J B, 1993, *Science* vol 261, pp 78–82.
[14] Hallegraeff, G M and Bolch, C J, 1991, *Marine Pollution Bulletin*, vol 22, pp 27–30.

water involved. The obvious solution might appear to be to change the ballast water during the voyage but that may not be effective in removing unwanted organisms. There is always some water and sediment left behind because of the positioning and pumping capacities of tank suction boxes. In bulk carriers, for example, there could be as much as 9 inches of water remaining in the bottom of a ballast tank.

9.76 Most States do not have ballast water controls, though the USA and Canada do have controls in the Great Lakes, and Australia and New Zealand have introduced voluntary codes of practice. Because there is no requirement to change ballast or keep records, there is no means at present of checking on general ballast operations in ships other than tankers.

9.77 IMO is discussing all ballast water contaminants, including pathogens and other harmful organisms. Guidelines[15] on minimising the risks from these substances have already been adopted by IMO and were issued as part of UK Merchant Shipping Notice No. M.1533 in August 1993. This Notice urged compliance with the voluntary guidelines and warned of the need for care when exchanging ballast at sea. It stated that the Government was reviewing the need for regulatory controls, based on the guidelines, for UK waters. Suggestions have been made at IMO for research into alien organisms and into possible solutions. There have been no conclusions so far on the identification of a common problem or control measures, but we understand that IMO is aiming to develop the guidelines further so as to provide the basis for a new MARPOL Annex. **While the UK so far may not have been seriously affected by ballast water releases, experience in the rest of the world highlights the potential dangers, and it is important that the threat be recognised. We recommend that the Government should encourage relevant studies and should support the IMO working group on this topic.**

Anti-fouling paints

9.78 The underwater surfaces of a ship's hull are treated with special paints to keep down the growth of weeds and encrusting animals which reduce the speed of the ship and increase fuel consumption. The substances in the paint leach into the water and can have an effect on shellfish, fish farms and the marine ecosystem generally.

9.79 For many years copper was the active agent in anti-fouling marine paints, but tributyl tin (TBT) was introduced in the mid-1960s and turned out to be very much more effective. TBT treatment can save operators hundreds of millions of dollars each year in fuel costs, and the reduced use of fuel has positive environmental implications.

9.80 Unfortunately, TBT affects a wide range of marine organisms beyond those it is aimed at. The most notable reactions have been shell deformation in oysters which have adversely affected the shellfish industry and reproductive damage to dogwhelks, with catastrophic effects on the populations of these animals. Although TBT on pleasure craft is

---

[15] *International Guidelines for Preventing the Introduction of Unwanted Aquatic Organisms and Pathogens from Ships' Ballast Water and Sediment Discharges*, adopted as Resolution MEPC.50(31), 4 July 1991.

beyond our terms of reference, there is evidence that an EC ban on its use on boats of less than 25 metres is resulting in improvements in the vicinities of marinas. It is relevant that the impacts were greatest in marinas where large numbers of boats are concentrated and where water exchange and dilution are low.

9.81 As a result of these effects many countries have banned TBT or have restricted its use to copolymer based paints which have low leach rates with maximum retention of anti-fouling efficiency. **We recommend that monitoring of TBT be continued and that its substitutes be carefully evaluated.** We were pleased to note that the Intermediate Ministerial Conference (paragraph 9.5) has agreed to request IMO to develop, as a matter of urgency, regulations for the strict control of emissions from ships of TBT and to consider a ban on its use, taking into account the environmental impact of the use of TBT and its alternatives.

Chapter 10

Hazardous and Noxious Substances

10.1 Some substances may be particularly harmful because they are highly volatile, highly toxic, or both. An accident involving a potentially flammable cargo such as liquified natural gas (LNG) can result in fire and explosion with possible major loss of life and damage to property. The spillage of other, toxic, cargoes can cause serious damage to humans and the marine environment. Such damage may be short-term or may develop gradually depending on the type of substance spilt, its concentration and the nature of the marine environment affected. The possible danger to humans was highlighted in February 1994 when the roll-on, roll-off vessel *NORSE LAGAN* collided with the gas carrier *CORAL ACROPORA*. The ammonia gas involved is toxic when inhaled and had the cargo escaped it could have affected the centre of Belfast and a total area of 42 square kilometres. MPCU class the incident as a potential disaster (see Appendix L).

10.2 Some substances, including certain biocides[1] and synthetic industrial compounds such as PCBs, are persistent and may build up in the food chain because they are taken up and retained by marine organisms in greater concentrations than are found naturally – a process known as bioaccumulation. Others, such as camphor oil, taint seafoods making them unpleasant to eat or inedible. And products such as creosote (coal tar) may reduce the use of amenities by forming slicks and floating scum and giving off foul smells. International recognition of the dangers posed by such substances has led to very tight controls on the carriage of a range of dangerous and polluting goods including radioactive materials and certain gases and chemicals whether carried in bulk or in freight containers or packages.

Carriage of non-nuclear dangerous goods

Carriage in bulk

10.3 As we discuss in paragraphs 7.19 – 7.20 and 7.26, ships carrying hazardous chemicals and gases in bulk need to be constructed and operated to higher levels of cargo containment, monitoring and control than oil tankers. Their construction and operation are regulated by detailed international codes agreed through SOLAS and MARPOL and aimed at keeping risks as low as reasonably practicable. Many of those concerned with the operation of such ships, ashore and afloat, attend special training courses which maritime colleges in the UK have taken the lead in providing.

10.4 The condition of these and other ships is regularly monitored through Port State Control inspections (see Chapter 11). *The Memorandum of Understanding on Port State*

---

[1] Insecticides, fungicides and herbicides.

Control 1992 Annual Report, which we refer to in Chapter 7, showed that almost 4 per cent of gas tankers inspected were detained, well below the average detention rate of just over 5.6 per cent for all ship types. However, over 6 per cent of chemical tankers inspected and almost 8 per cent of oil tankers/combination carriers inspected were detained (see **Figure 7.ii**).

10.5   As we say in paragraph 7.8, we have not looked at the source data for these figures and various factors, such as targeting, may have affected the results. The Report notes that above average detention rates for oil and chemical tankers have been observed over a prolonged period. The authors of the Report expect that Paris MOU countries will continue to pay special attention to these ships' types to curb this disturbing development. **We agree that they should. We recommend that the reason for this worse than average detention rate should be investigated and remedial measures considered.**

Carriage in packages or containers

10.6   Dangerous goods are also carried by sea, packaged either individually or in freight containers. As we note in paragraph 7.21, requirements in Chapter VII of SOLAS covering such cargoes relate to packaging and labelling rather than ship structure. Detailed requirements are contained in the International Maritime Dangerous Goods (IMDG) Code which has been developed by IMO. A key point is that packages and containers must be properly labelled, with pollutants identified by a distinctive symbol, not only to assist those handling cargo but also to help rescue services make the correct response if there is an accident.

10.7   Packaging must meet set standards and pass a range of performance tests, including tests to simulate lifting the container, dropping and stacking, to ensure that lower containers cannot be crushed. The basic principle is that the integrity of the packaging provides the primary protection so that safety is assured when packages are moved between various modes of transport, or are lost at sea.

10.8   There are also stringent requirements for the stowage and segregation of packaged dangerous goods, with a total ban on the carriage of some types on passenger ships. The IMDG Code recommends that, wherever possible, potentially polluting cargoes should be carried below deck. However, the Code stipulates that certain cargoes that are dangerous to human life should be carried only on deck because they require constant supervision, such as temperature control, or to avoid the build up in enclosed spaces of toxic or flammable vapours or undetected corrosion of the ship itself. There may also be a particular need for direct, all-round access to such cargoes in an emergency.

10.9   Segregation of incompatible materials may also require that some cargoes be stowed on deck. They are then kept apart from goods with which they may react violently or which they may otherwise contaminate, such as foodstuffs. Not only locations but also distances between incompatible cargoes in the ship are specified along with the need to keep dangerous goods from crew and passenger accommodation.

10.10   Good seamanship demands that all cargoes, of whatever type, are stowed securely before a ship leaves port. This basic safety measure may be enforced by Port State Control inspectors who can detain a ship which, because of poor stowage, is unsafe to proceed to sea.

10.11   Special emergency procedures have been developed internationally to deal with fire and spillage incidents involving dangerous and polluting goods including medical First Aid guidance for treating people accidentally exposed to such substances.

10.12   We are aware of recent incidents where containers whose contents have included hazardous substances have been lost overboard and subsequently broken up, and which have led to detonators and sachets of pesticides being washed up on beaches in France. The pesticide came from containers lost overboard from the French registered vessel *SHERBRO* near the Channel Islands (see Appendix L). This is an important subject which was not raised in evidence to us and which we have consequently not considered. We look forward with considerable interest to the findings of the French Senatorial investigation, and we hope that the UK Government will feel able to cooperate with the French and in taking forward measures emerging from that investigation.

Tagging

10.13   Electronic tagging has been suggested as a means of rapidly locating containers of dangerous or polluting goods lost overboard. This is not feasible for individual packages but is technically possible for the freight containers in which they would be placed. However, false alarms could be caused by heavy seas washing over a container on the decks of a vessel or by leaving a transmitter on containers which were later loaded with non-dangerous goods. Acoustic devices using a sonar pulse have a limited range and function only if the container is submerged. Clearly a number of drawbacks remain with the methods currently available and these will need to be resolved before tagging can make a contribution to protecting the marine environment. **We recommend that the UK Government, with its European partners, should encourage the development of a workable system.**

Reporting and routeing

10.14   Harbour authorities must[2] be notified of any dangerous goods arriving either from the sea or from inland so that they are aware of all the dangerous goods within their area of jurisdiction. Ship Masters must inform Harbour Masters about dangerous goods on board ship at least 24 hours before arrival.

10.15   Any incident involving discharge of oil or other noxious liquids or packages of hazardous substances into the sea or the likely loss of these substances must be reported to the nearest Coastal State in accordance with Protocol I of MARPOL. An EC Directive

---

[2] Under The Dangerous Substances in Harbour Regulations 1987.

with similar requirements about advance notice and reporting of incidents was agreed in 1993. We discuss the MARPOL provision, the Directive and additional proposals for ship position reporting in Chapter 15.

10.16   Existing voluntary routeing and reporting measures are aimed largely at bulk carriers and tankers but there is no power in UK law for the Department of Transport to order a seaworthy ship to take a particular route because of the type and nature of its cargo or weather conditions or both. We return to the issue of routeing in Chapter 14.

Enforcement

10.17   Generally, the regulations are enforced during normal port inspections of ships, or in response to incidents or complaints. Prosecution is considered for all but the most minor offences. Department of Transport surveyors also visit ports to carry out intensive inspections of all aspects of the carriage of dangerous goods, paying particular attention to roll-on, roll-off ships and to chemical tankers loading or discharging hazardous cargoes.

10.18   Freight container inspections have been coordinated with other North European countries to ensure that ships are not diverted to nearby ports in the hope of avoiding the localised increase in inspections. There is frequent contact through informal links over the proper classification of hazardous substances and particularly close cooperation where fast moving roll-on, roll-off traffic is involved.

Carriage of nuclear materials

10.19   Nuclear materials are carried in secure containers or packages rather than in bulk to prevent cargo entering the sea if the ship's hull is breached. Broadly similar rules to those set out above for packaged dangerous goods apply to nuclear materials but other, more stringent, safeguards are added.

10.20   Where a ship is to carry material that exceeds set radioactivity levels through a country's territorial waters, seven days' notice must be given to the competent authority. In the UK the Department of Transport is notified before movements of irradiated nuclear fuel or plutonium nitrate solution take place.

Carriage of irradiated nuclear fuel

10.21   Packages for radioactive materials are generally designed, tested and approved to standards well above those required for other dangerous substances. For example, flasks intended for carrying irradiated nuclear fuel and other materials with a similar level of radioactivity are required to be able to withstand temperatures of 800 degrees Celsius for 30 minutes in an all-engulfing fire test. Very considerable precautions are taken during the whole transport operation to ensure that pollutants cannot escape into the environment in the event of any accident.

Routes taken

10.22 Irradiated nuclear fuel is transported to Sellafield, on the coast of Cumbria, for treatment. The main sea routes within UK waters are from the Continent via Dunkirk and Dover and from Japan directly to Barrow in Furness in Cumbria: onward journeys are by rail. Shipments from Japan are carried out in double-hulled vessels with high standards of fire protection and stability under damage conditions. These UK flagged ships are operated by British Nuclear Fuels with its subsidiary Pacific Nuclear Transport.

10.23 Occasional shipments are made from the Continent to Dounreay on the north coast of Scotland. These shipments are from experimental reactors where the hazard is lower than for irradiated fuel from a power reactor.

Carriage of plutonium nitrate solution

10.24 The sole shipment of plutonium nitrate in UK waters is from Dounreay, where plutonium is recovered from irradiated fuel in the form of a nitrate solution, to Sellafield where it is processed into fuel suitable for further use. The journey is highly controlled.

The prescribed route

10.25 The plutonium nitrate is transported by road from Dounreay to Scrabster near Thurso and driven aboard the *ABERTHAW FISHER*, a UK flagged ship which sails for Workington near Sellafield, following a prescribed route within territorial waters. The ship goes through the Minch not only because that is the shortest and most direct route but also because there is less risk to the ship in the more sheltered waters of the Minch than in the rougher seas of the Deep Water Route to the west of the Western Isles. We explain the problems connected with the use of the Deep Water Route in Chapter 14. All deviations from the prescribed route have to be approved in advance. The journey from Workington to Sellafield is completed by road.

The prescribed precautions

10.26 The solution is packaged in containers designed and tested according to the IMDG Code and approved by the Department of Transport. The ship used to carry the plutonium nitrate containers, the *ABERTHAW FISHER*, is suitable on structural grounds having been designed originally to carry heavy electrical generating equipment and transformers. Her progress is monitored independently from shore using satellite systems. The sailing time is under 36 hours but the Master is instructed by AEA Technology at Dounreay not to sail unless the area weather forecast indicates that he can complete the passage safely.

Additional precautions

10.27 Additional precautions beyond those required by law are taken primarily to provide further reassurance on security, but there is no doubt that they also improve safety. The *ABERTHAW FISHER* is fitted with extra navigational and communication systems, and the containers have devices that transmit signals to aid location and recovery if the ship sinks. Initial tests showed that containers could be located and retrieved in waters up to 700 feet deep off the west coast of Scotland. A salvage company is contracted to act immediately to recover the containers if needed.

Safety studies

10.28   In May 1987, the United Kingdom Atomic Energy Authority (UKAEA) reported[3] on the consequences of the release into the English Channel and North Sea of radioactive materials from typical cargoes, including irradiated nuclear fuel. In 1988, the National Radiological Protection Board reported[4] on the radiological impact of the transport of radioactive material by sea worldwide. Both reports concluded that the risks are negligible.

10.29   The Advisory Committee on the Transport of Radioactive Materials (ACTRAM), set up in 1985 to provide independent advice to the Secretary of State for Transport and the Health and Safety Commission, has also produced a report, *The UK Regulation of the Transport of Radioactive Materials: Quality Assurance and Compliance Assurance*[5]. One of the many conclusions reached was that regulations for transporting radioactive materials were efficient and effective.

10.30   More specifically, the Health and Safety Executive[6] assessed the safety of the combined road and sea transport of plutonium nitrate from Dounreay to Sellafield in 1978. It concluded that the probability of an accident severe enough to breach the container, in places where the public might be harmed, was no more than one in a million per year. If an individual near such an accident were to inhale some plutonium the chance of being killed was assessed as no more than one in a hundred million per year. The risks are substantially lower than those common in industrial operations, transport and everyday life.

10.31   A further assessment by the UKAEA[7] in 1984 confirmed these findings and also concluded that the impact on the marine ecosystem from any plutonium nitrate leakage would be negligible.

Developments in the transport of nuclear materials

10.32   In November 1993, IMO agreed a Code of Practice[8] for ships carrying irradiated nuclear fuel, plutonium and high level radioactive wastes under its duty to keep safety standards under review, taking account of improvements in technology and growing public expectations.

---

[3] *The consequences of release of radioactive materials from typical cargoes carried in the English Channel and the North Sea*: (May 1987—SG2(87)10) Safety and Reliability Directorate, UKAEA, Culcheth, Warrington, WA3 4NE.
[4] *Radiological Impact of the Normal Transport of Radioactive Materials by Sea*: R Gelder NRPB August 1988.
[5] HMSO 1988—ISBN0 11 752087 X.
[6] *The transport of plutonium in the form of nitrate solution between Dounreay and Windscale: A safety assessment*: The Nuclear Installations Inspectorate (NII/R/39/78) December 1978.
[7] *An assessment of the radiological consequences on the release into the sea of the contents of a plutonium nitrate package in transit from Dounreay to Sellafield*: (May 1984—SRD R 244) S Nicholson and A R Taig, Safety and Reliability Directorate, UKAEA, Culcheth, Warrington, WA3 4NE.
[8] *Code of Practice for the Carriage of Irradiated Nuclear Fuel, Plutonium and High Level Radioactive Materials in Flasks on board Ships* A18 RES 748(18).

10.33   The UK Government supported adoption of the Code because of the additional complementary safety it would provide in the design, construction and equipment features of ships used worldwide to transport such material over deep-sea areas where recovery of containers from a sunken ship would be difficult. International transport of irradiated nuclear fuel by sea to and from the UK is already carried out in vessels which are expected to meet all the relevant provisions of this Code. The Department of Transport is considering draft regulations to give effect to the Code and we understand that these could be introduced by the summer of 1994.

10.34   The International Atomic Energy Agency and IMO have agreed that no change is needed in packaging standards as there is no evidence that standards are inadequate. However, they are committed to keeping standards under review as part of their regular work programmes.

THORP

10.35   In December 1993, the Secretary of State for the Environment and the Minister for Agriculture, Fisheries and Food announced[9] decisions on radioactive discharge authorisations from the British Nuclear Fuels site at Sellafield which allowed for the operation of its thermal oxide reprocessing plant, known as THORP. Earlier that year, the Government said[10] that it considered existing arrangements were sufficient to ensure that the transport of nuclear materials remained safe, and that the transport requirements arising from THORP operation did not adversely affect the case for proceeding. The Government pointed out that the bulk of the spent nuclear fuel for the first 10 years of THORP operation had already been delivered to Sellafield; and that spent nuclear fuel had been transported in the UK for over 30 years, during which time over 30,000 tonnes of fuel had been moved in flasks, covering several million miles, without a single accident involving the release of radioactivity.

Conclusions on the transport of dangerous and nuclear materials

10.36   Apart from some doubts about the record of chemical tankers in Port State Control (paragraph 10.5), we were generally impressed by the thoroughness and care devoted to the regulation and operation of ships carrying cargoes of hazardous and noxious substances, including nuclear materials. We were also impressed by the signs of real day-to-day international cooperation displayed in evidence from the regulators in the Department of Transport[11]. **We accept that standards are generally far higher than those of other vessels, including oil tankers, and we have no recommendations to make on those standards.**

10.37   Compensation for those affected in the event of an accident is another matter. Compensatory arrangements already exist for persistent oil carried in bulk and for the transport of nuclear materials but **there is an urgent need to establish a compensatory regime for other hazardous and noxious substances.** We discuss this in Chapter 19.

---

[9] Hansard 15 December 1993, cols. 1094–6.
[10] *Statement of Government Policy on Reprocessing and Operation of the Thermal Oxide Reprocessing Plant at Sellafield,* July 1993.
[11] Oral evidence, 1 July 1993.

Chapter 11

Port State Control

Introduction

11.1   Internationally agreed standards intended to produce safer shipping are not so high as to be unattainable. This is illustrated by the fact that some shipowners operate to standards over and above those set out in the Conventions. Against that background one might expect that foreign vessels visiting our ports would only occasionally fall below those standards. This is not the case.

11.2   In 1992, over 6,000 different foreign flag ships visited the United Kingdom. Of the 2,000 or so inspections carried out, 60 per cent revealed deficiencies of one sort or another. Whilst some of these deficiencies may have been relatively minor, 6 per cent of inspections revealed deficiencies serious enough to warrant detention of the vessel until they had been remedied. These figures are broadly similar to those for inspections carried out in other European countries. The problem is thus as much one for the States of the region as for the United Kingdom (see paragraphs 11.15 – 11.22 below).

11.3   The condition of some ships is such that they are detained more than once. The inspection of one particularly poor vessel, the *STELLA*, in November 1993 is described in Appendix E and shown at Plates 10 – 12. She had been detained in various European ports on no less than three previous occasions. This is exceptional but she is not the only ship to have been detained more than once: in UK ports alone 11 ships were detained twice out of a total of 298 individual detentions in the two years up to February 1994.

11.4   In other sectors of the transport industry such a situation would not be tolerated. One can imagine, for example, the public outcry if it was revealed that 6 per cent of foreign aircraft landing at UK airports were so unsafe that they were not allowed to take off until they had been repaired. The situation is just as intolerable for shipping.

The need for Port State Control

11.5   As we say in Chapter 6, the long-term aim must be to improve the standards of Flag State Control so that the international rules are properly and consistently applied by all Flag States. But for as long as Flag State Control continues to be ineffective to the extent demonstrated in paragraphs 11.2 above and 11.21 below, Port State Control will be the United Kingdom's first line of defence against the pollution of its coastline. Safer ships mean safer seas. Safer seas mean less pollution. It is as simple as that. Port State Control as practised at present undoubtedly has some effect in maintaining standards of safety, but it is a very long way from being fully effective. The strategy for the future outlined in paragraphs 11.37 – 11.85 below is designed to remedy this deficiency.

11.6   In making our recommendations we recognise that no system of Port State Control can be fully effective without collaboration between the States of a particular region. We therefore seek to build upon and improve existing regional cooperation.

The legal basis of Port State Control

11.7   This is discussed in paragraphs 5.79 – 5.86 and for present purposes it is sufficient to say that the UK is entitled to impose and monitor compliance with any reasonable preconditions to a right to enter and load or discharge cargo at UK ports and anchorages which are compatible with its international obligations. Such conditions could and should be designed to improve safety at sea and to reduce the risk of marine pollution.

The international dimension

11.8   Regulation 19 of Chapter I of SOLAS expressly recognises the right of Port States to satisfy themselves that foreign ships visiting their ports carry valid Flag State certificates of compliance with internationally agreed standards. The more significant of the certificates concerned are listed in Appendix D. Regulation 19 goes on to provide in paragraph (b) that "such certificates, if valid, shall be accepted unless there are clear grounds for believing that the condition of the ship or of its equipment does not correspond substantially with the particulars of any of the certificates or that the ship and its equipment is not in compliance with the provisions of Regulation 11(a) and 11(b)". Those paragraphs prohibit any change in the structural arrangement, machinery, equipment and other items covered by the survey upon which the certificates were based without the sanction of the Flag State and require the shipowner to maintain the condition of the ship and her equipment in conformity with the Regulations "to ensure that the ship in all respects will remain fit to proceed to sea without danger to the ship or persons on board."

11.9   Regulation 19 goes on to provide in paragraph (c) that if any certificate has expired or ceased to be valid or if there are clear grounds for believing that the condition of the ship does not accord with the certificates, the officer of the Port State carrying out the control "shall" – **not** "may" – take steps to ensure that the ship shall not sail until she can proceed to sea or leave the port for the purposes of proceeding to the appropriate repair yard without danger to the ship or persons aboard. SOLAS does not define the word "port" for the purpose of detaining ships. When a ship is tied up at the quayside she is quite clearly "in port" but there are cases where the lack of a precise definition can cause difficulties. We discuss this further in Chapter 17 (paragraphs 17.36 – 17.43).

11.10   Regulation 19 paragraph (d) provides that "in the event of this control giving rise to intervention **of any kind**" (our emphasis), the Flag State and nominated surveyors or recognised organisations responsible for the issue of the certificates "shall" – again, not "may" – be notified. Paragraph (e) extends this duty to notifying the authorities at the next port of call if the ship is allowed to proceed there, the deficiencies not having been fully made good.

11.11   The Regulation concludes by providing in paragraph (f) that "when exercising control under this Regulation, all possible efforts shall be made to avoid a ship being unduly detained or delayed. If a ship is thereby unduly detained or delayed, it should be entitled to compensation for any loss or damage suffered".

11.12   Control procedures similar to those contained in SOLAS are also provided in Articles 5 and 7 of MARPOL (paragraphs 5.41 – 5.42 and Chapter 9), Article 21 of the International Convention on Load Lines 1966 (paragraph 5.45), Article X of STCW 1978 (paragraph 5.44 and Chapter 8) and Article 4 of the Convention Concerning Minimum Standards in Merchant Ships 1976 (ILO Convention 147) (paragraph 5.49 and Chapter 8). All of these Conventions, as amended, contain a "no more favourable treatment" clause which implies that ships flying the flag of a State that is not a party to the Conventions will be treated in the same way as a ship registered with a State which is a party to the Conventions. Between them the Conventions ensure that Port State Control covers not only safety, in terms of structural, mechanical and operational aspects, but also environmental considerations.

IMO Resolutions

11.13   There are a number of IMO Resolutions which provide guidance on procedures for the control of ships. These include:

(a)   Resolution A.466(XII) of 1981 as amended by Resolution A.597(15) of 1987 which provides guidance on control procedures under SOLAS and the Load Line Convention and includes advice on ways of checking compliance with the Collision Regulations. Perhaps more importantly it allows an inspector to look beyond the certificates if he is acting on reliable information from a crew member, a professional body or anyone else concerned with the safety of a particular ship, that the ship appears to be substandard;

(b)   Resolution A.742(18) of 1993, which replaces Resolution A.681(17) of 1991, provides guidelines covering operational requirements including those covered by SOLAS, MARPOL and STCW. If a Port State Control inspector has clear grounds for believing that the operational condition of the ship is inconsistent with the requirements of the Conventions he can check on-board procedures such as whether key crew members can communicate adequately with each other or if officers in charge of the navigational watch are familiar with bridge control and navigational equipment. His checks should not include any operational tests or impose physical demands which could, in the opinion of the Master, jeopardise the safety of the ship, her crew or passengers, or her cargo. The Resolution provides a number of examples of "clear grounds" for further inspection including the absence of an up-to-date muster list; and

(c)   Resolutions A.542(13) and MEPC 26(23) which provide detailed guidelines on the procedures for the control of ships and discharges under Annex II of MARPOL.

Weaknesses in the system

11.14   There are two obvious weaknesses in the system of control envisaged by the international Conventions. First it does not fully protect good shipowners from inspections at every port of call with the consequent inevitable, if often minor, disruption to the ship's routine when Port State Control officials board and require production of the relevant certificates. Second it does not adequately deal with substandard ships. This is because the system of control provided in SOLAS and other Conventions is based upon the assumption that notification of deficiencies to the Flag State and, if they have not been fully remedied, to the authorities at the next port of call, will ensure that for the future the ship will meet the international standards. This is an entirely false assumption given the lamentable state of much Flag State Control and the fact that the next port of call may be in a State which has an equivocal attitude towards Port State Control or has inadequate resources to follow up the notification. Once a ship has been found to be substandard, she needs careful watching for the future. All ports at which she may thereafter call, and not just the next port, need to be alerted to this fact.

The Paris Memorandum of Understanding (Paris MOU)

11.15   The Paris Memorandum of Understanding of 1982 (Paris MOU) has sought to address these problems by coordinating and harmonising the efforts of the parties in relation to Port State Control with the objective of achieving greater success in securing the compliance of ships with international standards regarding safety of life at sea, pollution prevention and on-board working and living conditions[1]. It is the prototype for other regional Port State MOUs which IMO is encouraging throughout the rest of the world[2].

11.16   In April 1994, the parties to the Paris MOU are the UK and fourteen other European States (Belgium, Denmark, Finland, France, Germany, Greece, Ireland, Italy, The Netherlands, Norway, Poland, Portugal, Spain and Sweden). The operation of the Paris MOU is coordinated by the Port State Control Committee which includes representatives from each of the Member States and the EC. IMO and the International Labour Organisation (ILO) act as observers. Day-to-day coordination is carried out by a secretariat based in The Netherlands. The results of each Port State inspection carried out anywhere in the Paris MOU region are entered in an abbreviated form on a computer database, known as SIRENAC (Système d'Information Relatif aux Navires Contrôlés), maintained by the Centre Administratif des Affaires Maritimes (CAAM) at St Malo, France. UK Port State inspectors also have access to a Ship Inspections And Survey (SIAS) database. This includes details both of surveys and inspections of UK flagged ships and of Port State Control inspections carried out in UK ports. The advantage of this database is that it is capable of holding more detailed Port State Control information than SIRENAC.

---

[1] The Paris MOU specifies that each member will maintain an effective system of Port State Control to ensure that foreign merchant shipping visiting its ports comply with the standards laid down in the following international Conventions and all amendments thereto in force: the International Convention on Load Lines 1966; the International Convention for the Safety of Life at Sea 1974, as amended by the Protocol of 1978; the International Convention for the Prevention of Pollution from Ships 1973, as modified by the Protocol of 1978 relating thereto; the International Convention on Standards of Training, Certification and Watchkeeping for Seafarers 1978; the Convention on the International Regulations for Preventing Collisions at Sea 1972; and the Merchant Shipping (Minimum Standards) Convention 1976 (ILO Convention No. 147).

[2] IMO Resolution A.682(17) on Regional Cooperation in the Control of Ships and Discharges invites Governments to consider concluding regional agreements on the application of Port State Control measures in cooperation with IMO. The Resolution invites members of the Paris MOU and any other countries participating in Port State Control to assist in the conclusion of regional agreements elsewhere in the world and to consider how inter-regional cooperation can be enhanced.

11.17   Each State agrees to inspect not less than 25 per cent of the foreign ships entering its ports in a year. The Paris MOU members have agreed to avoid inspecting ships outside targeted categories (see paragraph 11.19 below) if they have been inspected within the previous six months unless there are clear grounds for doing so. Some ships may well go much longer than six months between inspections. It is estimated that about 80 per cent of ships entering Paris MOU ports are inspected at least once a year – a precise figure is not available because the number of individual ships entering the Paris MOU region as a whole is not known.

11.18   The UK has set itself a higher target of 30 per cent which it has more than met over the last two years. This higher target would be objectionable as undermining the need for inspections to be kept to a minimum, were it not for the fact that so high a proportion of ships inspected were found to be substandard. As things are, not only is this level of inspection reasonable, but also, until such time as the proportion of substandard ships falls, there is a strong case for increasing it, subject to improved targeting so that ships and shipowners with good records may be sheltered from continual inspection.

11.19   Some progress has been made towards targeting ships of types where the consequences of deficiencies would be particularly serious or which are more likely than others to be substandard. This has been achieved by an agreement between the Paris MOU States which currently requires them to pay special attention to:

(a)   passenger and roll-on, roll-off ships;

(b)   ships with a special hazard such as oil, chemical or gas carriers;

(c)   ships which are known, from Paris MOU data, to have had several recent reported deficiencies; and most recently

(d)   ships of specified Flag States that have a poor safety record as measured by their detention rate within the Paris MOU; and

(e)   bulk carriers.

11.20   Discriminating between States by targeting ships of specified Flag States for inspection represents a major development which was long resisted by some Paris MOU Member States. It recognises that failings may lie not only with the operators of the substandard ship but also with the supervision and control exercised, or not exercised, by her Flag State.

11.21   The most recent Paris MOU annual report shows that over 45 per cent of the 14,783 inspections carried out in 1992 revealed deficiencies judged by the agreed international standards (see **Figure 7.ii** in Chapter 7 above). Of the ships inspected, 5.6 per cent were so deficient that they had to be detained in the interests of the safety of the crews and of the environment.

Geographical extension of the Paris MOU

11.22   Poland joined the Paris MOU in 1991 and we support efforts to extend the agreement further to include Russia and the Baltic States. Canada, which has had observer status for a number of years, is likely to become the sixteenth member of the Paris MOU in May 1994. The extension of the Paris MOU, particularly to include part of North America, will significantly extend its scope. **Standards of inspection will have to be carefully reassessed to ensure consistency of approach.**

The limitations of Port State Control

Passing traffic

11.23   Port State Control cannot be applied to a vessel before her first arrival at a Paris MOU port. Nor can it be applied to passing traffic, notwithstanding that such ships are almost as much a potential threat to our coastline as those calling at UK ports. The reason is that, quite apart from any practical difficulties, this would involve an interference with the right of innocent passage. Fortunately most traffic passing the UK coast comes from, or is destined for, ports in States which are parties to the Paris MOU and therefore should not escape inspection. The exceptions are ships sailing through the Paris MOU area to or from Russia or the Baltic States. This gap will remain unless and until those States join the Paris MOU.

The conclusiveness of Flag State certificates

11.24   This problem stems from Regulation 19(b) of Chapter I of SOLAS (see paragraph 11.8 above) and similar provisions in the other major Conventions. Theoretically it is difficult for a Port State Control inspector to see sufficient of the ship to acquire "clear grounds" for believing that the ship does not correspond with the certificates, unless he can make a fairly detailed inspection. Indeed one of the purposes of such certificates is to protect ships' Masters and crews from the disruptive effects of such an inspection. Yet we know from the results of the Paris MOU Port State inspections that many Flag State certificates cannot realistically be taken at their face value.

11.25   Whilst the problem is real, it is not as serious as it might at first appear. Witnesses from MSA have told us, and we fully accept, that substandard ships have a "feel" or "smell" which is usually detectable on a fairly brief acquaintance, particularly if inspectors take the "scenic route" from the gangway to the bridge. Furthermore substandard ships are usually deficient in more than one respect. In practice a surveyor will not be greatly inhibited by apparently valid certificates from acquiring "clear grounds" sufficient at least to justify a limited inspection. Should that reveal deficiencies, he can expand the scope of his inspection as far as may be necessary.

11.26   Nevertheless the potentially inhibitory effects of Regulation 19(b) of Chapter I of SOLAS and similar provisions in other Conventions should not be overlooked. What is intended as a legitimate protection against harassment by Port States must not be allowed to become in practice an instrument of deceit. **Should this occur, consideration should be given to amending the Conventions.**

Inability to discover latent deficiencies

11.27　A Port State Control inspector has access to a ship only whilst she is in port, which may be for a very short period. If the ship has no previous Port State inspection history the inspector will probably have no previous knowledge of the ship and no access to her construction details and history. Many features may not be available for inspection: for example, the use of fire-protecting materials may be hidden by decorative facings and the hull may be unavailable for inspection because cargo or ballast tanks are full. Nor can the inspector check the accuracy of the calculations of a ship's stability. In short, a Port State Control inspector is limited by practicality in what he can inspect. An inspector's report of a particular ship will reflect deficiencies only in items he has been able to inspect rather than the deficiencies which may actually exist. Consequently many deficiencies which should become patent during a detailed Flag State survey are latent in the context of most Port State Control inspections in the sense that they are not discoverable by the exercise of due diligence by the Port State inspector.

The difficulty in checking on the human factor

11.28　It is now widely recognised that human failure lies at the root of most marine casualties, whether or not it is the immediate cause. It was this which led IMO to approve the extension of Port State Control to the management, manning and operation of ships by Resolution A.681(17) which was superseded in November 1993 by Resolution A.742(18) (see paragraph 11.13 above). But this presents considerable practical difficulties. Whilst it is sometimes possible to check on instructions given to Masters, it is extremely difficult to check on such vital aspects as the existence of an appropriate safety policy and arrangements for management auditing. It is almost as difficult to check on operational efficiency in terms of voyage planning, bridge manning and linguistic proficiency and compatibility amongst the officers and crew. And it is impossible to assess the application of skills and experience in the varied and often unpredictable conditions arising at sea.

The grant of temporary dispensations by the Flag State

11.29　As we note in paragraph 6.29, less conscientious Flag States have been known to seek to defeat the purposes of Port State Control by granting temporary dispensations when deficiencies are found or expected to be found in relation to safe manning. This makes it more difficult for the Port State to detain the ship on the basis of those deficiencies, although it can do so if satisfied that the dispensations are wholly unjustified.

The threat of a claim for compensation

11.30　Ships should not be unduly detained or delayed by Port State Control, but what is or is not "undue" gives considerable scope for argument. Inspectors thus will always be inhibited, consciously or subconsciously and to a greater or lesser degree, by a wish to avoid any suggestion that they have unduly delayed or detained the ship. We welcome the recent agreement between the members of the Paris MOU whereby a ship should always be detained if the inspector believes it is necessary for him to inspect essential repairs before she leaves: this removes some of the pressure from the individual.

The availability of resources

11.31   Resources, whether human, material or financial, are always limited. Port State Control work must compete for these resources with other work which may be given a higher priority.

Follow-up action

11.32   Given the need to avoid undue delay or detention, many ships will be given permission to proceed on a limited voyage pending the effecting of repairs. This will often be justified, particularly if the port for which she is bound has better repair facilities. If, however, this port is in another State, particularly one which is not party to the Paris MOU, there are obvious difficulties in making sure that remedial action is in fact taken by the ship.

The UK system of Port State Control

11.33   As we mention in Chapter 6, MSA surveyors are responsible for carrying out both Flag State surveys and Port State Control inspections in the UK: their organisation is described in Appendix C. We believe that the exchange of secondments which we recommend in paragraph 6.46 will help improve best practice for both survey and inspection. Port State Control inspections are based upon the procedures laid down by the Paris MOU. They are often carried out by a single inspector who can summon assistance if he feels that he needs the specialist knowledge of a surveyor from one of the other two ship surveying disciplines. The way in which Port State Control inspections are carried out is described in Appendix E, which also includes some case histories.

Resources available for survey and certification work, and for inspections

11.34   In the UK, Flag State and other survey work is statutory and so takes precedence over Port State Control of foreign ships and other inspections which are non-statutory. Because it is more detailed, survey and certification work is also more time consuming. The MSA Business Plan for 1994-95 indicates an annual cost of statutory survey work of about £3.8 million, which is largely recoverable from survey fees. Overall it is estimated that around 25 per cent of MSA staff time is devoted to survey and certification.

11.35   Inspections of domestic shipping generally involve ships not covered by international Conventions, such as small passenger ships and other commercial and inland waterway craft and fishing vessels, and cost about £1 million each year. Although there is no charge for initial inspections the cost of follow-up visits is recovered. It is estimated that this work accounts for about 6 per cent of MSA staff time.

11.36   Port State Control inspections involve about 7 per cent of MSA's staff resources, also at an annual cost of about £1 million, approximately £60,000 of which is recovered in charges for follow-up visits. In addition MSA contributes a small sum each year – about £16,000 in 1993-94 – towards the cost of the Paris MOU Secretariat and database. In Chapter 21 we discuss the UK's standby capacity for dispersant spraying of oil spills which has an annual cost of some £3.5 million. This capacity may not be used and is designed to deal with the effects of an incident after it has happened. Whilst we believe that the spraying capacity is valuable we consider it surprising to say the least that less than one-third of the amount of money spent on it is spent on Port State Control inspections which are aimed at prevention by trying to ensure that ships are safe.

A strategy for the future

The strategic objective

11.37 No ship operator, whether owner or manager, has any valid excuse for being ignorant of the state of his ship and of the standards to which she is operated. The figures in paragraphs 11.2 and 11.21 therefore show quite clearly that some shipowners have reached the conclusion that the balance of commercial advantage lies in ignoring the effects of Paris MOU Port State Control. In reaching this conclusion they will have weighed up:

(a) the chances of being inspected;

(b) the chances of the substandard condition and operation of their ships escaping detection upon an inspection; and

(c) the degree of the adverse consequences of an inspection which reveals that the ship is substandard.

The strategic objective must be to produce a drastic alteration in the balance of this equation by improving both the apparent and the actual chances of the ship being inspected, improving the detection rate amongst ships inspected and increasing the financial and other disincentives to being found to be operating a substandard vessel.

The risk of detection

11.38 We have no quarrel with the Paris MOU criteria for targeting set out in paragraph 11.19 above in the sense that ships falling within them are undoubtedly more deserving of attention than other ships. On the other hand it is all too clear that owners of substandard ships believe that the chances of the true condition of their ships being detected are low. Clearly it is impracticable to inspect every ship on every call at a Paris MOU port. In any event this would impose an intolerable burden on the owners and managers of ships which are maintained to or above the appropriate agreed international standards. Some other pattern of inspection has therefore to be developed which not only supplements the Paris MOU criteria but also, and crucially, concentrates the minds of errant shipowners on the risk of detection.

Self-targeting

11.39 At present targeting is entirely a matter for Port State Control authorities. In reaching decisions they are dependent upon information from harbour authorities which may come too late or be inaccurate. They then have to consult the SIRENAC database and other information available to them in order to decide which (if any) ships to inspect.

If ship operators played an active part in the process, not only would this simplify the task of Port State Control authorities, but it would also concentrate the minds of ship operators wonderfully.

11.40 Our principal recommendation designed to increase the perceived and actual rate of detection is a system of self-targeting which would be introduced throughout the Paris MOU region. The foundation of this scheme would be a shipborne record of the result of Paris MOU inspections – the Paris MOU log book (paragraph 11.42) **coupled with a new notice requirement** (paragraph 11.45). Self-targeting is not to be confused with self-regulation. Under our recommended scheme ships would be obliged to report themselves to the regulators: they would not in any sense be self-regulated.

11.41 The self-targeting system would apply to ships belonging to the register of a Paris MOU country even when visiting ports in their own country of registration.

The Paris MOU log book

11.42 **We recommend that the UK Government, together with its Paris MOU partners, should introduce a Port State Control log book for ships calling at Paris MOU ports.** This idea is conceptually the same as the MARPOL requirement that from mid-1995 a survey history file must be carried by certain oil tankers (paragraph 7.24). The form of the log book would be determined by agreement between the Paris MOU States and it would be issued to the ship upon first inspection by a Paris MOU Port State Control authority. The log book might take the form of a folder made up of copies of the Paris MOU reports which are already given to Masters following inspection but the existing forms might need to be revised to include all the necessary information.

11.43 The introduction of Paris MOU log books would in no way displace the need for the Paris MOU database (paragraph 11.16). The fact that a log book had been issued would be included in the computer record. It would be needed in order to check that no unauthorised additions or omissions had occurred in the new log books and in order to provide statistical and other information such as the proportion of ships in particular categories which were subject to a notice requirement.

11.44 However, the capacity of the SIRENAC database is limited. It records whether deficiencies were found and, if so, the broad category of the deficiency but it does not reveal two very important facts, namely the extent and nature of the inspection (bridge, communications, machinery or whatever) or a detailed description of the deficiencies. **This information could and should be recorded in the Paris MOU log book.**

The notice requirement

11.45 Once the scheme had started, every vessel bound for a Paris MOU port which had not been subject to a Paris MOU inspection within (say) the previous 12 months – or perhaps six months for some types of vessels such as tankers – would be required to give the Port State Control authority of the State concerned 48 hours notice of her intended time and place of arrival. So far as resources permitted – and it would be important to ensure that they did so permit – that ship would be subject to as thorough an inspection on her arrival as international law allows.

11.46   Ships would be required to continue giving notice at each Paris MOU port until inspected for the first time under the new system. At that inspection she would be issued with a Paris MOU log book. This requirement would also apply, once the system was established, to any ship visiting a port in the Paris MOU region for the first time. Failure to give advance notice would lead to the application of the sanction described in paragraph 11.74.

11.47   It may be objected that the Port State Control authorities could find out whether a ship had been the subject of a Paris MOU inspection, and if so when, by consulting the Paris MOU database without troubling the shipowner. This is correct, although obtaining access to this database can be subject to delays as we saw for ourselves on a visit to a Marine Office. Furthermore harbour authority information as to whether and when the ship will arrive is not as easily come by as information from the ship herself or her owners. However this is not the point. The primary object of the exercise is to draw the attention of the shipowner to the fact that his ship is highly likely to be inspected.

11.48   The subsequent self-targeting regime would depend upon the result of the first inspection. There are several possible scenarios:

(a)   **no deficiencies are found.** If no deficiencies are found, this fact would be recorded in the Paris MOU log book which the Master would be able to produce whenever he entered a Paris MOU port. *Prima facie* it would be a passport to freedom from inspection for the next 12 months (or six months for some vessels) in the absence of clear grounds for suspecting that deficiencies have been overlooked or that deficiencies have arisen subsequent to the inspection. This should be appreciated by shipowners and managers who take trouble to ensure that their ships are maintained to or above the appropriate international standards. At the end of the 12 months, or other appropriate period, the ship would be required to report again on her next visit to a Paris MOU port. It would be for the authorities concerned to decide whether or not to inspect her. Ships which were consistently found to be free of deficiencies should expect to be inspected progressively less frequently;

(b)   **deficiencies are found which do not justify detention and are remedied or said to have been remedied before the ship sailed.** The ship would be required to give advance notice of her arrival at subsequent Paris MOU ports of call until an inspection resulted in a report that no deficiencies were detected;

(c)   **deficiencies are found which would justify detention, but for the fact that the owners undertake to effect the repairs at a subsequent port of call.** There would be two consequences. First, the specified port would be informed regardless of whether it was a Paris MOU or other port. Second, the notification requirement would be longer lasting than if the deficiencies had been remedied before the ship sailed. At the ship's next Paris MOU port of call she would be inspected to confirm that the deficiencies had been remedied, but the notification requirement would be removed only if on a subsequent inspection she emerged with a clean bill of health. If inspection at the next visit to a Paris MOU port revealed that the deficiencies still had not been put right the ship would be subject to detention. Continuing the notice requirement would help to meet the problem of following up on ships which were given leave to remedy deficiencies at a subsequent port of call.

(d) **deficiencies are found which lead to the detention of the vessel.** A notice requirement would be imposed or, if already in existence, maintained for a further period of 12 months after which, the normal initial notice requirement (see paragraph 11.45) would again apply to the ship. Such a ship would be liable to inspection on every visit to a Paris MOU port within the 12 month period even if inspections during that period found her free of deficiencies. Whether she was or was not inspected on each occasion would be a matter for Port State authorities in the light of the results of subsequent inspections, but the shipowner would know that his ship was peculiarly at risk of being inspected.

The position of fleet owners and managers

11.49   We think that it is a mistake to concentrate attention simply upon individual ships. It is trite that there are no substandard ships without substandard owners or managers. If one ship in a fleet in the same ownership **or** management failed to meet international standards, there is a high probability that others will. **We therefore recommend that if more than one of several ships in the same ownership *or* management is found to be substandard on inspection in Paris MOU ports, a notice requirement should be imposed on all the ships in the same ownership or management.** This would be removed ship by ship as each achieved a clean sheet on inspection.

11.50   To enable the targeting of certain shipowners and managers **we recommend that:**

(a)   **ships with a notification requirement should be required to disclose the names of their owners and managers when giving notice to Paris MOU authorities; and**

(b)   **the names of owners *and* managers should be recorded both in the Paris MOU log book and on the SIRENAC database. SIRENAC already records the names of owners but will need to be amended to include managers as well.**

11.51   We expect that any prudent potential customers will enquire of fleet operators whether or not a notice requirement applied, and we also expect that any failure to disclose such information would be actionable at the suit of the customer if he chartered the ship.

Taken together, these two points should ensure that the application of a notice requirement to fleet owners and managers (in addition to ships) will act as a considerable incentive to them to improve their performance.

The position of classification societies

11.52 Whilst initially we do not contemplate any notice requirement being imposed on the basis that a ship is classed with a society which has a poor record, we do not rule this out as an option if, over a period, statistical evidence points a finger at them.

Combined reporting

11.53 We would not wish to burden Masters with a multiplicity of communications even when they are in command of a ship with a record of deficiencies. Advance notice of arrival under our recommended self-targeting scheme should therefore be capable of being combined with any other reports required by MAREP (paragraphs 15.39 – 15.42), the EC Directive on vessels carrying dangerous goods (paragraphs 15.43 – 15.44) or any other scheme. If this might result in the notice being given to an authority which was not responsible for Port State Control, it would be for that authority to ensure that it was passed on to Port State Control without delay.

Exceptions

11.54 The exceptions to the self-reporting system should be as few as possible, but for reasons of practicality the notification requirement should not be applied to cross-Channel and other short-sea ferries which call at Paris MOU ports several times a day. Special attention should of course be paid to such vessels because of the risk to passengers but this is better achieved by a regime of inspection tailored to their special voyage patterns.

Monitoring self-targeting

11.55 There would be little difficulty in monitoring self-targeting under the scheme outlined above since if any ship arrived in a Paris MOU port without having a Paris MOU log book on board and without having given advance notice of her arrival, she would be in obvious breach of her obligations under the scheme. Equally the log book, if produced, would show whether the ship was subject to a requirement to give advance notice of arrival.

The effect of self-targeting upon the nature of inspection

11.56 Self-targeting would not remove the need for some degree of discretion in the nature and depth of inspection undertaken in the case of individual ships. Indeed we attach great importance to the maintenance of this discretion in Port State Control inspectors. Shipowners and managers with a good record are deserving of consideration and in such cases an inspection may reasonably be of limited scope. At the other end of the spectrum general targeting criteria or information from third parties may dictate that the inspection should be as rigorous as human ingenuity and the status of international certificates permits. Whilst we accept that Port State Control has an important educational role in helping to develop an understanding of the need for meeting international safety standards, it is also a means of upholding international standards by detecting and discouraging seriously antisocial conduct on the part of owners and managers who know, or ought to know, that their ships are substandard.

The effect of self-targeting upon existing Paris MOU targeting and quotas

11.57   The effect of our self-targeting proposals would be to place greater emphasis on the Paris MOU criteria relating to ships with known recent defects, but the other criteria would still remain in place. They would be taken into account in two situations: first, as a guide to the use of resources not committed to other inspections as a result of self-targeting; and second, in order to provide a check on the extent to which self-targeting was proving effective in high risk categories. There would continue to be a need for some random inspection independent of self-reporting in order to ensure that ships were complying with the notification requirement.

11.58   The Paris MOU quotas were originally introduced in order to:

(a)   provide a net of uniform mesh throughout the Paris MOU region through which it was hoped it would be difficult for substandard ships to pass for more than a limited period; and

(b)   spread the burden of cost equally, it being accepted that this was a cost to be borne by the national taxpayers rather than the industry.

They have not wholly achieved either of these objectives. As we pointed out, the UK has voluntarily imposed upon itself the target of 30 per cent rather than 25 per cent as its inspection quota. If the only objective had been to catch substandard ships, the UK's quota, and those of some other Paris MOU members, should have been much higher. By contrast we understand that Finland complains of what has been described as "the end of the line syndrome". Few ships call at Finnish ports which have not previously called at one or more Paris MOU ports and Finland has difficulty in meeting its Paris MOU quota without being accused of harassment. The problem with the present standard quota is that it is not based upon actual shipping patterns.

11.59   Under our proposed system of Port State Control, it would be self-targeting which dictated the proportion of the work undertaken by each State party to the Paris MOU and the existing quotas would be both inappropriate and irrelevant. The work would be demand-led – the demand being that of the public interest – and not quota-led. We have no doubt that a major part of the burden in the north east Atlantic would fall upon the UK, France, The Netherlands and possibly Germany as the countries providing a first and often only port of call in the area. Not only is it likely that the considerable burden of a "first time" inspection would fall on them, but they would be responsible in many cases for imposing notice requirements and for passing on information as to deferred repairs, although this information would also be contained in the Paris MOU log books.

The effect of self-targeting upon the need for information from third parties

11.60   Self-targeting would be a primary criterion for inspection, but given the difficulty which sometimes exists in detecting deficiencies, we attach considerable importance to Port State Control inspectors having access to the widest possible sources of information which might lead them to suspect that a ship was substandard and decide to inspect it.

11.61   As we mention in Appendix E, Port State Control in the UK relies heavily upon information from harbour authorities on impending arrivals at UK ports. It is obviously very important that this information is passed on to the Marine Offices as quickly as possible and we believe that this is not usually a problem. **However, if it becomes clear that harbour authorities are not providing this information as required we recommend that the UK Government should consider imposing a statutory obligation to ensure that they do so.**

11.62   Apart from self-targeting, the information from harbour authorities and the SIRENAC database, the other source of information which we have in mind would be based on informal links with organisations connected with the shipping industry. The observations of pilots, harbourmasters, port authorities and others are potentially very useful. There are also several bodies which carry out inspections of ships for their own purposes. These include:

(a)   the major oil companies which carry out tanker inspections. We received evidence from one major oil company that of the 3,500 tanker inspections it carried out in 1991 about one in five were substandard to the extent that they could not be recommended for charter;

(b)   the Salvage Association[3] which conducts surveys on behalf of the Joint Hull Committee of the Institute of London Underwriters and Lloyd's Underwriters' Association. We understand that by June 1993, full Structural Condition Surveys had been carried out on 147 ships of which only 30 passed first time without the need for recommendations. Almost 800 less intense Condition Surveys had also been carried out, a number of which matured into full Structural Condition Surveys. The Salvage Association also has information on worldwide marine casualties and incidents which, until 5 April 1994, it made publicly available on a daily basis. We regret the Association's decision to halt this practice and **recommend that the UK Government asks the Salvage Association to reconsider;**

(c)   the Protection and Indemnity Clubs. The UK Club, for example, has a programme of ship visits which concentrates on various aspects of a ship's performance including standards of operation and management. Between June 1990 and July 1992, 832 ships were visited. Of these 349 were in an acceptable condition, 403 had minor deficiencies which required attention and 80 received such adverse reports that they were required to undergo a condition survey under Club rules[4]. The programme is ongoing; and

---

[3] The Salvage Association was founded in 1856 by underwriters in London to carry out and coordinate surveys on behalf of underwriters. The Association now acts as the technical arm of the London insurance market.

[4] The United Kingdom Mutual Steam Ship Assurance Association (Bermuda) Limited—Analysis of Major Claims 1992.

(d)   the classification societies who carry out surveys on behalf of Flag States and shipowners.

11.63   This clearly illustrates that a great deal of additional information exists. Although at one time we considered whether there should be a statutory obligation to make these reports and observations available to MSA, we have come to the conclusion that this would be undesirable as creating conflicts of interest and confidentiality and incurring the risk that reports would be characterised by tact rather than realism. It must also be recognised that inspections carried out by other bodies are necessarily tailored to their own needs and may not reflect international standards. Nevertheless **we recommend that the Department of Transport should foster the closest possible relations with these sources of information and, to the extent that they too have a need to know, should make their own information available to them.** Information, on request, on whether a ship was subject to a notice requirement should form part of this, as should information on ships which ignore routeing advice (paragraph 16.56). We hope and expect that the flow of information, on however informal a basis, would not be entirely in one direction. **We further recommend that the UK Government should encourage other Paris MOU countries to adopt a similar approach.**

11.64   We are encouraged by the example of the Oil Companies International Marine Forum's (OCIMF) Ship Inspection Report Exchange (SIRE) which was launched in October 1993. SIRE involves the voluntary submission of tanker inspection reports by the 34 members of OCIMF to a central database. Information is available to all OCIMF members and also to some non-member organisations. We hope that this initiative will help to encourage a greater exchange of information between all those involved in shipping. **We fully support the current efforts within IMO to establish an international ship database.**

Saturation inspections

11.65   As we have said, the perceived risk of inspection is at least as important as the actual risk. Our new system of self-targeting is designed to increase both. But no system is infallible and it is impossible to inspect every vessel on every visit to a Paris MOU port. We therefore need a way of reinforcing self-targeting to discourage errant shipowners from trying to slip through the net.

11.66   **We recommend that the UK Government should establish occasional inspections of *all* ships entering a particular UK port in a particular period.** This is already undertaken by UK Port State Control on an occasional basis, the ships affected being those carrying hazardous and noxious substances. Although at any particular time a saturation inspection in one port may reduce the **actual** risk of being inspected in other ports because resources have been diverted from those ports, the shipowner will have to weigh the risk that his ship may be destined for a port where there is 100 per cent inspection.

11.67 The psychological effect of saturation inspections would be much increased, and the burden on resources much decreased, if the Paris MOU States agreed upon a programme for such inspections with the aim of having one saturation inspection in one Paris MOU port at any one time. **We recommend that the UK Government encourages its Paris MOU partners to cooperate in extending the policy of saturation inspections to the whole Paris MOU region.** The fact that such a programme had been agreed should, of course, receive maximum publicity as should the results of the inspection, but it would be important that no advance notice should be given of where such inspections were due to take place.

Publicity

11.68 Publicity can also help to raise the profile of inspection and the perceived risk. The case of the *STELLA* (see Appendix E) was featured on the local television news. **We recommend that the UK Government should highlight such cases more frequently and persuade its Paris MOU partners to do so as well.**

Enforcement

11.69 As we point out in paragraph 11.37 above, our proposals are designed to meet a strategic objective which has three facets. Our proposals for self-targeting and saturation inspections are designed to deal with the first two facets, namely improving both the apparent and actual chances of inspection and improving the detection rate amongst ships inspected. We now consider the third facet, namely increasing the seriousness of the consequences of deficiencies being found.

11.70 The Australian report *Ships of Shame* recommended that a penalty surcharge should be imposed on substandard vessels. This was rejected by the Australian Government on the grounds that detention, and the cost incurred thereby, is a sufficient sanction. We do not doubt the severity of the consequences of detention. But this very fact, taken with the threat of a claim for compensation under SOLAS Chapter I Regulation 19(f) (see paragraph 11.11) or under equivalent provisions in the other Conventions, and the strength of the representations which are usually received from those with an interest in the vessel, renders detention a sanction which is used with extreme reluctance. What is required is a scale of increasing sanctions to be applied not only in cases of detention, but in other cases where detention is deemed inappropriate. In a word, the consequences of any inspection which reveals deficiencies must **hurt** the shipowner.

11.71 Under our new self-targeting system, the notification requirement would in itself be a sanction, with the heaviest burden of self-reporting falling upon a ship which had been detained. However this sanction, which would be applied automatically, does not sufficiently meet the problem of what is to be done about the shipowner or manager who fails to operate the self-targeting system or persistently operates substandard ships. We now turn to that.

Denial of the right to enter UK ports

11.72   We have considered whether the UK and other Paris MOU States should exercise their undoubted right to refuse entry to their ports to substandard ships. This we have rejected for more than one reason. First, in the last analysis it could only be made fully effective by the use of force. Second, it would be contrary to all maritime traditions to deny entry to a port of refuge, yet it is the substandard ship which is most likely to be in need of such a port. Third, a substandard ship may well be a greater menace to our coastline if she is at sea off the coast in adverse weather conditions than if she is in port. Fourth, so drastic a sanction could not be applied in the case of minor deficiencies and it would be necessary to institute a complex system of warnings for minor and first time offenders coupled with rights of appeal.

Denial of the right to discharge and load

11.73   None of these objections applies to the equally undoubted right of the UK and other Paris MOU States to refuse permission to discharge and load cargoes. It is a sanction which hits the bad shipowner where it hurts most – in his pocket – since, apart from refuelling, reprovisioning and effecting repairs, the sole purpose of entering a port is to discharge and load cargo. Furthermore it is a flexible sanction since time is money to a shipowner and a ban could be imposed for differing periods which reflected the gravity of the offence. We recognise that in some circumstances such a sanction may affect others connected with a ship such as stevedores and distribution interests. Such interests already suffer in a similar way if a ship is detained and, to the extent that they are adversely affected, may be able to increase pressure on the owners of substandard ships to improve. As we said in Chapter 4, it is our **intention** that our recommendations should force bad operators out of business or force them to improve. The imposition of a delay or a ban on loading or discharging would clearly be the result of a failure on the part of the shipowner. As such he would be liable to direct or indirect claims for breach of contract from those dependent upon the timely delivery of the cargo. Those who had chartered the vessel would also think twice before engaging such a vessel again.

11.74   A failure to comply with the self-targeting requirement that a ship should give 48 hours advance notice of arrival with a view to inspection could be met with a ban on discharging or loading within 48 hours of arrival. The punishment would thus precisely fit the crime.

11.75   Where ships persistently enter Paris MOU ports in a substandard state, different bans might be imposed reflecting the seriousness or persistence of the offence. Thus in cases of extreme gravity the sanction could be absolute in the sense that the ship or fleet would be banned from discharging or loading at the relevant Paris MOU ports for a specified period, perhaps several months. In less serious cases the sanction could take the form of imposing a ban on discharging or loading until the expiry of a waiting period beginning with the arrival of the ship in port – a special form of a refusal to grant *free pratique*[5]. This waiting could and no doubt would be used for inspections, the previous record of the vessel or fleet providing "clear grounds" justifying such inspections.

---

[5] "Permission granted by the Authorities at a port, being satisfied as to the state of health of those on board a ship on arrival, for them to make physical contact with the shore"—*Marine Encyclopaedic Dictionary, IIIrd Edition* published by Lloyd's of London Press—ISBN 1 85044 371 8.

11.76 Detention is the severest sanction of all and it would be inappropriate to combine it with any discharging and loading ban to operate contemporaneously. Discharging will almost certainly be necessary to facilitate a full inspection and loading may well be inhibited by the need to effect repairs and obtain confirmation that they have been completed satisfactorily.

11.77 Given the discretionary element in a discharging or loading ban, we think that in the case of the UK it would have to be imposed and, if it was not for a defined period, lifted at the discretion of the Chief Executive of MSA on behalf of the Secretary of State. We hope that analogous arrangements would be put in place in other Paris MOU States. We also consider that such bans should apply only in the State whose own authorities imposed it, but the fact that a ban had been imposed in one Paris MOU State should be a ground upon which the authority in any other Paris MOU State could impose a similar ban if it thought it appropriate. **We recommend that the UK Government should encourage other Paris MOU countries to take powers to impose the sanctions we suggest and should take similar action itself.**

11.78 It has been suggested to us that the imposition of bans or waiting periods in relation to loading and discharging might be regarded as a breach of paragraph (f) of SOLAS Regulation 19. We do not agree for two reasons.

11.79 First, paragraph (f) is related to "exercising control under this regulation", that is to say undertaking inspections "directed towards verifying that the certificates issued under Regulation 12 or Regulation 13 of this Chapter are valid" (paragraph (b)) and, if they are found not to be so, taking the steps contemplated by paragraph (c). In other words paragraph (f) requires that there be no undue detention of the vessel or undue delay in undertaking the process of inspection. A ban on discharging or loading or the imposition of a compulsory waiting period does not involve the detention of the vessel. She is free to sail away. Nor do they prolong any inspection which may take place. Indeed whilst ships subject to such measures are likely to be inspected there is no necessary connection between the imposition of the sanction and "control" under Regulation 19 of SOLAS. The sanctions which we propose, like SOLAS itself, are designed to improve safety of life at sea, but they would not be applied in pursuance of SOLAS, but in pursuance of an independent Port State Jurisdiction.

11.80 Second, even if, contrary to our view, Regulation 19 of SOLAS has any relevance, it would be difficult to contend that a system agreed by the Paris MOU States with the sole objective of improving safety of life at sea "**unduly** detained or delayed" the vessel.

The problem of ship identification in enforcement

11.81 In the course of our consultations it was suggested that the ability of ships to change their flags and names and the ability of owners to transfer their vessels into new ownership or management would make it difficult to operate any sanctions in relation to a particular ship. We do not agree. All ships have permanent and immutable IMO numbers which would be used for identification. A change of flag, ownership or management might in some circumstances justify the revocation of the sanction (it would not do so automatically because of the risk of manipulation by disreputable owners) but it would be no obstacle to identification.

Geographical extension of Port State Control agreements

11.82   The Paris MOU was the first regional Port State Control agreement. IMO recognised the importance of the Paris MOU in its Resolution A.682(17) of November 1991 which encouraged the development of other regional agreements. In 1993 the Viña del Mar Agreement came into effect in Latin America and in December 1993 agreement in principle was reached on an Asia/Pacific system which is likely to come into effect in mid-1994. It is vital that emerging Port State Control regimes should have the same formal basis as existing systems and this will need to be taken into account in developing our proposals.

Coastal shipping

11.83   Small coasters and other ships which are engaged solely in voyages between ports in the same State pose special problems. In some cases they do not require the degree of Flag State survey and certification required by ships which trade internationally. In all cases they pose a greater potential threat to the coastline since, by definition, they are close to the coast not only on entering and leaving ports of call, but also throughout their voyages between such ports.

11.84   There is a strong case for imposing a special supervisory regime upon such ships, but since they confine their voyages to the waters of a single State, this is a matter for individual States rather than the Paris MOU.

11.85   **We recommend that the UK Government considers imposing a special inspection regime in relation to ships engaged primarily in UK coastal waters, the regime being based upon the principle of self-targeting and the use of either a Paris MOU or a UK log book with sanctions on the lines already recommended in a Paris MOU context.** That this problem is far from negligible is shown by the fact that UK port-to-port voyages account for 20 per cent of all tanker traffic in terms of quantities lifted and that it is thought that some 240 tankers – 30 of which are over 75,000 dwt – are regularly involved. Whilst most of the vessels are flagged in the UK or with other "Red Ensign" registers (defined in Appendix G) or with EC or EEA States, almost a quarter belong to other foreign registers.

Conclusion

11.86   We believe that our recommendations will go a long way towards removing substandard ships from Paris MOU waters. But we do not delude ourselves that any such improvement will be cost free. The problem is how this burden should be shared equitably, for it would cripple our proposal if States were reluctant to apply Port State Control rigorously and wholeheartedly because of considerations of cost. We believe that it should be the potential polluter rather than the taxpayer who shoulders the burden of Port State Control and we discuss this further in Chapter 22.

11.87 Whilst we recognise that there is work to be done in terms of negotiating agreement through the Paris MOU, certain of our recommendations such as "saturation inspections", better informal links with other sources of information and the inspection regime for coastal shipping are not dependent on such agreement and we would expect the UK Government to implement these quickly and encourage its Paris MOU partners to follow suit. Whilst the UK **could** act unilaterally to implement our other recommendations on Port State Control we believe that they will be fully effective only if implemented on a regional basis. We urge the UK Government to negotiate with its Paris MOU partners to bring this about as soon as possible.

11.88 Whilst we would welcome any *bona fide* application of our suggested Port State Control system to UK and other Paris MOU ships outside the Paris MOU area, we also recognise that it would be possible for less scrupulous authorities to use similar measures in a retaliatory way. We do not believe that this risk is sufficient to undermine the justification and practicality of our proposals.

Draft EC Directive on Port State Control

11.89 A few days before this Report was due to be submitted we saw, for the first time, a draft EC Directive, dated 24 February 1994, on Port State Control. In the time available we have not been able to evaluate this in detail but our initial impression is that the proposal may be too prescriptive in trying rigidly to enforce many of the existing practices of the Paris MOU without tackling effectively some of the basic problems we have identified. For example, the draft Directive requires Member States to take measures to refuse access to Community ports to some ships until the owner has provided evidence that certain deficiencies have been rectified. Better enforcement is vital if Port State Control is to be more effective but as we discuss above (paragraph 11.72) we do not believe that a ban on entry to ports is the best way forward. We believe that our suggestion of a ban or a delay on discharging or unloading cargo (paragraphs 11.73 – 11.75) would be a more practical and effective sanction because it could be varied to suit the offence. We are also concerned that the draft Directive's reinforcement of a quota-led system leaves no scope for the evolution of an improved targeting system along the lines we have suggested (paragraphs 11.39 – 11.55). In at least one respect the Directive appears to go beyond our understanding of what international law permits – in seeking to apply Port State Control to purely transit traffic. We took the view that this would involve a breach of the right of innocent passage which is of fundamental importance (paragraph 11.23).

11.90 There is clearly much work still to be done in developing the EC's proposals for Community action. We hope that the EC will include consideration of our recommendations before finalising its approach and **we recommend that the UK Government takes all steps necessary to persuade it to do so.**

Chapter 12

Accident Investigation and Developments in Safety Regulation

12.1   Any safety regulation system needs to be based on a methodical approach, with a realistic assessment of likely risks. An analysis of actual incidents is an important part of this.

Accident investigation

The Marine Accident Investigation Branch

12.2   In July 1989 the Marine Accident Investigation Branch (MAIB) was set up[1] to investigate accidents involving or occurring on board United Kingdom registered ships worldwide, and any ship within UK territorial waters. The creation of MAIB separated the investigation of marine accidents from the regulation of ship safety: the SGO (now MSA) had up till then been responsible for both. The Chief Inspector of Marine Accidents reports directly to the Secretary of State on the investigation of accidents.

12.3   Regulations[2] under which MAIB operates set out that:

> "The fundamental purpose of investigating an accident ... is to determine its circumstances and the causes with the aim of improving the safety of life at sea and the avoidance of accidents in the future. It is not the purpose to apportion liability nor, except so far as it is necessary to achieve the fundamental purpose, to apportion blame."

Draft revised Regulations were circulated to interested parties for comment in February 1994. The Department of Transport hopes that the new version will come into force soon. No changes are envisaged for Regulation 4, quoted above.

Reports on accidents

12.4   MAIB takes several factors into account in deciding which accidents need to be investigated and which should be simply logged in statistics. MAIB receives something like 2,000 reports a year; in 1992 there were 743 reports of accidents to ships (including fishing vessels), 723 of accidents to persons on board and 387 of incidents with accident potential. Many incidents are relatively minor and are adequately covered by the initial report. In deciding which reports need further investigation, and at what level, MAIB takes several factors into account including an assessment of the likely value of inquiry as well as the seriousness of the incident. Again in 1992, 579 incidents were subject to an essentially

---

[1] Under Section 33 of the Merchant Shipping Act 1988.
[2] The Merchant Shipping (Accident Investigation) Regulations 1989 Regulation 4.

office-based administrative inquiry and 84 to full investigation by an Inspector. Such investigations are detailed and thorough, and may be carried out in conjunction with the accident investigation organisation of the relevant Flag State, or Coastal State where an accident to a UK registered vessel outside UK territorial waters is involved.

12.5   A small number of investigations are the subject of individual published reports. These reports normally include recommendations, most of which are addressed to the Department of Transport. It is entirely up to the organisation to whom the recommendation is made to decide whether and how to implement it.

12.6   Some of the remaining investigations are briefly described in a Summary of Investigations, issued every few months, which includes comments but not specific recommendations; the accounts are anonymous and where the investigation has yielded recommendations they are dealt with separately. The Chief Inspector's Annual Report gives statistical details and analysis and outlines the number and type of recommendations made during the year. MAIB often also produces a summary for interested parties. Again this does not include recommendations. Although these summaries are mainly intended for those closely concerned with the accident, occasionally they have wider circulation when there has been considerable local interest in the case.

12.7   Although we fully understand and appreciate the reasons for separating accident investigation from the consideration of recommendations and the development of regulation, this system does have its disadvantages. MAIB cannot keep fully abreast of national or international developments in safety regulation, because of its necessary isolation from the mainstream of the Department of Transport, though both MAIB and MSA go to some trouble to try to ensure close liaison, and involve MAIB in relevant committees, including IMO sub-committees. We were pleased to hear that MAIB frequently discusses intended recommendations with those to whom they are addressed, to ensure that they are practicable and will achieve the effects intended: we have taken a similar approach ourselves.

The production of major accident reports

12.8   The purpose of MAIB investigations is to identify the causes of an accident in order to establish what action, if any, should be taken to reduce the risk of a similar accident happening in future. Obviously, the sooner the causes of the accident can be made known, the sooner remedial action can be taken – or the sooner the public can be reassured that action is not needed if that is the case. Unfortunately, MAIB reports do not, under present arrangements, come out as quickly as we – or, we believe, the Chief Inspector – would like.

12.9   There are two problems here. The first is the possible conflict between the interests of justice and the interests of accident prevention. When a prosecution is pending, it may be necessary to hold up the publication of an accident report until the trial is completed. In the case of the collision between the *MARCHIONESS* and the *BOWBELLE* in August 1989, the report[3] of the accident could not be published until nearly two years after the

---

[3] ISBN 0 11 551025 7.

accident because of action in the courts. In that case, MAIB's interim recommendations were issued within a few days of the accident and all the recommendations were published when the report was finalised, a year before the full report could be published.

12.10   The second problem lies in the need to give those whose conduct may be criticised a fair opportunity of defending themselves against such criticism. If the normal system for accident investigation by MAIB involved public hearings, they would have such an opportunity there. As it does not involve public hearings, and in normal circumstances there is no reason why it should, some other method has to be employed. The current regulations accordingly require the Chief Inspector to send a draft of his report to all persons whose conduct is criticised. They then have 28 days or such longer period as the Chief Inspector may allow in which to answer the criticism and to propose an alternative draft. The Chief Inspector then considers this and, if appropriate, modifies his draft. If he does not accept the suggested changes, he must then give persons whose conduct is criticised a further 28 days, or again such longer period which he may allow, for them to submit an alternative text. When the Chief Inspector reports to the Secretary of State he must set out the substance of the representations made, and the published report must include as an appendix any alternative texts which have been submitted.

12.11   Although, so far as we are aware, this approach has never been questioned, it does have a number of serious disadvantages:

(a)   it can cause unnecessary delay in the publication of the final report. For example it may have become apparent at an early stage in the investigation that the ship was proceeding at an excessive speed in fog. Why should the whole report have to be completed in draft before the Master and officer of the watch are invited to answer this criticism?

(b)   it may deprive those criticised of an opportunity of answering potential criticisms at an earlier time when their recollection is fresher. Indeed at the late stage of a completed draft, there may be difficulty in communicating with them because they may be in different employment or have changed their home address;

(c)   there is an element of actual unfairness in a system which requires the Chief Inspector to decide upon criticisms and commit them to paper, before he has heard the answer (if any) of those criticised. It is no real answer to this objection to say that the criticisms are at that stage tentative or subject to the effect of further evidence or representations. To have reached that stage as part of a private mental process is one thing. To commit the result to paper and, in effect, publish an interlocutory judgement, albeit to a limited number of addressees, is quite another; and

(d)   there is an element of apparent unfairness in the premature release of a conclusion, tentative though it may be, on the basis of only part of the evidence and representation. The Chief Inspector is put in the false position of appearing to have made up his mind.

12.12   Whilst we cannot say that on some occasions the sending of a draft of the report to those who may be criticised is not the most appropriate procedure, we think that it would usually be better for the Chief Inspector to write to those concerned saying, to take the example given above:

> "I have evidence that your ship was proceeding at X knots with only Y metres visibility. Do you agree with this assessment? If you do agree, what reasons have you for contending that this speed was not excessive given the conditions? If you do not agree, what, in your opinion, was the speed of the ship and the level of visibility? Any reply, including any evidence to support your comments, must reach me by Z."

12.13   The only justification for a mandatory requirement that a draft report be prepared and circulated to those who are criticised is that there is no other way of ensuring that the Chief Inspector gives them a fair opportunity to respond. Given the seniority and experience of the Chief Inspector, we cannot accept that such a precaution is necessary.

12.14   The task of speeding up the process of justice is, fortunately or unfortunately, beyond our remit. Clearly the publication of an MAIB report must never be allowed to muddy the waters of justice. But, as the Contempt of Court Act 1981 recognises, not every publication concerning matters which are or are due to come before the courts will have this effect.

12.15   In this context a distinction must be drawn between criminal and civil proceedings. In neither case will the report be admissible in evidence. In the case of criminal proceedings before a jury, there can be a risk that premature publication of the Chief Inspector's conclusions in an MAIB report may have come to the attention of the jury, be remembered or misremembered by them and, contrary to the judge's direction, be taken into account in reaching a verdict. But that risk will vary according to the public interest in the incident and the interval of time between publication and trial. If a significant risk exists, publication of the MAIB report should be deferred, but the Chief Inspector is not best qualified to assess this risk. We understand that it is proposed to amend the Regulations so that whether or not to defer publication will become discretionary, the decision resting with the Secretary of State. No doubt he will in difficult cases seek and be guided by advice from the Law Officers.

12.16   In the case of civil proceedings before a judge alone, there is no risk of his taking account of the MAIB report. The only objection would be to simultaneous or nearly simultaneous publication of findings which might be inconsistent, thus damaging the reputation of one or the other or both tribunals. Against this must be weighed the fact that prior publication of the MAIB report might well render the civil proceedings unnecessary or lead to a settlement. We understand that the summary reports for interested parties (see paragraph 12.6) often have this effect. **We recommend that the Department of Transport should take the approach we outline.**

Interim reports

12.17 Subject to the overriding requirement that an MAIB investigation and report should not interfere with the administration of justice, the public interest requires that the facts of an incident be established and made known as soon as possible. Any other course provides a rich feeding ground for rumour. **We see no reason why the Chief Inspector should not be entitled in an appropriate case to publish an interim report finding that certain things did *not* occur or, if they occurred, had no causal connection with the accident, adding that other matters were still under investigation.** Curiously, under the existing Regulations the Chief Inspector cannot do this unless he also makes recommendations. The proposed revision of the Regulations will remove this anomaly.

12.18 Subject to the same qualification, **we believe that the Chief Inspector should not hesitate to make interim recommendations, even if at a particular stage he cannot publish findings of fact** – perhaps because he is awaiting replies from those who may be the subject of criticism. One recent example of the Chief Inspector doing just this is the interim recommendations issued in relation to fish factory ships on 26 November 1993. These are described in paragraph 17.20.

The present scope of accident investigations

12.19 At present accident reports produced by MAIB are mainly restricted, as one might expect, to describing the sequence of events, establishing the causes of an incident and making specific recommendations. But whilst a few incidents are clearly unique, others may have a wider applicability. Every accident is an opportunity to investigate not only how a malfunction which led to an accident **did** happen but also how it **might have** happened. We are pleased to see that MAIB does sometimes make recommendations on matters thrown up by an investigation even though they had no direct relevance to the incident concerned: and we accept that a detailed investigation of all aspects of all incidents is not practicable or sensible. A great deal has to be, and is, left to the judgement of the individual Inspector.

Possible causes of failures

12.20 One way of improving the value of accident investigations in helping to prevent future incidents would be to widen their scope. To take one example, if a ship is crippled because of a fire in the main electrical distribution panel, it would be instructive to consider not just how this came about but other ways in which it might plausibly and reasonably have done so. The Chief Inspector should consider not only why this occurred, but the vulnerability of the panel and indeed key elements in the electrical system as a whole. Such an approach would, of course, need to look carefully at the degree of risk involved in the various alternatives.

Near misses

12.21 Equally, an accident-based investigation regime is unlikely to spend much of its time investigating "near misses" – in which term we include failures which could lead to a grounding as well as narrowly-averted collisions – though MAIB does have the power to investigate incidents with the potential to lead to accidents. During our Inquiry we heard of three incidents in the busy Dover Strait and its approaches when a ship lost all power, to the extent that communication was impossible other than visually or over a very short range. These cases of dead ships are listed in Appendix L. They are the *ODIGITRIA B*, which became a dead ship in the Dover Strait, the *PACIFIC MARCHIONESS* in the English Channel and the oil tanker *OLYMPIC BREEZE* in the southern North Sea. All these cases ended happily: but they could have ended in disaster. We do not know how they came to be dead ships. Their Flag States, if they are even aware of the incidents, may not know either, though at least one of these cases was investigated (the *ODIGITRIA B*, by Vanuatu), albeit rather inconclusively. In some cases, it is even possible that the owners and Masters do not always get to the bottom of the trouble. Nor do we know how many dead ships there were in potentially dangerous positions throughout the world in the same period: probably nobody knows.

12.22   There is a particular irony here in that the causes of the loss of power to the *BRAER* have been examined as exhaustively as is possible when the physical evidence lies in the sea, smashed to pieces by the violence of the waves. There are two differences between our group of "near misses", the *ODIGITRIA B*, the *PACIFIC MARCHIONESS* and the *OLYMPIC BREEZE*, on the one hand and the *BRAER* on the other. The *BRAER* grounded and lost her cargo, while the others did not; and the difficult-to-investigate *BRAER* was investigated, while two out of the other three, although comparatively easy to investigate, were not. There is no mechanism, either national or international, by which the UK authorities could investigate them: and no mechanism to ensure that Flag States are alerted to the desirability of an investigation. UK flagged merchant ships are required to report specific minor or potential accidents (known under the Regulations as "dangerous occurrences"): only if other Flag States have made similar rules will they be informed.

Aviation "occurrences"

12.23   It was to deal with similar problems that the Civil Aviation Authority (CAA) introduced its Mandatory Occurrence Reporting (MOR) Scheme, whose objectives are:

(a)   to ensure that the CAA is advised of hazardous or potentially hazardous incidents and defects;

(b)   to ensure that knowledge of these occurrences is disseminated so that other persons and organisations may learn from them; and

(c)   to enable an assessment to be made by those concerned (whether inside or outside the CAA) of the safety implications of each occurrence, both in itself and in relation to previous similar occurrences, so that they may take or initiate any necessary action[4].

---

[4] CAP 382 *The Mandatory Occurrence Reporting Scheme - Information and Guidance*, Civil Aviation Authority January 1993—ISBN 0 86039 532 4.

The overall objective of the CAA in operating occurrence reporting is to use the reported information to improve the level of flight safety and not to attribute blame.

12.24　Under this scheme, not just flight crew members but aircraft manufacturers, maintenance engineers, airport managers and civil air traffic controllers are obliged to report a variety of potentially hazardous occurrences taking place in UK airspace or involving UK aircraft anywhere in the world. An important part of the scheme is that reports are treated in confidence, to encourage full reporting.

12.25　Many of the occurrences reported to the CAA under this scheme are also reported to the Air Accidents Investigation Branch (AAIB), the equivalent of MAIB, for formal investigation.

12.26　The system has been successful for two reasons:

(a)　it provides an opportunity for alerting colleagues to potentially hazardous situations. Corrective action can then be taken through the offices of, for example, the manufacturers. The CAA's independence is a considerable strength in this regard; and

(b)　the reports create awareness of trends and potentially hazardous occurrences which so often can accompany the build-up to a serious accident: small incidents which may not be capable of causing an accident on their own can certainly do so when linked together in a chain of events.

12.27　The CAA is also responsible for the Confidential Human-factors Incident Reporting Scheme (CHIRP) which is run for it by the Institute of Aviation Medicine. This allows pilots and air traffic controllers to report errors that they may not wish to admit to their employers or the CAA. The EC is also considering a Confidential Aviation Incident Reporting Scheme and is currently sponsoring a trial scheme in Germany.

The International Marine Accident Reporting Scheme (MARS)

12.28　In 1992 the Nautical Institute[5] launched an entirely voluntary confidential reporting system, based on the CAA's, through its magazine *Seaways*. Reports are sent in confidence to the Institute and an edited version removing any means of identification is published by it. Although the scheme is based on the MOR Scheme, because there is no mandatory element it is in practice more akin to CHIRP. We commend this scheme, which should help expand and share experience and highlight problems. The particular value of this confidential scheme is that it is international and projects an awareness of potential accidents without being restricted by consideration of liability. The difficulty with it is that it is entirely voluntary and that there is no direct link to a regulatory body able to consider what action is needed.

---

[5] 202 Lambeth Road, London SE1 7LQ. The MARS scheme is sponsored by The Swedish Club, Det Norske Veritas, the UK P & I Club, The Marine Society and the journal *Safety at Sea International*.

The MAIB near miss system

12.29   MAIB also operates a near miss reporting scheme. In 1992 MAIB received 233 voluntary reports of hazardous incidents, and 154 reports of (mandatorily notifiable) dangerous occurrences. A large proportion of the voluntary reports take the form of a complaint by one ship about another ship's navigation. MAIB would welcome more reports of other types of incident, especially system failures where the causes are procedural or human rather than mechanical.

The future of accident investigation

12.30   In Chapter 20 we discuss the means needed to ensure that help is available when necessary for crippled ships. Here we are concerned with analysis to identify the possible causes of "near misses" – which are likely to be at least as instructive as the causes of actual accidents. **We wish to stress the importance of adopting a more forward-looking approach to accident investigation. This would maximise the information gained from accidents and so increase the benefits in terms of future accident prevention.**

Broader based investigation

12.31   The first step must be an improvement in reporting arrangements, so that all significant near misses, including those not involving UK flagged ships, are reported as well as actual accidents. Immediate causes of accidents and near misses also need to be reported where practicable. If there are reports of a number of similar "near misses", it may not matter that the precise facts of each may not be ascertainable. The message that there is a problem will be loud and clear.

12.32   There already exists a requirement under MARPOL[6] for a report to be made if there is a probability of a pollutant being discharged: we describe this in paragraphs 15.73 – 15.74. Obviously all such reports should be copied to MAIB. We recommend in Chapter 15 a study of the effectiveness of this system, with improvements if necessary which would remove the scope for value judgements, and the eternal optimism of Masters that faults will not lead to significant problems. Reports under any new system should also be copied to MAIB as a matter of routine.

12.33   Improved reporting arrangements would make possible the **selection of themes for analysis: all incidents, large and small, involving a particular cause or linked series of causes should be considered together to see what general lessons can be learned. One such theme might be total electrical and communication failure. The purpose of the analysis would be to discover how severe a problem a particular type of failure is in terms of the number of times it occurs, the size and type of vessels involved and the likely potential for disaster.** We were pleased to learn that MAIB has developed a database with this type of analysis as one of its aims, though we understand that a great deal more work is needed on it.

---

[6] Article 8.

12.34 Analysis of themes should reveal what the most significant problems are. Work may then be needed on how to solve them. We cannot judge whether it would be best to replicate the CAA/AAIB division between near misses and actual incidents or whether some other division of work between MAIB, MSA and COASTGUARD is sensible, but clearly all three have a significant input. **There should be a dialogue between them on technical and human matters, though care may be needed to ensure that this does not compromise MAIB's independence of action. There is also likely to be scope for significant input from shipping interests.**

12.35 We do not believe that a significant net increase in effort is needed here: simply a redirection of existing effort. We therefore see no need for any increase in resources.

Research

12.36 Research may often be sensible either to pursue the best means of solving a particular problem or to investigate probabilities. MAIB does sometimes commission research, but only if it is needed to give direct support to an investigation; more often it includes a suggestion for research to be carried out among its recommendations. **We agree that this is sensible: not only would undertaking research during an investigation slow the production of the report, but the small MAIB is less well equipped to commission and oversee research projects than MSA or COASTGUARD. We believe that MAIB should, as a matter of routine, continue to consider the areas which may be suitable for further research and that accident reports should make recommendations accordingly.**

International cooperation in accident investigation

12.37 There is no absolute international requirement laid down for administrations to enquire into accidents generally, though Article 2(g) of ILO Convention 147 states that:

> "Each member which ratifies this Convention undertakes to hold an inquiry into any serious marine casualty involving ships registered in its territory, particularly those involving injury and/or loss of life, the final report of which inquiry normally to be made public."

12.38 In addition, IMO Conventions and UNCLOS 1982 provide that certain accidents should be investigated while IMO Resolution A.637(16) "urges States to fulfil their obligations to carry out investigations of maritime casualties". IMO requests information on serious casualties from Member States and a Working Group meets annually to consider the data. There is also some exchange of reports between Administrations.

12.39 The Conventions in question include SOLAS[7]. Chapter I Regulation 21 of SOLAS reads:

---

[7] The others are the International Conventions on Load Lines, 1966; for the Prevention of Pollution from Ships, 1973, and for the Safety of Fishing Vessels 1977, though the last has not been ratified by the UK.

"(a) Each Administration undertakes to conduct an investigation of any casualty occurring to any of its ships subject to the provisions of the present Convention when it judges that such an investigation may assist in determining what changes in the present regulations might be desirable.

"(b) Each Contracting Government undertakes to supply the Organization with pertinent information concerning the findings of such investigations. No reports or recommendations of the Organization based upon such information shall disclose the identity or nationality of the ships concerned or in any manner fix or imply responsibility upon any ship or person."

12.40   We believe that IMO should take a more active role in examining accident and incident information, identifying themes for investigation and the development of remedies. We urge the UK Government to press this upon IMO. The first step must be the removal of the ban on publication of accident investigation results in SOLAS (Chapter I Regulation 21). This ban not only limits proper investigation of the underlying causes of accidents but also prevents proper public appreciation of the varying record of different Flag States. That is simply unacceptable.

Scientific safety regulation

12.41   A broader research-based and international approach to the investigation of accidents and near accidents should go a long way towards identifying the most important areas for action, but it will still be looking backwards at past accidents rather than forwards to possible future ones. To a large extent this is both inevitable and right, but a more forward-thinking approach is also needed. The "safety case" principle provides this.

The "safety case" principle

12.42   In its 1992 report *Safety Aspects of Ship Design and Technology*[8] the House of Lords Select Committee on Science and Technology, chaired by Lord Carver, considered the whole issue of safety standards and regulation. The Committee observed that progress in advancing shipping safety is generally reactive, with new regulations generated by particular disasters and designed to prevent such accidents from happening again. The Committee proposed a new system to prevent accidents from happening in the first place based on realistic analysis of the risks involved rather than prescriptive standards. It recommended that in the longer term a safety case regime for ship operations based on primary safety goals should be agreed through IMO and administered by Flag States.

Primary safety goals

12.43   IMO would set primary safety goals for all aspects of ship operations. These would consist of standards for structural strength, stability, performance in a seaway, operational competence and safety management for every type of ship operation. Standards

[8] ISBN 0 10 482192 2.

would be based scientifically on quantified risk assessment, on cost benefit analysis and on international agreement of the level of acceptable risk. Standards would need to be revised as technology advanced.

The safety case

12.44   The primary safety goals would form the basis for a safety case for every merchant ship. The safety case would demonstrate that a vessel's operations would meet the relevant primary safety goals, subject to prescribed conditions. These conditions would cover aspects not only of vessel structure, such as maintenance, stresses on the hull and safety equipment, but also of vessel operation, including manning levels, crew competence and safety management systems. The safety case, which would be produced by the operator and audited by the Flag State, would be reviewed every five years to take account of changes in a ship's operating pattern and overall condition. The prescribed conditions would form a "user's manual" for successive Masters of the ship and a checklist for Port State Control.

The advantages of a safety case regime

12.45   The Committee's report envisaged numerous advantages in adopting a ship safety regime. Ship safety regulation would be based wholly scientifically rather than on a mixture of science, political and commercial compromise and rule of thumb. The present system – divided between Flag State responsibilities, class matters and matters not presently covered by regulation – would be unified. Primary responsibility for safety would be placed on the operator rather than the Flag State – encouraging a safety culture instead of one based on compliance and evasion. Perhaps most importantly it would enable more realistic and effective safety standards to be set because the vessel, her crew and her managers would be assessed as an operational unit rather than as separate elements.

Difficulties in applying a safety case regime

12.46   We agree that the safety case regime is an attractive approach in an ideal world and we are pleased to see that some of the principles are already being usefully developed in the UK for other forms of transport. For example, the Health and Safety Executive is involved in implementing The Railways (Safety Case) Regulations 1994. The Regulations require every railway operator in the UK to prepare and secure acceptance of a safety case to demonstrate his ability and commitment to adequately controlling risks to the health and safety of staff, passengers and the general public. Elsewhere in this Report we discuss the importance of the human factor as part of vessel operation and emphasise the need for all those involved in shipping to have a better understanding of risk to inform decision-making. But we also agree with the Committee's own assessment that the adoption of a safety case regime for international shipping is a possibility only in the very long term, although we might add, if at all. In our view, the main problem is enforcement. Under the new regime Port State Control would be able to check the conditions prescribed by the Flag State only on the basis of the shipowner's safety case. If the conditions imposed by the Flag State were inadequate but the ship met those conditions, the Port State would be powerless to act.

12.47   The existing limitations of Port State Control would also become more apparent. The Flag State, with, one would hope, detailed knowledge of the way in which the vessel is constructed, maintained and operated, is in the best position to judge whether she is seaworthy. A Port State, with inevitably lesser knowledge, is less able to do so. To take a doubtless absurd example, under a safety assessment regime a ship might be constructed without bulwarks or rails, on the grounds that the crew always wore safety harnesses and lifejackets when on the deck and needed no extra protection. This might be true: but it is not capable of being checked under Port State Control.

12.48   Our absurd example also shows the potential dangers of balancing operations against structure in a world of tight margins, fierce competition and some unscrupulous owners. A Flag State might satisfy itself that a vessel was equipped with enough lifejackets, safety harnesses, lines and fixing points to make a ship without bulwarks or rails wholly safe in the roughest of seas: but it cannot check whether the crew **actually** use the harnesses at all times. And there is nothing to stop owners from changing flags if they cannot agree a safety case with a particular Flag State.

12.49   The Committee acknowledged these sorts of problem and identified three conditions which would have to be satisfied for there to be any chance of developing a safety case regime for international shipping. Firstly, there would have to be progress in ship science and in maritime risk analysis. Secondly, a "safety culture" would have to emerge across the whole of the shipping industry. And thirdly, there would have to be a high and uniform standard of Flag State Control to meet the point about enforcement. We discuss vessel structure and operation in Chapters 7 and 8 and Flag State implementation in Chapter 6. It is clear that there is a very long way to go before the last two conditions can be met.

Ship science

12.50   The Committee felt that international research had been stimulated significantly by recent events to the extent that the first condition was satisfied, but stressed that further progress was desirable particularly in the UK. However the decline of the UK shipbuilding industry has reduced the funding for UK research. **We agree that access to good quality research is essential, not only in developing the scientific approach to decision making but also to support the UK's leading role in IMO. We note that the UK Government accepted the Committee's recommendation that it should encourage ship science. We recommend that the UK Government should continue to assess the current state of ship science in this country and consider what further action is needed to ensure that there is sufficient capacity to support the UK's work in IMO.**

The UK Government's approach

12.51   The Government response[9] to the Committee's report, which discussed the safety case approach in far more detail than we do here, pointed out the considerable difficulties

---

[9] *The Government Response to the House of Lords Select Committee on Science and Technology Report on Safety Aspects of Ship Design and Technology*—Cm 2121—ISBN 0 10 1212127.

in developing the concept. It also expressed particular concern about the transferability of the safety case concept which is being developed in the offshore industry, but broadly accepted that the safety case concept does have a role to play if it can be approached in stages.

Formal Safety Assessment (FSA)

12.52 The UK Government has adapted the safety case idea in an attempt to formulate practical proposals which can be taken forward through IMO. This modified concept is called "Formal Safety Assessment". The UK Government sees considerable merit in moving away from the sole use of prescriptive regulations and instead placing a greater emphasis on the totality of a ship's performance and on the hazards and risks that she may encounter, and applying scientific methods so as to manage and reduce risks.

12.53 FSA is seen as comprising five basic steps: the identification of hazards; the assessment of risks associated with those hazards; ways of managing the risks identified; cost benefit assessment of the options identified; and decisions on which options to select. In essence FSA would enable safety goals to be set by identifying particular hazards and risks, which could be dealt with by risk management.

12.54 The Government believes that the five steps of FSA can and should be applied first to the operation of IMO itself. At present, a number of sub-committees work on specific subjects but there is no body within the Organization charged with taking an overall view of safety or with identifying particular procedures in one safety or pollution prevention area that might have a bearing on the totality of a ship and its operation. The UK Government believes that the framework of FSA could provide the machinery to enable the work of IMO's individual bodies to be assessed in the round. The aim would be to ensure that total safety, risk assessments and compliance cost assessments become part of the IMO safety culture.

12.55 Given the realities of human nature and the necessity of progressing FSA through international agreement we believe that there will always be a need for prescriptive international regulation. But we have no doubt that an increase in the use of practical, performance-based regulation can improve marine safety and we hope that satisfactory progress can be made through IMO. **We support the UK Government's efforts in pursuing Formal Safety Assessment through IMO**. An IMO correspondence group has been set up and the issue of FSA is due to be discussed at the next session of the Maritime Safety Committee in May 1994.

Chapter 13

Navigation and Guidance to Mariners

13.1   A great deal of advice and information is available to mariners using UK waters. The first and most essential source of information is Admiralty charts, described below, which contain much information about routeing measures in addition to being maps of the sea. The key passage planning chart for the English Channel[1] includes a wide range of invaluable information. The Hydrographer of the Navy publishes Radio Navigational Warnings and weekly Admiralty Notices to Mariners and as well as predictions of tidal heights and tidal streams, lists of lights, Admiralty Sailing Directions and so on. In addition, MSA issues Notices to Mariners (Merchant Shipping Notices or M Notices) on more general issues. All of these should be carried on board.

13.2   There is also a wide range of publications giving very useful information, advice and best practice on a variety of topics – examples include:

> *Ships' Routeing*[2]
>
> *Bridge Procedures Guide*[3]
>
> *Shipping and the environment – A code of practice*[4]
>
> *International Safety Guide for oil tankers and terminals*[5]
>
> *Peril at Sea and Salvage – A Guide for Masters*[6]
>
> *A Guide to the Planning and Conduct of Sea Passages*[7]

A recent and valuable addition is *Guidelines on Safer Oil Tanker Navigation (SOTNAV)*[8], published by INTERTANKO in January 1994, which gives excellent general guidance on planning and undertaking a voyage. Simpler guidance is often also available: for instance, MSA has recently issued a laminated leaflet emphasising key safety points as part of its fishing vessel safety campaign.

13.3   The UK Chamber of Shipping[9] produced in April 1993 an *Interim Voluntary Code on routeing in UK waters for ships carrying oil or other hazardous cargoes in bulk*. While this was

---

[1] Admiralty Chart 5500 *Mariners Routeing Guide English Channel and Southern North Sea.*
[2] Published by IMO—ISBN 92 801 1266 X.
[3] Produced by the International Chamber of Shipping (ICS)—ISBN 0 948691 42 5.
[4] International Chamber of Shipping, 2-5 Minories, London, EC3N 1BJ.
[5] Produced jointly by ICS, the Oil Companies International Marine Forum (OCIMF) and the International Association of Ports and Harbours (IAPH)—ISBN 1 85609 026 4 revised 1991. (The 1984 version is available in Spanish—ISBN 0 948691).
[6] Produced by ICS and OCIMF—ISBN 1 85609 032 9.
[7] Published by the UK Government (HMSO 1980)—ISBN 0 11 5129235.
[8] The International Association of Independent Tanker Owners, PO Box 7518 Skillebekk, N-0205 OSLO, Norway.
[9] 2-5 Minories, London EC3N 1BJ.

largely designed to give routeing advice pending an IMO decision on extended routeing measures (see paragraph 14.18), it also gives excellent guidance on such matters as passage planning and factors to be considered in deciding on an appropriate minimum distance of vessels from shore.

13.4   Some of this guidance is written in admirably clear and simple English: some of it is not. Official guidance which is too long or unclear to those using it (who may well not be native English speakers) may be rewritten and simplified by trade associations or owners – or it may be ignored.

The Seaway Code

13.5   We believe that there is simply too much guidance, and that much of it is likely to remain unread by those who most need it. Despite our reluctance to add to the volume of paper, we are convinced of the need for a clear, simple and above all short text outlining the main points which Masters of vessels transitting UK waters are expected to observe, and giving them some essential information in a single reference text. This we call the *Seaway Code*.

13.6   The Code should have no legal status: we do not believe that ships should be legally required to carry it, though we very much hope that owners of all ships using UK waters would instruct their Masters to carry and use it. The Code should outline briefly the more important legal requirements – including those arising from the implementation of this Report. The consequences of ignoring new rules imposed under Port State Jurisdiction need to be carefully explained and widely advertised.

13.7   The Code would also list key points essential for navigation in UK waters. Owners should ensure that their Masters know and understand everything listed in the Code.

13.8   The Code should give information on UK facilities available, such as MARPOL reception facilities in ports. It should outline the use of emergency communications channels. It should explain the system of reporting which we recommend – with a brief explanation of **why** this is helpful to both vessels and shore-based authorities. It should describe the surveillance system, again with the improvements we recommend. It should outline the system of pilotage, emphasise the areas – such as the Dover Strait and the Pentland Firth – where deep sea pilotage is likely to be particularly helpful, and give contact numbers. It should outline the new system for emergency assistance which we recommend in Chapter 20. It should also describe the service provided by HM Coastguard with details of where rescue centres are and how they may be contacted.

13.9   The Code should also give guidance on the most vulnerable areas of coast, including Marine Environmental High Risk Areas (MEHRAs) which we recommend in Chapter 14. It should give routeing advice, including all advisory and mandatory IMO measures. It should outline particular hazards, such as accident black spots and the (broad) areas in which vessels are most likely to encounter severe or rapidly changing weather, strong tides and currents and shoals. It might also usefully draw attention to the importance attached by the UK to the MARPOL rules on oily discharges and the surveillance patrols flown by MPCU day and night.

13.10   The details in the Code should be extremely short: the main point of the Code is to act as a brief guide to fuller advice and instructions, listing sources where further information can be found, and the main part of the Code should do just this. Those references should include domestic legislation and international Conventions, and should also list useful publications, which will no doubt include those mentioned in paragraphs 13.2 and 13.3 above.

13.11   There may also be a case for the Code to include brief general advice on points to remember when planning and undertaking a voyage, similar to INTERTANKO's *SOTNAV*, described in paragraph 13.2: the alternative is a direct reference in the Code to *SOTNAV* or similar guidance.

13.12   We recommend that the Department of Transport draws up a concise outline of a *Seaway Code* along the lines we suggest and then consults widely with shipping, maritime and navigational interests on matters to be covered and the best means of publication. A careful judgement will be needed to keep it as short and simple as is compatible with coverage of the main points. We believe that such a publication should find a wide market and we expect that the shipping industry – perhaps the Chamber of Shipping, which has already taken a constructive and responsible attitude towards guidance on routeing – will want to take on a major part of the task of production, circulation and updating.

Other guidance

13.13   One of the publications we expect that the *Seaway Code* will refer to is the Department of Trade (now Department of Transport) publication *A Guide to the Planning and Conduct of Sea Passages*, published in 1980. We believe that this is out of date, and hope that it will be revised and reissued.

Hydrography and charting

13.14   Charts are a fundamental tool of safe navigation. Charting – the drawing-up and publication of charts – is the responsibility within the UK of the Office of the Hydrographer of the Navy, an agency of the Ministry of Defence. Hydrography – the surveying of the sea – is also mostly the responsibility of the Hydrographer of the Navy, but the larger harbour authorities are responsible for surveying within their harbour limits. The Department of Transport refunds to the Ministry of Defence the part of the hydrographic surveying programme which relates to non-naval use of the sea. This is currently worth over £6 million a year. Hydrographic information is shared worldwide through the International Hydrographic Organisation. The Hydrographer publishes Admiralty Charts for most of the world: those relating to other countries' waters are based on information provided by the relevant country's hydrographic office.

13.15   Charts are updated to include new information of five types:

(a)   previously unknown hazards, which come from surveying or from reports from mariners;

(b)   established clear routes, which come from surveying;

(c)   recent wrecks, on which the information usually comes from the relevant General Lighthouse Authority, which also investigates, clears wrecks hazardous to shipping, marks wrecks outside harbour areas, and issues warnings;

(d)   new man-made hazards (such as oil installations and pipelines), which come from the relevant organisation; and

(e)   information on navigation, which comes from the relevant Government authority: in the UK, MSA.

Hydrography

13.16   Some areas of unstable and shallow seabed need to be resurveyed at regular intervals, and this takes top priority in the civil hydrography programme. A major problem is a phenomenon called sandwaves. These are banks of underwater sand which move both horizontally and vertically. Some of the sandwaves near the channels to the east of the Dover Strait can stand anything up to 16 or 17 metres high in really quite shallow areas. Other areas with sandwaves include parts of the east coast and the Bristol Channel.

13.17   Beyond that, it is very difficult to judge what level of surveying is needed. There are estimated to be some 24,000 unlocated wrecks in UK waters, but many of them will be in deep water or away from shipping routes. The chances of an accident happening because of inadequate charts are very low; we know of no evidence to suggest that any accident has been caused or worsened by chart deficiencies in UK waters, as opposed to deficiencies in the holding of charts. Nevertheless, there remain some areas of UK waters which have not been surveyed to modern standards, and there may still be uncharted wrecks or pinnacles of rock in accepted routes. Before any agreed routeing measures can be implemented through IMO a full survey is carried out to ensure that there are no hidden hazards. The survey of the Deep Water Route off the Western Isles (see Diagram 3 on page 198) between 1981 and 1985 did find such a pinnacle.

13.18   Priorities for civil surveying are decided by the Department of Transport in consultation with other interests, including the Chamber of Shipping, the General Lighthouse Authorities and UK ports. There is a five year rolling programme of surveys, divided into three categories of priority. First comes resurveying of important areas of unstable seabed; then surveying to full modern standards of areas which have not been so surveyed; and finally resurveying to full modern standards of other areas where both hydrographic risk assessment and commercial interest indicate a lower priority.

13.19   Since the early 1980s there has been an increased level of hydrography but financial pressures have ensured that the original impetus has not been kept up, though all the areas identified as top priority in 1984 have now been surveyed. **We recommend that the Department of Transport should make every effort to preserve the current civil hydrography programme in real terms at least until all the remaining priority areas have been surveyed.**

13.20   Although the Department of Transport is responsible financially for the civil surveying programme, its responsibilities do not cover all the Hydrographer's civil work, including the preparation and sale of charts. We do not know to what extent, if any, these are subsidised by the Ministry of Defence and thus a possible candidate for defence cuts, but we believe that **it would be wrong for defence cuts to affect the part of the Hydrographer's work which is essentially for civil purposes and that the UK Government should protect the budget concerned.**

13.21   Surveying for civil purposes is required only to a depth of about 100 metres. Any surveying below that depth is for naval purposes, or non-shipping purposes such as pipeline deployment. **In neither case should the Department of Transport pay.**

The use of charts

13.22   All vessels are obliged under national and international rules to carry full and up-to-date charts appropriate to the class of vessel and the voyages undertaken. Up-to-date charts obviously give the most recent results of survey work and thus include more potential hazards than older ones. They also include all IMO approved regulations and guidance.

13.23   While it is important that charts do not become so cluttered with information that they are difficult to read, **they should include all approved IMO routeing measures and (depending on the scale of the chart) should in future include information on matters which we recommend, including Marine Environmental High Risk Areas (Chapter 14).**

13.24   Charts need to be updated frequently: the Hydrographer issues weekly Notices to Mariners listing necessary changes. Correcting charts is a chore, but an essential one. There must be a temptation to save money or effort by using out-of-date or uncorrected charts, but this is misguided and could lead to a major accident. **We recommend that there should be active and frequent checks on whether vessels do have the right charts, corrected up-to-date, as part of Port State Control.**

13.25   The importance of using up-to-date charts was illustrated by the case of the Liberian tanker *MARION*. In March 1977 her anchor fouled and severely damaged an oil pipeline from the Ekofisk Field to Teeside. Although the pipeline was clearly marked on up-to-date charts, the Master was unaware of its existence because he was navigating with an uncorrected chart nearly 20 years old. A Flag State Control inspection a year earlier had stated among other things:

"... Navigational charts for trade of vessel corrections omitted for several years ..."

13.26   The House of Lords' conclusion on this case[10] was that owners and managers were personally at fault for not ensuring that up-to-date charts were provided to the *MARION* and used by her Master, and that their liability for damage to the pipeline should not be limited. Damages were estimated at over $25 million.

13.27   The increasing – and welcome – inclusion of guidance on charts expands their use from simple maps, in which language is largely irrelevant, to maps with instructions for which a comprehension of English is essential. We are not convinced that the wording on charts is likely to convey the right flavour to a foreign Master or navigating officer with little English. **We recommend that the wording on charts should be examined critically with this in mind, with non-native English speakers being asked to help.**

Electronic charting

13.28   Electronic charting – or more precisely, the Electronic Chart Display and Information System (ECDIS) – is a development in electronic navigation. It is not yet ready to replace paper charts, but the Hydrographer of the Navy suggested to us that it might be ready for approval by IMO by 1995[11]. The means by which electronic charts will be updated is not yet decided, but both satellite broadcasting for automatic updating and semi-automatic updating through a disc are possibilities. The Hydrographic Office intends launching an electronic chart service later in 1994, with both charts and Notices to Mariners issued on compact disc. Broadcasting corrections may become an option at a later stage. Under this system, up-to-date charts will always be available and will be immediately accessible to navigators: this should greatly enhance safety.

13.29   The new system will also allow the mariner to select the data to be displayed on the chart. There is a minimum level which cannot be removed, but the remainder can be tailored to the ship's needs in different circumstances. Information from navigation sensors, including the ship's position, can be integrated into the system so that the vessel can be tracked and a record kept of her voyage. It will be possible to set visual and audible warnings of hazards such as when the vessel is approaching shallow water or deviates from her course.

13.30   It will also be possible to put radar information, including the position of other ships, on the electronic charts: it is not yet clear whether IMO will agree to the use of ECDIS for anti-collision manoeuvres instead of a dedicated radar as at present.

---

[10] The Marion [1984] 2 Ll.L.R., 1.
[11] Oral evidence, 27 April 1993.

13.31 The development of electronic charting requires careful appraisal to ensure that problems are not built in to the system. Users would obviously need training. It will be very important to ensure that there is a fall-back position when the electronic charting equipment fails.

13.32 The existing system of paper charts and corrections, which electronic charting may replace, is not inherently unsafe. There is nothing wrong with present day charts provided the ship is properly equipped and those on board know how to use them. While there is obviously great potential for transfer and selection of information in the new system, it must for the present remain largely for shipowners to decide whether they see justification for investing in electronic charts, although given the rapid advances in computing, it may well not be long before electronic charts are the norm.

Weather forecasting

13.33 The routes ships take, and their safety when they take them, can depend heavily on the weather. Good information on weather forecasts is important.

13.34 Weather information for shipping for the UK coast and the Eastern Atlantic to 40° West is provided by the Meteorological Office. For the Atlantic area outside coastal waters, weather bulletins are issued twice-daily by British Telecom International and Irish Coast Radio Stations. Broadcasts at specified times on wireless telegraphy and telex consist of Storm Warnings; a General Synopsis of weather conditions, Area forecasts and a Surface analysis. Coastal areas receive twice-daily forecasts detailing visibility, wind speed and direction. Navigational warnings are issued by telex and the International Maritime Satellite Organisation. Weather bulletins for shipping are broadcast daily on BBC Radio 4 at 00.33, 05.55, 13.55 and 17.50, local time. In addition, HM Coastguard transmits at four-hourly intervals (two-hourly in the case of Strong Wind and Gale Warnings) shipping forecasts and regional inshore waters forecasts. From March to October it also transmits three-day fishing fleet forecasts from Aberdeen, Falmouth and Humber Rescue Centres.

13.35 The Meteorological Office also provides a Weather Fax service and a Meteorological Routeing service which covers pre-voyage advice and route planning and a voyage monitoring and advisory service. No charge is made for Weather Fax; the other services operate on a commercial basis.

13.36 The system seems generally satisfactory.

General principles of voyage planning

13.37 A Master planning a particular journey should take fully into account international – and if necessary national – rules and guidance, including (when it becomes available) the *Seaway Code* outlined above, local conditions, including the weather, and of course the policy of the shipowner. Beyond those constraints, the choice of route, including the distance offshore, must be his clear responsibility. **It is essential that everyone with a financial interest in a particular voyage – including the owners, cargo owners, charterers and insurers – should take into account the guidance issued, and should expect the Master to adhere to it. The Department of Transport should issue advice and reminders to this effect.**

13.38 The British Petroleum Company plc (BP) issues distance tables which are widely used. The distances quoted in them do cater for mandatory routeing schemes, but the last edition was published in 1976 and no schemes agreed by IMO since then are included. Advisory schemes, such as the advice endorsed by IMO that laden tankers over 10,000 grt should not pass through the Minch (see paragraph 14.44), are not taken into account in the distances. As Masters may have to explain to their owners why they take routes longer than those in the BP tables, this is unfortunate.

13.39 **We would like to see the BP distance tables updated at regular intervals to include all routeing measures agreed by IMO, advisory as well as mandatory. We appreciate that this may not be a practicable undertaking for a single company, and recommend that the Department of Transport should ask the International Chamber of Shipping to consider whether it could take over publication. Owners and Masters should be warned not to rely entirely upon out-of-date editions by a note in all future editions and by Notices to Mariners issued by the UK Government.**

13.40 Shipowners' standing instructions to Masters should include clear guidance on appropriate safety margins which need to be made to allow, for example, for possible engine or equipment failure or unexpectedly bad weather. These should take normal weather – including normal bad weather – and tides into account. As the Chamber of Shipping's *Interim Voluntary Code* makes clear, there are many other variables. **We recommend that the Department of Transport and the Chamber of Shipping, acting through the appropriate international bodies, should seek to persuade all shipowners to issue such guidance and to monitor regularly Masters' compliance with it.** The INTERTANKO publication *SOTNAV* makes an excellent start.

13.41 Inevitably, the introduction of more guidance on routeing makes planning voyages more complex. This task has to be fitted in with other preparations for a voyage, and all tasks need to be scheduled so as to ensure that the right people are available, having had sufficient rest, at the right time, and that engines are at an appropriate state of readiness.

13.42 The responsibility for proper passage planning lies with shipowners, Masters and officers. Good shipowners regularly monitor Masters' compliance with their standing instructions on passage planning: all shipowners ought to do so. They should ensure that adequate time is allocated for proper planning.

Navigational equipment and position fixing

The provision and funding of navigational aids

13.43   The three General Lighthouse Authorities (GLAs – Trinity House, the Northern Lighthouse Board and the Commissioners for Irish Lights) are responsible for providing and maintaining aids to general navigation in UK waters, including lighthouses, buoys, radio beacons and the Decca navigation system. The cost is met from the General Lighthouse Fund, which is administered by the Department of Transport and which comprises light dues paid by ships calling at UK and Irish ports, together with contributions from the Irish Government and the Ministry of Defence. Pleasure craft of less than 20 tonnes and Royal Navy vessels are exempt from light dues. The GLAs also have the power to remove wrecks which are a hazard to shipping and to mark wrecks which lie outside harbour areas and are thought to present a danger to navigation.

13.44   Most other EC States fund marine navigational aids not through light dues but by other means, such as general taxation. The European Commission, in its communication *A Common Policy on Safe Seas*, recognised that different approaches lead to some ports operating at a competitive disadvantage. It therefore agreed that there should be a study of the funding of navigational aids with a view to achieving a consistent basis throughout the Community, based on the "user pays" principle.

Developments in navigational aids

13.45   As the Chamber of Shipping points out in its *Interim Voluntary Code*, traffic routeing schemes in the past had to take account of the need for ships to approach close to land to check their geographical position, using visual positioning by bearings of land objects and lighthouses. Shipborne electronic aids such as radar and echosounders, shore-based electronic aids such as Decca and Loran and satellite positioning have made such approaches to land increasingly unnecessary.

13.46   All these and other methods of position fixing are now available for use on board the modern merchant vessel. Given the risk of system error and system/machine breakdown, no one system should be used in isolation.

Global Maritime Distress and Safety System (GMDSS)

13.47   GMDSS[12] uses both radio and satellite communications. It is designed to alert search and rescue authorities, and other ships in the area, to a distress incident. GMDSS also provides for emergency communications and the promulgation of urgent safety information such as navigational and meteorological warnings.

13.48   Implementation of GMDSS began in February 1992 and will be completed by February 1999. By then it will apply to all passenger ships and cargo vessels over 300 grt engaged on international voyages. Such ships are required under SOLAS[13] to carry a record of shipborne communication equipment.

---

[12] Implemented in the UK by the Merchant Shipping (Radio Installations) Regulations 1992.
[13] Chapter I, Regulation 12(iv), as amended by GMDSS amendments.

The Global Positioning System (GPS)

13.49   GPS is a highly accurate worldwide electronic positioning system based on the interrogation of satellites. The system was developed by the United States of America Department of Defense. By December 1993 GPS had achieved initial operational capacity and it is now available for civil use at a guaranteed level of service. The accuracy provided by the system is deliberately downgraded for the general user. Greater accuracy can be achieved by the use of a Differential GPS signal. Encrypted Differential Global Positioning System (DGPS) signals are transmitted for United Kingdom waters by a commercial company under the terms of a contract with the GLAs.

13.50   The current requirement under SOLAS[14] is for carriage of a radio direction finder. Amendments to the SOLAS Convention are being considered to replace this largely obsolete requirement with one for the carriage of an electronic positioning system. **We recommend that the UK Government pursues this vigorously.**

Electrical failure

13.51   It is not compulsory for large vessels to carry a GPS receiver, or backup shipborne navigational aids, to guard against equipment failure. The Liberian Investigating Officer into the *BRAER* incident (Appendix Q) recommended that:

> "Consideration should be given to the requirement for vessels having on board battery powered GPS or SATNAV in order to be able to easily fix vessel position and drift when vessel is without electrical power."

We agree with this and **recommend that the UK Government should press for the Liberian Inspector's recommendation to be implemented.** GPS will become particularly important as maritime transponders (discussed in Chapter 15) are developed and adopted.

13.52   However, the problem goes wider. SOLAS[15] presents a number of options for ships' emergency electrical systems. Information which has reached us during the Inquiry indicates that, in some cases, these systems are inadequate, improperly maintained or operated, with the result that the ship is immobilised and deprived of its communication and navigational capabilities.

13.53   It is essential that a ship is able to re-establish main propulsion after a "black-out" and maintain emergency lighting, radio communication and a capability to determine position and drift, even if the engine room is untenable. An emergency power supply (or supplies) is needed outside the engine room. This could take the form of an emergency generator with an independent fuel supply; banks of storage batteries; or battery supplies for individual instruments.

---

[14] Chapter V Regulation 12 (p).
[15] Chapter II-1 Regulation 43 and Chapter IV Regulation 13.

13.54 The requirements for emergency electrical systems should be reassessed in the light of recent accidents and near misses. This review should examine the design, maintenance and operational requirements of systems against their ability to provide essential services.

Pilotage

13.55 A pilot is defined[16] as a person not belonging to a ship who has the conduct thereof. The pilot is there to assist the Master and crew, not to take over from them: the owner and Master of a ship remain liable for any damage caused by a ship when it is being navigated by a pilot, and the Master remains clearly in charge. **We see no reason to seek a change in this clear division of responsibilities.**

13.56 There are two sorts of pilotage – **harbour pilotage** which is generally compulsory within some – but not all – harbour authority areas and **deep sea pilotage** which is a commercial service available to Masters and crew who want it.

Harbour pilotage

13.57 The present statutory basis for harbour pilotage is the Pilotage Act 1987. "Competent Harbour Authorities" (CHAs) are responsible for the provision of pilotage services within their areas, for which they may charge. They may, in the interests of safety, impose compulsory pilotage on ships above a certain size, or only on ships of a specified description, within those areas. The CHA must grant Pilotage Exemption Certificates on application by a Master or mate with the necessary skill, experience and local knowledge, allowing them to dispense with pilots. The conditions to be met before a certificate is granted must not be more onerous than those for an authorised pilot in the area: a sufficient knowledge of English is required where necessary in the interests of safety. An exemption may be withheld only where there are unusual hazards involved in shipping movements within a harbour. In practice, because of these exemptions, many vessels are able to proceed without a pilot in harbours where pilotage is compulsory.

13.58 If no pilot is available, a Master may proceed without one. The British Ports Association have assured us that this is extremely rare. One large CHA reported to them that out of a total of 48,000 pilotage acts since 1988, on only three occasions have ships been permitted to sail without a pilot for this reason. Others, large and small, have not reported any occasions on which this has happened.

13.59 The Secretary of State is responsible for approving applications from ports to have CHA status, or from a CHA to change its area of jurisdiction. His powers are limited: for instance, he cannot initiate an extension of jurisdiction in order to impose new duties upon a harbour authority. Extensions of a CHA's area can only be made through a Harbour Revision Order, and only for the reasons specified in legislation[17], which are broadly limited to the interests and purposes of the harbour in question. Orders cannot be used to impose general control over vessels in transit near the authority's area.

---

[16] Section 742 of the Merchant Shipping Act 1894.
[17] Section 14 of the Harbours Act 1964.

Deep sea pilotage

13.60   There is not, and we understand that there never has been, any provision in UK law for compulsory deep sea pilotage, but the UK and its EC partners have agreed[18] to ensure that vessels using deep sea pilots in the North Sea and English Channel should be provided with pilots who are adequately qualified. Deep sea pilotage is mainly used in the Channel and the North Sea. The service is an optional and commercial one.

13.61   The service provided by deep sea pilots has two elements. One is that a pilot, who is effectively a skilled freelance navigator, can act as a deputy to the Master or simply as an extra navigator. The second element is detailed knowledge of particular areas or routes, which is of especial value to Masters who are unfamiliar with them. Pilots are not likely to have detailed knowledge of areas other than the ones in which they normally operate. Masters who regularly ply a route can be expected to know it and its hazards well: they are thus unlikely to require the services of a deep sea pilot for his local knowledge alone, which may be less than the Master's. A deep sea pilot may nevertheless be taken when the Master's own navigating officer cannot give him the support he needs, perhaps because of inexperience. In addition, since no Master can be on his feet for the whole of a lengthy and difficult passage, he may, in these circumstances, benefit considerably from the assistance provided by a deep sea pilot.

The cost of pilotage

13.62   We are told that some Masters are under instructions from their owners not to use pilots because of the cost. It is obviously difficult to establish the truth or otherwise of this allegation: we certainly have no reason to suppose that any such policy is widespread. If the policy does exist, it is shortsighted. **We hope that owners will encourage Masters to take pilots whenever they feel they would benefit.**

More widespread use of deep sea pilotage

13.63   It has been suggested to us that deep sea pilotage should become much more widespread. We believe that deep sea pilots can be of great benefit to Masters and crews who are unfamiliar with particular routes, or on routes which present more than the usual difficulties. We also agree with the view put to us that having an extra navigator on board is in some circumstances very useful.

13.64   We cannot judge whether more use of deep sea pilotage is necessary or justified: that must be a matter for Masters and owners. Where both owners and Masters are satisfied with the competence and knowledge of their crews, it would be quite wrong to seek to impose unnecessary regulation and costs upon them.

13.65   Positive advice on pilotage is given on the Admiralty routeing guide (Chart 5500) for the English Channel, together with details of how to obtain pilots' services. The first advice section on this chart, headed *How to plan your passage using this guide*, includes the advice:

---

[18] EC Directive 79/115 of 21 December 1978.

"Masters of vessels passing through the English Channel and Dover Strait should take into account the possibility of availing themselves of the services of an adequately qualified deep sea pilot in connection with the requirements of safety of navigation."

It goes on to give details of arrangements for embarkation, but does not point out the advantages of either an extra navigator or an expert on routes. **The Department of Transport should examine the wording on charts to see whether the advantages of pilotage in some circumstances can be more clearly stated.** Beyond that, and brief coverage in the *Seaway Code*, there is little that the UK Government can do to disseminate information on deep sea pilots: Notices to Mariners are normally seen only by UK ship Masters. The deep sea pilot organisations may wish to take the necessary steps to promulgate detailed information on their pilotage services to shipowners worldwide.

Compulsory deep sea pilotage

13.66   It has also been suggested that deep sea pilotage should become compulsory in some areas, in order to raise standards of navigation. **We do not believe that this is realistic.** It would remove the discretion of the Master, who may well know the route in question as well as, or better than, the pilot. We know of no reason to suppose that the problems of poor navigation apply to more than a small minority of merchant shipping, and it would be unreasonable to impose a substantial and unnecessary financial burden on the virtuous majority. Even worse, compulsory deep sea pilotage would in some cases increase the risks. Except where pilots can be safely embarked or disembarked by helicopter, vessels would need to come close to shore for this purpose, increasing the risks of grounding and of collisions such as that involving the *BRITISH TRENT*, described in Appendix L. That would also involve crossing the line of traffic, risking collisions, and would increase the risks of bunching.

Deep sea pilotage off northern and north western Scotland

13.67   The particular problems of navigation off northern and north western Scotland are explained and discussed in Chapter 14. For convenience we discuss here the possibility of pilotage in those areas.

13.68   There are no organised arrangements for boarding or disembarking deep sea pilots off northern and north western Scotland, though the Pentland Firth (see Diagram 2, page 196) in particular may pose difficulties for the Master unfamiliar with it. It has been suggested to us that compulsory deep sea pilotage through the Minch (see Diagram 3, page 198) would be of particular benefit, as it would act as an inconvenience, and thus a deterrent to using the Minch. The two aims, of achieving higher standards of navigation in the Minch and deterrence, are incompatible: a deterrent effect would be likely to destroy any pilotage service. It might also act as a deterrent in those circumstances – such as foul weather in the Deep Water Route – when there is a good case for ships to be in the calmer waters of the Minch.

13.69   Compulsory pilotage through the Minch is impossible under existing law. Compulsory pilotage can be required only in the area of a CHA. There is no CHA with relevant jurisdiction in the Minch. The jurisdiction of a harbour authority can be extended (for any purpose) only if it can be shown to be in the interests of the efficient management of that authority's operation. It seems unlikely that any authority in the Minch could pass this test: none has tried. Even if a CHA's jurisdiction over the passages through the Minch could be established, Masters who used the Minch frequently would soon gain the right to dispense with a pilot. This would act as a positive incentive for Masters to use the Minch regularly.

13.70   These rules could be changed only by new primary legislation. **We do not think it would be right or sensible to seek to change the system of pilotage, which was only recently revised, in order to provide at best a flawed solution to the problem of the Minch.**

13.71   Nevertheless, there may be a case for a deep sea pilotage service to be made available off northern and north western Scotland. We do not know of any demand for such a service: but as there is no obvious outlet for any suppressed demand there may be, it does not necessarily follow that demand does not exist. It is customary for deep sea pilots to work from port to port on short sea voyages, and it may well be reasonable for a ship loading at Sullom Voe for, say, the Mersey and faced with a bad long range weather forecast for the Atlantic to take a pilot in order to facilitate the passage through the Minch if weather dictates using that route.

13.72   We are unable to judge whether there is sufficient demand to justify a system for regular pilotage in northern and north western Scotland. **We recommend that the relevant Marine District Safety Committee** (see Appendix C paragraph 7) **should seek to establish whether demand does indeed exist, and if so whether there is any way in which it can sensibly be met.** Any such service would, of course, need to be fully commercial.

Congestion at pilot stations

13.73   It has also been suggested to us that pilotage might be made compulsory in Lyme Bay (see Diagram 8, page 209) but unless a harbour authority and a CHA can be set up, there is no possibility for this under current legislation. Nor do we see any reason to suppose that navigation within Lyme Bay is difficult – it is just that some guidance is needed. Even without the legal difficulties, we see no benefit from the imposition of compulsory pilotage in Lyme Bay.

13.74   We were distressed by the tragic collision between the *BRITISH TRENT* and the *WESTERN WINNER* near a pilot station off Ostend in Belgium on 3 June 1993 (described in Appendix L), and by the similar incident in the Bosphorus on the evening of 14 March 1994 when an explosion and fire, claiming 31 lives, resulted from a collision between the bulk carrier *SHIP BROKER*, which had just dropped her pilot, and the tanker *NASSIA*, which was about to take a pilot on board. **We believe that the lessons of these collisions should be considered in relation to each pilot station – except where this has been done already – and decisions reached on whether improved arrangements at UK pilot stations are necessary and desirable.** So far as stations for the embarkation of harbour pilots are concerned, the relevant Competent Harbour Authority should take on the job. So far as stations used by commercial deep sea pilots are concerned, the Department of Transport should consult with local interests, including the pilots themselves. We believe that the District Marine Safety Committees are the best mechanism for this. The areas studied should include Lyme Bay (see paragraphs 14.75 – 14.82).

Pilotage and Port State Control

13.75   Pilots are, of course, skilled mariners well accustomed to a wide variety of vessels. They are already under a statutory obligation[19] to ensure that defects on tankers are reported to the Harbour Authority. This provision will be extended in due course to ships carrying hazardous cargoes under a recent EC Directive[20] (see paragraph 15.43). Pilots also sometimes report to MSA on the faults of the vessels they have piloted.

13.76   It has been suggested that pilots might go further than this reporting provision and carry out specific checks – a kind of Port State inspection – while on board. We have doubts on the practicability of this, given both that the pilots are paid, directly or indirectly, by the Masters of the vessels which they pilot (so a conflict of interest might arise) and that pilots when on board should concentrate on navigation. Nevertheless, we hope that pilots will continue to report any faults they see on all types of vessels. We also note that pilots are at liberty to decline to take the conduct of an unseaworthy vessel and to report their reasons to MSA or any other authority.

Escort tugs

13.77   We discuss in Chapter 20 the use of tugs in emergencies. Here we discuss a suggestion put to us that all large oil tankers and other potentially polluting vessels should be attached to tugs by hawsers, or have tugs standing by, whenever they are within a fixed distance of land.

13.78   Large vessels moving into a berth or steaming in a canal often need the assistance of tugs attached by a hawser. Large vessels going into and out of ports are sometimes attached to tugs by hawsers simply for insurance: so that the tugs can help immediately if something goes wrong. In the confined area of a port and its immediate surroundings that can often be a very sensible precaution.

13.79   If a tug is made fast to a large vessel outside a harbour area, there is a fundamental problem of who is in charge. In nearly all circumstances the tug, pulling on her line and manoeuvring very close to the big ship, risks being more trouble than she is worth.

---

[19] Under the Merchant Shipping (Tanker) EEC Requirements (Amendment) Regulations 1982 SI 1982 No. 1637.
[20] Directive 93/75/EEC of 13 September 1993 concerning minimum requirements for vessels bound for or leaving Community ports and carrying dangerous or polluting goods.

13.80   The escort tugs used in harbours are comparatively small – up to 60 tonnes bollard pull[21] – and incapable of dealing with a large vessel in the open sea in poor weather. To be effective in a real crisis, a full scale salvage tug would need to be attached to each vessel. We regard this as self-evidently ridiculous: it would also be massively expensive and extremely poor value for money.

13.81   To make matters worse, such a system could only be applied through Port State Jurisdiction: it could not be applied to passing traffic. There would be substantial additional costs for vessels coming into UK ports, which would represent a significant disincentive to trading with the UK. We see no merit in this idea.

---

[21] An explanation of this term is given in Chapter 20.

Chapter 14

Routeing

The value of routeing

14.1   We stress throughout this Report that prevention of accidents, and thus prevention of subsequent dangers of pollution and loss of life, is vital: there is no absolute "cure" for pollution, and no "cure" at all for lost life. The best prevention is for ships to avoid getting into difficulties: the second best is for ships in difficulties to be able to avoid disaster.

14.2   Routeing measures are designed on exactly this principle. Their prime purpose is to encourage ships to follow routes where they are least likely to collide with each other, to run aground or to get into difficulties of any sort. The best example of this in UK and adjacent waters is the chain of Traffic Separation Schemes (TSSs) – which divide through traffic into two lanes, rather like a dual carriageway – stretching from off Ouessant (Ushant) in Brittany through the pinch point of the Dover Strait to the mouth of the River Elbe in Germany. They are illustrated in part on Diagrams 8 and 9 (pages 209 and 212). The formal TSSs form only a small part of the through route, but lay a clear path from which ships have little reason to deviate. It is perhaps worth stressing that no Master will deliberately put his ship in a position where she is likely to ground or be involved in a collision. He has absolutely no reason to do so.

14.3   The second aim of routeing measures is to reduce the scope for disaster if a ship does get into difficulties, by encouraging Masters to keep their ships well away from shores or sea areas where problems are likely to arise. Simple information on hazards printed on charts is usually, but not always, the best way of alerting Masters to dangers. The third aim becomes relevant only if the first two have failed: it is to ensure so far as practicable that ships keep out of areas where pollution would cause particular damage to the environment. This third aim is a comparatively recent addition: originally routeing measures were designed primarily for safety, though they also benefitted the environment.

14.4   The second and third aims can conflict. It may be better in some circumstances for a ship to take a safer route fairly close to a vulnerable coast than a more dangerous one further away: the best example of this in UK waters is the Minch, discussed in paragraphs 14.38 – 14.61. Where there are specific measures to protect a particular area, they may not be effective in a crisis. The *BRAER* was several miles away from the Shetland Area To Be Avoided when she lost power, but was driven into it by the gale force winds. No line on a chart can prevent weather and tides driving a crippled ship or pollutants into a protected area.

14.5   Environmental interests have to be carefully balanced with the interests of shipping, and particularly shipping safety. It is unrealistic to expect all large ships to stay a long way from land, or even from all sensitive areas. Virtually all the UK coastline is sensitive in one way or another – most of the parts which are not built up are of ecological value, often a very high ecological value, and most of the built up parts are very important to the people who live there. It must also be borne in mind that limiting the areas where vessels can go can create potentially dangerous congestion.

14.6   Those unfamiliar with the sea need to remember that generally speaking, the closer a ship is to a shore which provides shelter from the wind, the greater the protection she will have. Prudent mariners will stay well clear of exposed shores in harsh weather, or even in weather which is capable of turning harsh quickly. In some circumstances it will be best for a ship in difficulties to stay as far as practicable from land: in others to head for a recognised sheltered position, or failing that, any shelter. The *BRAER* attempted to head for the recognised safe anchorage of the Moray Firth when she got into difficulties: had she succeeded in getting there she might well have been safe.

14.7   This may mean, paradoxically, that a ship in difficulties can in some circumstances best preserve both safety and the environment by going close to an environmentally sensitive shore. The chances of her being saved may be much greater: the unavoidable problem is that if she cannot be saved, the risk to the environment may well be greater.

14.8   Despite this, we were struck by the fact that, while hazards are marked on marine charts in considerable detail, there is little mention on those charts of environmentally sensitive areas. Maps do exist showing environmental features in great detail – the *Nature Conservancy Council Atlas of Nature Conservation Sites in Great Britain Sensitive to Coastal Oil Pollution* is the best example, but it is very expensive and ships would be unlikely to carry it. An environmentally-aware owner or Master cannot easily find out where the most sensitive areas are.

Routes taken by shipping

14.9   The first point to be considered is where ships actually go within UK waters. We were surprised to discover that there is virtually no clear information available on this. There is no obligation on ships to report their origins and destinations to a central statistical point, and no sample counts are taken routinely. Some origin and destination data can be obtained, but information derived from them is fallible in two ways: it gives no indication of the route actually taken, and it can take no account of transit shipping which does not call at UK ports. A European wide study would be needed to get fuller information. Just such a study is being undertaken – the EC sponsored EURET programme of research on a maritime vessel traffic management programme, which is partly funded by the Department of Transport. Unfortunately the results will not be available until the autumn of 1994.

14.10   We do not believe that there is a case for an enormous expansion of information: the need to know has to be carefully balanced against the cost of acquisition. Only necessary information should be sought and only necessary areas should be covered. The general principle should be that the simplest and cheapest means to obtain information should always be used. Only when this fails should more complicated and expensive means be used.

14.11   We recommend that the UK Government should consider with its European partners whether further information is necessary to implement properly the recommendations in this Report, and jointly or individually commission any necessary studies. These could include paper surveys based upon commercial information and information collected by bodies such as harbour authorities for other purposes.

14.12   Some limited information is available. Recent studies showed an average of just under nine vessels a day in the Little Minch[1] (see Diagram 3, page 198) and 21 a day (two-thirds of them fishing vessels) in the Fair Isle Channel[2] (see Diagram 1, page 193). HM Coastguard[3] estimate that in the Strait of Dover (Diagram 9, page 212) there are between 420 and 440 ship movements a day: about 200 through the Strait, 180–200 across it and 30–40 fishing vessels operating within it (see paragraph 16.7).

14.13   At our request, the Department of Transport commissioned a paper survey of origins and destinations to plug at least part of the gap. Appendix H explains the way in which the study was conducted and outlines its principal findings. The map at Plate 1 is derived from this information. It shows the density of traffic of shipping, **excluding** ferries, warships, fishing vessels and pleasure craft, based on data from the mid to late 1980s. Plate 4 shows actual traffic density on a single day in the Dover Strait, and Plate 5 shows actual traffic density on a single day in the Fair Isle Channel. The information on which Plates 4 and 5 were based was taken from radar data.

14.14   It is clear that by far the greatest traffic density of merchant shipping around our shores is in the Dover Strait, and that the Strait is the natural route between most of northern Europe and much of the rest of the world. It is likely that much, perhaps most, of the traffic passing through the Strait has no connection with the UK – not in port of origin, not in port of destination, not in ownership and not in flag. The Dover Strait is thus a prime example of a strait used for international navigation, with the constraints (discussed in Chapter 5) which that status brings.

Routeing measures

14.15   Routeing measures are always agreed through IMO, so that they will be notified to and observed by the ships of all nations. They are promulgated in the IMO publication *Ships' Routeing*[4], and are marked on charts.

---

[1] Survey carried out by the Maritime Operations Centre of the Southampton Institute of Higher Education for the Department of Transport in September and October 1989.
[2] Study commissioned by the Department of Transport from the Defence Research Agency at the request of the Inquiry. It was carried out in June 1993, as an extension of a study previously commissioned by the Shetland Islands Council.
[3] Using figures derived from the radar-based Channel Navigation Information Service (CNIS)—see paragraphs 16.6–16.13.
[4] ISBN 92 801 1300 3.

Traffic Separation Schemes (TSSs)

14.16   Traffic Separation Schemes[5] are the only internationally agreed compulsory routeing measures: and they are compulsory only in the sense that, once within them, ships must obey the rules which apply there. It is not compulsory to use TSSs if there is an alternative. TSSs are agreed (by IMO Resolutions) only where the density of traffic or other difficulties, such as the narrowness of a particular sea route, make traffic management important. Identified offending vessels are reported to their Flag State for prosecution or other action. Although under the Collision Regulations the UK authorities can theoretically prosecute for offences by ships of any flag within territorial waters, in practice, for the reasons explained in paragraph 14.102, this is virtually impossible. There are eight TSSs in or partly in UK waters, including a group of three around the Isles of Scilly. They are all shown on the Diagrams in this chapter.

Recommended routeing measures

14.17   Other routeing measures are approved by IMO Resolutions[6]. These Resolutions are advisory, and Member States are not required to enforce them. Like TSSs, they are marked on charts and included in *Ships' Routeing*. They are:

(a)   **Areas To Be Avoided (ATBAs)**, which can be established for either navigational or environmental reasons. All vessels are advised to stay out of navigational ATBAs, but only certain types of vessel are advised to stay out of environmental ones. There are nine ATBAs in UK waters, five established for environmental reasons (shown on Diagrams 1, 2 and 6, pages 193, 196 and 205) and four for navigational reasons (three, in the English Channel, are shown on Diagram 8 (page 209): the fourth, in the Dover Strait, is not shown);

(b)   **Precautionary areas,** which are areas within defined limits where ships must navigate with particular caution and within which the direction of traffic flow may be recommended. They are established for safety reasons in congested areas: the only ones in UK waters are in the approaches to Shetland ports;

(c)   **Inshore Traffic Zones (ITZs)**, which can be established by the Coastal State, subject to approval by IMO. They are always associated with Traffic Separation Schemes, and they are established between the TSS and the adjacent coast. Unless proceeding to or from a port or anchorage within the ITZ, vessels over 20 metres in length are excluded from those zones to strengthen the effects of the Traffic Separation Schemes;

(d)   **Deep Water Routes (DWRs)**, which are routes within defined limits which have been accurately surveyed for obstructions to a specified depth. There are two DWRs in UK waters, one for environmental reasons (shown on Diagram 3, page 198) and one for navigational reasons (shown on Diagram 9, page 212); and

(e)   **Recommendations on navigation and recommended routes**: many TSSs include associated recommended routes, but *Ships' Routeing* also includes other recommended routes and recommendations in relation to the use of certain routes. In addition to those we describe in paragraphs 14.23 – 14.90, IMO have

---

[5] In accordance with Article 22 of UNCLOS 1982.
[6] In accordance with Article 21 of UNCLOS 1982.

endorsed a recommendation that all laden tankers should avoid the southern passage between the Bass Rock and the Scottish mainland in the Firth of Forth; and another that laden tankers of over 10,000 grt should not use the Needles Channel between the western part of the Isle of Wight and the English mainland.

New routeing measures in 1993

14.18 After the *BRAER* incident in January 1993, the Department of Transport invited the Chamber of Shipping to develop a voluntary routeing code[7]. This was produced in April 1993 and was circulated widely to members of the International Chamber of Shipping. Most of its routeing provisions were proposed by the UK Government to IMO's Maritime Safety Committee in May 1993 and approved by the IMO Assembly in November 1993. They comprised an extension of one ATBA (with associated precautionary areas) and two new ones; recommendations on navigation in eight areas and one recommended route. With the exception of the recommended route, where hydrographic surveying was required, they all came into effect on 28 November 1993. Both IMO and the UK Government are to be congratulated at the speed with which these measures were introduced.

14.19 IMO also endorsed UK Government recommendations for Masters to report to HM Coastguard before transitting four specified areas, and extended the existing reporting scheme for the Dover Strait. The reporting scheme is described in Chapter 15.

14.20 We have carefully considered all these measures. We note that they are designed to protect vulnerable areas and that they are therefore based on types of ships rather than on an assessment of traffic. While we regret that it was not possible to make decisions based on accurate knowledge of where ships actually go, and on the extent to which existing recommended routes are adhered to, we do not dissent from any of them. Indeed, we would have recommended most of them ourselves.

Areas with particular routeing problems

14.21 In evidence we heard a great deal about the particular problems of certain areas. We have great sympathy for those who are worried about the effects pollution could have on their local environments and economies, but we are convinced that it is essential to look realistically at the likely benefits of any new measures. Unfortunately, it is also necessary to recognise that some problems are intractable.

14.22 Our recommendations throughout this Report will affect these areas as much as anywhere else, and should substantially reduce the risks of pollution to them. In the following paragraphs we discuss the particular problems of some key areas one by one: problems and solutions which relate to more than one area are discussed later.

---

[7] *Interim Voluntary Code—Routeing in UK waters for ships carrying oil or other hazardous cargoes in bulk.*

Fair Isle Channel

14.23   The UK Government has accepted in Parliament[8] that the Fair Isle Channel is an international strait with the right of transit passage. It is in two parts: that between the northern tip of Orkney and Fair Isle, some 23 nautical miles wide, and that between Fair Isle and the southern tip of Shetland, some 20 nautical miles wide (see Diagram 1 opposite). The *BRAER* was in the northern Fair Isle Channel, some ten miles from Shetland, when she lost power on the morning of 5 January 1993. Just over six and a half hours later she struck the rocks at Garths Ness.

14.24   Since the *BRAER* incident, the Shetland ATBA has been extended and supplemented by precautionary areas, and new ATBAs have been established around Fair Isle, and around the Orkney Islands, with the exception of the Pentland Firth and the entrance to Scapa Flow. Recommended routes, for all traffic in the area, have been agreed in principle for the Fair Isle Channel. They will come into force only after the hydrographic work necessary for any internationally agreed routeing measure has been completed: we understand that this is likely to be in the autumn of 1994. There will be two west bound lanes, one to the north of Fair Isle and one to the south west of Fair Isle, and a single east bound lane to the north east of North Ronaldsay, at the north eastern edge of the Orkney Islands. A reporting scheme for all large laden vessels using the Fair Isle Channel has also been instituted, and is described in the next chapter.

14.25   When we took oral evidence in Shetland in May 1993, it was put to us that Shetland was in a special position because of the number of hazardous cargoes moved around its shores, the exceptionally stormy weather and the economic dependence of the islands on the sea. It was therefore suggested that exceptional measures should be taken to protect the islands from the possibility of pollution from merchant shipping. While we have a great deal of sympathy with the worries of the islanders, we believe that it is essential to assess carefully whether any proposed measure will have the desired effect. We also believe that it is equally important to remember other areas where the coast is particularly vulnerable, and yet further areas where the density of traffic or other special features increase the risks. It is also worth remembering that Shetland does now have exceptional protection: the islands are completely surrounded by a combination of Areas To Be Avoided and Precautionary Areas.

14.26   We were hampered by a lack of information on the density of traffic in the Fair Isle Channel. At our request, the Department of Transport arranged for a radar survey of the Channel to be carried out for 10 days in June 1993, as an extension to a survey already agreed for the Shetland Islands Council. Our letter to the Secretary of State requesting this survey is reproduced at Appendix O. The survey, carried out by the Defence Research Agency of the Ministry of Defence, showed an average of one tanker, 14 fishing vessels and seven other vessels each day passing through the Fair Isle Channel during the 10 day survey period. All of the tankers appeared to be on transit passage, not calling at Shetland. The tracks of the vessels on the busiest day (14 June 1993) are shown in Plate 5. The survey observed that:

---

[8] During discussion of the Territorial Sea Bill on 5 February 1987: Lords' Hansard col 382.

192

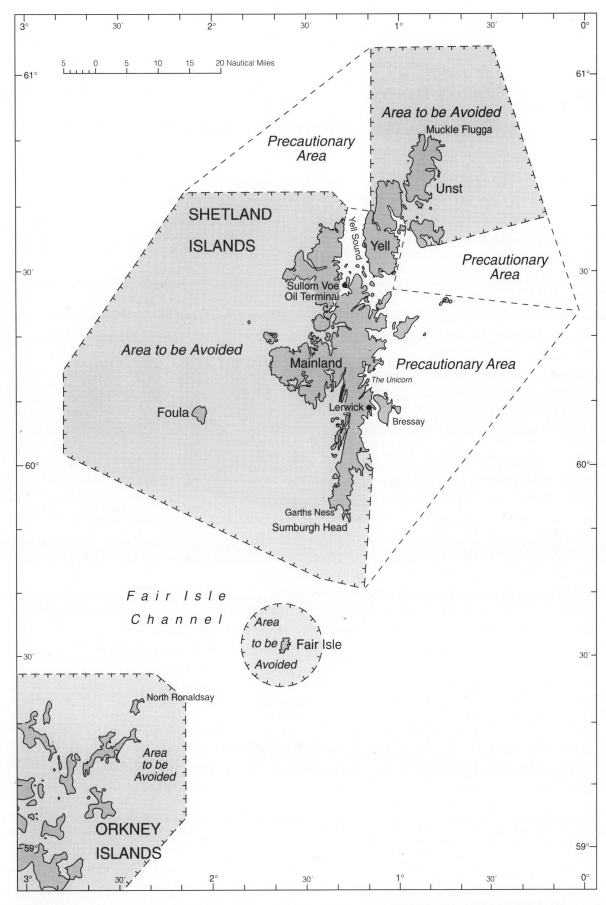

Diagram 1

Shetland and the Fair Isle Channel

"The average number of tankers per day between Shetland and Orkney was observed to be one a day compared to 40 per day through the Dover Strait."

14.27 It was suggested to us that changes in the UK tax regime at the end of June may have reduced the amount of oil in transit from Sullom Voe. As traffic to and from Sullom Voe makes little use of the Fair Isle Channel, and as non-UK tanker traffic was not affected, we do not accept that this will have made any appreciable difference to the level of traffic through the Fair Isle Channel. We do however accept that tanker traffic is likely to be slightly increased in winter, when demand for oil is greater. But even if one assumes a 50 per cent increase in winter – and it is probably far less in reality – there would still be only three tankers using a wide strait every two days.

Excluding traffic from the Fair Isle Channel

14.28 It has been suggested that large tankers should be banned from the Fair Isle Channel. This would not be possible under international law as it now stands, and perhaps more to the point would be very unlikely to reduce the overall risk of pollution. The Channel is wide with little traffic and no obstacles apart from Fair Isle itself. If large tankers could not use it, they would be obliged to go to the north of Shetland – where there is a greater risk of collision because of the substantial number of oil installations and vessels going into Sullom Voe. Alternatively they would go through the Pentland Firth which is narrow and has its own problems, which we describe in paragraphs 14.34 – 14.37. The risks must be **less** in the Fair Isle Channel.

14.29 It was also suggested to us that in foul weather it might be better for tankers to go through the North Sea, Dover Strait and Western Approaches rather than through the Fair Isle Channel. This would add very substantially to many journey times and thus to costs, and in a highly competitive market would be very strongly resisted. But it would also route vessels away from the wide and sparsely trafficked Fair Isle Channel into the comparatively narrow and very much busier Dover Strait. This cannot be sensible.

14.30 Another suggestion, one that was pressed upon us very strongly in Shetland, was for immediate and permanent radar coverage of the Channel, and indeed all round the Shetland coast. We discuss radar surveillance in Chapter 16.

A Traffic Separation Scheme for the Fair Isle Channel?

14.31 After the *BRAER* accident, considerable thought was given by the Department of Transport, the Chamber of Shipping, the local authorities and other interested parties as to whether a Traffic Separation Scheme should be established within the Fair Isle Channel. Despite the *BRAER* incident, the case was weak.

14.32 TSSs are necessary only when traffic needs to be managed because sea routes are narrow or so busy that there is a significant risk of collision or grounding. The Fair Isle

Channel is wide with (so far as is known) few hydrographical problems and there was and is no evidence of a significant risk of collision. A TSS would have made some journeys longer – increasing the length of time which potentially polluting vessels would take to pass the islands, and thus increasing slightly the risk that if something did go wrong the vessel concerned would ground on the islands. In addition a TSS might have brought vessels closer to exposed shores than is now the case. Furthermore the rules of a TSS have to be obeyed by all vessels, including fishing vessels, whose activities would have been badly hampered. It was agreed by all concerned that a TSS was not a sensible solution. **We also agree.**

14.33   Instead, the United Kingdom proposed, and IMO agreed, an extension of the Shetland ATBA and recommended routes outlined above, and also recommended reporting in to HM Coastguard. The ATBA is now large. To the west it extends thirty miles from land. Extensions in other directions would be impracticable because they would restrict access to ports or narrow to an unacceptable degree the passages through the Fair Isle Channel. There are probably few tankers operating in the area below the limit of 5,000 grt applying to the ATBA. Smaller ships would anyway be more likely to need to seek shelter in adverse weather, so any lowering of the limit could adversely affect safety.

Pentland Firth

14.34   The Pentland Firth, between the north of the Scottish mainland and Orkney, is subject to a right of innocent passage, (see paragraphs 5.21 – 5.27). The Firth provides the only practicable access for large vessels to Scapa Flow and the oil terminal at Flotta, and the shortest route around the north of the Scottish mainland. It is shown on Diagram 2 overleaf. As Plate 1 shows, it has a greater density of traffic than all other areas of Scottish waters except the North Channel and the area of the coast south of the Firth of Forth.

14.35   The Firth is narrow – 2.6 miles wide between Stroma and Swona Islands, the narrowest point on the route used by through traffic – and subject to strong tidal flows, including cross tides. It is particularly tricky to navigate for those unfamiliar with it, as the case of the *BETTINA DANICA*, described in Appendix L, shows. It is monitored by radar belonging to the Orkney Islands Council Department of Harbours. In the year from 15 January 1993 to 14 January 1994 they identified an average of 108 vessels a week going through the Firth, including eight tankers, two chemical carriers and four liquified petroleum gas (LPG) carriers. Nearly a third of vessels did not reply to interrogation and the actual figures may have been higher. The Council stopped requesting vessels to identify themselves from the end of January 1994, shortly after the IMO-approved scheme for voluntary reporting to HM Coastguard (see Chapter 15) came into effect: the two authorities will continue to cooperate very closely.

14.36   A Traffic Separation Scheme would be impracticable in the Firth – it is too narrow to provide two passages and a separation zone – but given the problems of navigation clear guidance is needed. Measures taken during 1993 were:

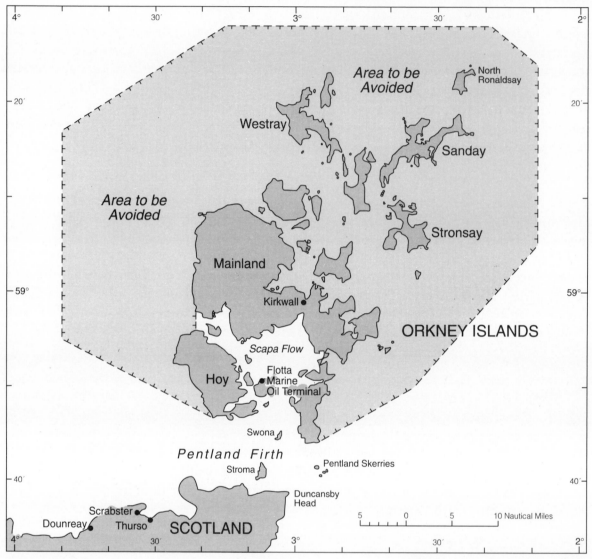

Diagram 2   *Orkney and the Pentland Firth*

(a)   IMO have agreed that "laden tankers not bound to or from Flotta should not transit the Firth against the tide or in restricted visibility or other adverse weather";

(b)   in addition, the larger scale charts of the area now include the legend:

"**Laden Tankers** not bound to or from Flotta and Scapa Flow should not transit the Pentland Firth against the tidal flow or in restricted visibility or other adverse weather.

"**All Vessels**. Mariners intending to transit the Pentland Firth should be aware of the strong tidal streams within the area. Details are given in the notes on the chart, Admiralty Sailing Directions NP52, and Tidal Stream Atlas NP209. Difficulties in maintaining course and speed can be encountered when transitting either with or against the tide. Masters should therefore ensure that a close watch is kept at all times on the course and speed of their vessels."; and

(c)   Orkney Islands Council have issued detailed recommendations for navigation for vessels bound to or from the Flotta Oil Terminal and Scapa Flow.

14.37   We discuss the possibility of making deep sea pilotage more readily available through the Pentland Firth in paragraphs 13.71 – 13.72.

The Minch

14.38   For our purposes, the Minch consists of the Little Minch, the North Minch and the Sea of the Hebrides. This is the area of sea between the Inner Hebrides (Tiree, Coll, Rhum and Skye) and the north west of the Scottish mainland on the one hand, and the Western Isles or Outer Hebrides (Barra, South Uist, Benbecula, North Uist, Harris and Lewis) on the other. It is shown in Diagram 3 overleaf.

14.39   The Minch is a singularly beautiful unspoiled area, containing many Sites of Special Scientific Interest and reserves of the Royal Society for the Protection of Birds (RSPB) and Scottish Wildlife Trust. It supports a large number of fish and shellfish farms which are vital to the local economy. There are no very strong tides and currents – the maximum tidal rate is one knot at "springs" – and any pollutants spilled would be likely to take a long time to disperse. There is no doubt that a significant pollution incident in the Minch could be catastrophic. Understandably, local people fear that the passage of large laden tankers through the Minch could lead to an accident and consequent pollution, and would like to see them avoiding the area.

14.40   The Minch is wide for most of its length, with a comparatively narrow section some three miles wide between Harris and the Shiant Islands. The available depths mean that the navigable passage for large tankers is about one and a half miles wide – rather wider than the narrowest part of the Deep Water Route through the very much busier Dover Strait (see paragraph 14.86).

Innocent passage

14.41   As we explain in Chapter 5, internal waters such as the Minch which have been used by foreign-flagged ships for many years are subject to a right of innocent passage. This right of innocent passage might not matter, even in such an ecologically sensitive area as the Minch, if it was not used by potentially polluting vessels. Unfortunately the Minch is on the natural route for oil tankers *en route* from Norway or Shetland to Milford Haven and other destinations in the Irish and Celtic Seas, and may well also be used by tankers *en route* to south western Europe. Neither tankers nor any other vessel can be banned from the Minch.

Measures taken to protect the Minch

14.42   In 1987 a Deep Water Route (DWR) was established to the west of North Uist, Harris and Lewis: the only one in UK waters established for environmental reasons. It was

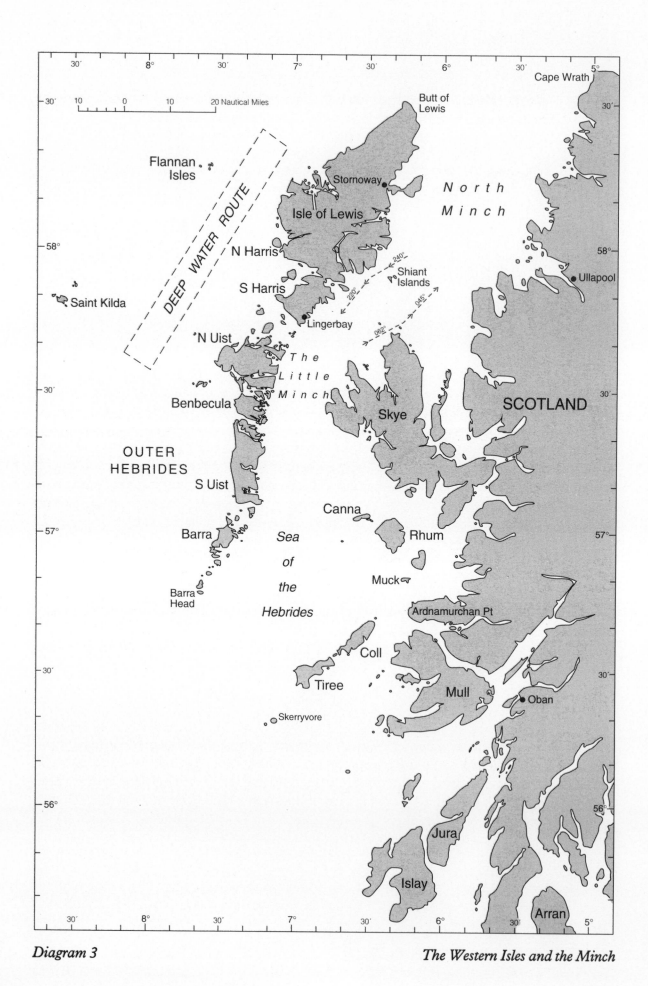

Diagram 3

The Western Isles and the Minch

approved by IMO and marked on charts. Notices to Mariners are issued to the Masters of tankers leaving Sullom Voe advising them to use the DWR, weather conditions permitting. The advice applies only to laden tankers of 10,000 grt and above. Recommended routes through the Minch were established and marked on charts many years ago. They advise north bound traffic to use the eastern side of the Minch, going to the east of the Shiant Islands, and south bound traffic to take the western side, to the west of the Shiants.

14.43   More recently the Department of Transport, the Highland Regional Council and the Western Isles Islands Council have jointly asked anyone seeing a vessel which they believe to be a large laden tanker in the Minch to report it to HM Coastguard. Reports are checked, and the owners of large laden tankers identified going through the Minch are asked to explain why they chose that route. At least one Norwegian company has changed its policy as a result, instructing its Masters to use the DWR routinely. The UK Government cannot, however, take any legal action against anyone who ignores the advice. Flag States could only do so if they had enacted specific domestic legislation to that end.

14.44   The Chamber of Shipping's *Interim Voluntary Code* of April 1993 and the measures proposed by the UK Government and adopted by IMO in November 1993 both recommended that laden tankers over 10,000 grt should not pass through the Minch, except due to stress of weather or any other case of *force majeure*. The effects of this have yet to be seen, though we were pleased to note that INTERTANKO[9] has advised all its members to follow the advice on using the DWR, and has asked that any charterers' instructions to the contrary should be reported to it[10]. Unladen tankers are not advised to avoid the Minch, on the grounds both that they pose a lesser risk to the environment than laden tankers and because this reduces the chances of a head-on meeting between tankers travelling in opposite directions: most laden tankers off north western Scotland are *en route* southwards, and most unladen ones northwards. Smaller tankers and other vessels are not advised to avoid the Minch. Large vessels, both laden and in ballast, which do use the Minch are asked to report to the Stornoway Coastguard at least one hour before doing so.

Traffic in the Minch

14.45   A traffic count taken in 1989 (paragraph 14.12) suggested that fewer than one large laden tanker went through the Minch every day. Only about one fifth of large laden tankers used the DWR in preference to the Minch during the study period: the remainder used the Minch. A quarter of those using the Minch – a fifth of the total – did so because of severe weather.

14.46   The survey also observed an average of just under nine other vessels a day in the Little Minch. These may have included unladen tankers, naval vessels and ordinary merchant shipping in transit, and smaller tankers, ferries, fishing vessels, pleasure craft and other vessels with business in the islands. If a proposal for a large quarry at Lingerbay on the eastern side of Harris goes ahead, 120,000 grt ore carriers will also need to manoeuvre across the Minch on about 400 occasions a year.

---

[9] The International Association of Independent Tanker Owners.
[10] INTERTANKO General Circular Letter to Members No. 02/1994.

14.47   We were interested to note when we flew along part of the Minch in a helicopter in May 1993 that there were no vessels to be seen at all. It is clear that, as with the Fair Isle Channel, traffic is sparse by the standards of busy straits such as Dover. For every tanker going through the Minch, there are probably over 40 tankers going through the Dover Strait, as well as other large vessels carrying potentially dangerous or polluting goods. Traffic in the Dover Strait is confined to traffic lanes which, because of the constricting sandbanks, are generally narrower than the passages through the Minch, or the Fair Isle Channel.

14.48   The only incident we know of involving a tanker in the Minch took place in August 1993 when a ferry leaving Oban had to change course to avoid a tanker following the recommended route on the eastern side of the Minch. The Collision Regulations make special provision where large vessels are confined to narrow channels, and as we understand that the tanker would have put herself on a hazardous course had she given way, it is likely that she was right not to do so.

14.49   The Minch is well charted with a stable seabed and excellent radar targets, and there are safe anchorages available for any vessel in difficulties. In all these circumstances, the chances of a collision or grounding which could lead to pollution must be remote. To describe the Minch as "dangerous", as some journalists have done, is a gross misrepresentation.

Alternatives to the Minch

14.50   A large tanker which does not use the Minch may go around the eastern side of Great Britain instead and through the Dover Strait. Given the much higher chances of a collision in the Strait, such a change is unlikely to be in the overall best interests of the UK coastline. A more likely alternative is the western route, using the Deep Water Route which goes roughly half way between Lewis and the outlying Flannan Islands and between North Uist and the outlying St Kilda.

14.51   There are financial and operational disadvantages for owners in taking this route as the passage is likely to take several hours longer. We believe that this should be disregarded in the interests of the environment. However, the rougher seas and stronger winds in the open Atlantic will inevitably put greater stress on both a vessel and her crew. While ocean crossings in severe weather are routine for both, the stresses may very slightly increase the chances of mechanical or structural failure or human error. What is certain is that if something does go wrong, help is further away, there are no safe anchorages available, and winds and tides are liable to push a crippled vessel onto the western coast of the main chain of the Western Isles. A vessel suffering a mechanical breakdown, like the *BRAER*, is more likely to come to grief on the western rather than the eastern side of the islands.

14.52   The ecology and economy of the western coast are almost as vulnerable as those of the eastern coast of the main chain of the Western Isles – just over a quarter of the fish and shellfish farms in the Western Isles are on the western coast which is even less accessible in an emergency. And if there were a pollution incident on the western coast of these islands, the winds and currents would tend to drive at least some of the pollutants between the islands into the Minch. So the net effect of transferring tanker traffic from the Minch to the outer route is to reduce but not eliminate the already small risk to the Minch from a collision or grounding, and to transfer a slightly increased risk to the outer coastline. For this reason, it has been suggested to us in evidence that the DWR ought to be moved further west. This could only be done by moving it to the western side of the Flannan Islands and St Kilda.

St Kilda and the Flannan Islands

14.53   St Kilda, which is owned by the National Trust for Scotland and managed in association with Scottish Natural Heritage, was designated Scotland's first World Heritage site by UNESCO in 1987. It has unique wildlife and nearly 30 per cent of the world gannet population. It clearly merits at least as much protection as the Minch, so any new DWR would need to be several miles to the west of it. The Flannan Isles are a group of rocky islands and skerries notified as a Site of Special Scientific Interest in 1983 and a Special Protection Area in 1992. The islands support breeding populations of guillemots, razorbills, puffins, storm petrels and Leach petrels, the last in internationally important numbers.

14.54   The area to the west of St Kilda has not been surveyed to modern standards, and a survey would clearly be needed before any recommendations could be made. More to the point, St Kilda is 45 nautical miles from the nearest part of North Uist and going to the west of it would be a substantial, and time-consuming, diversion for many vessels. **We do not believe that this makes sense, or that IMO – let alone the shipping industry – would accept it. There is no point in giving guidance if its recipients are likely to consider it ridiculous and ignore it. Worse, such guidance would tend to devalue routeing guidance all over the world.**

14.55   **Whilst St Kilda and the Flannan Islands deserve protection, they may not need it because of their remoteness. We recommend that ships proceeding to the west of the main chain of the Western Isles and on courses west of Ireland should be advised to keep well to seaward of the Flannan Islands and St Kilda in bad weather. This advice should be printed on charts. Particular measures may be needed to deal with cruise ships which visit the islands: these we discuss in paragraphs 14.109 – 14.111.**

The Deep Water Route to the west of Harris and Lewis

14.56   The DWR covers only part of the route taken by tankers along the western coast of the islands, and there is no guidance to vessels on how close they can sensibly go to the Butt of Lewis at the northern end of the chain or to Barra Head at the southern end. The temptation must be for them to take the shortest route, going very close to these headlands, and anecdotal evidence suggests that they do just this. **It should be made very** clear in guidance, preferably by an extension of the DWR both north and south, that vessels should keep several miles off the entire western coast of Barra, the Uists, Harris and Lewis and the intervening islands. Again, the guidance should be marked on charts. We understand that there should be few problems with this, because the whole of the relevant area has been surveyed to modern standards.

Compulsory pilotage

14.57   It has also been suggested to us that compulsory pilotage should be introduced in the Minch, partly to ensure the highest standards of navigation through the Minch and partly because the inevitable inconvenience of taking on a pilot would act as an added incentive to use the outer route. We discuss and dismiss this idea in Chapter 13.

Resolving the problems

14.58   Unfortunately, there is no real solution to the problem of the Minch. For the foreseeable future large tankers will continue to go past the north western coast of Scotland, and there is no means of eliminating the risk they pose to beautiful and valuable coasts. That said, a real effort must be made to ensure that everyone whose actions might affect the special character of the Minch realises the potential problems and takes well informed decisions. The recommendations set out elsewhere in this Report will go a long way towards achieving this.

14.59   **The key point is that the Masters of large and potentially polluting ships should use the DWR as a matter of routine.** *All* **large vessels should do so; given the damage that bunker oil can cause, the current distinction between large laden and unladen tankers, and between large tankers and other large vessels, is mistaken and should be changed.** We recognise that this will make it possible for vessels to meet head on in the DWR, with a small increased risk of collisions, but we believe that the DWR is wide enough, and traffic sparse enough, for the risk to be very small.

14.60   **In normal weather, the balance of advantage to the environment lies in tankers using the DWR. In severe weather, it does not. Masters of all large vessels should retain the option of using the Minch when** *exceptional* **weather or other conditions make it safer for them to do so. There can be no set criteria: Masters must be free to act in the best interests of safety, which are normally also the best interests of the environment. The Department of Transport should continue the cooperative monitoring arrangements and continue to seek explanations from the owners or Masters of vessels using the Minch. This should be done both when Masters report in under the arrangements agreed by IMO and subsequently when tankers are seen in the Minch.**

14.61   **We expect that these measures will result in a steady reduction of the number of large vessels using the Minch. The position should continue to be monitored. If after a reasonable period has elapsed – say a year – there has not been a major improvement, the Government should raise the problem with IMO.**

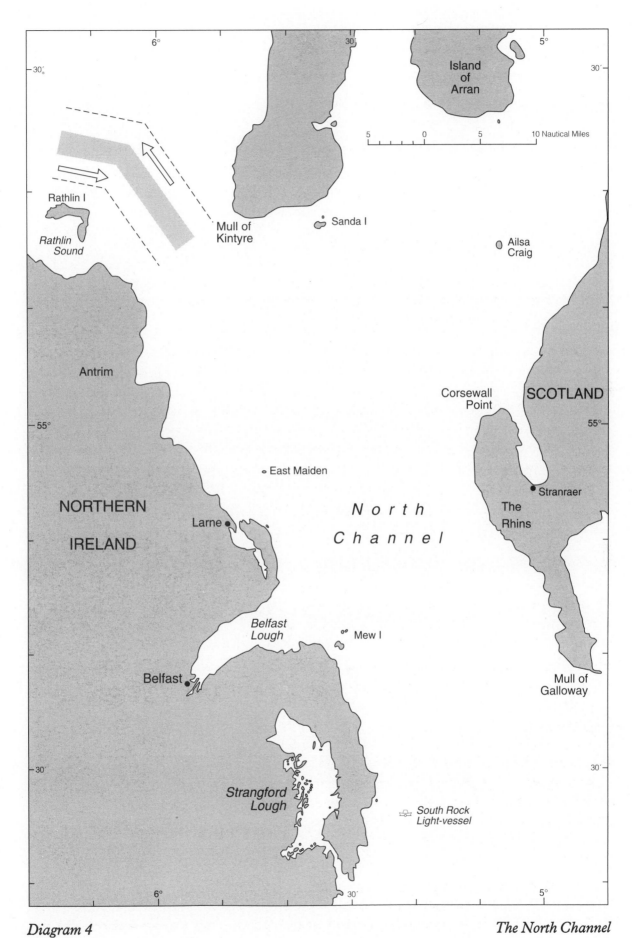

Island
of
Arran

5   0   5   10 Nautical Miles

Rathlin I

*Rathlin
Sound*

Mull of
Kintyre

Sanda I

Ailsa
Craig

Antrim

Corsewall
Point

SCOTLAND

The
Rhins

Stranraer

55°

55°

30'

30'

NORTHERN

IRELAND

East Maiden

N o r t h

C h a n n e l

Larne

Mull of
Galloway

*Belfast
Lough*

Mew I

Belfast

Strangford
Lough

South Rock
Light-vessel

6°

30'

5°

Diagram 4

The North Channel

The North Channel

14.62   The North Channel, the passage between Scotland and Northern Ireland, has two pinch points: one between the Mull of Kintyre and County Antrim, some 11 nautical miles wide at its narrowest point: and the other between the Galloway coast and Belfast Lough, some 20 nautical miles wide at its narrowest point. There is a Traffic Separation Scheme in the northern pinch point, and a recommendation on charts that large tankers should not use the area between the TSS and the ecologically sensitive Rathlin Island. The routeing advice approved by IMO in 1993 added the stipulation that laden tankers should not use the narrow passage through Rathlin Sound, between Rathlin Island and the Antrim coast. The North Channel is shown on Diagram 4 overleaf.

14.63   As Plate 1 shows, the North Channel between Belfast Lough and the Galloway coast is one of the three areas with densest traffic off the Scottish coast, the others being the Pentland Firth and the coast south of the Firth of Forth. It also has substantial ferry traffic, which is not shown.

14.64   The density of traffic makes it likely that the North Channel is at greater risk from a collision and subsequent pollution than the Minch, and its coasts are also of significant ecological and economic value. Because there is no sensible alternative route the traffic density is probably significantly higher. We were surprised that the recommendations to IMO for voluntary reporting did not include the North Channel. The Department of Transport explained to us that there are no navigational difficulties in the Channel and

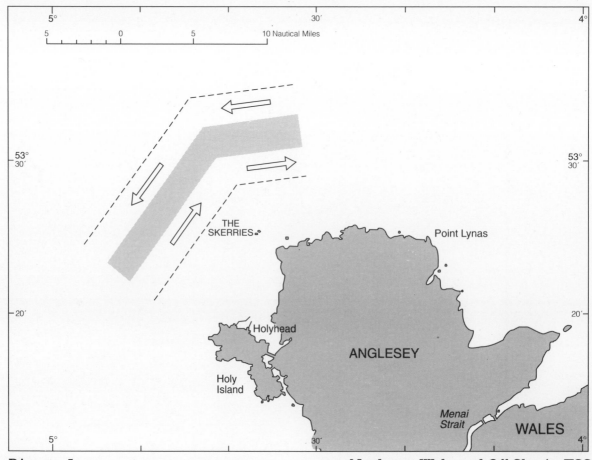

Diagram 5   *North west Wales and Off-Skerries TSS*

that they had no reason to suppose that ships do not use the lanes correctly. **We recommend that the Department of Transport should establish, by surveillance, whether there are any problems and consider voluntary reporting in the light of the results.**

North west Wales

14.65   Although we are unaware of any problems connected with it, we mention for completeness the Traffic Separation Scheme off the Skerries, a group of rocks to the north west of Anglesey, shown in Diagram 5 on page 204. As Plate 1 shows, there is substantial traffic to and from Liverpool which uses the TSS. The incident involving the *CITY OF LIMASSOL*, mentioned in Appendix L, took place there.

South west Wales

14.66   Skomer Island, off Wooltack Point at the southern end of St Brides Bay in south west Wales, is a particularly important bird site. Unfortunately it is also very close to the oil refinery in Milford Haven and alongside the natural route into Milford Haven from the north and west, and for tankers moving into and out of Milford Haven from the anchorage in St Brides Bay. It is shown in Diagram 6 below.

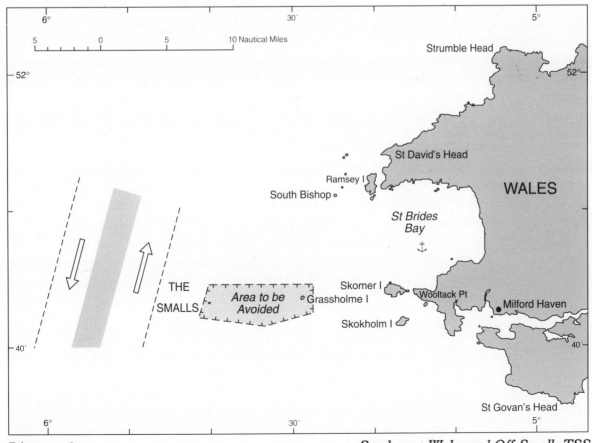

Diagram 6   *South west Wales and Off-Smalls TSS*

14.67   The passage between Skomer Island and Wooltack Point is only half a nautical mile wide and too constricted for large tankers to use. IMO has accepted as part of its 1993 package that tankers over 10,000 grt should be advised not to use the Grassholme Channel, between Skomer Island and Grassholme Island some six miles to the west, unless they are moving between the anchorage in St Brides Bay (to the north of the channel) and the port of Milford Haven (to the south). There is an ATBA, established for environmental reasons, between Grassholme and the Smalls (a group of rocks and a lighthouse) some 8 nautical miles further west. There is a Traffic Separation Scheme off the Smalls (aligned with that west of the Isles of Scilly) which includes a recommendation that laden tankers should avoid the area between the TSS and ATBA. The only approved route therefore for large tankers moving between St Brides Bay and Milford Haven is through the channel between Grassholme Island and Skomer: tankers are recommended to avoid this passage in any other circumstances.

14.68   This is another clash between two necessary uses of the same area. Neither Skomer nor the Milford Haven refinery can be moved: the two uses have to be made as compatible as possible. When tankers are waiting for a berth at Milford Haven it is safer – and thus less risky for the environment – for them to anchor there than to drift unanchored. St Brides Bay offers the most sheltered – and therefore safest – anchorage available.

14.69   Again, we were surprised that there was no recommendation to IMO for a voluntary reporting scheme in the TSS off south west Wales. The explanation from the Department of Transport was the same as with the North Channel: that there were no difficulties in navigating the TSS, no incentive to break the rules and no evidence that any vessels did so. **Our recommendation is the same: that the Department of Transport should check through surveillance that this is correct before coming to a final decision on reporting.**

14.70   We also note that there is nothing to stop tankers going close to the shores of Skomer Island *en route* from St Brides Bay to Milford Haven: indeed it would be natural for them to go as close to Skomer as safety permits. **The Department of Transport should also survey traffic using the Grassholme Channel for a limited but representative period, and consider whether there is a case for an ATBA to be established to protect the western side of Skomer Island and Skokholm Island to the south of it.** Without doubt Skomer Island should be designated a Marine Environmental High Risk Area (MEHRA), a concept which we describe below.

The Isles of Scilly

14.71   The Isles of Scilly are another group of beautiful and ecologically sensitive islands located at a shipping crossroads. There are three TSSs around the islands, to the east, south and west, which between them have the effect of creating a clockwise movement between 5 and 7 nautical miles and an anticlockwise movement between 10 and 12 nautical miles from the islands. Plate 1 shows how busy they are. ITZs have been established between the TSSs and the coast of the Isles of Scilly.

14.72   Although there is no legal obligation to use the TSS (see paragraph 14.16), the 1993 IMO-endorsed package of advice includes the recommendation that laden tankers of over 10,000 grt going through the 21 nautical mile gap between the islands and the Cornish mainland should use the lanes of the relevant TSS. There is an equally safe but longer alternative to this route for ships going between the Irish Sea and the English Channel, using the schemes to the west and south of the islands. The area is shown in Diagram 7 below.

14.73   During our Inquiry (in May 1993) a merchant vessel, the *GRAN PIEDRA*, lost engine power some 20 miles south west of the Isles of Scilly: HM Coastguard were notified ten hours later by which time the vessel was only five miles from the Bishop Rock Lighthouse. The Scillonians were more fortunate than the Shetlanders: the *GRAN PIEDRA's* anchors held and a potentially very damaging pollution incident was averted. A fuller description of the incident is in Appendix L.

14.74   We are not convinced that the TSSs and ITZs between them provide enough protection for the Isles of Scilly: as Diagram 7 shows, there are large gaps between the ITZs. As with Skomer, there may be a case for an ATBA or ATBAs,

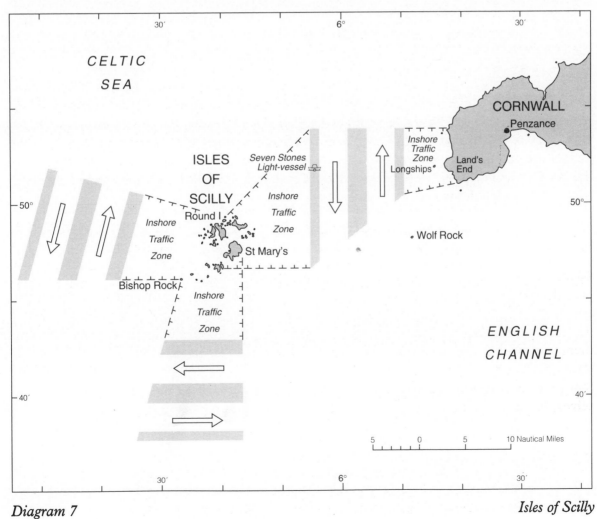

Diagram 7   *Isles of Scilly*

207

though we appreciate the need for the approaches to ports to be left unobstructed. The islands are, again like Skomer, an obvious candidate for MEHRA status – see below. The Department of Transport should consider the options.

Lyme Bay

14.75   The bounds of Lyme Bay are not precise, but for our purposes the key area is from Exmouth to Dartmouth. This area is a significant anchorage. Large vessels visit it to embark and disembark Channel pilots or to anchor while waiting for orders. Some of these large vessels are obliged to cross the lanes of the TSS off the Casquets to reach Lyme Bay – an action which is wholly within the rules of the TSS but which must have some dangers. Some guidance is given on Admiralty Chart 5500 *Mariners' Routeing Guide English Channel and Southern North Sea* on routes to be taken to Lyme Bay: see Diagram 8 opposite.

14.76   There is inevitable conflict between the use of Lyme Bay by large vessels and the fishing and pleasure craft which abound in the area. In May 1990 there was a collision to the south of Prawle Point between the tanker *ROSEBAY*, which was going to pick up a pilot from Brixham, and the fishing vessel *DIONNE MARIE*. Less than 0.5 per cent of the *ROSEBAY's* cargo was spilled but a major clean-up was needed – this is described in Chapter 21. The potential disaster of the Cowes Classic race which we mention in paragraph 3.35 took place in Lyme Bay. In both cases the vessel other than the tanker was principally at fault.

14.77   The fears expressed to us by some of the local authorities in the area were given added point when in June 1993 the *BRITISH TRENT* was struck by the *WESTERN WINNER* at a pilot station off Ostend on the Belgian coast, with tragic results: again, the incident is described in Appendix L. A similar tragic incident occurred at a pilot station off the Bosphorus in March 1994 when the bulk carrier *SHIP BROKER* and the tanker *NASSIA* collided with the loss of 31 lives.

"Parking" in Lyme Bay

14.78   It is normal and acceptable practice for large vessels to "park" for fairly short periods while waiting for repairs or for a berth in port. What is not acceptable is for laden tankers to "park" for months at a time, apparently while waiting for the price of oil to increase, as happened a few years ago in Lyme Bay. We entirely agree with the Government's view that these vessels were not in any sense on passage and that the right of innocent passage was thus irrelevant. We recommend in paragraphs 5.30 and 5.88 – 5.94 that powers should be taken in UK law to require vessels not on passage to remove themselves, but so far as we are aware the problem of "parked" tankers has not recurred.

Ships manoeuvring for pilots

14.79   It was suggested to us in evidence that a particular problem in Lyme Bay is that there is no single source of advice or control for ships manoeuvring for pilots, no authority

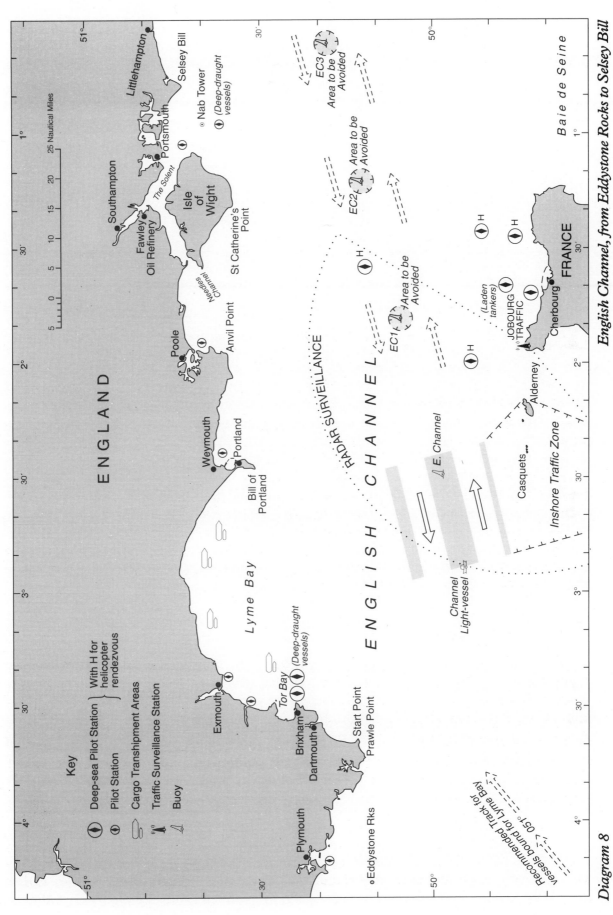

Key

- ⬗ Deep-sea Pilot Station ⎱ With H for
- ⬗ Pilot Station ⎰ helicopter rendezvous
- ◻ Cargo Transhipment Areas
- 📡 Traffic Surveillance Station
- ⚓ Buoy

ENGLAND

Littlehampton

Selsey Bill

Nab Tower ⊙

⬗ (Deep-draught vessels)

Portsmouth

Southampton

The Solent

Fawley Oil Refinery

Isle of Wight

St Catherine's Point

Needles Channel

Poole

Anvil Point

Weymouth

Portland

Bill of Portland

Lyme Bay

RADAR SURVEILLANCE

E N G L I S H   C H A N N E L

E. Channel

Channel Light-vessel

Casquets

Inshore Traffic Zone

Alderney

JOBOURG TRAFFIC

(Laden tankers)

Cherbourg

FRANCE

Baie de Seine

EC3 Area to be Avoided

EC2 Area to be Avoided

EC1 Area to be Avoided

H

H

H

H

H

Exmouth

Tor Bay

⬗ (Deep-draught vessels)

Brixham

Dartmouth

Start Point

Prawle Point

Plymouth

Eddystone Rks

Recommended Track for vessels bound for Lyme Bay

51°

30'

2°

30'

3°

30'

4°

51°

30'

1°

30'

50'

50'

30'

2°

30'

3°

25 Nautical Miles

5 0 5 10 15 20 25

Diagram 8

English Channel, from Eddystone Rocks to Selsey Bill

to whom Masters can report, no means of separating the various uses of Lyme Bay and no means of keeping tankers well away from shore – for instance, by insisting on the embarkation of pilots by helicopter where possible. Figures supplied to us by the Torbay Borough Council suggest that there are about 2,400 calls for a pilot each year in Torbay, Weymouth and Portland combined. Assuming that traffic is evenly spread throughout the year, about five vessels a day call for a pilot at Torbay, the busiest of the ports.

14.80   There are several fairly small harbour authorities around Lyme Bay, dealing mostly with pleasure craft and fishing vessels. All of them have restricted seaward limits, reflecting the nature of their businesses, and none approaches the area where tankers anchor. None of them is therefore empowered to exercise any control over tankers. While it would be possible, as we explain in Chapter 13, for one of them to apply to the Secretary of State for Transport to extend its area and its powers to cope with this problem, this could be agreed only if the Secretary of State was satisfied that the change was:

> "desirable in the interests of securing the improvement, maintenance or management of the harbour in an efficient or economical manner or of facilitating the efficient and economic transport of goods or passengers by sea."

14.81   This might not be easy to demonstrate. There would in any case be disadvantages: the harbour authority would acquire duties in relation to safety and other matters within the extended area, and there would be nothing to stop tankers anchoring immediately outside any extended area. While this might have benefits in removing them further from land, it would mean that the harbour authority would acquire extra responsibilities but would not be able to get new revenue from the tankers to cover them.

14.82   We recommend in paragraph 13.74 that the Department of Transport's District Marine Safety Committees should consider the problems which may arise from congestion at pilot stations. We do not believe that further measures are necessary.

Transfers of oil between ships

14.83   As we explain in paragraph 8.80, it has been the practice of oil companies for many years to transfer crude oil from large to small tankers to enable heavily-laden tankers to enter northern European ports. The sheltered Lyme Bay is particularly suitable for such transshipments and is a recognised area for them: we understand that in recent years about four transshipments have taken place there a year. It was made clear to us in evidence that local people object strongly to transshipments.

14.84   Transshipments have to take place somewhere: the only alternative is an increase in shipping costs, which is likely to affect the prices of finished goods and thus UK trade. It is obviously sensible for transshipments to take place at recognised safe anchorages and under close supervision. The draft Regulations proposed by the Department of Transport and described in Chapter 8 would do just that. The four existing transshipment points in Lyme Bay (shown in Diagram 8 overleaf) would remain, but transshipments would be able to take place only after both COASTGUARD and MSA had been given 24 hours notice and in accordance with an approval given by the Department of Transport.

14.85   We believe that the draft Regulations could go further towards meeting the wishes of local people without increasing any risks from transshipment. **We consider that there should be a single, large transshipment area rather than four specified points, and that this area should be in an area of Lyme Bay which is suitable in terms of depth and shelter. Most important, the inshore boundary of the area should be at least 9 miles away from land. We recommend that draft Regulations along these lines should be brought into force as quickly as possible.**

The Dover Strait

14.86   Curiously, we have had very little evidence relating to the Dover Strait, one of the world's busiest international straits. The TSS in the Dover Strait is the oldest established in the world. At its narrowest point the Strait is just under 19 nautical miles wide, but because of sandbanks the useable traffic lanes can be narrow: the north east bound DWR through the Dover Strait is 1.3 miles wide at its narrowest point off Sandettié.

14.87   The TSS in the Dover Strait and adjacent waters includes a DWR, established for navigational reasons, as part of its north east bound lane, north of the Sandettié Bank. A second TSS is off the Casquets (between the Channel Islands and Lyme Bay). Both TSSs have ITZs separating them from their respective shorelines. *Ships' Routeing* includes warnings on the use of these Schemes. The English Channel passage planning chart (Chart 5500) also contains a great deal of information, and the 1993 IMO-approved package of advice includes a recommendation that all vessels navigating in this area should carry the latest edition.

14.88   These two TSSs are aligned together and form part of an integrated chain of TSSs (or dual carriageway) stretching from Ouessant (Ushant) on the Brittany coast to the mouth of the Elbe river in Germany. Recommended routes between some of the TSSs are marked on charts, and there is a series of small ATBAs (established for navigational reasons) between the Dover Strait and Casquets TSSs. These mark the "central reservation" of the route between the TSSs. They are shown on Diagram 9 overleaf.

14.89   Radar monitoring is provided by the United Kingdom and France to cover the Dover Strait Scheme (the Channel Navigation Information Service or CNIS, described in paragraphs 16.6 – 16.13) and by France to cover the Casquets Scheme. Contravening vessels are reported to their flag authorities for enforcement action. A voluntary maritime reporting scheme (MAREP)[11] applies in the English Channel to ships of 1,600 grt or more carrying oil, chemicals or gas in bulk and to vessels with manoeuvring or navigational difficulties. This Scheme, and its recent extension to other areas, is described more fully in paragraphs 15.39 – 15.42.

---

[11] MArine REPorting: this reporting scheme follows IMO Resolution A.531(13).

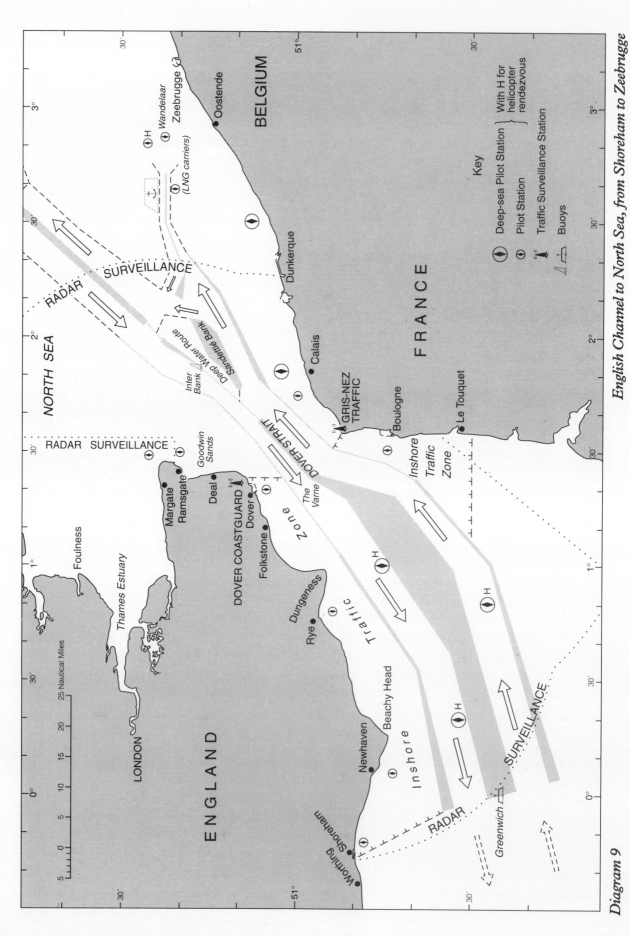

English Channel to North Sea, from Shoreham to Zeebrugge

Key

Deep-sea Pilot Station ⟩ With H for helicopter rendezvous
Pilot Station
Traffic Surveillance Station
Buoys

Diagram 9

212

14.90 As we mention in paragraph 14.12, it is estimated that the Dover Strait has an average of 420-440 traffic movements a day, 200 of them passing through, 180-200 crossing from side to side. 30-40 fishing vessels operate daily within the Strait. Vessel tracks over a 24 hour period are shown in Plate 4: these include ferries and fishing vessels which are excluded from Plate 1 and therefore give a more accurate picture. Because of the density of traffic and the consequent risk of collision, fast action may be needed to deal with a "rogue". One potentially dangerous incident, involving the *ODIGITRIA B*, is described in Appendix L. While we are generally satisfied with arrangements in the Channel, we believe that HM Coastguard should take a rather more active approach towards traffic management. We discuss this in Chapter 16.

Increasing the effectiveness of routeing measures

14.91 We accept the Government's view that only routeing measures agreed internationally through IMO have any chance of being observed by ships of all flags, and that any development of routeing measures is best conducted through IMO. Unilaterally applied routeing measures, implemented through Port State Jurisdiction, would inevitably be second best because of the severe limits on their enforceability. There may still be some scope for them. Port State Jurisdiction also provides the best means of improving observance of routeing measures. We return to this point later on. We note with interest that the harbour authority at Sullom Voe imposes rules, which include routes to be taken, on ships using the port. This it does as a condition of use of the port facilities.

The status of advisory measures

14.92 Many people assume that compulsory measures are more effective than advisory ones. We understand that moves are under way at IMO, based on this assumption, to consider the development of mandatory routeing measures, which might, for instance, include making ATBAs mandatory. But so far as we know, no study has ever been carried out of the extent to which ships' Masters heed IMO endorsed advice – or, indeed, of the extent to which they heed IMO endorsed rules in TSSs. We have been assured in evidence that Masters routinely follow advice printed on charts without considering whether it is "voluntary" or "mandatory", and we have no reason to doubt that this is true of the vast majority of Masters. We do however note that HM Coastguard estimate that about three vessels – 0.6 per cent of traffic – ignore the very well publicised traffic rules in the Dover Strait every day. The figures include a large number of contraventions by (mostly French) fishing vessels. Many of the contraventions are minor or technical.

14.93 Masters must be free to exercise their judgement in the best interests of the safety of their ships, but we firmly believe that Masters should always follow internationally sanctioned advice unless they have very good safety reasons to do otherwise. We accept that many, probably most, routeing measures around the world are not routinely monitored and that detailed information on the extent to which they are observed cannot be made available. We also accept that such evidence as there is in UK waters suggests that there is a reasonable degree of compliance – indeed, if routeing measures are properly designed, mariners have no good reason to ignore them. Nevertheless, we believe that **the UK Government should ask IMO to consider, on the basis of such information as is** available, the extent to which Masters do accept IMO endorsed advice. If it is found that Masters are not accepting IMO endorsed advice, **the UK Government should ask IMO to consider why that advice is being disregarded.** In particular cases it may, of course, be because the advice is not as sensible as its supporters thought it was: but general non-observance of routeing advice would be more worrying.

14.94   We believe that voluntary routeing measures should be made compulsory only if there is evidence that there is a significant difference in the level of observance of voluntary and mandatory measures. If there is such evidence, the UK Government should press IMO to speed up and resolve its consideration of ways in which existing voluntary measures can be made mandatory on all vessels. In some cases an element of judgement must remain in the best overall interests of safety and of the environment.

14.95   However, if it transpires that voluntary measures endorsed by IMO are, in practice, as well observed as mandatory ones, then the next point to consider is whether the level of observance of either is good enough. We have little evidence to go on, and what evidence we have is inevitably confused by recent changes to the advice given, which will take some time to be fully absorbed. Nevertheless, we suspect that observance is not good enough. If that is right, the next question is whether shortcomings are due to ignorance of advice or deliberate flouting of advice. We suspect that there are elements of both, and that both better promulgation of advice and better powers of enforcement are needed.

Publicising routeing rules and advice

14.96   There is no point in establishing routeing measures, or any other type of advice, guidance or instruction to seamen, if the advice does not reach those to whom it is addressed.

14.97   All routeing measures and advice endorsed by IMO, whether mandatory or voluntary, are published in *Ships' Routeing* and marked on larger scale charts. Given the obligation in SOLAS[12] to use up-to-date charts, all advice should thus be clear to all who use the relevant waters. But human nature being what it is, charts may not always be as up-to-date as they should be: Appendix L describes one case, the *SEIKO*, where the necessary charts did not appear to be available at all. As we recommend in Chapter 13, the checking of routes and charts should figure in Port State Control.

14.98   Routeing advice may be emphasised, explained or reiterated in Notices to Mariners which all ships are required[13] to carry. The new routeing measures agreed during 1993 were given wide publicity in the specialist press and promulgated through Notices to Mariners on 28 August 1993. They were also fully described in the papers circulated in June 1993 to the UK Safety Of Navigation Committee, on which the pilots' associations are

---

[12] Chapter V.
[13] SOLAS Chapter V Regulation 20.

represented. Given this, we were surprised to be told by one of the pilots' associations that they were not aware of them until October 1993.

14.99 It is important that pilots should be very well aware of the advice endorsed by IMO, as in the normal course of their jobs they can do much to point out to Masters both what the advice is and the importance of keeping to it. It is disturbing that some of them appear not to keep up to date with developments, though they were of course aware of the measures before they became effective. Although we see no reason to suppose that the Department of Transport was at fault, we consider that it would be useful for it to **review its mechanisms for consultation and the circulation of information to ensure as wide a coverage as practicable, both within the UK and internationally.**

14.100 Beyond that, ensuring that individual Masters know of the advice and its importance is likely to be a time-consuming process of checking with individuals and their companies. This patient checking has already proved very worthwhile in the Minch – see paragraph 14.43. We discuss how this should be expanded in Chapter 16.

Enforcement of routeing measures

Effectiveness of existing enforcement

14.101 At present, the UK Government makes systematic attempts to seek a change in behaviour in relation to only two routeing measures in UK waters. One is the recently established system whereby owners of large laden tankers seen in the Minch in fair weather are asked to avoid the Minch in future. The other is the policing of the Dover Strait TSS through radar.

14.102 Under the Collision Regulations it is possible for the UK to prosecute ships which transgress against the Traffic Separation Scheme within UK territorial waters. In practice this is difficult. There are no means by which information on the identity of transgressors and their next port of call can be routinely added together quickly enough for action to be taken at the next port of call. But even if such arrangements existed, except in rare cases of a particularly dangerous infringement there would be no justification for the severe penalty of arresting the ship, so any action taken against foreign flagged ships would depend on the return of the ship, with the same Master, to a UK port at a later stage. Because of these practical difficulties, the UK Government normally takes action only against those offenders which fly the UK flag.

14.103 Figures provided by the Department of Transport showed that in 1993 there were 994 infringements of the Dover Strait Traffic Separation Scheme (in both UK and French waters) and that 297 (30 per cent) of the vessels breaking the rules were identified. That compares with an average of 1,338 infringements and 35 per cent identification over the previous seven years. The problems of identification are addressed in the next chapter. Of those identified between 1985 and 1992, an average of 5 per cent were UK flagged: the remainder were divided roughly equally between French flagged vessels – almost entirely fishing vessels – and other flags.

14.104   Masters of UK flagged vessels infringing the TSS are summoned by the Department of Transport for official warnings. Prosecutions are mounted in the most serious cases where evidence is sufficient. The French Government also uses warnings more than prosecutions, and is well aware of the dangers that rogue fishing vessels can pose to other larger vessels.

14.105   All verified infringements by non-UK or non-French flagged vessels are reported to the Flag State for action. An analysis of such infringements in 1989 showed that other Flag States prosecute in about two-thirds of cases but that no action had been taken for various reasons in a third of cases. Only two fines were above £500 in value, both imposed by the Panamanian authorities. There have been no follow-up studies to see whether any action taken has persuaded offenders not to reoffend, but the proportion of "rogues" is decreasing. If the Department of Transport becomes aware that a vessel keeps reoffending it will notify the relevant Flag State.

Identifying offenders

14.106   Enforcement must depend on information on where vessels are and whether they are observing routeing measures. This is discussed in the next chapters. All we need note here is that IMO has accepted that mandatory routeing measures do not need to be permanently monitored by radar, and the Dover Strait is the only one of the eight mandatory Traffic Separation Schemes in or partly in UK waters which is so monitored by the UK authorities: the Casquets TSS is monitored by radar by the French authorities. Other areas where routeing measures apply are not regularly monitored by Government, for reasons of practicality and cost, and enforcement must largely rely on information coming to the attention of the authorities by chance or through informal arrangements. We are not aware of any evidence that this lack of an enforcing regime causes any difficulties – but nor are we aware of any studies carried out to check whether this is so.

Vessels to which routeing measures apply

14.107   Different routeing measures sometimes apply to different types of vessels. Traffic Separation Schemes, for instance, apply to all vessels, while much routeing advice applies only to large laden tankers. The same is true of the reporting arrangements discussed in the next chapter. We are happy with this in principle, because different precautions are sensible in different places. Nevertheless, there are two categories of vessel which we believe merit special attention.

Vessels with large bunker capacity

14.108   As we point out in Chapter 3, bunker oil can be a major pollutant – some large bulk carriers or unladen tankers carry more oil in their bunkers than small tankers do in their cargo tanks. An example of pollution by bunker oil during 1993 is the incident involving the *BORODINSKOYE POLYE* described in Appendix L and discussed in Chapter 17. **We believe that in general unladen tankers and other vessels with large bunker carrying capacity should be subject to the same routeing and reporting** requirements and recommendations as laden tankers, and recommend that the UK Government should press IMO to ensure this.

Cruise ships

14.109   Most merchant ships have no reason to choose to go close to wildlife sites in preference to other routes. The exception is cruise ships which go into environmentally sensitive areas so that their passengers can admire the scenery and the wildlife. For instance, the Royal Society for the Protection of Birds (RSPB) sponsors a cruise which visits the Isles of Scilly, Rathlin Island, St Kilda, Orkney, Shetland and Fair Isle among other places. The gross tonnage of the ship (over 6,000 grt) is above the limit for the Shetland, Orkney and Fair Isle ATBAs (5,000 grt). We have no reason to doubt the quality of the ship or the skill of her Master and crew, but inevitably the ship, her bunkers and her garbage present a risk to the bird colonies the passengers want to see. Similar problems can be caused by any pleasure vessel, in the broadest sense.

14.110   We have considered whether there is a case for excluding cruise vessels from environmentally sensitive areas. We have no views on whether the visits put the species and habitats directly at risk through human intrusion and disturbance: we are concerned only with possible pollution from the vessel. On the whole we believe that it is right to allow cruise ships, or any other type of pleasure vessel, to go close to environmentally sensitive sites in order to allow their passengers to appreciate them. But **it is incumbent upon the organisers and sponsors of such cruises and trips to ensure that the vessels concerned are built, maintained and operated to the highest standards, that IMO rules and guidance are strictly observed so far as is consistent with the presence of the vessel in an ATBA, and that no garbage of any sort is thrown overboard from them. They should report to HM Coastguard to indicate that they are going into a sensitive area, so that the authorities can be aware of their presence and be in a position to act very quickly if anything goes wrong. This can apply to safety as much as pollution: going ashore from cruise vessels on remote islands can be dangerous. They should also heed any advice HM Coastguard may give them on particular hazards, including adverse weather.**

14.111   **We recommend that the Department of Transport ensures that all sponsors and organisers of cruise ships are aware of the importance of these points, that a reporting requirement should be considered, and that the Department, with other interested bodies, should consider the case for a code of practice.**

New routeing measures

14.112   As we explained at the beginning of this chapter, routeing measures for environmental reasons are not a panacea. They can help keep ships away from particularly sensitive areas, but they cannot give them complete protection. There is also an unpalatable dilemma to be faced: measures to protect one area can increase risks to another, and even increase risk overall. The Minch is the chief example of this dilemma in UK waters, but it occurs in lesser form in any area where sheltered routes are also ecologically vulnerable.

14.113 With the adoption by IMO in November 1993 of the new routeing advice described in this chapter, much of the UK's waters were covered by routeing measures of one kind or another. They cover busy areas, such as the Dover Strait, potentially danger-ous areas, such as the Pentland Firth, and environmentally sensitive areas such as Shet-land, the Minch and the Isles of Scilly.

Blanket bans

14.114 The UK has a long, varied and ecologically sensitive coastline, much of which can fairly be regarded as important in international terms. While it has no single area of ecological significance and ecological vulnerability equivalent to the Australian Great Bar-rier Reef – the only existing area designated by IMO as a Special Protection Area – much of it is high in landscape or ecological value or both. Most of the rest is residential or town centres where amenity is important. Such areas can also support ecologically valuable sites. The only exceptions are likely to be those very few parts of the coast which are industrial or derelict – but even the most unpromising of areas can be rich in wildlife.

14.115 It was suggested to us in evidence that because so much of our coastline is valuable, equal protection for all of it is needed in the shape of a blanket ban. It was suggested that all large, potentially polluting vessels should at all times keep a fixed dis-tance from shore: 10 and 50 nautical miles were proposed. An alternative suggestion was that these vessels should keep at a minimum distance from shore in bad weather.

14.116 We do not accept this because of the severe practical problems. Many inter-national straits, including Dover, are simply too narrow for traffic to keep ten – let alone fifty – miles from both shores. A fixed distance from shore might encourage dangerous bunching. Vessels obviously need to come close to the shore, both to reach ports and to pick up pilots. In bad weather, a vessel is likely to be safest either in shelter close to shore or a long way from shore – it depends on the circumstances of the weather and the shore concerned. There is thus no reason to suppose that a fixed distance off shore would benefit either safety or pollution prevention.

The problems of identifying sensitive areas

14.117 If a blanket approach is unworkable, selection is essential. Identifying the key sensitive areas is extraordinarily difficult. During our study, in the late summer and early autumn of 1993, the Department of the Environment coordinated work by the Joint Nature Conservation Committee, the Countryside Council for Wales, The Department of the Environment for Northern Ireland, English Nature and Scottish Natural Heritage, designed to establish which marine coastal areas were particularly sensitive. The work was being done in the context of the EC report *A Common Policy for Safe Seas*. We are grateful to the Department of the Environment for keeping us in touch with the developing work here. We were interested to note that the expert conservation bodies had great difficulty in establishing on a consistent basis the areas which were of the greatest sensitivity.

14.118   We have concluded that it is impossible to give high level protection to all areas which might deserve it: there are so many, embracing so many genuine problems of navigation, that the concept would become meaningless. The more numerous and the larger the areas highlighted as particularly sensitive, the greater is the risk of assumptions that the remainder is of no environmental significance – which cannot be true. **It must follow that only limited areas can be singled out for any special status.**

The need for information

14.119   The routeing measures so far adopted are essentially reactive. They advise or require a Master to take a particular route or avoid a particular area: they do not explain to him **why** he should do so. **We consider that the first purpose of any new measure must be to *inform* Masters of areas where there is a real prospect of a problem arising. This prime purpose stands alone and regardless of any consequential defensive measures.** At present no ship Master has any knowledge of the sensitivity of the coast which he is passing. He may assume that where there is an ATBA a sensitive coastline lies behind it, but that apart he has no guidance. Recommended routes and TSSs may reasonably be regarded by him as being designed purely for traffic regulation.

Marine Environmental High Risk Areas (MEHRAs)

14.120   **We therefore recommend the establishment of *Marine Environmental High Risk Areas* or MEHRAs: comparatively limited areas of high sensitivity which are also at risk from shipping.** The mere identification and publicising of MEHRAs will give the ship Master additional information relevant to passage planning and many will take it into account. In addition we hope that shipowners and insurers (particularly P & I Clubs) would, in their own self-interest, regard a MEHRA as an area from which their ship should keep well clear. We accordingly believe that the establishment of MEHRAs is an important concept, irrespective of whether anything further is done to protect them.

14.121   We would obviously like to see the concept of MEHRAs adopted and promoted by both the EC and IMO. **The UK Government should seek to achieve this result, incidentally resisting any attempt by others to produce too many MEHRAs with the inevitable result that they would not be taken seriously. However, there is no need for the Government to wait for international agreement:** individual States are after all best placed to put forward lists. The initiative must come from them. There would be no problem over unilateral promulgation of UK MEHRAs in Notices to Mariners, Admiralty "Pilots" and the *UK Seaway Code*.

Defining MEHRAs

14.122   We are very keen that MEHRAs should be seen as both an environmental concept and a shipping concept: even the most sensitive areas should only become classified as MEHRAs if there is a realistic risk of pollution from merchant shipping. Giving special protection to areas which are at no real risk from merchant shipping merely serves to cheapen the concept. For this reason, we would not expect areas like Strangford Lough in County Down (see Diagram 4 on page 203) to qualify for special protection. Strangford

Lough is an enclosed inlet with mudflats, sandbars, saltmarshes and dune grassland – very difficult to clean if oil is spilled – which supports seals, otters, terns, Brent geese, redshank and bar-tailed godwit amongst others, and some very diverse marine communities. A major pollution incident in such an enclosed area would be a catastrophe – but as Strangford Lough is enclosed and major merchant shipping would have difficulty in getting into it, protection of the kind we envisage of the Lough itself is not needed. Despite that, the entrance to the Lough might be a candidate for MEHRA status to minimise the risk of pollutants reaching the Lough through tidal movements.

Criteria

14.123   The choice of areas will inevitably be controversial, and we believe that it is important to establish criteria, based on both shipping patterns and environmental importance, to use as guidelines. IMO has already[14] established guidelines for the designation of Special Areas (under MARPOL: as explained in Chapter 9, the North Sea and English Channel are already Special Areas for garbage disposal purposes) and the identification of particularly sensitive sea areas. These should obviously be taken into account. We need to identify areas of special environmental, ecological or economic value which are subject to a high risk of damage from pollution from shipping. In determining whether such an area exists, regard should be given to the following **maritime** considerations:

(a)   the number, type and size of vessels passing and the nature of their cargoes;

(b)   the distance of the usual shipping lanes from the shore;

(c)   any circumstances giving rise to an increased risk of collision such as a significant amount of traffic going across the normal flow;

(d)   hydrographical conditions relevant to safe navigation, such as a lack of safe anchorages; and

(e)   prevailing meteorological and tidal characteristics.

14.124   Regard should also be given to the following **environmental** considerations:

(a)   existence of wildlife feeding or breeding sites of international significance or the presence of biological communities of either flora or fauna or both of particular interest or rarity: designation as a Special Protection Area under the EC Birds Directive[15] or an Area of Special Conservation under the Habitats Directive[16] will normally be regarded as evidence of this.

(b)   the existence of commercially exploitable biological resources and mariculture sites; and

---

[14] Assembly Resolution 720, adopted on 6 November 1991.
[15] The EC Council Directive on the Conservation of Wild Birds 79/409/EEC.
[16] The EC Council Directive on the Conservation of Natural habitats and of Wild Flora and Fauna 92/43/EEC.

(c)   the extent to which the area provides a public recreational amenity.

14.125   These outline considerations will no doubt need more refinement. A particular area would obviously need to qualify on **both** sets of consideration to be a candidate for special treatment. It is unlikely to be enough for an area simply to meet one of each set of criteria: it should score highly on both sets. While subjective decisions on the areas to qualify are probably unavoidable, they should be minimised as far as possible by setting "points" for each criterion. Any particular area would need to "score" a minimum number of points in each group. To ensure that MEHRAs are kept to a minimum, for the reasons set out above, the criteria should be set in such a way that not more than about a tenth of the UK coastline qualifies.

Examples of MEHRAs

14.126   We obviously cannot identify all sites which deserve MEHRA status, but we can suggest some examples. We have already suggested Skomer and the Isles of Scilly. There will no doubt be plenty of candidates in Scotland, including the Bass Rock in the Firth of Forth, Fair Isle and parts of other Shetland islands, parts of Orkney, parts of the coasts of the Minch (but only those close to shipping routes) and parts of the west coast of the main chain of the Western Isles, with the same proviso. St Kilda is not likely to be a candidate, because (so far as we know) very few ships go anywhere near it. Rathlin Island is a likely candidate but not Strangford Lough, for the reasons set out in paragraph 14.118. Lundy Island in the Bristol Channel and the Farne Islands off the coast of Northumberland are not likely to qualify, but some of the headlands of the English south coast may well do so because of the density of traffic in the English Channel.

Protecting MEHRAs

Monitoring

14.127   **Providing owners, Masters, shippers and insurers with information on the existence, significance and location of MEHRAs is the vital first step.** They should be marked on charts and publicised as widely as possible, both nationally and internationally, by all the means discussed in this chapter. After that, the authorities will need to find out what effect their promulgation has. Do ships give them a wider berth than they did before?

14.128   We do not envisage a vast monitoring exercise. The pre-existing pattern of shipping will to some extent be known from the research which will have been undertaken to decide whether or not that pattern combined with ecological sensitivity justified the declaration of a MEHRA. Informal surveillance from shipping itself – asking the Master in the course of a Port State inspection what **other** shipping he saw on radar nearer to MEHRAs than he was – from fishing vessels and local inhabitants will give much information and this can be supplemented by concentrated aerial surveillance over a limited period. There is no reason to believe that the pattern changes significantly day by day. **We recommend that the Department of Transport should carry out such a monitoring exercise once MEHRAs have been set up.**

Defensive measures

14.129   If promulgating MEHRAs is not producing results, or if the results are inadequate, **the UK Government will need to discuss with IMO the need for protective measures.** Despite the attractions of simplicity, we have found it impossible to devise a single type of protective measure which could apply to all sensitive areas, because the areas to be protected, and the navigational problems, vary so widely. We discuss the types of area below.

Protected headlands

14.130   Despite the problems of a blanket ban designed to keep shipping a fixed distance from shore, **there may be a case for vessels being obliged to keep a minimum distance from some headlands, as a form of protection for sensitive areas at and on either side of the headland.** For example, there are a series of headlands along the southern coast of England, most of which are themselves sensitive areas – Dungeness, Beachy Head, St Catherine's Point, Portland Bill, Start Point and Lizard Point. If shipping was not allowed to pass between the tips of these headlands and a point a certain distance – perhaps two or three miles – out to sea, ships would normally travel in a straight line from one protected headland to another, avoiding the areas in between, but would still be able to use the often well-established anchorages in the lee of the headlands concerned. Both shipping and environmental interests would thus be protected. Much larger areas of sea than the small and rare MEHRAs which we envisage would be protected: but we can see no harm in that.

14.131   The chief problem would be the risk of head-on collisions between vessels going in different directions. If different distances off headlands were specified for ships going in different directions, ships' paths might well still cross because of the need to move into and out of ports. It is therefore possible that in some areas a protective zone would create more problems, and more risks of collision, than it would solve.

14.132   The headlands quoted are simply examples: each would need to be considered on its merits, against the criteria we suggest.

Protected areas

14.133   **Some sea areas will need protection on a similar basis. The areas concerned might be between two islands** – for instance, between islands in the Orkney or Shetland archipelagoes. **They might be between islands and the mainland** – for instance, between Rathlin and the County Antrim mainland (see Diagram 4, page 203). **Or they might surround an island or a group of islands,** such as the Isles of Scilly (Diagram 7, page 207).

Compulsory ATBAs and compulsory routes

14.134   There are, broadly speaking, two ways of achieving the aim of eliminating traffic from the areas which need this kind of protection: compulsory Areas To Be Avoided and compulsory routes. A **compulsory ATBA** would be identical to an existing ATBA in everything except its compulsory nature, and like an ATBA would need exceptions. Islands or groups of islands surrounded by compulsory ATBAs need some arrangements for access, whether it is occasional access by small boats or regular access by ferries, as is the case with the Isles of Scilly. This can be done either through gaps in the circle or exemptions for particular types or sizes of vessel.

14.135   Other exemptions which might be needed are for fishing vessels (though not their mother ships) and pleasure craft, which are outside our terms of reference, and for cruise ships visiting sensitive areas to show to tourists the very areas which need protection. These will need to be considered case by case. Exemptions will be needed for *force majeure*. The Government will no doubt also want to consider the position of Royal Navy vessels.

14.136   The alternative (or complementary) approach is to adopt sea lanes or **compulsory routes**, with associated "no go" areas between the routes and land. One way of implementing a policy of protected areas and headlands would be to establish short compulsory routes to the outside of the headland, with an associated "no go" area between them and the headlands concerned.

14.137   Recommended routes already exist: we describe those in UK waters earlier in this chapter: and as we describe in paragraph 14.88, the chain of TSSs and recommended routes through the English Channel and North Sea provides clear routes over several hundred miles. We envisage something less formal and with fewer restrictions than a TSS, which would still make it clear to the Masters of vessels that they should not go close to land in certain areas or take short cuts close to headlands. The most obvious immediate candidate for a compulsory route would be the Deep Water Route to the west of the Outer Hebrides, which, as we recommend in paragraph 14.56, should also be extended both north and south to keep ships well away from the Butt of Lewis and Barra Head. Again, some exemptions might be needed.

Recommendations on Marine Environmental High Risk Areas

14.138   To summarise, **we believe that there is a good case for establishing a new type of *area*, the Marine Environmental High Risk Area, which needs protection from shipping because of both its sensitivity to pollution and the likelihood of damage occurring.**

14.139   **We believe that the most important function of these areas is to inform owners, Masters, insurers and charterers of the key significant areas. We hope that simply highlighting these areas will lead to a change in behaviour. If, after a monitoring exercise of the type we describe, it is clear that further steps are needed, we conclude that there is more than one way of protecting these areas. One option is new *compulsory ATBAs* with exemptions for access, for *force majeure* and perhaps some small vessels. Another option is *protected headlands*: a third is *compulsory routes*, again with the minimum of necessary exceptions. Compulsory routes are one way of establishing compulsory ATBAs: they are also valid in their own right as a means of protecting longer coastlines while preserving the essential right for ships to shelter in recognised anchorages.**

Enforcement

14.140   Assuming that MEHRAs are widely and effectively publicised, we believe that enforcement of any new rules on routeing will arise only in the context of a tiny minority of "rogue" ships. There is no doubt that enforcement will be difficult, but we believe that sooner or later any rogue ship will be identified and reported: we discuss this in the next chapter. **She should then be subjected to a special entry reporting condition, along the lines of the reporting conditions we recommend in Chapter 11. The condition might be to report her position and proposed route 24 or 48 hours before arrival at a UK port. To this could be added a compulsory routeing condition, ie she has to follow a route notified to her when she reports. Compliance with the reporting condition is easily monitored and, once she has reported, it is easy to do a spot check on what route she follows. Breach of the reporting condition, or of compulsory routeing, would lead to a warning and, if repeated, to a ban on loading and unloading in the way described in Chapter 11.**

The way forward

14.141   Although many routeing measures are now established around the UK coast, there has never been any systematic evaluation of risks using the sort of criteria we recommend in paragraphs 14.123 and 14.124 above, and taking into account traffic information, aerial surveillance and Coastguard reports. A first step has been taken with the work commissioned by the Department of Transport on where ships actually go, but a great deal of work still needs to be done.

14.142   **We have concluded, with some reluctance, that we are not equipped to carry out such systematic analysis. We are therefore unable to make recommendations on which areas around the UK coast should qualify as MEHRAs, whether protection is necessary and if so what form it should take, what other areas could sensibly be given extra protection by compulsory routeing, and whether areas which already have some form of protection, such as ATBAs or Inshore Traffic Zones, should have protected area status instead.**

14.143   **We recommend that the Department of the Environment, with its Northern Irish, Scottish and Welsh counterparts and their statutory advisors, should work jointly with the Department of Transport to identify those areas which merit special protection based on our suggested criteria.**

14.144   **The Department of Transport should at the same time consider with IMO and the EC the best way of taking forward our proposals for identifying and publicising these areas on charts and in all other ways practicable, for monitoring the effects, and for protecting these areas by exclusion zones and compulsory routeing if necessary. We would expect wide public consultation before final conclusions are reached.**

Chapter 15

Identification and Reporting

15.1   In this chapter we discuss the means that a ship's owners, Master or crew adopt to identify her or to report her presence and position, and other relevant details, to land-based authorities or to other ships. In the following chapter we discuss the means which can enable land-based authorities to establish where ships are.

The need to know

15.2   Ships, unlike aircraft, travel the world in a cloak of virtual anonymity. Many merchant ships display no flag unless entering a port. Most carry their names on either side of the bow and at the stern, but these are often obscured by rust and dirt or are in characters which may be virtually indecipherable. They are often not identifiable from the air or by visual means at night other than from sea level at very close quarters.

15.3   Does this matter? We think that it matters very much for at least three reasons. First, in the event of any sort of emergency involving outside assistance, whether by sea or air, it is essential to be able to identify the target ship, and distress signals may not be enough. Second, if there is evidence of wrong doing on the part of a ship, whether it consists of negligent navigation or illegal discharges, no sanctions can be applied unless the ship can be identified. Third, the fact that a ship is readily identifiable, and known by the Master and crew to be so, is a great deterrent to wrong doing. The standards of driving on the roads would be frightening in the extreme if cars could not be identified by registration plates.

15.4   The difficulty of visual identification would matter less if radio identification was a reliable alternative. At the moment this can be done only by calling a vessel and asking her to identify herself. It is often difficult for the radio operator or Watch Officer of one vessel to realise that it is his vessel being addressed: he may not recognise the description which the shore authorities or other vessels give of his position. Recognition by this method is impossible if the vessel being called does not cooperate, and the experience of HM Coastguard is that on occasion they do not. Whether this is due to incompetence or to baser motives is immaterial.

15.5   Worse, this method of identification can create dangers, particularly when it is used by ships for communication between themselves. A vessel may believe that she is being addressed when in fact she is not. If the wrong vessel replies, and no one realises that a mistake has been made, there may be a greatly increased chance of a collision. For instance, ship A may tell ship B on her port quarter that she intends to turn to port and receive a reply from ship C, which thinks that she is being addressed by ship D. All four may be at risk.

15.6   The situation is compounded by conflicting advice given by Governments. Following the collision between the *YELLOWSTONE* and *EXXON CHESTER* the US National Transportation Safety Board recommended the US Coast Guard to promote the adoption by IMO of a requirement to use Ihs radio telephone for collision avoidance. By contrast the UK Government has issued M Notice M845 advising against the use of radio communication for collision avoidance. We believe that until automatic identification is in place this is the more prudent course.

15.7   An older form of communication, by Morse code using a signal lamp, had the advantage that there was little likelihood of confusion as to the addressee, but it is now rarely used.

The need for information to be provided by vessels

15.8   The remainder of this chapter deals with the information which a ship's owners or crew can and should make available to land-based authorities. Merchant ships are asked to report in some circumstances (see paragraphs 15.38 – 15.42 below) and we have had to consider whether this should be extended. This involves a consideration of the purposes of reporting.

15.9   The primary purpose of routine reporting of basic information such as identity, position, destination, estimated time of arrival and nature of cargo is to enable shore and sea-based assistance to be provided in any sort of emergency without first having to seek essential information. The need is enhanced if something occurs, such as a machinery breakdown, which may or may not develop into a situation in which such assistance is required by the ship either in her own interests or in the interests of other shipping for which she may constitute a hazard. The secondary purpose is as an aid to identification. The type of reporting we are considering here is quite different from the notice requirement envisaged in Chapter 11, which consists of giving advance notification of a vessel's estimated time of arrival at a port. There may be scope for the two systems to be linked administratively, but that is a different point, which we discuss in paragraph 11.53.

15.10   Routine reporting by ships could produce huge quantities of information. Collecting information is not, and must not be seen as, an end in itself: it should only be the means to a defined end. It is essential to consider just what those ends should be and how far they can be served practicably: otherwise there would be risks of much expensive effort going into the collection and collation of unimportant information, diverting effort from other areas where it would be more effective. There are always dangers in producing a mountain of facts: the temptation is to file and forget them, ignoring in the process the few that are really important. It is better to stick to simple basics.

15.11   We also consider a second type of reporting: the reporting by vessels at sea to the authorities on land (in the UK, HM Coastguard) of any difficulties they may be facing, so that HM Coastguard can plan, and if necessary set in motion, any necessary remedial action.

Identification of vessels

15.12   There is no means of knowing what vessels are in any part of UK waters at any time, except when they have identified themselves to HM Coastguard or to harbour authorities. Their precise position may well not be known unless they also appear on radar screens.

Visual identification

15.13   It will be some years before reliable means of automatic identification (described below) can be established. Even when they are fully in use, there will inevitably be operational failures – including, possibly, deliberate operational failures. A quick and simple alternative means of identifying ships more easily is thus needed for both the short and the long term. It is essential that the identification signs are prominent and unmistakeable, not least for the psychological effects on Masters who may be less tempted to cut corners if they are aware that they can be easily identified.

15.14   All vessels already have unique identification numbers in their call signs. We believe that all vessels should have their call signs painted in large characters on their sides (for identification by other vessels) and decks (for identification from the air), in much the same way as the Royal Navy paints pennant numbers on its ships. The characters should be white on dark backgrounds and black on light backgrounds for maximum visibility. Obviously regulation would be needed but the cost of applying the paint would be very small. It would be quick and simple to check that the call signs had indeed been painted.

15.15   This elegantly simple idea is not new: in 1991 IMO recommended that fishing vessels should be marked with their international call signs in just the way we suggest. Unfortunately, the reaction of the UK fishing industry was unhelpful. They considered that the existing markings of name and registration number, with the individual identification signals of their EPIRBs[1], was adequate. They pointed out that the initial letter of radio call signs allocated to the UK are also used by vessels from the Dependent Territories as well as by UK vessels and suggested that this might lead to confusion. As a result, there has been no progress on the idea in the UK.

15.16   We do not accept either of these arguments. We have already explained that existing identification marks are not always clear enough. We want to identify vessels before they get into difficulties, and EPIRBs are of use only after a vessel is in real trouble: and of course they have no psychological benefit. They are irrelevant to the identification of "rogues" contravening routeing measures. And we are not interested in country of origin, only in identifying vessels.

15.17   We do however recognise that radio call signs may have limited application after 1999 when MMSIs – Maritime Mobile Service Identities[2] will be more useful for radio

---

[1] Emergency Position-Indicating RadioBeacons. The signals transmitted from these beacons are primarily used to help search and rescue teams find the survivors of accidents.

[2] A series of nine digits which are transmitted over the radio path in order to identify uniquely ship stations, ship earth stations, coast stations, coast earth stations and group calls.

communications. It may be that IMO Ship Identification Numbers[3], which do not change when a vessel is sold or moved on to another register, would be more appropriate: this must be for international discussion. The system adopted must allow for quick and easy recognition of unique and permanent numbers. The ideal is a number (or combination of letters and numbers) which is short, which allows ready identification of the owner, and which remains with the vessel concerned throughout her existence.

15.18   The only possible valid objection we can think of is aesthetic – that boldly painted call signs would not improve the look of a ship. While we are second to none in our admiration of the beauty of ships, we do not think that aesthetic sensitivities should stand in the way of a very useful means of improving safety, and thus the prevention of pollution. **We recommend that the UK Government should work through IMO for early implementation of prominently painted unique recognition signs for all vessels.**

15.19   **While we want this visual identification system brought in at once, it should be retained after a transponder regime is introduced as a permanent and alternative simpler means of identification.**

Transponders

15.20   Widespread installation and use of transponders will allow vessels to respond automatically to interrogation by coastal authorities or by other vessels. Aircraft have been fitted with radar transponders for identification for many years. There are some technical problems involved with adapting aviation transponders for maritime use, chiefly that vessels go much closer to each other than aircraft, using only two dimensions, and the radar images may merge. Modifications may also be needed to the ship's own radar. A recently developed alternative is radio transponders which in turn need an electronic position fixing system such as the Global Positioning System (GPS) described in paragraphs 13.49 – 13.50.

The purpose of transponders

15.21   A prime purpose of transponders is the same as for visible call signs: identification of vessels to shore-based authorities and to other vessels, for the many and various purposes we identified at the beginning of this chapter. While we have no evidence that the existing means by which vessels identify themselves, their positions and their intentions to harbour authorities and pilot stations are seriously inadequate, transponders will provide an additional means of communication, which will be less dependent upon the initiative or cooperation of ships. More significantly, they will become an essential tool for MSA in identifying and pinpointing the vessels upon which it needs to keep a particularly close eye under the system of self-targeting for Port State Control which we recommend in Chapter 11.

15.22   A second, equally important purpose of transponders is that they will be capable of being programmed with information specific to a particular voyage. This will be able to

---

[3] Resolution A.600 (15).

include information on, for example, cargo and destination which can now be given only by individual reports, either direct to HM Coastguard through reports by passing vessels or direct to the shore-based authorities before the vessel concerned leaves port. We discuss the current and proposed future arrangements for reporting later in this chapter.

Developing transponders

15.23 The UK, like any other country passed by ships not bound for its ports, cannot sensibly develop a comprehensive system of transponders by itself. Any fully effective system needs participation from vessels of all flags using UK waters. The essential first step of a technical specification has been produced by the International Electrotechnical Commission (IEC) and accepted by IMO for a radio transponder. This uses Digital Selective Calling (DSC) techniques which are also used for distress and safety calling within the Global Maritime Distress and Safety System (GMDSS) (see paragraphs 13.47 – 13.48) being introduced during the 1990s.

15.24 Just as important is a requirement to carry transponders. This is being considered as part of a wider review of navigation requirements currently taking place in IMO committees. It appears to be progressing, albeit slowly. It was considered by IMO's Sub-Committee on Radiocommunications at its meeting in December 1993 and aspects of the problem associated with the technical application of transponders have been added to the work programme of the Sub-Committee.

15.25 A third essential is a means of finding the position of a ship identified by transponder from the land. This could be done by very expensive radar coverage or by the compulsory carriage of an accurate position finding system linked to a radio transponder: the second is clearly far more practicable.

15.26 We believe that a worldwide system of transponders would be immensely useful for safety and pollution prevention, both in ensuring that vessels do follow the rules and advice on routeing and in improving the ability to respond to safety or pollution incidents. We recognise that the Masters of some vessels would prefer the coastal authorities or Masters of other vessels not to know exactly where they are: in particular, the Masters of fishing vessels may well not want their rivals to discover through transponders where they are fishing. **We believe that any opposition on commercial grounds should be resisted: safety and the prevention of pollution are more important.**

Specification

15.27 We do not wish to express any concluded views on the respective merits of radar and radio transponders, but we believe that it is essential that the international community should decide soon on the applications of the different systems and agree detailed specifications to be adopted worldwide. The decisions on the systems to be adopted should be taken objectively, taking into account compatibility with existing equipment on the ship and on shore and with coastal radar and radio systems: transponders should be able to transmit information to computer controlled radar systems so that "blips" on screens can be easily identified, but should be equally useable with non-radar information systems. Worldwide coverage is essential, and cost is obviously important. We understand that it ought to be possible to install a transponder in a vessel, including all the necessary modifications or extensions to existing equipment, for less than £1,000, and that the cost of the essential equipment for interrogating transponders ought to be in the region of £10,000. We would hope that prices would come down once manufacturing in large quantities became practicable.

15.28 We expect transponders to be able to function automatically without crew involvement and to respond with the ship's name, callsign (or other unique means of identification such as the MMSI) or current position, as appropriate, when interrogated from the shore or from another ship by name, by identification number or by position. They should be able to receive requests for other information and alert the Watch Officer. They do not need to be able to respond automatically to interrogation in a particular area, to identify vessels which might be able to go to the assistance of a vessel in difficulties, because there are already GMDSS procedures for that.

15.29 **The current agreed specification for radio transponders includes these points but does not include a mechanism to record whether transponders remain continuously in operation. We believe this to be essential: otherwise there will be nothing to stop a Master disabling or turning off his transponder if he would prefer to remain anonymous. That can only help the rogues, including those who wish to evade the self-targeting for Port State Control which we recommend in Chapter 11. The relevant regulations will need to stipulate that it will be an offence to have a non-functioning transponder. Records should be kept available for Flag State and Port State inspection.** Provision also needs to be made for circumstances in which the transponder suffers a genuine malfunction: **there should be a requirement on ships carrying dangerous and polluting goods to report to coastal authorities in such circumstances with details such as cargo, position and destination.**

15.30 **We recommend that the UK Government seeks as soon as possible to amend the IEC specification.** We recognise that this addition to the specification will add to the costs of developing transponders: we cannot estimate how this will be reflected in the prices quoted above. We would like to see transponders made wholly tamper proof, provided that this can be achieved at a cost which is commensurate with the benefits.

Timetable

15.31 **We believe that transponders are so important that the international community needs to set itself a rigid timetable for agreeing carriage requirements for both transponders themselves and for an associated accurate position finding system.** Once these have been agreed different countries or groups of countries can to some extent opt for different timetables of implementation, particularly in relation to small vessels which do not travel long distances. Port and Coastal States could demand unilaterally that vessels using their ports and waters carry transponders, using Port State Jurisdiction (see Chapter 5), but this would be a last resort. Action through a club of States would be far preferable, not least in terms of practicality.

15.32 **IMO should aim to agree carriage requirements by the end of 1996.** From that date any transponder fitted, including any fitted voluntarily, should be to the agreed standard. IMO or, if necessary, clubs of States should aim to make regulations for all large vessels (and all vessels carrying dangerous goods) sailing under their flags or visiting their ports to have transponders installed and working within a short period thereafter – say by the end of 1998. Assuming a cost of £1,000 per vessel, the cost of fitting transponders to the entire UK owned merchant fleet would be some £1.2 million.

15.33 Small vessels ought also to carry transponders, partly for their own safety and partly because they can be the direct or indirect cause of major pollution (and safety) incidents. **All new fishing vessels should be obliged to carry and use transponders from the end of 1998 and all existing fishing vessels should do so from, say, 2004.** We recognise that this may be unpopular with the fishing industry, but believe that progress is essential. The cost of fitting transponders to the entire UK owned fishing fleet would be of the order of £11 million.

15.34 New larger sea-going pleasure craft should also carry and use transponders: consultation with user groups will be needed to establish a sensible definition of those types of vessel to be included. Again, new vessels in this category should carry transponders from the end of 1998 and existing ones from a later deadline. **The UK Government should press for international agreement on a timetable for the introduction of transponders on fishing vessels and larger sea-going pleasure craft.** The total cost in relation to UK owned pleasure craft would obviously depend on the definition adopted. If all pleasure craft on the small ships register[4] had transponders fitted the cost might be in the order of £65 million, but we expect that many will not require them.

15.35 The 21 Coastguard search and rescue centres will need equipment for interrogating transponders, at a cost of about £10,000 each, or a total cost for the Coastguard service of some £210,000. **We would expect the equipment to be in place in key Coastguard stations, particularly Dover, by the date on which the use of transponders became compulsory for large vessels.** Gradual introduction over a few years might be appropriate for the smaller stations. MPCU would of course make use of information from Coastguard stations: MSA could also do so but might also need interrogation equipment at the six Marine Offices for Port State Control purposes.

15.36 Transponders will have a use in ship-to-ship communications, particularly in identification, so long as ships are equipped with interrogation equipment as well as tran-

---

4 The Register of British Ships Part 3.

sponders themselves. It is too early to consider whether ships ought to have a requirement to carry interrogation equipment, but we expect that responsible shipowners will wish to install them. **An agreed specification for interrogation equipment is as important as for the transponders themselves. While the easier communications transponders may provide might be used to confirm Masters' intentions if those are not clear, they should not be used to agree to manoeuvres contrary to the Collision Regulations.**

Value for money

15.37   Although the total cost of the transponders, particularly for pleasure vessels, is potentially large, they represent only a minute fraction of the total cost of a merchant vessel and a very small proportion of the total cost of a fishing vessel or large pleasure craft. While we cannot assess their benefits in money terms, we believe that the advantages in terms of safety and protection of property to the individual owner and Master are such that we would expect responsible owners to install transponders and interrogation equipment of their own volition as soon as they become readily available on the market. We would also expect demise and time charterers, P & I Clubs and other insurers and shippers to insist that vessels in which they have an interest are equipped with properly functioning transponders. The benefits to the Coastal State are also substantial in terms both of monitoring (because Masters are far less likely to cut corners if they know they can be quickly and easily identified) and search and rescue, as vessels can be identified and then contacted without difficulty in an emergency.

Routine ship reporting – existing and planned arrangements

15.38   Ships transitting UK waters are generally under no obligation to report their presence to HM Coastguard. EC law requires all tankers, irrespective of nationality, proceeding to Community ports to report to the Harbour Master, and under the MARPOL Convention ships in difficulties should report to the nearest Coastal State so that remedial action can be taken. We discuss the MARPOL requirement in paragraphs 15.72 – 15.83.

Marine Reporting (MAREP)

15.39   In 1979 IMO promulgated the MAREP voluntary reporting scheme for the English Channel, to enable the movement of tankers and vessels carrying hazardous cargoes to be monitored. MAREP should ensure that communications are established to assist the timely reporting of defects and early provision of assistance in the event of an emergency. Originally, tankers and chemical or gas carriers over 1,600 grt were asked to report to the appropriate surveillance centres in the UK or France, using a standard IMO format. Other ships which have difficulties with manoeuvring or navigation are also asked to report. The French require certain classes of ships intending to enter their ports to report their movements in a zone out to seven nautical miles from their Channel coast.

15.40   An analysis carried out by HM Coastguard for the Inquiry in October 1993 (before the scheme was enlarged) showed that 10 per cent of **all** through traffic in the Dover TSS reported routinely to either the UK or the French authorities under the

MAREP scheme. A further 6 per cent of through traffic not covered by the scheme also reported. In 1980, when the scheme was first introduced, it was estimated that about a third of vessels asked to report under MAREP actually did so. A study carried out for the Department of Transport by British Maritime Technology in the summer of 1987 found that the proportion had gone up to about three-quarters. It is not known what the proportion is now, but it seems reasonable to suppose that it will have continued to increase as the benefits of reporting become more widely understood, though probably at a slower rate.

15.41   In November 1993 IMO extended the English Channel MAREP scheme to cover all ships of 300 grt or more, irrespective of the cargo carried. It is expected that this will eventually lead to increased participation in the scheme by vessels transitting the Strait, but no figures are yet available. At the same time, IMO also endorsed MAREP schemes in other areas around the UK coast. Specified types of vessels are asked to report to a named Coastguard station at least one hour before the estimated time at which they will enter the route concerned, and again on leaving the route. The areas concerned, and the vessels to which they apply, are:

(a)	Fair Isle Channel	tankers – laden;
(b)	Pentland Firth	tankers – laden;
(c)	The Minch	tankers – laden or in ballast; and
(d)	Isles of Scilly	tankers – laden.

Although similar reporting arrangements have been recommended by the UK Chamber of Shipping and the International Chamber of Shipping since April 1993, they did not come fully into effect until after IMO Assembly approval in November 1993 and no assessment of their effectiveness is yet available.

15.42   The changed arrangements in the English Channel and the new arrangements elsewhere are being promulgated through IMO and Flag States in the usual way and will be included as an amendment to the IMO publication *Ships' Routeing* in due course. They have also been promulgated by Notice to Mariners and by amendments to charts and publications by national hydrographic offices. So far as we are aware, no publicity campaign is planned to persuade Masters to use MAREP in either the existing areas or the new ones, and no individual approaches, similar to those in the Minch (see paragraphs 14.43 and 16.44 – 16.46) are planned either. **We recommend that the Department of Transport should consider carefully whether existing means of publicising and promoting these changes could be improved.**

EC Directive on vessels carrying dangerous or polluting goods

15.43   This Directive[5] will come into force on 13 September 1995. It covers all vessels bound for or leaving Community ports and carrying dangerous or polluting goods (as

---

[5] Directive 93/75/EEC of 13 September 1993 concerning minimum requirements for vessels bound for or leaving Community ports and carrying dangerous or polluting goods.

defined in international Conventions). Under it, ship operators will be required to provide the competent authority of the Member State in the country of departure, or first port of arrival in the Community if coming from a port outside the Community, with detailed information relating to the ship and her hazardous cargo. This will include the name and call sign of the vessel, her nationality, her size, her port of destination, her estimated times of arrival and departure, intended route, and details of the hazardous cargo. The details to be given include the pollutant's technical name and United Nations number, its hazard class, the quantities on board and their locations and the identification marks on any portable containers. The information must be given before a vessel leaves the port of loading or any Community port.

15.44 The competent authority for the UK is likely to be HM Coastguard: the work would be done on its behalf by commercial organisations. The information would be handled electronically so that it would be immediately available to HM Coastguard on demand via electronic data transmission channels into the information handling systems. The systems would be organised so that Coastguards are not inundated with irrelevant detail. **The systems should be organised so that any intended routes which would flout routeing advice should be immediately notified to the coastal authorities so that they can seek to persuade the Master to take a different route, and so that they can notify the owners that they have done so.**

EC draft Directive on a European vessel reporting system

15.45 The European Commission presented a proposal for a new Directive in December 1993[6]. This follows on from the existing Directive and would considerably extend its scope. All ships carrying dangerous or polluting goods, including those in transit and not calling at EC ports, would have to report the same information as the existing Directive when entering the "EUROREP Zone", which would extend up to about 150 miles beyond the coast. States receiving the information would be obliged to pass the information on to other States through whose zones the ship would pass. The draft Directive depends upon agreement within IMO to a change in SOLAS permitting mandatory reporting. It would require every vessel over 300 grt to report to a Vessel Traffic Service (VTS), which would have to have radar and communication equipment. We return to this proposal in paragraph 15.67.

The purpose of reporting

15.46 There is a fundamental difference in approach between the EC system and MAREP. The first relies on reports being made to the competent authority as a condition of entry to a Community port: there is no need for any direct contact at any stage between the vessel and HM Coastguard. MAREP on the other hand relies on just that direct contact, without the backup of computer based information. The two systems will thus operate independently of each other.

---

[6] Proposal for a Council Directive concerning the setting up of a European vessel reporting system in the maritime zones of Community Member States COM(93) 647 final—SYN 491.

15.47   The main aim of both types of report is to provide a form of insurance. A ship reports at a convenient time basic details which include a general indication of the nature of the cargo with particular reference to any hazardous component. The information is logged in a form which is easily retrievable by HM Coastguard and retained until the vessel has left Community waters. If an incident develops, HM Coastguard has instant access to information which the crew may be too busy or distracted to give them. Information on the nature of the cargo can be crucial in deciding the response to an incident: the crew of a rescue helicopter, for instance, need to know whether the cargo of a ship in difficulties is likely to explode.

15.48   We have no doubt that the majority of Masters will comply with any reporting system of which they are fully aware and which is easy to use, but there will always be some who do not bother unless they can see benefits for themselves. To be fully effective, a reporting system needs to be either compulsory and enforceable or to incorporate benefits for the Master. The EC system will be compulsory and enforceable, and will give HM Coastguard fast access to information on the cargoes being carried by particular vessels. However, there will be no direct contact between Coastguard and vessel, and even where waters are covered by shore-based radar the information will not be readily "tagged" to a particular vessel. It is of course too early to judge how effectively the system will be enforced in practice and what the effect may be on the levels of voluntary reporting. Nor do we yet know what the costs of operating it will be. We know even less about the proposed change to SOLAS and have difficulty in seeing how any regulations made under it for compulsory reporting by passing traffic could be enforced.

Developing existing reporting measures

15.49   It should be stressed that reporting of more than the barest minimum of information is a medium-term solution to a medium-term problem. As we pointed out in paragraph 15.22, transponders will be capable of being programmed with information specific to a particular voyage, including all the information which is now, or will be under EC proposals, the subject of reports to HM Coastguard. Clearly it is essential that reporting continues until transponders are mandatory, but in considering any developments in reporting systems it is important to remember that reporting systems will be made largely redundant by transponders. Reports will continue to be needed only to identify that a vessel has entered the reporting zone: the transponder will do the rest. Reports will also be needed as a backup when transponders fail.

15.50   There are only two elements of existing reporting schemes which will not be replicated by a transponder-based system. One is direct human contact between the Master or Watch Officer of the ship concerned and HM Coastguard, which we discuss in the next paragraphs. The other is the availability of information in the unlikely but possible event of a sudden disaster which destroys the transponder and its information while damaging or destroying the vessel concerned. Some duplication will probably be needed to deal with this point: within the EC, the systems being set up for the existing Directive can presumably be adapted so as to hold a minimum of necessary information on ships in transit.

Direct contact with Masters

15.51 We value the human contact of direct reporting by voice and will regret its passing, but routine reporting by voice will have no place in a transponder-based system, except when a transponder is not functioning for some exceptional reason. In the meantime, however, the potential benefits of human contact should be realised so far as practicable.

15.52 Although voluntary reporting in the Dover Strait appears to be reasonably successful, an incentive should be offered to Masters to encourage better reporting. That incentive must be that reports and warnings of possible hazards can be given to them. HM Coastguard does already issue warnings of this type: navigational and other safety information which may be useful to ships in the Dover Strait area is broadcast every 30 minutes on VHF Channel 11. **Masters should be encouraged to keep watch on this Channel as well as on Channel 16.** While such formalised arrangements may not be appropriate in less busy areas, **all Coastguards should recognise that part of their job is to pass on, to ships which report, any navigational information which they may not have and which may be useful to them.** Help can if necessary be arranged for dealing with small problems – though it should be stressed that HM Coastguard is not a cheap substitute for shipping agents.

15.53 **Coastguards should recognise that there can also be indirect benefits from direct contact between themselves and vessels moving into and through UK waters.** HM Coastguard has the opportunity to ask whether there are any small problems which could conceivably develop into bigger ones. Human nature being what it is, the vessel's crew are far more likely to report minor difficulties if asked than spontaneously. HM Coastguard may thus get advance warning of problems which could escalate. This benefit is limited however to those ships where the Watch Officer concerned is reasonably fluent in English.

Possible mandatory reporting

15.54 Mandatory ship reporting could take the form of either reports before a ship leaves port (as with the EC Directive) or by direct contact between ship and Coastguard (as with MAREP and the draft Directive) or a combination of the two. IMO has agreed in principle that mandatory ship reporting is acceptable where there is a demonstrated need for it and that SOLAS should be amended to allow for this: clearly care will be needed to ensure that reporting regimes do not become so onerous as to inhibit innocent passage.

15.55 IMO's Safety of Navigation Sub-Committee is working on criteria and guidelines on mandatory reporting to assist in the prevention of accidents and the protection of the environment. It is working on MAREP type reporting, as opposed to reporting before leaving port, as IMO believes that any reporting system should be interactive. We entirely agree with this.

Possible universal reporting

15.56   We considered the possibility of universal reporting, by which we mean reporting by all merchant vessels within, or perhaps in the approaches to, UK waters. It could be either mandatory or voluntary, and it could be MAREP type ship-to-Coastguard communication or reports filed before leaving port, or both.

15.57   We initially found the idea of universal mandatory reporting appealing. We were attracted by a widely held view that someone ought to know just what vessels were in all UK waters, even though we recognised that in most of our territorial waters there is no need for a policing role. We felt that there was considerable value in the human contact of reporting, as Masters would be more likely to report minor problems, thus giving advance warning of possible major ones. On reflection we have concluded that the problems are too great, bearing in mind that transponders will replace reporting systems within a few years.

15.58   The first problem is one of enforcement. As we have said, we believe that most Masters will cooperate with voluntary reporting schemes, so long as they are fully understood and not onerous. It is those who do not report voluntarily who pose the problems. If they do not report because they do not realise why reporting is valuable, then education is needed, and will be needed just as much for a mandatory system. If they have more sinister motives, they need to be identified and prosecuted. There are no simple means of identifying vessels which do not report, so enforcement would be difficult. It would not, however, be impossible since an unreported vessel which arrived at an EC or Paris MOU port could be asked for an explanation.

15.59   A major technical difficulty with a universal system of reporting based on direct contact between the ship and HM Coastguard is the frequency of reports – a vessel *en route* from, say, the north of Shetland to the Isles of Scilly through the Irish Sea passes through the areas of several Coastguard stations. Repeated reporting would be onerous and would act as a major disincentive to Masters to report: but without it Coastguard stations would find it difficult to know just when a ship passes from one sector to another. A computer-based automatic system to transfer a report from one Coastguard station to the next would be ideal, but could be very expensive. It could not solve the problem of knowing just where the ship was. We anticipate similar problems with the draft EC Directive, where information on a ship would be passed on from one State to the next.

15.60   We do not want to add to the burdens on Coastguards or on Masters without very good justification. **We do not believe that justification, in the form of mutual benefit for the coastal authorities and the Masters of vessels, exists for universal reporting. We recommend that the UK Government should resist any attempts to introduce a system of universal reporting by ships to shore-based authorities.**

Reporting in particular areas

15.61   The principle of reporting in areas to which environmentally-based routeing measures apply is already established, with the extension of MAREP to the Fair Isle Channel, the Pentland Firth, the Minch and the sea around the Isles of Scilly. We recommend in paragraph 14.111 that cruise ships should report to HM Coastguard before entering ATBAs. **Where ATBAs or other protected areas are involved, or in areas such as the Minch which Masters of specified types of vessel are recommended to avoid, the report should include the reasons why the route in question has been chosen. Reports should be made an hour or so before the area in question is likely to be reached: in some areas a longer reporting time may be sensible according to local conditions.**

15.62 The scope for reporting, whether voluntary or compulsory, to police routeing measures is limited. No vessel is likely to report that she is flouting routeing measures: she is far more likely not to report in those circumstances, and there is not much that can be done about this until transponders are widely used. However, there will always be some vessels which do not realise that they are going against routeing measures, and **the Department of Transport should ensure that, when they report, either under current systems or under the new arrangements we recommend in this chapter, they should be asked why they are doing so and requested not to do it again. The requests should be reinforced by letters to owners.**

Linking MAREP and the EC system

15.63 The reporting of particular types of cargo is also clearly established in principle, both by IMO and by the EC. We welcome these developments, but still have some reservations about how the EC's system will work in practice. We would prefer there to be a brief contact between Coastguard and vessel, to establish a human relationship, for HM Coastguard to check that all is well and for the vessel to be able to check on likely problems.

15.64 **Links need to be developed between the EC reporting system and MAREP.** It would be unfortunate if Masters thought that because they had reported under the EC system they had no need to do so under MAREP: but it would be understandable if they resented having to give the same information twice. We hope that it will be possible for ships which have reported under the EC scheme to report also under MAREP, but giving only the briefest details necessary – name or identification number ought to be enough – so HM Coastguard can tap into the EC databank and identify the vessel from there if necessary. **We believe that HM Coastguard should check whether the ship is experiencing any problems, and give warnings of hazards and any weather warning which might be appropriate.**

Reporting by vessels not covered by the EC system

15.65 Ships not covered by the EC scheme include vessels carrying dangerous goods but not bound to or from EC ports, and vessels calling at EC ports but not carrying cargoes covered by the EC scheme. The first category would be covered by the proposed Directive. **Reporting on the approaches to all MAREP areas should also be extended to all vessels over 300 grt, the new limit for MAREP in the English Channel, whether** they are laden or unladen. Most vessels carrying dangerous or polluting materials will be covered by this provision, but it should be clear that if there are any vessels of less than 300 grt carrying such goods they should also report.

Voluntary or compulsory reporting

15.66   We would like to see the system of reporting we outline in paragraph 15.65, based on a combination of areas and types of ship or cargo, made compulsory for all vessels, whatever their flags, origins and destinations. It would be difficult to police such a requirement without **both** a comprehensive radar network – which we discuss in the next chapter (paragraphs 16.15–16.19 and 16.23–16.25) **and** a guaranteed means of identification of ships. There will be no guaranteed means of identification until transponders are universally adopted, and that will make reporting unnecessary. That being so, we have to accept that effective policing is unattainable. Nevertheless, it should be possible to establish quickly and easily whether vessels using UK and other Paris MOU ports have reported properly as part of Port State Control.

EUROREP

15.67   We have considered whether the draft Directive outlined in paragraph 15.45 would fulfil our objectives. We concluded that it would not.

15.68   The first problem with the draft Directive is that its scope is too wide: it would cover all vessels carrying specified goods within a very large area indeed, whether or not they were going close to areas where information on cargoes would be useful. The second is that it would be unenforceable through policing because of the problems of identification: this should be recognised and the attempt to enforce in this way abandoned, adopting our suggested approach of enforcement through Port State Control instead. The difficulties of identification make it impossible to justify the cost of establishing radar-based Vessel Traffic Services around the coast: in paragraph 16.19 we estimate that the cost of equipment alone for a chain of radars around the UK coast would be some £50 million. Where VTSs and means of identification such as a spotter plane can be justified for other reasons unconnected with the policing of reporting, they should of course be used as well.

15.69   The third problem is that without detailed information of the position and progress of a vessel, handing over details from one State to the next is a fairly pointless as well as expensive exercise. The fourth is that the proposal is premature: we believe that it is unwise to contemplate amassing a very great deal of information in the way proposed before the first Directive is even in force, and at a stage when no one knows whether the information it will provide will prove significantly more useful than that already available.

Conclusions on routine reporting

15.70   **We recommend that the UK Government should seek to modify the draft Directive to bring it into line with our proposals in paragraph 15.66 that the compulsory reporting system should:**

(a) **operate only in specified areas of high traffic density or particular environmental sensitivity, such as those now covered by MAREP;**

(b) **cover all large vessels and all those, whatever their size, that carry dangerous and polluting goods;**

(c) **be enforced only through Port State Control or through VTSs and spotter planes where those are justified for other reasons; and**

(d) **be brought into operation only after the existing Directive has been implemented and its effects assessed.**

15.71   **We also recommend that the UK Government should press the EC Commission to concentrate its efforts on transponders, which will solve so many problems, rather than on the reporting systems which they will largely supersede. Reporting arrangements will need to be retained only to the extent that ships will need to identify themselves on first entry to the reporting area and as a backup in case of equipment failure.**

The reporting of faults

15.72   We have already mentioned the value of human contact as an aid to the identification by the shore-based authorities of possible problems. Ships' officers tend to be reluctant to report apparently minor problems, simply because they are optimistic that they can be dealt with quickly. If specifically asked if they have any problems, they are more likely to give details.

The MARPOL requirement

15.73   As we record in paragraph 15.38, there already exists a MARPOL[7] requirement that a report should be made to the authorities of the nearest State – in the case of the UK, to HM Coastguard – if there is a possibility of a discharge of a pollutant. In deciding whether a report should be made, the nature of any damage, failure or breakdown of the ship, machinery or equipment should be taken into account as well as the sea or wind state, traffic density in the area and the time and place of the incident. The reports should be made when there is any damage, failure or breakdown which affects the safety of the ship, such as collision, grounding, fire, explosion, structural failure, flooding, cargo shifting, or the failure or breakdown of machinery or equipment which results in the impairment of the safety of navigation (breakdown of steering gear, propulsion plant, electrical generating system or essential shipborne navigational aids).

15.74   We do not know how widely this requirement is obeyed in practice. We suspect that in the majority of cases, reports are not made until it is entirely clear that major problems are developing. The case histories in Appendix L show different reactions: the Masters of some vessels, such as the *PACIFIC MARCHIONESS* and the *CITY OF*

---

[7] Article 8.

LIMASSOL, did report their difficulties at a fairly early stage, while others, such as the Masters of the *ICE STAR* or the *ODIGITRIA B*, did not. Even when reports are made, there may be delays: for instance, HM Coastguard was not advised of the problems of the *BRAER* until over an hour after she turned south to head for an anchorage off the Moray Firth. In such cases there may be doubt on the interpretation of MARPOL and whether a report should have been made earlier: but in many cases where no report was ever made, and the ship's problems are resolved without the involvement of the coastal authorities, those authorities will never know that a report should have been made.

Developing the MARPOL requirement

15.75   We believe that the first step in dealing with this problem should be to find out how widespread the failure to report promptly is. That could be done either through a specific research project or through examination of ships' logs in Port State Control. The former is probably the better: particularly as the study would be most useful if it covered the whole of the EC or, better still, of the Paris MOU. **We recommend that the UK Government explores with its partners in the EC and the Paris MOU the possibilities for cooperative research on this. It would be sensible for the research to cover how the coastal authorities react to reports which are made and whether their reactions could be improved upon.**

15.76   If, as we suspect, standards of reporting of comparatively minor failures which could have disastrous effects are not good enough, further action will need to be taken. **We believe that the MARPOL provision outlined in paragraph 15.73 should be strengthened so as to include mandatory *immediate* reporting to HM Coastguard (and its equivalents in other countries) of:**

(a)   **any casualties, such as a collision or fire; or**

(b)   **any propulsion or steering failure; or**

(c)   **any failure of navigational equipment, unless duplicate equipment is carried and is functioning correctly; or**

(d)   **any other failure which has the potential for hazarding the safety of the ship; or**

(e)   **any problems (such as a leaking valve) which could cause pollution; or**

(f)   **any hazards to navigation, such as the ship being anchored or not under command in a fairway.**

This mandatory reporting requirement should be applied to transit traffic as well as to traffic calling at all EC ports. Ideally the mandatory reporting area should be roughly equivalent to 12 hours' drift time: that is, territorial waters and a further band of some 12 nautical miles beyond territorial waters, except of course where this impinged on the territorial waters or a similar outer zone of another State. Median lines would need to be established.

15.77 We recommend that the UK Government should press IMO to develop its thinking on mandatory reporting to include this provision on mandatory reporting of failures as they arise and regardless of whether the Master confides that there is any risk in terms of safety or pollution. The UK Government should, in parallel, ask the EC and the North Sea States to take the same approach. The sanction would be a notification condition, as set out in Chapter 11, for all ships in the same ownership or management. In extreme cases, a ban on loading and unloading might be appropriate, as envisaged in Chapter 11, in the absence of assurances for the future.

15.78 Enforcement is obviously a problem: if a ship in transit does sort out her own problems without any adverse consequences, as would often be the case, and if her Master does not report, who is to know? **This is a problem which must be tackled internationally.** A considerable effort may be needed to convince Masters sailing under all flags, including those with poor English, that reports should be made. We want to inculcate an attitude that minor faults are reported, and it is part of this that Masters should not fear the consequences of reporting comparatively minor faults. If enforcement proves necessary, the record of minor faults in the ship's deck and engine room log books will be available for checks in Port State inspection.

Action taken on reports of faults

15.79 We expect that in the vast majority of cases when a Master reports a fault, no action will need to be taken by the land-based authorities. A Coastguard would normally note any reports and call back after half an hour or so to check on progress: we record in Appendix L a case involving the *CITY OF LIMASSOL* where the Coastguard did precisely this. Only in a very few exceptional cases would he take any further immediate action. That action is likely to consist of warning salvage operators that there may be a casualty. The current procedure is described in paragraph 20.135: our recommendations in Chapter 20 will necessitate some changes. There is a fine balance to be struck here: it is important that salvors are alerted quickly when a genuine need is likely to arise, but the knowledge that salvors may be alerted to his predicament may discourage a Master from reporting.

15.80 It is clearly important that Coastguard Watch Officers, as the recipients of reports of failures, should be able to assess quickly the likely seriousness of those faults. At the major Coastguard stations, and particularly Dover, it is rare for the watch not to include an officer with bridge watchkeeping experience and qualifications. The problem is in some of the smaller stations, where the Watch Officers may have no qualifications as mariners and cannot be expected to judge what should be done. They need instant access to good advice. Some advice is already available: MPCU officers, who have considerable experience in assessing the risks to ships in difficulties, can be contacted at any time. The home telephone numbers of the MSA District Chief Surveyors are also available if needed.

15.81 We recommend that HM Coastguard should reconsider, in the light of the recommendations in this Report, whether this is adequate or whether further

advice needs to be made available by agreement with MSA, perhaps by establishing a panel of designated experts in MSA headquarters to be on call at all hours of the day and night.

15.82   The designated expert would advise HM Coastguard on how serious the reported fault appears to be. The Coastguard Senior Watch Officer would need to consider this advice alongside his standing instructions and his local knowledge and decide whether or not emergency assistance, of the kind described in Chapter 20, should be called out. If, as would usually be the case, this is unnecessary he should check with the Master after a period – say half an hour – that all is well. He might need to reconsider his action, and should certainly go on checking at regular intervals until the problem is resolved. He should also be able to offer positive help, for instance in communications with owners.

15.83   **All reports of failures should be entered on the Port State Control computer record,** to which HM Coastguard will need rapid access, though this need not be direct access. **In serious cases, the authorities at the port of destination should be alerted to the fault by telephone.**

Conclusion

15.84   We have established that **identification** is a fundamental issue. Transponders are vital, but in the meantime identification can be improved simply, easily and cheaply by painting a ship's number very prominently on her sides and deck. There can be no good reason for not doing this.

15.85   **Routine reporting** is essentially an information-gathering exercise, which will lose much of its significance once a transponder regime is operational. While it has a place in encouraging a safety culture, it is essential to consider just what use can be made of the information generated. We can see little justification for a significant expansion of routine information-gathering, but we believe that the system we advocate of **effective compulsory reporting of failures** in propulsion, steering or navigational instruments is urgently needed and would reduce the chances of "incidents" becoming "disasters".

Chapter 16

Surveillance and Tracking

16.1   Ships, unlike aircraft, are not normally tracked from the land. Aircraft are tracked because routeing, in terms of the route to be taken and the time at which it should be taken, is controlled from the land. Such land-based control of shipping is both unnecessary and undesirable. On the other hand tracking of ships is sometimes desirable for different reasons. Thus all shipping using the Dover Strait is tracked by radar, albeit often without individual ships being identified, in the interests of policing the observance of the Strait navigational rules and giving warning to other ships of the activities of "rogues". We need to consider whether there is a case for any extension of tracking.

16.2   Tracking is, of course, a special and concentrated form of surveillance, but we need to consider whether other forms of surveillance are necessary. Surveillance we take to mean action by someone other than a vessel's crew to identify her or to establish the position or route of a vessel. It may be undertaken from the sea, the land or the air. It has three distinct purposes. First is aid to a ship in an emergency – her position and drift may be of vital importance. Second is where, as a result of an incident, pollution has occurred and it is necessary to know the extent and likely consequences of that pollution. Third is a purely policing and detection role – policing against infringements of routeing or other measures and illegal discharges and, where they occur, detecting the ship responsible.

16.3   Routine tracking and any other form of routine surveillance present the same risk as routine reporting: that of creating an immense amount of information without any very clear purpose, and above all without considering whether the costs of compiling, storing and retrieving that information are commensurate with the benefits. We need to be reasonably certain of the benefits before embarking on any expansion.

Radar surveillance

16.4   Radar surveillance is used chiefly to track traffic. Tracking can serve both short-term and long-term aims. In the short term, it can be used to identify developing problems, to warn other vessels in the area of developing hazards, and very occasionally to observe erratic movements which could create a hazard for other vessels: two examples of this are given in Appendix L. It can also be useful in search and rescue (SAR) and other emergency operations. Surveillance can be used to identify vessels ignoring advice or regulations, though some means of identifying the vessel concerned is needed as well: we discuss the problems in Chapter 15. It can also be used to identify problem areas where further measures may be needed.

Vessel Traffic Services

16.5 Vessel Traffic Services (VTSs) involve a control centre which coordinates information, normally as a basis for regulating the traffic in a port. Every ship is identified; movements on and off berths are known and many ships have local pilots on board. Several UK ports have such systems, backed up by radar. These VTSs are the responsibility of harbour authorities, paid for through port dues. They vary in sophistication according to the needs of the harbour authority concerned.

The Channel Navigation Information Service

16.6 The only VTS system operated by the UK Government is the Channel Navigation Information Service (CNIS) at the Dover Coastguard station. CNIS is a radar based and computer operated system, linked to the similar French system at Cap Gris Nez, which gives HM Coastguard a detailed picture of the Dover Strait and its approaches, the Traffic Separation Scheme, the Inshore Traffic Zones and the vessels passing through. Plate 2 shows CNIS in use and Plate 3 reproduces the CNIS screen on 12 June 1993 at 22 01 hours. Before 1969 there were an average of 30 collisions in the Dover Strait each year: since the introduction of CNIS and the establishment of the TSS in the Dover Strait in 1972 there have been no more than four collisions in all but three years. During the same period movements have remained almost constant although tonnage has probably increased.

16.7 At our request, HM Coastguard counted the traffic in the Strait during a seven day period in October 1993, in the low season for ferries. It concluded that there were about 420 commercial movements a day on average, rising to 440 in the ferry high season. Of these, 200 commercial vessels pass through the Strait, 180-200 cross it and about 30-40 are fishing vessels operating within it. Plate 4 shows the tracks of vessels over a 24 hour period in the Strait, taken from CNIS information.

16.8 CNIS records show that most of the commercial vessels transitting the Strait stay within the designated traffic lanes, but each day, on average, three vessels break the rules of the TSS. Most breaches involve fishing vessels. Several vessels a week break down in the CNIS area.

16.9 CNIS cannot identify vessels automatically. The radar images of vessels reporting under MAREP (paragraphs 15.39–15.42) are "tagged" with a reference number for fast identification if necessary. The "tags" include a note of details such as name, cargo and destination obtained through MAREP. CNIS also projects courses and speeds, so that estimated positions in six minutes' time (or longer if so required) can be seen at a glance. The speed and course projections and "tags" can be seen in the photograph of a CNIS screen in Plate 3. These two very useful features are not found on less sophisticated radars. HM Coastguard can ask vessels which do not report under MAREP to identify themselves, but may not get a response.

16.10 A spotter plane permanently based 15 minutes' flying time from Dover is used to identify "rogues" breaking the rules of the TSS, but it is unusable at night or in poor weather. Only about 30 per cent of "rogues" are identified – on average, the spotter plane identifies some 72 per cent of these, that is about 21 per cent of the total. The spotter plane is also used by MPCU for pollution surveillance, as described in Chapter 21.

16.11   CNIS's first task is to prevent accidents by providing an information service. HM Coastguard regularly provides radio information to ships on the weather, tides, depths of water and any navigational warnings needed to assist safe passage through the Dover Strait. These are backed up, if necessary at very frequent intervals, by warnings of specific hazards to which they have been alerted by CNIS. This is probably CNIS's most effective role in safety and pollution prevention. CNIS is also a valuable addition to SAR in the Channel.

16.12   CNIS's second task is to identify "rogues" contravening the TSS regulations, using the spotter plane for identification, for the action described in paragraphs 14.101. **The system of reporting infringements of the Dover Strait TSS is slow. The Department of Transport should ensure that it is speeded up, so that Masters of ships infringing the TSS while *en route* to UK ports can be admonished immediately. It should also ask the French Government to take a similar approach.**

16.13   CNIS is not only an extremely sophisticated system, it is also expensive – the recent renewal of the control system alone cost some £4 million. In addition it requires permanent manning by some five staff at a total annual cost, including maintenance, of £410,000.

Other existing radar systems

16.14   Some port VTSs also overlook important areas of sea: for instance, the Orkney Harbour Authority's radar overlooks most of the Pentland Firth. The Port of London Authority not only has a system for watching much of the Thames Estuary, but also very sensibly shares one radar, at Margate, with CNIS. The Royal Navy has radar observation stations at Portland, Plymouth (from 1995), Culdrose, Hartland Point (from 1994), the Mull of Kintyre and Islay. Other national bodies such as the Civil Aviation Authority and the Royal Air Force also have radars facing the sea, but even in an emergency they may not be available for keeping an eye on shipping.

The limitations of VTS radar

16.15   Radar is not a panacea, and it would not be to the benefit of safety or the environment to treat it as though it were. Its limitations are considerable: the inability of systems – and operators – to predict or control events, and the difficulty of identifying vessels. The limitations are greater where sophisticated systems with "tagging" or projection of course and speed cannot be justified. It is highly unlikely that a dedicated identification aircraft could be justified in many areas: and even where a dual use could be arranged for an aircraft, it would be reasonable to expect a lower proportion of successful identification in areas with worse weather than the Channel.

16.16   It can be very difficult to find suitable sites for radar scanners. Scanners are ugly, and they need to be placed high up so that they can "see" a wide area. Inevitably, they tend to be very visible themselves. As we have already pointed out, the vast majority of our coastline is either of significant landscape and ecological value or residential. Intrusive scanners are not welcome in either type of area.

16.17   Radar scanners also have to be linked to the relevant Coastguard station, either by microwave links – which need clear lines of "sight" – or by landline. Either may well be difficult to arrange, particularly in mountainous areas. A reliable source of electricity and vehicle access for maintenance are also required. All these factors tend to add to the intrusiveness of radar installations and their cost.

16.18   The costs of new radar installations can be substantial. It was suggested to us in evidence[1] that the equipment for a remote radar station would cost upwards of £300,000 in capital costs, plus another £250,000 for the equipment at a Coastguard station. The capital costs of the site and buildings at the remote station would depend very heavily on whether road access and electricity were readily available. Operational and maintenance costs would be significant.

16.19   The range of a remote radar would be about 35-40 miles.[2] HM Coastguard now needs 120 remote sites in order to obtain the current level of 80 per cent VHF radio coverage of the UK coastline out to 30 miles, or 94 per cent of territorial waters. It considers that a similar number of radar scanner sites would be required. Making some allowance for existing radars, a complete chain around the UK coastline would require perhaps 100 remote radar sites. The cost of the equipment alone would be over £50 million, plus substantial extra costs for land, buildings and power supplies and greatly increased running costs.

Other types of radar

16.20   Although less effective than a full VTS, other types of radar are available and could in some cases be useful. One such type is a simple ship's radar to be used on land to keep HM Coastguard informed in busy areas. This would be comparatively cheap – a ship's radar costs about £25,000 – particularly if it could be installed at the Coastguard station rather than on a remote site, but would have limited use. HM Coastguard would have no better quality information than ships' Masters, and unless the scanner could be given enough height to provide a good "view", the information could be less good. There would also be no possibility of recording the radar images. The opportunities here are thus limited.

16.21   The second type is a mobile radar. The Defence Research Agency already has Quick Reaction Mobile Radars, which can be used at any site in the UK. The capability,

---

[1] Oral evidence from EDS Scicon UK Ltd April 1993.
[2] ibid.

which was established at the request of the Department of Transport over ten years ago, can be used in an emergency, for establishing sites for permanent radar or for surveillance. It can be hired, and was used in carrying out the survey of traffic in the Fair Isle Channel commissioned by the Secretary of State for Transport at our request (see Appendix O). The Quick Reaction Mobile Radar consists of a 9 foot scanner, full monitoring equipment and a recorder mounted in a four wheel drive vehicle. Other similar systems can be rented or bought.

16.22   **We believe that the Department of Transport should use a mobile radar facility more often in order to:**

(a)   **keep informed of ship movements during an emergency – but only when the emergency is a long-running one and the equipment can be moved on site quickly;**

(b)   **carry out traffic counts to establish whether routeing measures or permanent radar would be useful; and**

(c)   **monitor traffic from time to time, as part of a surveillance bluff – in the same way that television detector vans only sometimes work in a particular area. The possibility of surveillance would, of course, need to be widely known.**

The purpose of radar tracking

"Sea Traffic Control"

16.23   One possible use of radar tracking is to enable land-based authorities to **direct** traffic. Harbour authorities have powers to direct traffic within their areas. There is no corresponding power for national authorities to direct sea traffic outside port areas. As we have said, we cannot see any case for a system of "Sea Traffic Control" by analogy with Air Traffic Control, whereby aircraft are handed on from one zone to another with very specific instructions on the route to take. That system is simply unnecessary for most of the sea.

16.24   In some areas sea traffic is much more dense than air traffic – rendering control very difficult and thus extremely expensive – but because of their far slower speeds vessels can safely go much closer to each other than can aircraft. Ships also operate in two dimensions while aircraft operate in three, leaving more scope for directions. As we pointed out in the last chapter, there is as yet no certain means of identifying vessels. The number of variables involved in making decisions on ship manoeuvres is so high, the likelihood of unreported changes in some of them (such as the location of sand-banks) is so great, and the difficulty of ensuring that all craft are covered by a scheme is so large, that it has seemed essential to leave the final decision to the person in control of the ship. No system has yet been developed that would put central controllers in a position where their decisions could be guaranteed to be more reliable than decisions of those on board. **We therefore reject "Sea Traffic Control" as impracticable and undesirable.**

Universal tracking of vessels

16.25 Even if control from the land is impracticable, there may be a case for tracking vessels from land; by radar or by reporting or a combination of the two. We have already dismissed the idea of universal reporting. We conclude in Chapter 15 that very widespread radar tracking for the purposes of vessel monitoring and reporting, as suggested in the EC draft Directive on a European vessel reporting system, is not justifiable because of the very large costs and the uncertain benefits. The question is whether it is justifiable for any other reason: we conclude that it is not. Again, the benefits are unclear and are undoubtedly outweighed by the huge costs.

Radar surveillance to police routeing measures

16.26 Radar surveillance can help detect infringements of both mandatory and voluntary routeing measures, encouraging good behaviour and thus lessening the risks of collision. The first point to consider is whether traffic in TSSs other than the Dover Strait needs policing, and the second is whether permanent radar is the only or best way of doing this.

The need for policing

16.27 At the time of writing, the new routeing measures agreed by the International Maritime Organization had only recently come fully into force, and it was premature to try to assess the extent to which they were being heeded. There is no evidence that well-established routeing measures and advice are generally ignored: equally, there is no evidence that they are generally heeded. We know that only about 0.6 per cent of traffic a day in the Dover Strait ignores the rules (see paragraph 14.92). We do not know whether this is typical: common sense suggests that at least some adherence to the rules is a direct result of monitoring from shore. Most of the vessels disobeying the rules in the Dover Strait are fishing vessels.

16.28 The type of "policing" provided in the Dover Strait is needed because of the density of traffic, the conflicting paths of through and cross-Channel traffic and the narrowness of some of the traffic lanes. Similar permanent policing would be desirable elsewhere only if there is a sufficient density of traffic to require it. We suspect that there are few if any areas where this type of policing would be beneficial, particularly given that the extension of vessel reporting we have recommended is likely to affect behaviour. **We recommend that the UK Government resists any pressure for permanent radar coverage of shipping except in areas where the density and conflicting movements of traffic in restricted areas makes "policing" desirable. It should consider permanent radar surveillance for policing purposes only in areas where:**

  (a) **there is comparatively dense traffic – perhaps an average of, say, 20 large vessels (or a much larger number of small vessels) a day; *and***

  (b) **actual traffic movements conflict, leading to a risk of collision; *and***

  (c) **there is inadequate sea-room to accommodate all the traffic.**

16.29   Where areas meet the criteria, **the Department of Transport should consider what type of radar coverage is most suitable.** Where another body, such as the Ministry of Defence or a harbour authority, already has a radar system nearby **the best course, and certainly the first to be considered, might be for HM Coastguard to share the output of those radars.** The Department of Transport should clearly pay the marginal costs of any necessary equipment and extra operating costs incurred by the primary user.

16.30   Some areas which do not meet the criteria will no doubt be covered by harbour or Royal Navy radar. The operators of those radars may well want to keep an eye on passing traffic, and to pass on significant information gained to HM Coastguard, either on a regular basis through computer links or simply by telephone. That is very much to be welcomed. But it is important that these authorities do not usurp the role of HM Coastguard by taking reports or giving instructions outside harbour limits: that is a recipe for chaos.

Policing with temporary radar

16.31   Areas which do not need permanent policing by radar may still benefit from occasional radar policing. This should be organised on the same basis as police road speed cameras: Masters should not be told in advance whether a particular area is subject to temporary radar surveillance. They should, however, be made very well aware that radar policing is a possibility.

16.32   **We recommend that the Department of Transport sets up a few – probably no more than half a dozen – sites for temporary radars and advertises their presence.** Monitoring would be carried out by a mobile radar along the lines of that described in paragraph 16.21 and would normally be at only one site at any one time. Each site would overlook areas where voluntary or mandatory routeing or reporting measures apply, as described in Chapter 14. Monitoring could be carried out by a ship's radar if sufficient height could be provided or by a radar vehicle, as suggested above. The purpose of the surveillance would be twofold: to establish whether there was a case for permanent radar coverage for policing purposes, using the criteria we suggest above, and to police traffic. Special arrangements might be needed to identify any ship seen ignoring advice or regulation. Any identified wrongdoers should be followed up not only through the Flag State but also by direct approaches to the owners.

Radar surveillance to detect problems

16.33   A number of witnesses, particularly those who gave oral evidence in Shetland, suggested to us that radar is the key to the prevention of incidents such as the *BRAER*. They argued that if HM Coastguard had tracked the *BRAER* on radar as she went into the Fair Isle Channel, it would have noticed her unusual path first as she turned south to head for shelter in the Moray Firth and subsequently as she was driven north after her engines had failed. The local Coastguards, they argued, might have thus become aware that a vessel was in difficulties between half an hour and an hour before the crew of the *BRAER* got in touch with them, and so would have been able to initiate salvage action earlier. They therefore pressed us to make an immediate recommendation to the Secretary of State for

Transport for radar coverage of the Fair Isle Channel to be installed before the winter of 1993-94 to prevent a recurrence of the *BRAER* incident.

16.34   While we have great sympathy with the desire in Shetland to see protection against the possibility of another grounding in place, we do not believe that radar coverage of the Fair Isle Channel is the answer, and we declined to make the recommendation suggested. The recommendation we did make – on a traffic count in the Fair Isle Channel – is reproduced in Appendix O and its results are described in paragraph 14.26. The tracks of the vessels on the busiest day (14 June 1993) are shown in Plate 5.

16.35   We do not believe that a different outcome would have been likely if the last voyage of the *BRAER* had been monitored by land-based radar. Neither the MAIB nor the Liberian accident investigators suggested that radar could have played a part. We can see no reason to assume that if the local Coastguards had been tracking her on a radar screen, whether or not that tracking was automatic and alarmed, they would have become aware that she was in difficulties substantially earlier than was the case: certainly not early enough for the outcome to have been different.

16.36   At the time there was no MAREP system in the Fair Isle Channel. There is now: all laden tankers are asked to report to the Lerwick Coastguard an hour before they enter the Channel. Had the *BRAER* done this, we believe that there is a high chance that her Watch Officer would have mentioned the problems which were already evident, and that HM Coastguard would have had earlier warning of the difficulties she was in. Whether the extra notice would have made any difference to the final outcome it is impossible to say.

16.37   Under our proposals for mandatory reporting of faults as soon as they arise (paragraphs 15.72 – 15.78), Coastguards would have had significantly earlier warning of the *BRAER*'s difficulties than radar could possibly have given them. But no two incidents are ever the same, and it is more instructive to consider whether radar might help prevent future accidents, off Shetland or anywhere else.

16.38   It is certainly a theoretical possibility that a radar system, particularly if it is fitted with alarms to alert the operator to unusual occurrences, will give HM Coastguard warning of incidents as they happen. There are however a number of practical difficulties. Radar operators may very occasionally be able to help prevent collisions in busy areas by warning Watch Officers that vessels are on a collision course, but definition is rarely good enough for operators to be able to tell just how close vessels are to each other, and of course they cannot predict changes in direction. A "collision" which appears on a radar screen may be no such thing: it is quite possible that the radar echoes have merged and may separate again, perhaps some time later. Nor can radar normally help prevent grounding, though there may be rare occasions on which land-based authorities can alert a vessel to problems of which her crew appear to be unaware. However, crews which are unaware that they are heading into difficulties which can be seen on their own radar are unlikely to pay much attention to warnings from the shore: precisely this problem arose in the case of the *BETTINA DANICA*, described in Appendix L.

16.39 Radar obviously cannot prevent breakdowns. It cannot detect many types of failure, such as electrical failure leading to loss of navigational aids. In most cases, once a problem has started to develop, radar can at best give HM Coastguard a short additional warning of impending trouble if a vessel is seen on screen to be taking an erratic route or to have slowed down unexpectedly. The extent to which that can be picked up depends on the scale and level of definition of the equipment: and, to be realistic, on the degree of concentration of the individual Coastguard concerned.

16.40 Once a radar signal appears on a screen in a Coastguard station, someone has to keep an eye on it. Systems can include automatic alarms set to go off when vessels appear to collide or lose steerage, but even with those alarms HM Coastguard Watch Officers would need to spend a great deal of time watching the screens. If there is little traffic this task becomes very boring, and it is only human nature to start to lose concentration. We are convinced that if there was widespread radar coverage of areas with little traffic, such as the Fair Isle Channel, operators would inevitably mentally "switch off". There would thus be occasions on which radar coverage might have given some small extra warning but the operators, being only human, did not pick up the perhaps tiny indications of approaching trouble.

16.41 We therefore do not believe that radar coverage can be justified on the grounds of early identification of potential problems. Where radar coverage is required for a policing role, arrangements should be made to deal with those rare instances where radar can give warning of problems. We return to this point at the end of this chapter.

Radar coverage of particularly sensitive areas

16.42 It is tempting to suggest that particularly sensitive areas, including MEHRAs (see Chapter 14), should be surveyed by radar. The temptation needs to be resisted unless there are other good grounds for it. If radar surveillance is unlikely to be able to prevent or reduce the risks of an accident occurring or a dangerous situation worsening, then the sensitivity of the area is irrelevant to the potential usefulness of radar.

Non-radar surveillance

Cooperation in the Minch

16.43 As we explain in paragraph 14.39, there have for many years been fears of a devastating pollution incident in the Minch. Large laden tankers have been advised since 1987 to use the Deep Water Route unless weather conditions dictate otherwise, but the necessarily subjective decisions on what weather conditions did permit appeared to encourage Masters to use the Minch rather than the longer alternative. As we mention in paragraph 14.12, when a traffic count was taken in 1989 only about one in five large laden tankers was using the Deep Water Route in preference to the Minch. Local people saw very large vessels – by no means all of which were large laden tankers – transitting the Minch and concluded that the risks of pollution remained undiminished.

16.44   Formal measures have been taken to persuade large laden tankers to avoid the Minch, through the means described in Chapter 14. As we explain in paragraph 14.43, the Department of Transport has also joined with the Western Isles Islands Council and the Highland Regional Council in asking local people to report to HM Coastguard anything which looks like a large tanker transitting the Minch in good weather. As a result of the Department's subsequent checks and queries, at least one shipping company has decided to include in its Masters' standing instructions a direction that the Minch should not be used.

16.45   A scheme such as this needs a great deal of cooperation and good-will, including feedback to individuals who report specific vessels. It inevitably takes up staff time, but the cost of that is a very great deal less than high-tech radar coverage: it is probably also more effective. MAREP has now been extended to the Minch: **we recommend that the Department of Transport considers carefully any discrepancies between vessels reporting in under MAREP and those spotted by local people, and continues to follow up cases of tankers seen in the Minch without good reason. The Department should discuss the effectiveness of the scheme from time to time with the local authorities and other interests concerned. We also recommend that it considers setting up similar schemes elsewhere.** The Council of the Isles of Scilly expressed interest when we raised the idea with it informally: so did the South Wales Sea Fisheries Committee. People in other areas might well be equally cooperative.

16.46   It is important that reports are made to MSA, either directly or through HM Coastguard, for it to take up with owners and if necessary with Flag States, rather than local individuals or organisations taking them up direct. This is for two reasons. One is that no one other than the State Agencies has the authority to pursue these points with shipowners and Flag States. The other is that if MSA is not told of reports, it cannot build up a picture of what is going on and thus develop strategies to deal with problems. Clearly it is important that MSA deals with reports quickly.

16.47   This type of informal surveillance will normally be too slow for identification of immediate problems in time to deal with them. Nevertheless, HM Coastguard already relies very heavily upon a kind of informal surveillance, in the form of emergency calls, to alert it to accidents where search and rescue may be needed. It is sometimes similarly alerted to potential or actual pollution problems in the same way. **Ships' Masters, the crews of pleasure craft and the general public should be encouraged through publicity to report pollution and potential pollution incidents to HM Coastguard in the same way as they now report risks to safety. While we were pleased to see that the *Coastguard Charter Standard Statement 1994* encourages the crews of pleasure craft and the general public to report pollution incidents, more encouragement to report is needed.**

Aerial surveillance

16.48   We have so far discussed surveillance to police routeing measures and surveillance to give advance warning of potential problems. Aerial surveillance adds a new dimension:

it can be used to spot illegal discharges and sometimes to identify the ships responsible; to identify vessels seen on radar or reported by other vessels; and to monitor actual pollution incidents. We believe that aerial surveillance, which should be extremely noticeable from the bridge, can have a marked psychological effect on Masters.

16.49   As part of the cooperative scheme in the Minch the Scottish Office Fisheries Protection Service and the Ministry of Defence both agreed to provide information to the Department of Transport on vessels which they see in the Minch on their routine flights. **We consider that this idea should be expanded to other areas and other types of aircraft, such as Ministry of Defence training flights and perhaps private small aircraft** (which could be asked to report to their local airfield, with the airfield passing on reports to HM Coastguard). When small extra costs are involved, the Department of Transport may need to consider some reimbursement. Pilots of commercial aircraft are already required through Notices to Airmen[3] to report any pollution which they see.

16.50   The Marine Pollution Control Unit has on contract seven dispersant spraying aircraft, supported by two small aircraft equipped with remote sensing equipment which are also used for routine surveillance. They are described in paragraph 21.49. It also shares with HM Coastguard the Channel surveillance plane described in paragraph 16.10. We discuss possible additional uses for these aircraft in paragraphs 21.90 – 21.92. The fixed costs are so large that we do not think it appropriate to suggest an additional aircraft for surveillance, but **we do recommend that the existing contract aircraft should be used to the full for routine surveillance. After a trial period of, say, one year the Department will need to assess whether detection rates are significantly increased and whether there is a noticeable deterrent value from more flying. If this assessment suggests it to be worthwhile, a higher level of aerial surveillance should then be sustained during subsequent years.** The marginal costs should be a comparatively small addition to the MPCU contract.

16.51   Satellites may also be usable to identify vessels, or at least to identify the routes which vessels follow. One problem with existing satellites is the difficulty of combining the resolution needed to observe shipping with the frequency of coverage required to make observations useful. **We recommend that the Department of Transport explores this possibility, and that the Ministry of Defence cooperates as fully as practicable.** Satellite technology is a rapidly advancing field, and **the Department of Transport should keep track of developments with a view to introducing relevant procedures as soon as they become available at reasonable cost.**

Policing through checks on vessels

16.52   Routes are plotted in pencil on charts by ships' officers, usually in port before voyages are undertaken. The route followed can be identified by fixes and amendments to the course line made at the time and by entries in the deck log book. Although it is possible for a Watch Officer to rub out the planned route and substitute the one actually taken after

---

[3] Notices to Airmen or NOTAMs are the equivalent of Notices to Mariners and are mandatory.

the event, it must be rare that anyone would bother doing so: and traces would be likely to remain on the chart. Ships' positions and log book entries showing courses and speeds would also need to be doctored to back up any deception.

16.53 We welcome the emphasis put on passage planning, which means that the navigator must spend time in port on setting the courses for the next voyage, particularly if the ship is to use an unfamiliar route. It would be unreasonable to ask that the route marked on charts should be left undisturbed until shortly before the vessel is ready to leave port for her next voyage, but checks should still be possible. **We recommend that ships' Masters and navigators should be prepared to demonstrate to Port State inspectors by reference to log books and charts the routes followed on the inward voyage. We would like to see a routine established whereby Port State inspectors normally ask the Master or Watch Officer to confirm that the route indicated on charts and in the log book had indeed been taken, but we appreciate that not all inspectors will necessarily have the relevant expertise.** We understand that on badly-run ships there is sometimes little evidence available on board to trace the voyage of the ship. **That should in itself be "clear grounds" (see paragraph 11.8) for a Port State inspector to look very carefully at a particular ship.** Port State inspectors should at the same time check that charts are fully up to date, as recommended in paragraph 13.24.

16.54 The specification for electronic charts (see paragraphs 13.28 – 13.32) has a requirement to retain track information and voyage details, so checking routes taken will be easier once electronic charts are introduced.

16.55 **The Department of Transport should consider the scope for routine checks on the routes taken by vessels into and out of particular ports.** For instance, tankers arriving at and leaving Milford Haven should *always* be asked to confirm that they use the approved route between Grassholme Island and The Smalls *en route* to and from St Brides Bay (see paragraphs 14.66 – 14.68).

16.56 **Any cases where routeing advice is ignored should be taken up with owners and Flag States, and the information that advice is being ignored should be logged on MSA's SIAS database and, if other Paris MOU countries agree, on the SIRENAC database as well. The information would become available for insurers and potential charterers in the way we recommend in paragraph 11.63.**

An expanded role for HM Coastguard

16.57 In this and previous chapters we have made many references to HM Coastguard (HMCG), who together with the Marine Pollution Control Unit (MPCU) make up the Coastguard Agency or COASTGUARD within the Department of Transport. Their current roles are described in Appendix I. We discuss the role of HM Coastguard in relation to pollution emergencies in Chapter 20.

16.58 In the previous chapter (paragraph 15.81) we recommend a review of the arrangements whereby HM Coastguard has immediate access to expert advice. That advice should be of great help in incidents of many kinds, but it may not always be enough.

16.59   Coastguards at Dover who "see" a vessel on CNIS which appears to be breaking – or about to break – the rules of the Traffic Separation Scheme do not **instruct** her to change her behaviour. This is partly for fear of undermining the authority of the Master and partly for fear of the consequences if the advice is accepted and something goes wrong. Both fears are understandable, but the present warning of

"Your track may contravene rule 10 of the Collision Regulations"

is not forceful enough, particularly when addressed to someone with poor English.

16.60   **When a Coastguard Watch Officer becomes aware of an impending infringement of the rules, from CNIS or any other source, he or she should say clearly that if the vessel continues on her present course, she will break specified rules. If the rules are already being broken, that should be stated quite clearly.**

16.61   **Coastguards should not normally give advice unless that advice is based on the assessment of an expert: there is no need for them to be qualified mariners themselves.** Nevertheless there may be rare occasions on which the giving of navigational advice is the best or only way of averting an accident if a ship is in real difficulties or if her crew do not know where they are. The incidents involving the tankers *SEIKO* in December 1993 and *ETILICO* in February 1994, described in Appendix L, illustrate the sort of problem which may occasionally arise.

16.62   **We recommend that the Department of Transport should accept the principle that on rare occasions Coastguards should give navigational advice, and that it may be impracticable for them to seek the assistance of an expert. Advice of this kind should only be given by the Senior Watch Officer when there appears to be no other sensible way of reducing unacceptable risks. Individual Coastguards should not be constrained in these exceptional circumstances by a fear of potential personal liability for the possible consequences of advice given in good faith which turns out to have been at fault. The Department of Transport should make it quite clear to staff that it stands behind them. However, the individual Coastguard should be prepared to justify his actions in disciplinary proceedings if the Department has reason to believe he acted recklessly.**

The role of harbour authorities in surveillance

16.63   Harbour authorities have powers to direct traffic within their boundaries and several have VTSs to help them do so. Some of these VTSs also overlook a larger area, such as the radar belonging to Orkney Islands Council Department of Harbours which monitors the Pentland Firth (see paragraph 14.35). We understand that it sensibly works very closely with HM Coastguard in those areas where it may have information which the Coastguard lacks. In some areas there may be a case for the Coastguard to have direct access to harbour authorities' radar, in the way we discuss in paragraph 16.30. But despite this close cooperation, both harbour authorities and Coastguards need to be quite clear on their respective responsibilities. The same may be true of harbour authorities and MSA.

16.64 Broadly speaking, harbour authorities will be responsible within their harbour limits and COASTGUARD outside them for search and rescue, for any monitoring and reporting of through traffic (though harbour authorities may need to monitor incoming traffic while it is still outside their harbour limits) and for dealing with pollution (which we discuss in Chapter 21). The two authorities may wish to come to an arrangement for delegating tasks in a particular area: but if they do so, there must be absolute clarity. MSA is responsible for taking formal or informal action against ships which contravene routeing measures or routeing advice, and while it may sometimes be dependent on harbour authorities and others for the necessary information, the task cannot sensibly be delegated for the reasons we set out in paragraph 16.46.

16.65 We understand, for instance, that the Shetland Islands Council is considering the installation of a permanent remote radar at Fitful Head at the southern end of Shetland, overlooking the Fair Isle Channel (see Diagram 1, page 193). If it decides to do so, it will need to discuss with COASTGUARD whether there is a need for ships reporting to the Coastguard under MAREP to be identified and "tagged": if so, it is clear that the Coastguard will need a screen. There would also need to be an arrangement satisfactory to both parties to ensure that any information about an impending or actual emergency was passed on to the local Coastguards as fast as possible so that they can take any action they believe to be necessary. It is essential that there is no confusion of roles in an emergency: that could lead to delay and exacerbate any problems. There would also need to be an agreement with MSA, perhaps as part of an informal surveillance exercise of the type we advocate in paragraph 16.45, to ensure that MSA was told of any identifiable vessels contravening routeing advice, so that it could take action. **We recommend that the Department of Transport sets up systems to ensure that it receives any relevant information on the behaviour of civil shipping outside harbour authority areas which other authorities may obtain. It is important that there is no doubt in anyone's mind that COASTGUARD is responsible for any short-term action and that MSA is responsible for any long-term action.**

Chapter 17

Fish Factory Ships

17.1   Many of the problems discussed in this Report are illustrated by the activities of the fish factory fleet, sometimes known as "Klondykers", which operated off Lerwick, in Shetland, during 1993.

The fish factory fleet

The fleet at Lerwick

17.2   The transshipment of pelagic sea fish[1] to factory ships normally occurs at ports or locations specified in licences issued under sea fisheries legislation[2]. Lerwick is such a port. For several years about 40 to 50 fish factory ships, mostly from Eastern Europe and what is now the Commonwealth of Independent States (CIS), plus a small number of reefers[3] have clustered around Lerwick in autumn and early winter. In 1989 ten incidents involving these vessels were reported to HM Coastguard: in 1990 the figure was eight, in 1991 it was twelve and in 1992 it was nine. The vessels range in size from some 2,000 grt to 26,000 grt, and accommodate up to about 800 people, most of them engaged in fish processing.

17.3   Plate 20 shows some of the fish factory fleet off Lerwick in November 1993.

The fleet around the UK coast

17.4   The fish factory ships operate seasonally, following the fishing fleet around Shetland, in the eastern Minch off Ullapool, in the North Sea off the coast of Grampian, in the Forth, off Middlesbrough and along the south coast from Falmouth to Weymouth. These areas have not yet experienced a fish factory fleet as big as the one off Shetland, but given the increase in available vessels since the dissolution of the USSR, some may yet do so. Although many of those areas offer more sheltered anchorages than Shetland, and in general the waters off Shetland suffer more severe weather than those further south, in principle the problems which have arisen there could arise at any other point where the fish factory ships operate.

The casualties

17.5   In the autumn of 1993 the number of factory ships at Lerwick doubled to about 90, with a few bunker supply ships and reefers in support. The reason for the increase is not

---

[1] "Pelagic sea fish" in this context means wet, whole fish of the following species: mackerel (*Scomber scombrus*), herring (*Clupea harengus*), sprat (*Clupea sprattus*), pilchard (*Sardina pilchardus*) and horse mackerel (*Trachurus trachurus*).
[2] The Sea Fish (Conservation) Act 1967 as amended and The Receiving of Trans-shipped Sea Fish (Licensing) Order 1982 as varied.
[3] Refrigerated vessels which ferry processed fish from some of the factory ships to the country of destination. Some factory ships deliver their own processed fish to port.

known: there were rather fewer fish than in earlier years. It was suggested to us that a possible reason was the process of economic and industrial change taking place in Eastern European countries and the liberalisation of trading arrangements. It was also suggested to us that many of the factory ships had made losses during the 1993 season and that a smaller fleet could be expected in future years.

17.6   While the fleet merely doubled in size, the number of incidents shot up to 34, including two casualties in which a total of 133 people were rescued; another serious incident had occurred during the summer. These three casualties were:

(a)   the Russian *CHERNOMORSKAYA SLAVA*, which caught fire while anchored off Lerwick on 29 July 1993: this caused no oil pollution but an extensive ten-day operation by the shore fire brigade was required;

(b)   the Latvian *LUNOHODS-1*, which was wrecked at the southern end of Lerwick Harbour on 9 November 1993 with 60 people on board. Pollution was minimal because the vessel had very little bunker oil on board. The weather was not unusual for the time of year; and

(c)   the Russian *BORODINSKOYE POLYE*, which was stranded on The Unicorn shoal just north of Lerwick Harbour on 17 November 1993 with 73 people on board. Again, the weather was not unusual for the time of year. An extensive operation by MPCU recovered well over half – 575 tonnes – of the 942 tonnes of bunker oil on board. The remainder escaped to sea. Some oil reached beaches nearby but its effects were not serious. The salvage and clean-up operation cost the UK authorities some £650,000.

More details on the second two of these incidents are in Appendix L. The accidents have been investigated by MAIB, who will report on them in due course.

17.7   In addition, on 30 August 1993 the Russian *KANDALAKSHA* grounded near Peterhead, on the Scottish coast north of Aberdeen, and some bunker oil escaped. In January 1993 the Latvian *DARIUS* was on passage from Klaipeda in Lithuania towards Ullapool when she suffered main engine damage caused by her propeller racing in heavy weather (storm force 10, very rough sea and heavy swell). She was not totally disabled but required tug assistance to Shetland, which was nearer than Ullapool and to leeward. Further details of *KANDALAKSHA* are in Appendix L.

The condition of the fleet

17.8   Until the dissolution of the Soviet Union the fish factory ships formed a fairly coherent fleet, with some degree of mutual support. They are now privately owned and operated on a shoestring. It is often difficult for the UK authorities to contact their owners, and their UK agents (who do not act as shipping agents in the usual sense) have limited responsibility and authority.

Safety

17.9 Following the loss of the *LUNOHODS-1* and the *BORODINSKOYE POLYE* within ten days of each other and only five miles apart, the SGO (as MSA then was) arranged for an inspection of the fleet to be carried out. One inspection is described in Appendix E. The surveyors found that all the ships they visited had all the essential equipment in place to remain at anchor and to manoeuvre as necessary. None appeared to be in imminent danger. However, many had insufficient draught, because of inadequate ballast. This was because much of the tank capacity which could be used for ballasting was used to retain the dirty slops from the fish processing plant and engine room bilges. The fuel tanks could also be used for ballasting. The Masters were reluctant to use either, because the dirty ballast water would have to be discharged either ashore or out at sea, but could do so in an emergency. Many also had very low levels of bunker oil: while this would minimise any possible pollution, it might also be inadequate to get the ships out of difficulties.

17.10 Beyond that, some of the factory ships were in excellent condition with good manning, equipment and morale. Others were dirty (to the extent that some engine rooms were a fire hazard), rat or cockroach infested and with poor crew morale. Following the inspectors' visits there was evidence that the problems of the worst ships were being tackled.

Insurance

17.11 The worst problem from the point of view of the UK authorities was that many, possibly most, of the ships were uninsured: we understand that the casualties were uninsured. When they were State owned they were insured either through P & I Clubs or directly by the State concerned: private owners had evidently not replaced that system, presumably for financial reasons. The payment for the use of the fish factory vessels was usually by bartering fish for processing, and this system may have left little or no money available for insurance. Insurance premiums may also have been disproportionate to the market value of the vessels concerned.

17.12 Once the vessels got into trouble they appeared to be of no value, and of little further interest, to their owners. Some of the crew of the *DARIUS* were unable to leave Shetland for several months after she was arrested in January 1993 because they had no money to pay their fares, and they existed on the charity of the islanders. Rats escaping from the *DARIUS* infested the area, and the cost of dealing with that infestation could not easily be reclaimed. The cost of salvage and repairs was finally met in December 1993, nearly a year after the *DARIUS* first got into difficulties.

17.13 The owners of both the *LUNOHODS-1* and the *BORODINSKOYE POLYE* similarly washed their hands of their vessels. The UK Government will seek to recover the costs of pollution prevention and salvage from the owners, but as there is no insurance this is likely to be a difficult process. A claim against the owners of the *BORODINSKOYE POLYE* is being pursued through diplomatic channels.

Controls over the factory fleet

The transshipment licensing system

17.14   The transshipment licensing system is operated by the Scottish Fisheries Protection Agency, by the Ministry of Agriculture, Fisheries and Food (MAFF) in English and Welsh waters and by the Department of Agriculture for Northern Ireland. Its purpose is to ensure that certain pelagic species taken from UK waters (that is, up to 200 miles from the coast where no agreed boundary with another country's waters intervenes, as described in Chapter 5) are transshipped at certain specified locations, where the amounts of fish involved can be readily monitored for quota management and conservation reasons. Licences are issued free and on request to any Master who agrees to meet the conditions attached to the licence. The primary legislation does not envisage the conditions applying to anything other than the management and regulation of fisheries.

17.15   The fleet at Lerwick included both licensed and unlicensed fish factory vessels. The unlicensed ones did not take part in the transshipment of fish, but remained available in case the supply of fish increased: we understand that they did not normally stay for long. If required, the unlicensed vessels would have been granted licences automatically. This system allows for some flexibility to cope with unexpected developments in the movement and availability of fish.

17.16   The factory ships are not, of course, on "innocent passage": they are not on passage at all. Licensed ships clearly have a legitimate reason to be where they are, but unlicensed ones could quite properly be asked to move on in the same way that "parked" tankers in Lyme Bay were asked to move on (see paragraph 5.29). The difficulty here is that they would be likely to ask immediately for a transshipment licence, and on the current procedures and assumptions they would get one at once, giving them a legitimate reason to remain.

The harbour authority

17.17   In the Shetland area, fish can only be transshipped within the area of the Lerwick Harbour Trust, and the factory ships at Shetland therefore must enter the port area and pay port dues. The Harbour Trust monitors the movements of the fleet on radar and through monitoring VHF radio, the use of its own harbour vessels and occasional helicopter surveillance.

Safety inspections

17.18   MSA has the right to inspect vessels in territorial waters, but its powers of detention are limited to ships within a port. The definition of a "port" for this purpose is interpreted narrowly: we return to this point later in this chapter. MSA has no power of prior approval. Defects in the ships found in inspections were reported to the Masters and State maritime Administrations. Any unsafe ships would have been reported through diplomatic channels to the Flag State.

Action taken

17.19   Although the surveyors had no powers of detention and thus no effective power to insist on improvements, the inspection of a large number of vessels, in which the Masters and crews willingly cooperated, did appear to have a marked effect on standards. Ballasting and bunker levels were improved, as were cleanliness and maintenance.

17.20   The Marine Accident Investigation Branch (MAIB) issued interim recommendations on fish factory ships on 26 November 1993. It recommended that Lerwick Harbour Trust should expand its existing Multi Lingual Information Packs and ensure that they were issued to all fish factory ships visiting the area. The Trust was also advised to visit all vessels as they arrived. The Trust, which is not a large organisation, is complying with the recommendations so far as is possible. We understand that work on the Information Pack is well advanced, and that the Harbour Trust will include in it a requirement that fuel oil transfers take place only with the Trust's authority, which is to be given by means of an "Oil Transfer Request" form which must be submitted by the Master. As we make clear in paragraphs 8.76 – 8.78, there is plenty which can go wrong in a bunkering operation and vigilance is needed. The proposed Merchant Shipping (Ship to Ship Transfers) Regulations, which we discuss in Chapter 8, would ensure that bunkering operations could only take place within the limits of the harbour area and under the control of the Harbour Trust.

17.21   The Department of Transport accepted MAIB's recommendations to consider whether the licensing system described above could be adapted, to take action through Flag States, and to consider the problem for the UK as a whole.

17.22   MSA has also issued straightforward Guidelines to the Masters of the factory ships. These are reproduced in Appendix F. A Russian language version was due to become available in April 1994.

17.23   The Scottish Fisheries Protection Agency discussed the safety problems with the Herring Buyers Association and its agents, at which it was clear that the industry was anxious to cooperate. It has given unqualified support to the adoption of the Guidelines.

The benefits and problems of factory ships

The importance of the factory ships to UK interests

17.24   The total value of the UK pelagic catch is around £42 million a year and is of vital importance to the fishing industry and those who depend on it. The fish factory fleet buys some 40 per cent of UK mackerel and some 75 per cent of UK herring, including fish which may not be easily saleable on the domestic market. There is no readily available alternative market for them.

The problems caused by the factory ships

17.25   While the ships are not fundamentally unsafe, many of them are in a far from satisfactory condition, and their very density in a small area must give rise to increased risks of collision or other casualty in bad weather. There is also an increased risk to life-boatmen and rescue helicopter crews: the Masters of neither the *LUNOHODS-1* nor the *BORODINSKOYE POLYE* knew the precise number of people on board when their vessels went aground, and the rescuers risked their own lives searching for people who did not exist. The large numbers of people potentially involved could overstretch both the emergency rescue services and the medical services in Shetland and elsewhere.

17.26   Substantial problems also arise from the lack of insurance of many of these ships. Although the traditional form of salvage, on the principle of No cure: No pay, was not significantly influenced by insurance, newer arrangements for salvage (described in Chapter 20) are underpinned by insurance, as is the principle that the polluter pays. Insurance is even more important for elderly ships of little intrinsic value to their owners. Without it, salvors are likely to be reluctant to intervene when there is no insurance to guarantee payment, with possible consequences in terms of increased pollution and perhaps loss of life. Others, such as those who have to cope with infestations of rats, may also find it difficult to recover their costs. The polluted, rather than the polluter, would have to pay.

Changes needed

17.27   We commend the action taken so far, but more is needed. It is apparent to us that:

(a)   there were in 1993 too many vessels clustered together in a small area for safety, given the prevailing weather conditions; we understand that there were also more than were necessary for the quantities of fish which were or were likely to become available. This may prove to be atypical;

(b)   safety standards are not high enough;

(c)   MSA's Guidelines reproduced in Appendix F are a useful but very basic guide to safe operation. We welcome the apparent willingness of the fish factory fleet Masters and their agents to comply with the Guidelines, but simple compliance is not enough, even if it could be guaranteed;

(d)   the lack of insurance is a serious problem which must be tackled; and

(e)   any solutions should apply equally to all transshipment areas.

17.28   We believe that a system is needed to ensure that fish factory ships do not operate anywhere in UK waters unless they reach a minimum standard of safety and unless they are insured. In an ideal world the owners, or failing them the Flag States, would ensure that these simple and reasonable conditions were met. Although the problems are being discussed following the incidents in Shetland, it is not clear that effective action will be taken. So the UK Government must act.

17.29   We discuss in Chapter 18 the general issue of insurance and in Chapter 11 the system of Port State Control which gives States some powers to check the safety of vessels in their ports. We do not think that the general solutions recommended in those chapters are the best solution to the problems of factory ships. While our recommendations in Chapter 15 on the compulsory reporting to HM Coastguard of specified failures should be of significant assistance in any future incidents, we do not think that this goes far enough for these particular vessels. We are also keen to see a simple and evidently fair system which can be easily understood by the Masters and crews of factory ships, whose command of English may be limited.

Changes to the licensing system

17.30   **We believe that the best solution is to require that transshipment can only take place in any transshipment area in UK waters if the ship concerned carries adequate insurance and if she meets basic – and clearly spelled out – safety and pollution-prevention criteria to the satisfaction of MSA.** The criteria should include safe bunkering procedures. Permission for transshipment should be revokable if the conditions are subsequently breached: inspection is likely to be a necessary part of ensuring that they are not breached.

17.31   **We consider that much the simplest – and possibly the only effective – way of achieving this is to amend Section 4 of the Sea Fish (Conservation) Act 1967 so that transshipment licences can only be issued to vessels which meet basic safety standards.** We appreciate that the Fisheries Departments might prefer not to become involved in safety issues, but we believe that this is unavoidable. They could and should be advised by MSA. A single permit, covering both safety and fishery issues, is far simpler for the user than two different systems, and thus very much in line with the Government policy of eliminating unnecessary red tape. **We also believe that the Fisheries Departments should limit the number of licences issued in relation to the quantities of fish available, for reasons of safety and to limit congestion.**

17.32   In accordance with the principle that the polluter – or the potential polluter – should pay for pollution prevention measures, **the reasonable costs of checking the safety of the ship and her insurance, and of any inspection, should be charged to the vessel concerned.** It might be simplest to achieve this through a fee, payable on application, for the licence adequate to cover all costs. It may also be necessary to enlarge the approved transshipment areas for safety reasons, or to increase the numbers of such areas. **The Fisheries Departments should agree those areas with the Department of Transport and any harbour authorities affected.**

Changes in advance of legislation

17.33   **We believe that a revised system must be in place before the winter of 1994-95.** We accept that new legislation probably cannot be in force by then but, as a second best, we believe that the customary practice under which transshipment licences are issued on request should be changed. **The Fisheries Departments should declare straight away that from a specified date, well before next winter, they will not** consider any application for a transshipment licence unless the Master concerned produces evidence that his vessel is adequately insured and reaches minimum safety standards. Any licences issued under existing rules before that date should not run beyond that date.

Consequences of change

17.34 We recognise that these proposals may increase the operating costs of the factory ships and thus affect the prices at which UK fish is sold to them. We are comfortable with this because it is consistent with the polluter pays principle. At present, part of the costs of the fishing industry are quite wrongly borne by those who do not necessarily benefit from it: the general taxpayer and those who live in or otherwise benefit from the amenities of Shetland and other areas where fish factory ships congregate. That must be changed.

Unlicensed vessels

17.35 Changes to the licensing system would not directly affect unlicensed fish factory ships, though limits on the numbers of licences issued would limit the attractions of remaining in the transshipment areas without applying for a licence. We have already recommended (paragraph 5.30) that the UK Government should examine and if necessary strengthen its powers under domestic legislation to move on "parked" vessels. **It should also use those powers to ensure that unlicensed fish factory ships are instructed to leave UK waters when that is in the best interests of safety or the prevention of pollution.**

Changes to the definition of a port

17.36 In paragraph 17.18 we point out that MSA has the right to inspect vessels in territorial waters, but no power to detain them unless they are in port. The problems this gives rise to could in theory affect any aspect of Port State Control (see Chapter 11) but they appear only to have arisen in the context of fish factory ships.

17.37 The precise meaning of the word "port" is unclear. SOLAS Part I Regulation 19 (a) reads:

> "Every ship when in a port of another Party is subject to control ..."

without defining what is meant by a port. Subparagraph (c) continues:

> "... the officer carrying out the control shall take steps to ensure that the ship shall not sail until it can proceed to sea or leave the port for the purposes of proceeding to the appropriate repair yard ..."

which implies that a port is a specified area, but not necessarily a small one. MARPOL[4] has a similar provision that a ship is subject to the regulations while in the ports or offshore terminals of a State. The Paris Memorandum does not define "port".

---

[4] Article 6(2).

17.38   UNCLOS Article 220 gives a Coastal State power to prosecute for violation of its laws implementing international laws on pollution control. It begins:

> "When a vessel is voluntarily within a port or at an off-shore terminal of a State ..."

17.39   We conclude that a wider definition of a "port" than the limits of permanent harbour works is possible in UK law in the context of Port State Control.

17.40   UK law is very unspecific. "Port" is defined in Section 742 of the Merchant Shipping Act 1894 merely as including a place. In *Hunter v. Northern Marine Insurance Company*[5], where the meaning of the word "port" was in issue, Lord Herschell said that "A port is a place where a vessel can lie in a position of more or less shelter from the elements, with a view to the loading or discharge of cargo."

17.41   The power to detain in Section 692 of the 1894 Act does not say that a detention must take place only in port, though it implies it since the only offence is of proceeding to sea or taking a person on board to sea, and the words are not apt for a case when a ship is already at sea. The Department of Transport has taken the words as meaning that MSA's powers of detention extend only to the area within harbour walls or some fairly sheltered area. This does not necessarily equate to statutory harbour limits: for instance, the northern and southern limits of Lerwick harbour area are some six nautical miles apart and enclose a large area. The limits of larger ports can be substantially greater.

17.42   We believe that the UK Government should specify the areas within which the power to detain can be applied, by defining "port" for this purpose. The easiest solution would be to tie the definition of a port to an existing delineation. We recommend that a port, for the purposes of the power to detain, should be defined by legislation as "the area within harbour authority limits".

17.43   We recognise that this will give MSA a power to detain over a wide area within the statutory limits of some large ports, and that in some parts of that area there would be practical difficulties in exercising it. We do not believe that this matters, as the use of the power would be discretionary and we would expect it to be used sensibly. But we would have no objection if a more appropriate statutory definition of a port for this purpose were devised.

---

[5] *Hunter v. Northern Marine Ins. Co. (1888) 13 App Cas 717.*

Chapter 18

Insurance

Introduction

18.1   At the outset of the Inquiry it was put to us that the marine insurance industry ought to be able to give clearer signals to shipowners to improve standards. To many it seems obvious that insurers are in a strong position to influence the shipping industry. They must be able to reward good operators by lowering premiums and penalise those with a poor or unproven record by increasing premiums – rather like a no claims bonus on car insurance. It was suggested to us that the Government, through regulatory mechanisms, could cause the UK marine insurance industry to take a greater interest in improving shipping standards and that such action would be very effective because of London's leading role in the world market. This is all fine in theory but not so simple in practice.

18.2   The first point to make is that the "no claims bonus" analogy is a false one. Automobile insurance classifies cars into groups and then, within those groups, classifies owners by their claims records. This is the tariff system. There is no tariff system in marine insurance. Although marine insurers follow similar principles to automobile insurers they do so in a much more sophisticated fashion. Rather than fixing premiums on the basis of groups of similar vehicles, marine insurers assess each risk individually taking account amongst other things of the owner's claims record. There is thus a real maritime equivalent of the no claims bonus built into the system, but it is not immediately apparent.

18.3   By contrast, the scope for Government intervention in the London market is more apparent than real. The Government has established the regulatory framework for all insurance, including marine insurance, underwritten in the UK. It has also negotiated international liability and compensation systems for oil pollution, and attempted to do so, thus far unsuccessfully, for pollution by hazardous and noxious substances (see paragraphs 19.40 – 19.44). It has not sought to intervene in the operation of the marine insurance market or in hull or cargo insurance for a number of reasons.

18.4   Marine insurance is an extremely complicated industry. The London market for hull and cargo insurance and reinsurance is shared between Lloyd's and the commercial insurance companies of the Institute of London Underwriters. There are also the Protection and Indemnity Associations (P & I Clubs) which provide virtually all of a shipowner's liability cover.

18.5   London is the leading international centre for marine insurance but its position is open to challenge by competition from overseas markets. London must operate within a worldwide context and seek to maintain its competitive advantage within a world market. It is in the national interest that it does so. We believe that further unilateral regulation would succeed only in making the London market uncompetitive. There would be little benefit for shipping safety if significant business was lost to overseas competitors operating without comparable restrictions.

18.6   This is not to say that underwriters cannot and do not influence the shipping industry by imposing higher rates of premium, higher excesses or by refusing to accept the risk. After all, underwriters do not want to lose money by insuring bad risks. However, success in this respect breeds competitive pressures and they in turn breed misplaced optimism. Hence the cyclical nature of the profitability of the insurance market. We believe that there is room for further improvement in the assessment of risk, and trust that recent improvements will form part of an ongoing process which will temper optimism with realism to the benefit of the market as well as of safety at sea. Inevitably, some types of insurer are in a better position than others to influence the decisions made by shipowners and charterers. Insurance represents not one lever but several.

Hull insurance

18.7   Hull and machinery insurance covers the loss of, or damage to, a vessel and its machinery. It does not cover cargo but may cover some third party liabilities. Standard Marine Insurance Clauses are extremely varied and are often amended to delete or modify the protection which would otherwise be afforded. These modifications and the fundamental questions of premiums and deductibles are the subject of commercial judgements and dealings within a competitive international market.

18.8   The leading underwriters will, to a large extent, base a premium on experience. When fixing a premium for the first time, the underwriter will consider the age of the vessel and the shipowner's operational record. A vessel or owner with a bad record will be offered more onerous terms. The underwriter will also take account of the physical characteristics of the vessel, her classification, and where she will be trading.

18.9   Hull insurers have more direct contact with shipowners than, for example, reinsurers but the extent to which they are able to influence standards depends on their competitive position. Insurers want to avoid paying out large amounts in claims but equally do not want to turn down business. Some insurers are more optimistic than others and in a competitive market the shipowner is able to shop around.

18.10   In recent years, the increase in the size and number of claims has created a much tighter market and many hull underwriters have become far more careful in assessing the risks they insure. They have realised that they cannot necessarily rely either upon the inspection work of classification societies or upon Port and Flag States and IMO to enforce standards. The significant rise in the numbers of casualties in the late 1980s forced hull insurers to look more closely at the actual condition of the vessels they were insuring. In December 1991 the major insurers asked the Salvage Association to begin carrying out full Structural Condition Surveys. Only 20 per cent of the vessels examined passed first time without the need for recommendations (see paragraph 11.62). Hull insurers also now recognise the importance of the "human element" in assessing risk and are giving increasing

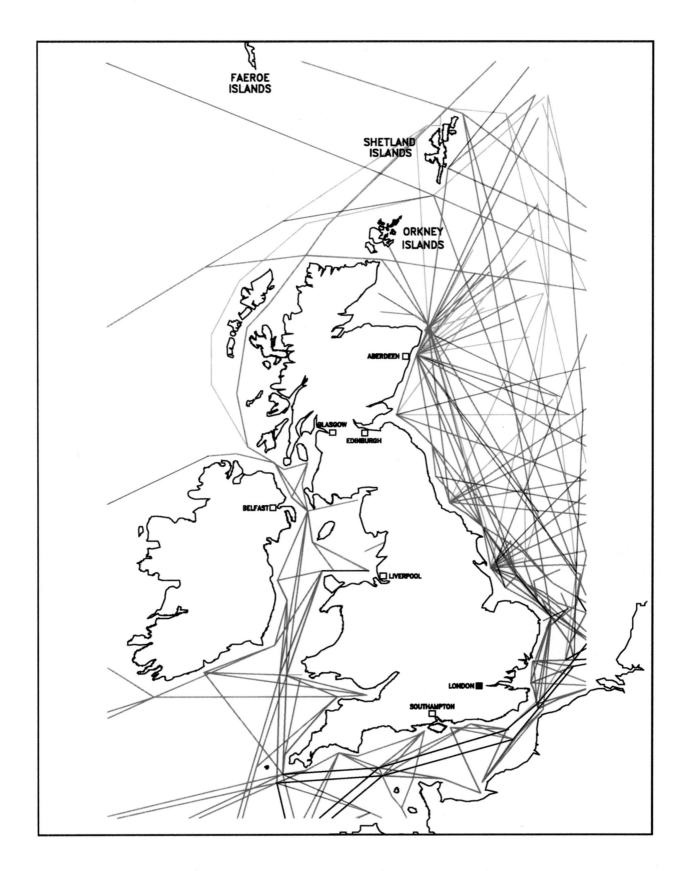

Key: Merchant vessels excluding fishing and ferry traffic

	Less than 0.5 vessels per day
	Between 0.5 & 1.0 vessels per day
	Between 1 & 10 vessels per day
	Between 10 & 30 vessels per day
	Between 30 & 150 vessels per day

Plate 1: Frequency of Shipping in UK and Adjacent Waters (DNV Technica Ltd). See also Appendix H.

Plate 2: *HM Coastguard monitoring Channel Navigation Information Service (CNIS) radar screens, Dover (Department of Transport).*

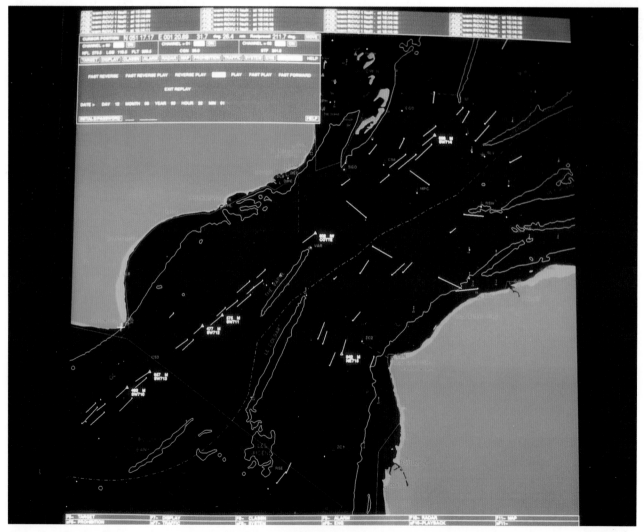

Plate 3: *Radar display information from CNIS at Dover, at 22.01 on 12 June 1993. Numbered images are "tags" for identified vessels. The line extending from the vessel shows her projected position in six minutes' time on the basis of current course and speed (see paragraph 16.9). (Defence Research Agency).*

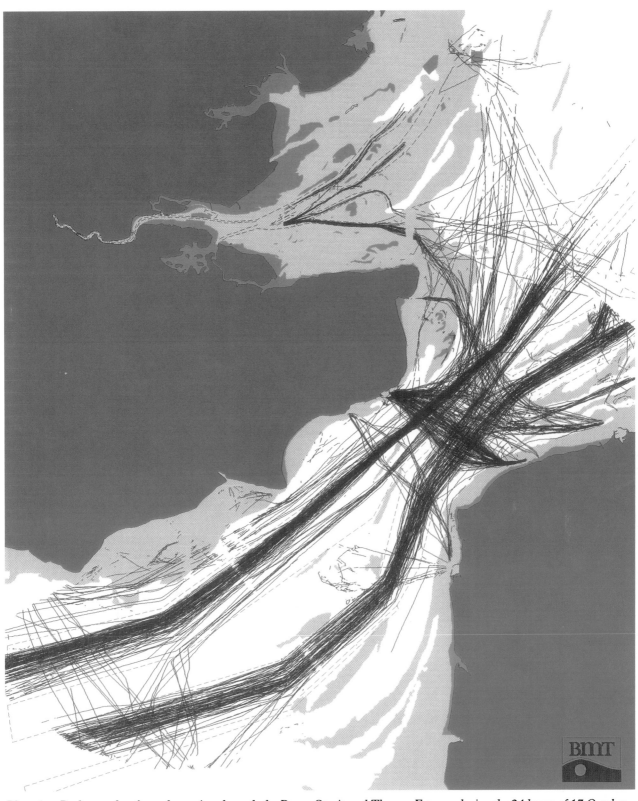

Plate 4: Radar tracks of vessels passing through the Dover Strait and Thames Estuary during the 24 hours of 17 October 1993 (BMT Group Ltd).

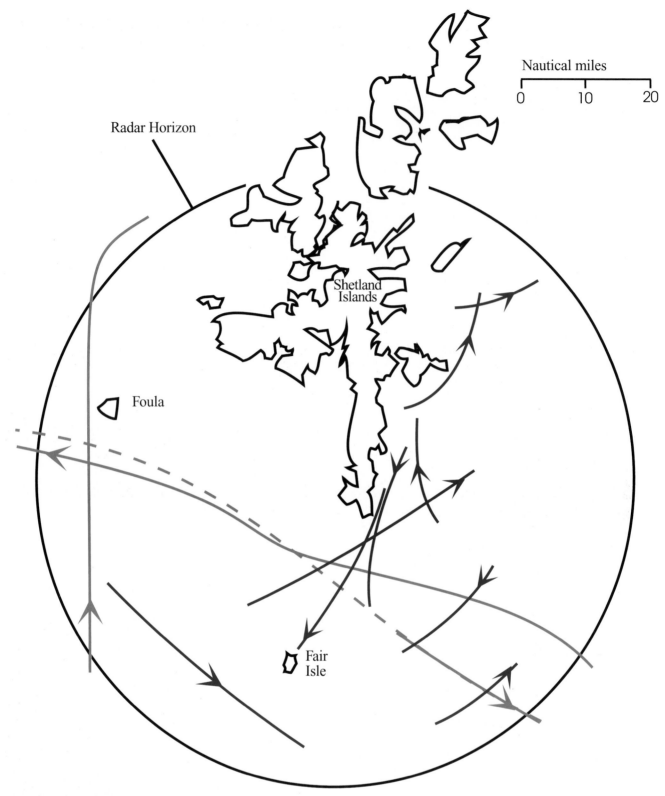

SHETLAND ISLANDS—not to scale

Diagram showing tracks of vessels from radar at Fitful Head on 14 June 1993, the busiest 24 hours of a 10 day survey.
Fishing vessels have been excluded.

Tankers are shown in red.
(dotted line shows vessel track in earlier 24 hour period of 13 June 1993.)

Non-tankers are shown in blue.
(weaker radar echoes from small vessels limit the distance over which the radar is able to track.)

Plate 5:   (Defence Research Agency).

Plate 6:   Bulk carrier VINE, 266 metres long and 114,975 deadweight tonnes (P&O).

Plate 7:   Container ship JERVIS BAY, 292 metres long and 59,093 deadweight tonnes (P&O).

VLCC Size Comparison

The VLCC shown here is 351 metres long and can carry 310,000 tonnes of crude oil. If the cargo space was loaded with petrol it would fill the equivalent of seven million cars. (based on a 55 litre fuel tank).

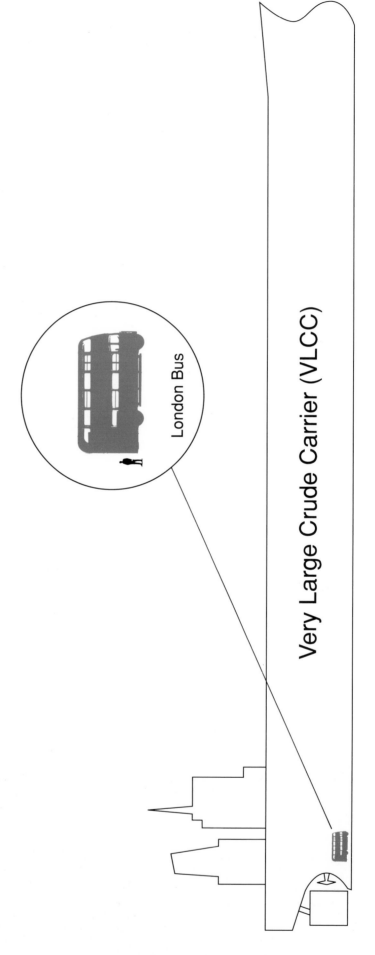

London Bus

Very Large Crude Carrier (VLCC)

Plate 8: *(Shell International Shipping Limited, London).*

Plate 9: Tanker EMMA MAERSK (343 metres long and 298,900 deadweight tonnes) being assisted by the Smit harbour tugs KWINTEBANK and TEXELBANK, Rotterdam/Europoort (Mr Hans de Jong, Smit International BV, Rotterdam). Compare size with Plate 8.

Defects found during Port State Control inspection of MV STELLA, Southampton, November 1993 (MSA). See also Appendix E.

Plate 12: Serious corrosion in Number 6 (port) ballast tank.

Plate 10: Hatch-end girder supporting brackets completely detached from the main deck.

Plate 11: Serious corrosion in Number 2 (port) ballast tank.

Plate 13: *MPCU Dakota DC3 spraying dispersant on the sea (Atlantic Air Transport Ltd).*

Plate 14: *Tanker PHILLIPS OKLAHOMA on fire in the Humber estuary, 1989 (United Towing Ltd, Hull).*

Plate 15: *Fish farms affected by oil sheen from the BRAER, Clift Sound, Shetland, January 1993 (Shetland Islands Council).*

Plate 16: *Oil slick from the ROSEBAY, Bigbury Bay, May 1990 (Nigel Rolstone, West of England Photo-News).*

Plate 17:   Removal of bulk oil from rocky foreshore using buckets (International Tanker Owners Pollution Federation Ltd, ITOPF).

Plate 18:   Clean-up of moderately oiled sandy beach by a small team working in sections, assisted by a front-end loader (ITOPF).

Plate 19:   Dead gannet caught in rubbish (Royal Society for the Protection of Birds).

Plate 20:   Fish factory ships in northern anchorage, Lerwick Harbour, November 1993 (MPCU).

attention to shipowners' flagging, crewing, maintenance and other operating policies, despite the difficulties in quantifying such aspects.

18.11   Obviously, there must be a correlation between future risk and the past level of claims because a high proportion of incidents giving rise to claims are avoidable. Other things being equal, vessels with high standards of management, operation and maintenance will be involved in fewer incidents with the potential for giving rise to claims than will those of lower standards. But whether a "near miss" becomes a "hit" may be fortuitous and, given an unmerited slice of good luck, it is entirely possible for a substandard vessel to trade for some time without serious incident. "Hits" feature in a claims record. "Near misses" do not. A vessel's or owner's claims record is thus only one of the factors to be taken into account in assessing the risk. We welcome the fact that hull insurers are now taking a closer and more direct interest in both the structural and operational quality of shipping they insure. **We believe that it is in the interests of insurers as well as those who want to eliminate substandard shipping that premiums are more closely related to quality and actual risk.** We fully support the joint efforts of the Lloyd's Underwriters' Association and Institute of London Underwriters both in instituting full scale structural surveys and condition surveys and in issuing questionnaires to brokers in an attempt to find out more about the operating policies of owners about whom they know very little. The questionnaire covers details not only of the vessels themselves but also aspects of crewing, training and communication.

Agreed values

18.12   The insured value of a vessel in the event of a total loss is agreed at the time of underwriting and fixed for the period of insurance. Not surprisingly the actual market value of many vessels fluctuates during the insurance period because of variations in the market or changes in condition. But in many cases underwriters will agree a value in excess of a vessel's current market value. There are a number of very good reasons for this. The hull insurance may include an element to cover loss of trade in the event of a total loss of a vessel. Again, the vessel may be mortgaged for more than her market value because of the fall in ship values. The mortgagee depends for his security upon the survival of the vessel and will reasonably require total loss insurance to the value of the shipowner's indebtedness. In some cases an owner may wish to repair a vessel at greater cost than the vessel will be worth when repaired because, for example, it will be difficult to find a suitable replacement vessel. It is quite right that hull insurance should take account of these elements.

18.13   However, an owner's enthusiasm for maintaining his vessel may be blunted if he knows that the consequence of the loss of the vessel will be ameliorated by the payment of a high agreed value well in excess of her market value. There is no evidence that this a significant problem but we are concerned that widespread use of unrealistic agreed values should not tempt owners by providing an easy way out of financial difficulties. **We believe that hull insurers should examine the problem and do everything they can to solve it.** It would, for example, be possible to provide that the insurer's liability in the event of a total loss should not exceed the amount of any sums lent on the security of the vessel or the vessel's market value immediately prior to the casualty plus x per cent, whichever is the greater.

Cargo insurance

18.14   Cargo insurance covers the loss suffered by the cargo owner in the event of total or partial loss of the cargo during the course of the voyage. In the event of a claim, the cargo owner, or more often his insurer, will seek (by no means always successfully) to recover the loss from the shipowner involved, usually on the grounds that the loss resulted from a failure by the shipowner to exercise due diligence to make the ship seaworthy. Underwriters base the premium for a particular cargo on a number of factors including consideration of management, ownership and the class and age of the carrying vessel. This is recognised in the requirements of the Institute Classification Clause. Where vessels do not conform to these requirements a scale of additional premiums is advised.

18.15   Originally, the Institute Classification Clause required the vessel to be classed with specifically named classification societies having full membership of the International Association of Classification Societies (IACS) and fixed an age limit of 15 years for those not operating on a Liner Service. But increased casualty figures for bulk carriers and large mineral oil tankers led to changes to the Clause. From 13 April 1992 the Clause has included an additional requirement limiting the age of bulk carriers and combination carriers to 10 years. Vessels which do not meet this requirement will be subject to an additional premium. There is also a new category for mineral oils carried in tankers over 10 years old in excess of 50,000 grt. The revised Clause and the scale of additional premiums has received wide acceptance by the international insurance community, with the notable exception of the United States which has its own arrangements.

18.16   The extent to which cargo underwriters can influence the behaviour of the shipping industry must be limited by the very nature of cargo insurance. The insurer will have no direct contact with the shipowner. He may be asked to insure goods which are already afloat or are in transit, the carrying vessel already having been nominated. Again he may be insuring a cargo owner who is not himself involved in arranging the transit of the goods. Last, but by no means least, it is immaterial to some cargo owners whether the goods arrive in sound or damaged condition or indeed whether they arrive at all, provided that they will be paid by the purchaser of the goods, the insurers or a combination of the two. The effect of increased cargo premiums is not to be ignored but the pressure which it brings to bear on owners of substandard vessels is indirect and limited.

18.17   We have been told that there is a highly competitive cargo insurance market. This further weakens the cargo underwriter's ability to influence shipping quality beyond avoiding patently unseaworthy ships. If a London underwriter takes a much stricter line over quality he will only succeed in losing the business to a competitor.

18.18   We appreciate that the insurance market is cyclical and that at some times cargo insurers are in a weaker position to influence improved standards than at others. We recognise that the circumstances of cargo insurance may limit the influence which underwriters may have. We also accept that the Institute Classification Clause is an understandable response to a perceived increase in risk. **Nevertheless, we would seek to encourage underwriters to achieve a more accurate assessment of risk, both in their own**

interests and to make it clear to those involved in buying and selling cargo that the selection of vessel will be reflected in the level of premium. Age alone is a blunt instrument for determining differentials in premiums. If cargo owners are given no incentive to discriminate between operators of similar types of older vessel they are likely to select the operator offering the cheapest freight rate. That operator may be able to offer a cheaper rate because his standards of maintenance and operation are lower. It must be in the interests of both insurers and those working to improve shipping quality that premiums are linked as closely as possible to actual risk.

Protection and Indemnity Clubs

18.19   P & I Clubs differ from all other marine insurers in that there is no "we" and "they" – "we" pay the premium and "they" pay the claims. Every member is both an insured and an insurer with an interest in seeing that the claims of his fellow members are as infrequent and as small as possible. The general underwriting principles of a Club are laid down by the Club's Board of Directors (or Committee) which is elected from the Club's shipowner members. The job of applying these principles to each individual fleet is entrusted to full-time Managers. They fix the premium rating for each fleet in accordance with their appreciation of the risk that each member brings to the Club.

18.20   This rating, which determines the proportion of the Club's liabilities which falls on each member, is highly individualistic and takes account of numerous factors. It is reviewed and revised annually. The Board of Directors decides what proportion of these premium ratings will be called up at the beginning of the year and how much will be left until later. Usually either 60 per cent or 80 per cent will be called in advance leaving the remainder to be called later once the size of overall claims for the year becomes apparent. If more money is needed, above 100 per cent of the premium ratings, the Board will meet the deficit either by using money from accumulated reserves or imposing further supplementary calls on all members at a standard percentage rate. If claims are lower than expected, the Board may decide that too much money has been called in and that a standard percentage should be returned to members.

18.21   Of all the insurers, the P & I Clubs have the best opportunity to, and do, influence shipping standards because every member is acutely aware that the extent of the call which he faces as an insurer will be determined by the standards of management, maintenance and operation which he and his fellow members adopt.

18.22   Although P & I Clubs compete with each other for business, the 18 members of the International Group of P & I Clubs[1] pool their larger risks. Some P & I Clubs operate

[1] The members are: The American Steamship Owners Mutual Protection and Indemnity Association Inc; Assuranceforeningen Gard (Gjensidig); Assuranceforeningen Skuld (Gjensidig); The Britannia Steam Ship Insurance Association Ltd; The Japan Ship Owners' Mutual Protection and Indemnity Association; Liverpool and London Steamship Protection and Indemnity Association Ltd; The London Steam-Ship Owners' Mutual Insurance Association Ltd; The Newcastle Protection & Indemnity Association; The North of England Protecting and Indemnity Association Ltd; The Shipowners' Mutual Protection and Indemnity Association (Luxembourg); Skuld Mutual Protection and Indemnity Association (Bermuda) Ltd; The Standard Steamship Owners' Protection and Indemnity Association Ltd; The Standard Steamship Owners' Protection and Indemnity Association (Bermuda) Ltd; The Steamship Mutual Underwriting Association Ltd; The Steamship Mutual Underwriting Association (Bermuda) Ltd; Sveriges Ångfartygs Assurans Förening; The United Kingdom Mutual Steam Ship Assurance Association (Bermuda) Ltd; and The West of England Ship Owners Mutual Insurance Association (Luxembourg).

outside the International Group but all the most important Clubs are members and together they insure over 90 per cent of the world's ocean-going tonnage. The pooling arrangement is regulated by a contractual agreement which defines the risks that are to be pooled and exactly how they are to be shared between the participating Clubs. The International Group Pool covers claims from $3 million upwards with no upper limit, except for oil pollution where cover is limited to $500 million. For individual claims over $25 million, the Pool purchases reinsurance from the fixed premium market. The upper level of this reinsurance contract is $500 million for oil pollution and a little over $1 billion for all other types of claims (above which the risk remains with the Pool but is not reinsured). Owners can obtain additional cover of $200 million for oil pollution, to meet the clause in major oil charterers' charterparties that cover should be $700 million, but this is provided on the fixed premium market not by the Clubs.

18.23   When a shipowner applies to become a member of a P & I Club the Club must first decide whether to accept the fleet at all. Only if the Club underwriter has decided that the fleet is of an acceptable standard will he come up with a proposed rate. In establishing a rate the underwriter will look at management quality, where the vessel will trade and the nationality of the crew. The age and flag of the vessel may also be considered but can be misleading indicators. The rating will depend to a great extent on the previous experience of the Manager of similar vessels. Factors such as changes in trading patterns or changes in types of cargo are taken into consideration in renewing the ratings of existing members but the claims record is the major feature in renewal rating. A member with a bad record will see his premium rating increase the next year by an amount which reflects the Manager's revised appreciation of the risk that the member is bringing to the Club in the light of his actual claims experience as shown by the member's claims record. A member with a better than expected record will receive a lower rating. Broadly speaking this is the same principle as a no claims bonus but is far more sophisticated because the rating is more closely tailored to the risk of the individual shipowner.

Insurance against fines

18.24   This has been criticised on the basis that it allows shipowners to escape punishment. This point of view is deserving of respect, but the matter is more complex than it might at first appear. We understand that in some countries "fines" are imposed for fiscal or political reasons and do not reflect any wrongdoing on the part of the shipowner. Furthermore, even when there is an element of "wrongdoing" in the sense that the shipowner has breached some local regulation, it by no means follows that this breach involved any departure from high standards of operation and maintenance. It may have been the purest technicality. Last, but by no means least, fines are usually for relatively small amounts which pale into insignificance when compared with third party liabilities which everyone agrees are properly the subject of insurance.

18.25   If a shipowner claims indemnity in respect of a fine, it is important that his P & I Club shall examine carefully whether the circumstances in which it was incurred evidence some departure from the standard of operation and maintenance which the Club requires of its members and, in particular, whether they evidence any failure to maintain internationally agreed standards. We understand that in the case of some fines Clubs do expel members if the circumstances indicate that operating standards have fallen below the minimum acceptable level. We hope that in serious cases this sanction continues to be used. Normally a fine would be looked at in the same way as any other claim and would be taken into account in fixing the member's rating for the following year. The risk of expulsion or an increased rating, and not the fine itself, is the real punishment. Ironically, the withdrawal of cover in respect of fines might well have the opposite of the intended effect since the Club might not learn of its member's transgression.

Reinsurance

18.26   Insurers limit their personal exposure by reinsuring part or all of the risk they have undertaken. Most of the world's marine reinsurance cover is provided directly or indirectly by the London market and this capacity is essential in providing the high levels of compulsory liability insurance cover sometimes required by international law.

18.27   Reinsurers are thus at least one step removed from the underlying insurance as they have no direct contact with the ship or the cargo owner. They must to a varying degree have regard to the information they receive from the original insurer and his reputation for skilful underwriting. We believe that other sectors of the insurance market are in a better position to influence shipping standards, although reinsurers have a part to play in reinforcing the resolve of their reinsured.

Confidentiality of ratings

18.28   There are those who suggest that ratings or premiums, from all insurers, ought to be made public. They argue that if shipowners could see how their rivals were rated it would act as an incentive to those paying higher premiums to improve quality. Although we agree that poorer quality owners ought to pay more in premiums than better quality owners, **we do not accept that the publication of ratings would give any clear signals to operators.** The range of variables in terms of size, type and age of ship, type of cargo and geographical area of operation is so large that no meaningful comparison between different rates can be made by an individual shipowner. The fact that ratings are confidential does not mean that they do not reflect differences in quality. Owners with a higher claims record will pay higher premiums and insurers will make it clear that owners can improve their rating by improving their claims performance.

18.29   The fact that ratings are to some extent confidential – information does leak – probably enables the P & I Clubs to give greater and not less effect to their perception of which members have high and which have low standards and thus bring pressure to bear for improvement. Were ratings to be published, the Managers would be confronted with a member's argument based not upon his actual standard of safety, which is what matters, but upon his perception of his standard as compared with other members. In other words the argument would cease to be about safety and become one about comparative ratings.

Deductibles

18.30 Deductibles are widely used throughout the marine insurance business. A deductible, as the word implies, is the sum which falls to be deducted from any claim in calculating the insurer's liability. It represents an initial tranche in respect of which the shipowner is uninsured. Following the rise in claims in the late 1980s, hull insurers have generally increased deductibles so that owners have a greater stake in the risk. The rise in deductibles, together with reductions in the cover provided, have not only improved underwriting results but have also made it less attractive for disreputable shipowners to carry out only the bare minimum of maintenance in the hope that the cost of consequential repairs can be recovered by a series of small claims.

18.31 Deductibles are also used in liability insurance. However, in the particular context of liability for oil pollution, the Clubs are averse to imposing them. There are two reasons. The first is that the Clubs wish to be in charge immediately an oil pollution incident occurs and take the view that they cannot reasonably expect their members to agree to this if the member and not the Club will be responsible for meeting the claim up to the amount of any significant deductible. The second is that where, as is usually the case, the Club has issued a Civil Liability Convention insurance certificate, the Club itself is liable to the third party for the whole claim regardless of any deductible agreed between it and its member. Whilst it can be argued that Club rules could put it in "the driving seat" regardless of whether there was any deductible and that the liability under the Civil Liability Convention is no different from that accepted by motor insurers in the case of compulsory insurance under the Road Traffic Acts, we think that the use of deductibles in the context of oil pollution claims would be of marginal efficacy in concentrating shipowners' minds, bearing in mind the Clubs' sophisticated rating systems.

Compulsory insurance for third party liabilities

18.32 We have heard a great deal of evidence from experts in hull and cargo insurance and from representatives of the P & I Clubs. It is clear that many people are taking the issue of loss prevention very seriously and we applaud the efforts made by certain sectors of the industry to raise standards and improve risk analysis by looking more closely at the actual condition of vessels and their operating policies.

18.33 The P & I Clubs have told us how important it is that the members of a Club are mutually compatible. If members fall below an acceptable standard and do not respond to the stimulus of more onerous rating terms or temporary suspension of cover they are thrown out. This is very encouraging. But we are worried about what happens to owners who are expelled from a Club.

18.34 In many cases they are taken on by another P & I Club. Generally, the new Club will be aware of the owner's record and will accept him "on probation" on onerous rating terms. If he does not improve he may again be expelled. This is all well and good but if all the P & I Clubs operate to the same high standards why is one Club prepared to take on a new member, albeit on onerous rating terms, whose record is such that another Club has expelled him regardless? In other words, how can a shipowner whose standards are incompatible with the high quality membership of one Club be compatible with the high quality membership of a different Club? The answer is that individual Clubs have either different standards or different perceptions of the risk posed by a particular shipowner. Differing perceptions are inevitable and do not of themselves matter. Different standards are another matter entirely and should be eliminated as far as possible.

18.35   The problem is that if a substandard owner is refused membership by all the P & I Clubs there is nothing to stop him from continuing to operate without liability insurance. Only tankers carrying more than 2,000 tonnes of persistent oil in bulk are required to have compulsory liability insurance. This is a condition of the 1969 Civil Liability Convention which we describe in Chapter 19. The 1976 Limitation Convention, which covers liability for most marine pollution damage not covered by the Civil Liability Convention, includes no such requirement. There is no requirement in any Convention that owners should take out hull or cargo insurance. In practice, most owners will take out hull insurance and most will have third party liability cover through membership of a P & I Club. But there must be a danger of an incident where the shipowner is not insured for third party liabilities. At least if the substandard owner is insured, victims of pollution damage caused by his vessels will have a better chance of being compensated.

18.36   Until recently there had been little evidence to suggest that some ships using UK waters lacked insurance cover. The series of incidents in 1993 involving the fish factory ships operating off Shetland (discussed in Chapter 17 and Appendix L) has made it clear that some ships are without any kind of insurance. The Australian report *Ships of Shame* (paragraph 1.28) identified the problem of lack of insurance cover and recommended that the Australian Government should require proof of adequate P & I cover as a prior condition of entry into Australian ports. In its response to the report the Australian Government saw compulsory P & I cover as a matter requiring discussion at an international level. **We believe that possession of at least adequate P & I cover but preferably also hull and cargo insurance is essential both to protect third parties and to ensure that salvage services are readily available.**

18.37   We did consider whether or not the UK could unilaterally impose a requirement for compulsory liability insurance. We decided that it could but **we concluded that, given the amount of passing traffic not calling at UK ports, international action is the best way of ensuring that all potentially polluting ships have adequate insurance to cover third party liabilities.** We discuss the issues of compensation and liability in more detail in Chapter 19 and recommend in paragraph 19.44 that a requirement for compulsory insurance should be incorporated into the revision of the 1976 Limitation Convention currently being discussed at IMO. Failing that, we support action on a regional basis.

Information

18.38   As we noted in Chapter 11, insurers possess a great deal of information about the standard of shipping. **We believe that it would be in the interests of reinsurers, hull and cargo insurers and P & I Clubs to pool their information both to cut down on**

duplication of work and to provide a clearer basis for risk assessment. We also believe that the insurance industry should allow the UK Government access to this information to assist Port State Control inspections. In Chapter 11 we considered whether or not there should be a statutory obligation on insurers and others to make information available. We concluded that there would be considerable difficulties in this because of conflicts of interest and confidentiality. In the case of the insurance industry we decided that the idea was not practicable for at least two reasons. The first is that there would be a real risk that this would incline shipowners to insure elsewhere than the UK market with the result that the UK would lose both the business and the information. The second is that we have been persuaded that reports of inspections on behalf of insurers and charterers would not be as full and frank as would otherwise be the case.

18.39 We therefore concluded that a less formal approach was preferable. We recommended, in paragraph 11.63, that MSA should foster closer links with the shipping industry to encourage a freer flow of information within the industry. **We urge the marine insurance industry to cooperate.** All concerned with shipping have a direct interest in being better informed and a wider dissemination of relevant information will also serve the greater public interest in increasing safety at sea.

Conclusion

18.40 We have already made it clear that we welcome the efforts being made by various sectors of the marine insurance industry to improve the evaluation of risk and to discourage substandard shipping. We also recognise that the prime concern of the insurance industry is to improve business rather than standards, although the two are not inconsistent. The retreat of capital from the market, particularly the hull insurance market, in the late 1980s certainly contributed to a hardening of rates and positive pressure on the shipping industry to improve standards. We hope that the resolve of marine underwriters will not be weakened as capital returns to the market and pressure to soften rates and terms of insurance increases.

Chapter 19

Liability and Compensation for Pollution Damage

Liability and compensation for oil pollution

Liability

19.1 Shipowners, like anyone else, are liable for damage caused by the negligence of themselves, their servants and agents. However for centuries this liability has been limited or capped in the interests of encouraging shipowning in times when this was a much more hazardous venture. Originally the limit of a liability was a sum equal to the actual value of the ship but this limit has long since been replaced by a notional figure based on the ship's tonnage. The only circumstances in which the shipowner's liability could exceed this limit was if the damage was caused by his "actual fault or privity"[1]. In more recent times, the Convention on Limitation of Liability for Maritime Claims 1976 (1976 Limitation Convention), as enacted in UK law by the Merchant Shipping Act 1979[2], has made it easier for a shipowner to limit his liability[3] and has revised the formula for establishing that limit[4]. The concession of making it easier for shipowners to limit their liability was made in exchange for, what were then, significant increases in the actual limits. Unfortunately the passage of time and changes in rates of exchange have eroded the advantage of these increases.

19.2 This remains the position in most instances although there are a number of exceptions. The most important of these from our point of view are claims for oil pollution damage by tankers carrying persistent oil in bulk, nuclear damage covered by international or national legislation which governs or prohibits limitation of liability for such damage and claims against the owner of a nuclear ship for nuclear damage. These are the subject of separate international Conventions. The rules applying to nuclear transport are discussed below in paragraphs 19.33 – 19.39.

19.3 In the case of pollution by tankers carrying persistent oil in bulk the liability of the shipowner will be affected by the International Convention on Civil Liability for Oil Pollution Damage 1969 (the 1969 Civil Liability Convention), if his ship is registered in a

---

[1] That is, his personal fault or privity to the cause of the damage or, in the case of a shipowner who was a body corporate, the fault or privity of some servant or agent of the company of sufficient authority to be considered the *alter ego* of the company.

[2] The 1976 Limitation Convention was enacted in United Kingdom law by Sections 17 to 19 of and Schedules 4 and 5 to the Merchant Shipping Act 1979. The Convention entered into force both in the United Kingdom and internationally on 1 December 1986.

[3] Part VIII of the Merchant Shipping Act 1894, which enabled a shipowner to limit his liability unless the damage was caused with his actual fault or privity, was repealed by the Merchant Shipping Act 1979. Article 4 of Schedule 4 to the latter Act states that "a person liable shall not be entitled to limit his liability if it is proved that the loss resulted from his personal act or omission, committed with the intent to cause such loss, or recklessly and with knowledge that such loss would probably result". We know of no case in which a shipowner has been unable to limit his liability using this test.

[4] Article 6 of Schedule 4 to the Merchant Shipping Act 1979, provides formulae for calculating the limits of liability. There are two formulae. The first applies to claims for loss of life and personal injury. The second applies to any other claims including those for pollution damage. The limits of liability for claims for pollution damage are calculated as follows: (i) 167,000 Units of Account for a ship with a tonnage not exceeding 500 tons, (ii) for a ship with a tonnage in excess of 500 tons, the limit is 167,000 Units of Account plus (a) 167 Units of Account for each ton from 501 to 30,000 tons, (b) 125 Units of Account for each ton from 30,001 to 70,000 tons and (c) 83 Units of Account for each ton in excess of 70,000 tons. A Unit of Account is the Special Drawing Right—see footnote 5 below.

Convention State. The effect of the Convention is twofold. First it creates a "strict liability" regime: the shipowner is liable whether or not anyone for whom he was responsible was negligent. The only exceptions are where the damage resulted from an act of war or a grave natural disaster, was wholly caused by sabotage or was wholly caused by the failure of authorities to maintain navigational aids. Second it raises the limitation on liability to an amount specified in the Convention, namely 133 SDR[5] (about £127) per ton of the ship's tonnage or 14 million SDR (about £13.4 million) whichever is the less. This limit will be "broken" and cease to apply if the damage resulted from the actual fault or privity of the shipowner.

Compensation

19.4   Since shipowners might well not be able to meet this increased liability from their own resources, a further Convention came into existence, namely the International Convention on the Establishment of an International Fund for Compensation for Oil Pollution Damage 1971 (the 1971 Fund Convention). Only States which are parties to the Civil Liability Convention can become parties to this Convention. Its purpose is to guarantee the payment of appropriate compensation to claimants in Convention States, notwithstanding that the shipowner is able to limit his liability to a lower figure or is unable, for whatever reason, to meet his liability. The International Oil Pollution Compensation (IOPC) Fund has its own limit of liability of 60 million SDR (about £57 million) for any one incident. So far, the Fund has paid out a total of about £67 million in respect of 63 incidents. There was concern at one stage that claims in the case of the *BRAER* might exceed the Fund limit but by March 1994 the total claim stood at £24 million. The final total is expected to be between £40-45 million which is still well within the limit.

19.5   The contributors to the Fund are importers in member States who receive more than 150,000 tonnes of crude and heavy oil (contributing oil) in a calendar year. The IOPC Fund sometimes suffers from cash flow problems and Government loans may occasionally be used to fill the gap. This happened in the case of the *BRAER* but such arrangements are very much the exception rather than the rule.

19.6   In order to reduce the burden on the Fund the Civil Liability Convention further provides that member States shall require that all tankers carrying more than 2,000 tonnes of persistent oil as cargo which enter or leave ports in Convention States (whether or not registered in such a State) should carry a certificate demonstrating that the owners are adequately insured. Such certificates are normally provided by the ship's P & I Club. The Convention also allows direct action against the insurer.

Claims settlement procedures

19.7   Claims are accepted for payment by the IOPC Fund for proved economic loss and reasonable expenditure caused by the incident. Since the primary liability is that of the

---

[5] Special Drawing Rights (SDR) of the International Monetary Fund. The value expressed in SDR is converted into national currencies by referring to its market exchange rate. At the end of March 1994 one pound sterling was equal to 1.0481367 SDR.

shipowner and his insurers, the IOPC Fund cooperates closely with those insurers in its claims settlement procedures and every effort is made to ensure that legitimate claims are met promptly, payments on account being made where appropriate. If the IOPC Fund cannot reach agreement with a claimant, the claimant may pursue his claim against the Fund before the courts of the State where the damage occurred.

19.8   There are only two respects in which we feel that criticism of the administration of the Fund is justified. One is described in paragraph 20.55. The other is that in meeting claims for dealing with oil pollution, the IOPC Fund pays for the cost of operations during an incident with only a small degree of "uplift" towards the standing costs of maintaining a response capability. Standing costs are often considerable: the annual cost of maintaining the UK's aerial dispersant spraying capacity is some £3.5 million (see paragraph 21.50). A response capability is valuable insurance for the IOPC Fund because by preventing or limiting oil pollution damage it may substantially reduce the cost in claims which might otherwise have been incurred by the Fund.

19.9   Inadequate recognition of standing costs is a positive incentive to Governments to be improvident by not preparing for oil spills. Whilst it would not be reasonable to expect the Fund to pay the full cost of maintaining the ability to spray we believe it should pay a larger part. There are good precedents for this. Salvage awards include an "uplift" intended to reward the salvor for incurring the overhead costs involved in keeping a salvage vessel on station and available in case of need. **We recommend that the UK Government, in concert with other Governments if possible, should seek to agree with the IOPC Fund a formula for the uplift of marginal costs by a fixed percentage so as to reflect a reasonable proportion of fixed costs.**

Deficiencies in the 1969 and 1971 Conventions

19.10   It has long been apparent that a major defect within the Civil Liability and Fund Conventions is that they do not apply to preventive measures which are so successful that no oil is spilled. Nor do they apply to spills from tankers during ballast voyages or to spills of bunker oil other than when combined with a spill of cargo oil from a tanker. There is also widespread concern that limits for liability and compensation are too low.

19.11   Attempts have been made to address these deficiencies. In 1984 an international conference adopted two Protocols amending the present Civil Liability and Fund Conventions. These Protocols provide higher limits of liability and compensation and a wider scope of application. By 1991 it was clear that the 1984 Protocols stood little chance of coming into force. However in 1992 an international conference adopted two new Protocols which retain the substance of provisions of the 1984 Protocols but with lower entry into force conditions.

19.12   Amongst a number of changes the 1992 Protocols substantially increase the limits of liability and compensation and introduce an accelerated procedure to secure international agreement on future increases.

19.13   The Protocol to the Civil Liability Convention sets significantly higher limits on the level of the owner's liability. Owners of smaller ships of less than 5,000 units of tonnage can limit their liability to 3 million SDR (about £2.9 million). The liability of owners of larger ships is based on the tonnage of their ship to a maximum of 59.7 million SDR (about £57 million) for ships over 140,000 units of tonnage[6]. The Protocol makes it easier for a shipowner to limit his liability by adopting the same test as the 1976 Limitation Convention (see paragraph 19.1 above)[7].

19.14   The Protocol to the Fund Convention increases the limit of compensation payable by the IOPC Fund to 135 million SDR (about £129 million). This limitation figure will be increased automatically to 200 million SDR (about £191 million) when there are three member States of the "1992 Fund" whose combined quantities of contributing oil received in a given year exceeds 600 million tonnes.

19.15   The Protocols extend the geographical scope of the Conventions to include the Exclusive Economic Zone (EEZ) established under UNCLOS, or equivalent area for those Contracting States which have not established such a zone.

19.16   Coverage is also extended to damage by spills of persistent bunker oil from **unladen** tankers.

19.17   Expenses incurred for preventive measures are recoverable even when no spill of oil occurs, provided that there was a grave and imminent danger of pollution damage.

19.18   The Protocols introduce a new definition of pollution damage retaining the basic wording of the present definition with the addition of a phrase to clarify that, with regard to environmental damage, only costs incurred for reasonable measures to restore the contaminated environment are included in the concept of pollution damage.

19.19   The 1992 Protocol to the Civil Liability Convention requires for its entry into force that it be ratified by ten States, including four States each with not less than one million tonnes of gross tanker tonnage. The 1992 Protocol to the Fund Convention will enter into force when ratified by at least eight States, when the total quantity of contributing oil received during a calendar year in all the ratifying States is at least 450 million tonnes. Unfortunately the 1992 Protocols are not yet in force and by the beginning of 1994 no countries had ratified them. We are, however, encouraged to hear that a number of countries are well on the way towards doing so.

19.20   **We gave the Secretary of State advance warning on 10 June 1993 that we believe that the 1992 Protocols should be ratified as soon as possible** (see

---

[6] The revised limits are: (a) for a ship not exceeding 5,000 units of tonnage, 3 million SDR (about £2.9 million); (b) for a ship with a tonnage between 5,000 and 140,000 units of tonnage, 3 million SDR plus 420 SDR (about £401) for each additional unit of tonnage over 5,000 units of tonnage; and (c) for a ship exceeding 140,000 units of tonnage, 59.7 SDR (about £57 million).
[7] Article 6 paragraph 2 of the Protocol of 1992 to Amend the International Convention on Civil Liability for Oil Pollution Damage 1969. Article V paragraph 2 of the 1969 Convention states that "if the incident occurred as a result of the actual fault or privity of the owner, he shall not be entitled to avail himself of the limitation provided in . . ."

Appendix P). We welcome the introduction to Parliament of the Merchant Shipping (Salvage and Pollution) Bill (see paragraph 1.35) which will allow the UK to ratify the Protocols. Once the UK has ratified the Protocols, the Government will be in a much stronger position to encourage other States to follow suit – and **we strongly urge it to do so.**

19.21   Without prejudicing our support for ratification of the Protocols, we believe that the working of the test for limiting a shipowner's liability specified in the 1976 Limitation Convention and the 1992 Protocol to the Civil Liability Convention should be closely monitored because a limit which in practice can scarcely ever be broken is no encouragement to a shipowner to adopt high standards. We believe that the test is derived from Article 25 of the Warsaw Convention 1929 as amended by Article 13 of the Hague Protocol 1955 which relates to aircraft. Given that there are far fewer types of aircraft, that the regulatory system is much tighter and that the consequences of failure to take certain precautions is much more predictable, a test for air carriers of "with intent to cause damage or recklessly and with knowledge that damage would **probably** [our emphasis] result" may be acceptable in that context. However, in a marine context with innumerable different types of ship and a far laxer regulatory structure it is likely to be extremely difficult to prove that reckless shipowners knew that any particular damage would probably result. **If this proves to be the case we recommend that the UK Government takes action with other States signatory to the Conventions to implement the necessary revisions.**

Voluntary industry schemes

19.22   In addition to the compensation regime for oil pollution established by the international Conventions, there are two voluntary industry schemes, the Tanker Owners Voluntary Agreement concerning Liability for Oil Pollution (TOVALOP) and the Contract Regarding a Supplement to Tanker Liability for Oil Pollution (CRISTAL). They were set up at the same time as the corresponding international Conventions were negotiated with the aim of providing comparable benefits in States which are not party to the Conventions. TOVALOP and CRISTAL were intended to be interim solutions and to remain in operation only until the international Conventions had been universally adopted. Unlike the 1969 and 1971 Conventions, the voluntary schemes cover preventive measures taken if no oil is spilled and TOVALOP applies to spills from tankers in ballast.

19.23   TOVALOP applies to virtually all tankers and is covered by the shipowner's P & I Club. The TOVALOP Standing Agreement provides a basic limit of cover but a higher limit is available under the TOVALOP Supplement in cases where the tanker is carrying a cargo owned by a member of CRISTAL. The TOVALOP Standing Agreement does not apply in cases where there is any liability under the Civil Liability Convention.

19.24   If the limits of the TOVALOP Supplement are exceeded, a claim can be made against CRISTAL. CRISTAL is financed by cargo owners and covers a major part of all cargoes of oil carried by sea. If damage occurs in an IOPC Fund member State, claims against CRISTAL are only likely to be made if the aggregate amount of damage exceeds the amount of compensation available under the Fund Convention. In these cases recovery under CRISTAL can be obtained only if the owner of the cargo is a member of CRISTAL and compensation has been paid by the shipowner up to the applicable limit of the TOVA-LOP Supplement. Contrary to the procedure under the Fund Convention, a claim will be paid by CRISTAL only if the claimant has taken all reasonable steps to obtain compensation from other sources, for example the owner of the ship involved.

19.25   To ensure that CRISTAL members in Fund States do not bear a disproportionate share of the costs of oil pollution settlements through having to contribute to settlements made under both CRISTAL and the Fund Convention, there is a reimbursement mechanism written into the TOVALOP Supplement and CRISTAL. Through this mechanism, CRISTAL members who have been required to contribute to the Fund settlement of an incident involving a tanker carrying a cargo owned by a CRISTAL member will have those contributions reimbursed by the tanker owner (up to the applicable TOVALOP Supplement limit) and, above that, by fellow CRISTAL members. In cases involving compensation payments by the IOPC Fund where the tanker involved in the incident is carrying a cargo owned by a CRISTAL member, it also results in CRISTAL member oil companies resident in States party to the Fund Convention receiving contributions from tanker owners and other CRISTAL members for a significant proportion of their contributions to the IOPC Fund.

19.26   The present voluntary schemes have global application and were designed to operate until 20 February 1994. In November 1993 agreement was reached to amend the schemes to increase the limits of compensation and extend the schemes for a further three years until 20 February 1997. The revised limits mean that the maximum amount of compensation available under the voluntary schemes has been increased by about 24 per cent. The revised limits of financial responsibility under the TOVALOP Supplement are identical to those in the 1992 Protocol to the Civil Liability Convention. The limits of CRISTAL have also been increased but the maximum amount of compensation available is still less than that under the 1992 Protocol to the Fund Convention.

19.27   We welcome the improvements to TOVALOP and CRISTAL and the extension of the schemes for a further three years. However, we recognise that these schemes were set up as temporary arrangements pending widespread ratification of the Civil Liability and Fund Conventions and support the industry view that the 1992 Protocols must be ratified before the voluntary schemes expire in 1997.

The United States and "unlimited liability"

19.28   The United States has not ratified the Civil Liability or Fund Conventions and has established a separate domestic liability and compensation system under the Oil Pollution Act 1990 (OPA 90). Prior to its enactment, Federal maritime law preempted State law on marine limitation matters but OPA 90 allows the development of State liability and compensation laws for oil pollution. Ships operating to the United States therefore face varying State provisions as well as those of Federal statute.

19.29   Under OPA 90 the owner is strictly liable for oil pollution but is allowed to limit his liability to an amount based on the tonnage of his ship. The provisions of OPA 90 differ from those of the Conventions in that the limits for liability are significantly higher and that it is much easier to break the owner's right to limit his liability. Many observers consider that despite the references to limitation in most cases, owners involved in an oil spill in United States waters effectively face unlimited liability. In addition to clean-up costs and economic loss, OPA 90 allows claims for non-economic environmental damage but the basis for such claims is not specified in the Act. Those who insure owners' third party liabilities are subject to direct action. It is this provision, together with the risk of unlimited liability, that has made insurers reluctant to provide the certificates of financial responsibility required under the terms of OPA 90.

19.30   Under OPA 90 claims which exceed the shipowner's limit can be made against a revolving Federal Fund of $1 billion financed by a tax on US oil. This Federal Fund, which has yet to be tested by a major incident, is intended to provide early compensation. It appears that the Federal Fund will initiate recourse action against shipowners to recover any payments it makes including breaking the owner's right to limit his liability. The owner is responsible for initiating and monitoring any clean-up operations following a spill and any failing by the owner in this respect can affect his right to limit his liability. The United States is unique in placing responsibility for the clean-up of pollution outside the ship on the owner. Responsibility for dealing with pollution from ships in UK waters is described in Chapter 21.

19.31   The main problem with the liability and compensation regime established under OPA 90 is that it creates great uncertainty for operators and insurers. The threat of unlimited liability already seems to have deterred some shipowners from operating to the United States and insurers levy additional premiums for ships intending to operate in US waters. The shipowner's liability is limited in practice by what he can pay before becoming bankrupt and insurers are understandably reluctant to accept responsibility for payments beyond the agreed cover. The best way for shipowners to protect their assets under the threat of unlimited liability may be to create one ship companies, thus limiting their liability to the point at which bankruptcy occurs. This does not encourage responsible operators.

19.32   We reject arguments that the United Kingdom should adopt a liability and compensation regime similar to that operating in the United States. The regime established under OPA 90 is, as yet, untested. It has received no support internationally, even from those who have reservations about the 1992 Protocols. And there is no guarantee that the bad operators will be deterred from operating to the US. Instead, it is more likely that the better operated, larger fleets will be deterred because of the unreasonable level of risk. There is no doubt that OPA 90 has driven insurance costs up significantly and we believe that this money would be better spent on improving standards and on preventive measures. We also consider that it is undesirable to place the responsibility for the clean-up of pollution on the shipowner who is most unlikely to have the expertise of a national body such as the UK's Marine Pollution Control Unit.

Liability and compensation for other types of pollution

Nuclear materials

19.33 Liability and compensation for pollution by nuclear cargoes are covered by the provisions of the Paris Convention on Third Party Liability in the Field of Nuclear Energy 1960 (the Paris Convention) and the 1963 Brussels Convention supplementary to it, as amended by subsequent Protocols, which are enacted in UK law by the Nuclear Installations Act 1965 as amended. The Paris Convention was agreed within the framework of the Organisation for Economic Cooperation and Development (OECD). Under the Paris Convention, the operator – in the UK the holder of a nuclear site licence – is strictly liable for damage to third parties and all such claims are channelled to the operator. The operator's liability is limited. The liability limit is absolute, and the Convention contains no "test" under which it may be broken. Damage arising from reactors powering a means of transport are specifically excluded under the provisions of the Paris Convention and the 1965 Act.

19.34 The 1965 Act applies the same limit of liability to the operator for the transport of nuclear materials as it does to nuclear sites. The 1965 Act, as amended[8], requires a nuclear operator to hold £20 million financial security in respect of any one incident. If an inventory of his site allows it to be prescribed under Section 2 of the 1965 Act the financial security required is set at £5 million per incident. These amounts were increased to £140 million and £10 million respectively from 1 April 1994. The nature of this financial security must be approved by the Secretary of State for Trade and Industry with the consent of HM Treasury in accordance with Section 19(1) of the 1965 Act. The financial security is required to meet claims only. Interest and other costs fall to the operator.

19.35 The Brussels Convention, as amended, which provided for increased compensation beyond the operator's limit of liability under the Paris Convention, requires Contracting Parties to make available 300 million SDR (about £286 million) in respect of any single incident. Therefore, the 1965 Act provides that claims in excess of £20 million for a single incident will be met from public funds. Where claims exceed 175 million SDR (about £167 million) the Brussels Convention, as amended, provides that all Contracting Parties are to provide funds on the basis of a formula set down in Article 12 of the Convention. In the case of an incident involving an operator from another Contracting Party to the Brussels Convention, as amended, the UK would contribute to this tier of funds. For accidents where the aggregate of claims exceeds 300 million SDR the Secretary of State for Trade and Industry (or, in the application of the 1965 Act to Scotland, the Secretary of State for Scotland) may with the consent of Parliament increase the amount of public funds available for compensation.

19.36 Under the Paris Convention and the 1965 Act compensation is payable for loss of life, personal injury and damage to property, provided that the damage is suffered in the territory of a Paris Convention Contracting Party. Damage to property does not include damage to the installation where the incident occurred. In the case of a transport accident,

---

[8] Section 27(8) of the Energy Act 1983.

the carrier may claim for damage to the means of transport. It is, however, common practice in transport cases for the operator who is liable to indemnify the carrier against any loss he may suffer.

19.37 It is unlikely that compensation for damage resulting from nuclear transport incidents would exceed in amount the levels of compensation provided in the UK under the 1965 Act as amended. This is recognised in foreign legislation, where operators are required to hold lower amounts of financial security for transport risks than for risks at sites. It is because of the provisions of the 1965 Act relating to transport incidents that the UK has not ratified the provisions of the IMO Convention Relating to Civil Liability in the Field of Maritime Carriage of Nuclear Material 1971.

19.38 The international regime on third party liability for nuclear damage is in the process of revision in the wake of the Chernobyl incident. Agreement was reached internationally in 1990 that Contracting Parties to the Paris Convention should increase the limit of financial security required by operators to 150 million SDR (about £143 million). In addition, the 1963 Vienna Convention on Civil Liability for Nuclear Damage, which is similar to the Paris Convention but covers countries which are not members of OECD, is in the process of revision by the International Atomic Energy Agency (IAEA). An important aim is to increase the adherence to the international liability regime, especially of States with nuclear power programmes. The amount of compensation available to victims under the Vienna Convention is likely to be increased.

19.39 We have no reason to doubt that the 1965 Act as amended provides adequate compensation in the event of a pollution incident involving a vessel carrying a nuclear cargo in UK waters but if the international community decides that limits need to be raised **the UK Government should make the necessary changes to the 1965 Act.**

Hazardous and noxious substances

19.40 There is currently no international liability and compensation system for pollution from ships other than oil tankers carrying persistent oil in bulk. This is in spite of twenty years of negotiations in IMO to establish a Convention on liability and compensation for damage caused by accidents involving ships carrying cargoes of hazardous or noxious substances (HNS). As we have seen, nuclear cargoes are dealt with separately under general legislation covering nuclear installations.

19.41 Claims made in the UK in respect of HNS damage arising from ships are currently subject to the right of the shipowner to limit his liability under the 1976 Limitation Convention (see paragraph 19.1 above). The limits to compensation are well below the levels of even the unamended 1969 Civil Liability and 1971 Fund Conventions and are widely acknowledged to be inadequate. There is a real danger that claimants will receive insufficient compensation for even limited HNS accidents unless they can break the owner's right to limit his liability. Even within the limit, the claimant still has to prove that the shipowner was negligent in respect of any HNS related claim to which the 1976 Limitation

Convention and the Merchant Shipping Act 1979 apply if any liability is to be admitted. This is in contrast to the strict liability regime in relation to persistent oils.

19.42   Generally, the shipment of hazardous and noxious substances has a good safety record, and as we record in paragraph 10.36, we are generally impressed by the thoroughness and care devoted to the regulation and operation of ships carrying hazardous and noxious substances. But this does not mean that a major HNS incident is impossible. Whatever measures are taken by the shipowner to ensure the safety of his cargo there is always the danger that another vessel may be the cause of a collision. If such a collision occurred near to a centre of population the results could be catastrophic, particularly if the cargo was explosive or a poisonous gas. The safety record of shipments of nuclear materials is excellent with no cases of deaths, serious injuries or significant environmental damage in over 30 years. Given that there must be far fewer shipments of nuclear materials than of other HNS it is surprising that a satisfactory liability and compensatory regime exists to cover the former but not the latter.

19.43   The IMO Legal Committee agreed in March 1993 to start immediate work on the revision of the 1976 Limitation Convention in parallel with its continuing work on a future HNS Convention. IMO has set a target date of 1996 for the adoption of an HNS Convention. **We strongly support this work and the UK Government's commitment to it. We also support the Paris Ministerial declaration (Belgium, France, Germany, The Netherlands and the UK) of 29 January 1994 that if IMO negotiations fail, work will immediately start on a regional compensation system.**

19.44   **We believe that any HNS Convention, whether fully international or regional, should cover claims in respect of spills of bunker fuel oil and non-persistent oil-based pollutants not already covered by the oil pollution compensation regime. It should also allow for compensation in the event of pollution from an unidentified ship. It is also vital, in our opinion, that the revision of the 1976 Limitation Convention includes a requirement for compulsory liability insurance in line with the provisions of the oil pollution compensation regime.** Whilst international agreement is preferable, we note that the UK Government is taking steps to impose strict liability for spills of bunker fuel in UK waters and support this sensible step.

Punitive damages

19.45   It has been suggested to us that punitive damages would make potential polluters more careful. We disagree. Punitive damages would be designed to deter those who deliberately set out to cause pollution. As we point out in paragraph 4.1, no operator, even the bad operator, aims to cause a major pollution incident and although he may cause minor pollution by tank cleaning or garbage disposal this is extremely difficult to prove. Proof that a major pollution incident was deliberate or was committed recklessly in the knowledge that such damage would probably result would break a shipowner's right to limit his liability and he would be open to prosecution through the courts. The costs of clean-up and compensation are so high that punitive damages would not make much difference.

Chapter 20

Dealing with Emergencies – Emergency Towing and Salvage

20.1   Our Report and recommendations so far have dealt largely with ways of persuading or compelling a wide variety of people to change their behaviour so as to reduce the risk of pollution by decreasing the chances of a ship getting into difficulties which may result in a breach in the integrity of her hull. We are convinced that this is much the best way of reducing risks of accidents which can lead to both pollution and loss of life.

20.2   Nevertheless, it would be idle to imagine that anything we or anyone else could recommend or do would ever eliminate risk. The sea is a dangerous place and humans are fallible. Ships will continue to get into difficulties, though our recommendations should ensure that they do so less often.

20.3   Once a vessel gets into difficulties, or risks becoming a hazard to other vessels, it is vitally important to do everything possible, as quickly as possible, to save life, to prevent her going aground or creating a hazard, and to prevent her cargo or bunkers from spilling. The first step is for information on problems and potential problems to reach the coastal authorities. MARPOL[1] and the International Convention on Oil Pollution Preparedness and Cooperation (OPRC) 1990[2] both include provisions for incidents and likely incidents of pollution to be reported immediately to the Coastal State. Our recommendations in Chapter 15 on reporting of all failures which could develop into a dangerous or polluting incident should improve actual reporting standards.

20.4   The next stage for the coastal authorities is the decision on whether to intervene. We recognise that the UK Government, through the Marine Pollution Control Unit (MPCU), often gives instructions to Masters or owners to ensure that the risks of pollution after a breakdown or an accident are minimised. We also recognise that it is unusual for events to move so fast that tugs are needed as a matter of urgency, but the *BRAER* incident showed not only that this can happen but also that if a tug is not available the consequences may be disastrous. But we believe that MPCU is struggling with inadequate resources, and that it needs access to better emergency assistance if this vital chance to avert disaster is to be seized.

20.5   Following the *BRAER* incident, and the Salvage Working Group report (see paragraph 20.76), the Department of Transport commissioned a study by a firm of consultants, Murray Fenton and Associates Ltd, into the availability of emergency towing vessels

---

[1] Article 8.
[2] Article 4. OPRC, which is discussed in the next chapter, is not yet in force or ratified internationally but the Merchant Shipping (Salvage and Pollution) Bill, currently before Parliament, will allow it to be implemented within the UK.

and the case for providing additional tugs. We are grateful to the Department for showing us a copy of the report.

Salvage, tug assistance and the environment

20.6 "Salvage" in the strict sense of the word is the remuneration to which the law entitles someone who, in the absence of a contractual duty so to act, renders a salvage service. The salvage service is one which preserves or contributes to the preservation from danger at sea of a ship or cargo or other recognised subject of salvage. This is a complex branch of the law, the standard text book[3] running to over a thousand pages. However in a popular sense the word is synonymous with salvage assistance, a salvage service or a salvage situation and it is in this sense that the word is used in this chapter. Tug assistance is one of the commonest forms of salvage service. It may be rendered as such or under contract. In any emergency situation it will be likely to be rendered as a salvage service, the rights and duties of the ship and the tug and the remuneration of the tug's owners being determined by law or under the terms of Lloyd's Open Form (see paragraph 20.38).

20.7 Generally speaking the provision of salvage services is a purely private sector commercial activity carried out by specialised, experienced and well equipped professional salvors, most of whom are members of the International Salvage Union. Although emergency towage, like all other salvage services, is primarily directed to saving the ship and cargo, it may often be the only way of protecting the environment as an incident develops.

20.8 Historically salvage services have been rendered on the basis of "no cure – no pay". "Cure" in this context meant that some part of the ship or cargo was saved. The remuneration for the services was higher than it would have been under a contract providing for payment whatever the result, but it could never exceed the value of the property which was in fact saved – "salved values". In these circumstances the salvor would not be concerned to undertake measures which were designed to preserve or to minimise damage to the environment, if they did not contribute to increasing the quantity or value of the property saved. It is to this problem, *inter alia*, that Lloyd's Standard Form 90 (LOF 90), the International Convention on Salvage, 1989, and the Merchant Shipping (Salvage and Pollution) Bill currently before Parliament are addressed (see paragraphs 20.44 – 20.47).

The assistance process

20.9 Emergency towing may be used to:

(a) assist the rescue of crew and passengers: generally speaking helicopters and life-boats are more effective than tugs in search and rescue (SAR), but tugs may also have a role, for instance to rescue large numbers of passengers from ferries in the Channel, to tow a ship away from danger (so that crew or passengers do not have to be rescued) or to tow her to a place of shelter where crew and passengers can be disembarked more safely than in the open sea; and to

---

[3] *Maritime Law of Salvage* (2nd edition) by Geoffrey Brice QC—ISBN 0420 484 906.

(b) secure the safety of ship and cargo: removing the ship and cargo from a place of danger to one of safety, such as a sheltered anchorage or port of refuge. A damaged or disabled ship may be at risk of grounding or sinking in weather conditions with which she cannot cope unaided in her damaged or disabled state. Or she may constitute a hazard to navigation and so risk being involved in a collision with other vessels. In either event there is a consequential risk of pollution damage.

Assistance to avert a grounding or collision

20.10   The breakdown of vessels in busy shipping lanes is a frequent occurrence. 150 breakdowns were reported to Dover Coastguard during 1993. Most vessels make repairs and get under way within a few hours. Occasionally the Department of Transport decides that the risk of collision is unacceptable and will make a formal request to the owner or Master to arrange a tow to a safe anchorage. Examples of this are when a vessel is anchored in the traffic lane of a traffic separation scheme, or is a laden tanker, or is badly lit at night, or the visibility is low or the weather is deteriorating. A vessel drifting down on an off-shore oil installation would also be dangerous.

20.11   If a vessel breaks down completely, or is too far from a safe anchorage to be able to reach it, one sure way to prevent a grounding is for a tug to reach her, attach a line and prevent her from drifting towards hazards. A breakdown in a busy shipping lane may represent a major risk of collision, and as much of a hazard as a ship about to go aground: sometimes more so, as a small dead ship is capable of holing a large ship carrying pollutants.

20.12   If assistance is going to be successful, a tug has to be able to reach the crippled ship quickly. The tug has to be strong enough for the job, properly equipped and furnished with an expert crew. There must be some way to make a very strong connection between the two vessels, sometimes in atrocious weather: we discuss some of the issues in Chapter 7. The tug also needs to be called out early enough for her to be able to make any difference.

Assistance following a collision or grounding

20.13   Tug assistance can be just as important after a vessel has grounded or collided with another. A salvor or other tug operator may be able to save the vessel and return her to a port where she can be repaired. Failing that, or as part of the salvage process, he may be able to remove part or all of her fuel or cargo oil or other cargo – a process called lightening[4]. If the vessel is already beyond saving and lightening or other salvage operations are required to prevent or minimise pollution, the cost of salvage is likely to be a great deal more than the benefits to the owner, and again Government intervention may be called for.

Delay in summoning assistance

20.14   If an emergency arises at sea, instant assistance is usually impossible. SAR can be provided by air, but seaborne assistance in the form of a salvage tug may be many miles,

---

[4] An example of lightening during our inquiry was the *APACHE* incident (May 1993), described in Appendix L. An earlier example was the *PHILLIPS OKLAHOMA* (September 1989), described in Chapter 21.

and therefore hours, away. This being the case, we cannot over-emphasise the need for Masters and owners to request assistance at the earliest possible moment. Unfortunately delay in taking this essential step is not uncommon, particularly in the context of a breakdown in the propulsion machinery.

20.15   There appear to be two reasons for this. The first is a mixture of optimism and pride on the part of Masters. They feel that any problem which is not immediately life threatening should be, and is, capable of being overcome by the skill and persistence of themselves and their crews. It takes time before it dawns upon them that they may not succeed and even more time before they appreciate that they are unlikely to do so.

20.16   The second reason stems from the improvements in worldwide communications. The ship Master's traditional awesome and all embracing authority over his ship and all who sailed in her – "second only to that of God and then only by virtue of seniority" – was based upon his inability to consult his owners. The authority still remains, but Masters are unwilling to exercise it if they can talk to the ship's owners or managers. It may take time to establish communication and, when this is done, the owners or managers, to whom the problem is considerably more remote, may wish to explore what other options are open and to consult underwriters. Owners and managers should trust their Masters and make it clear that they do so. Owners, managers and Masters should appreciate that an early call for assistance is a worthwhile premium to pay with a view to avoiding far greater liability. We return to this point in the context of the 1989 Salvage Convention (see paragraph 20.46).

20.17   Even after a tug has been called out, it may be important to continue to seek assistance until it is clear that the first tug can cope with the task she is being asked to do. The report of the Liberian investigators into the *AMOCO CADIZ* incident suggested that the Master of the *AMOCO CADIZ* should have appreciated that the tug *PACIFIC* would not have sufficient power to pull his vessel away from the shore and that he should have urgently required further assistance.

20.18   If a Coastal State is aware of an emergency situation and the Master or owners fail to summon adequate assistance sufficiently promptly, it may become necessary for the State to intervene in order to minimise the risk of pollution to its seas and shores.

Government intervention

Powers of intervention

20.19   The United Kingdom is a party to the 1969 Intervention Convention[5] (implemented through the Prevention of Oil Pollution Act 1971[6]) and its 1973 Protocol[7], implemented through a Statutory Instrument[8].

---

[5] The International Convention relating to Intervention on the High Seas in Cases of Oil Pollution Casualties 1969.
[6] Sections 12 to 16, inclusive.
[7] The Protocol of 1973 Relating to Intervention on the High Seas in Cases of Marine Pollution by Substances Other than Oil.
[8] SI 1980 No. 1093 made under Section 16 of the 1971 Act.

20.20 The legislation gives the Secretary of State extensive intervention powers in relation to all ships within United Kingdom territorial waters and United Kingdom registered ships outside them. The powers, which are detailed in Appendix J, include powers to take action himself and to issue directions to owners, persons in possession of the ship, Masters and salvors in possession of the ship or such salvors' servants or agents, if there has been an accident to a ship which:

> "... will or may cause pollution on a large scale in the United Kingdom or in the waters in or adjacent to the United Kingdom up to the seaward limits of territorial waters;"

and

> "... in the opinion of the Secretary of State the use of the powers conferred by this section is urgently needed."[9]

20.21 The Secretary of State has only limited powers of direction in respect of a foreign ship outside territorial waters. In the latter case, the powers[10] are triggered if he is satisfied

> "... that there is a need to protect the coast of the United Kingdom, or water within the seaward limits of the territorial waters of the United Kingdom, against grave and imminent danger[11] of pollution by oil or by substances other than oil."

20.22 The powers are broadly defined and include the power to require the removal of oil remaining on board a vessel. The Secretary of State's directions or actions have to be reasonable and proportional and there is a right to recover compensation from the Secretary of State in respect of unreasonable loss or damage arising through his actions or directions. The 1969 Convention, the 1973 Protocol and the 1971 Act are silent on the recovery of expenses incurred by a Coastal State or the Secretary of State – a point to which we return in Chapter 22.

The use of the intervention powers

20.23 The intervention powers have for some years been exercised in practice by the Director of Marine Emergency Operations (DMEO), now the Chief Executive of the Coastguard Agency or COASTGUARD. He is supported by the Marine Pollution Control Unit (MPCU) and HM Coastguard. Their roles are described in Appendix I.

20.24 The Government has implemented the recommendation of the Chief Inspector of Marine Accidents, in his report on the BRAER incident, that the powers should also be delegated to the Chief Coastguard. The recommendation is reproduced in Appendix Q. The Government has also agreed that the intervention powers should be delegated to the new Director of MPCU, and that if necessary they may be further delegated to a senior Coastguard officer in the area concerned to deal with a specific incident.

---

[9] Section 12(1) of the 1971 Act.
[10] Article 7, paragraph (1) SI 1980 No. 1093.
[11] The "grave and imminent danger" test derives from the 1969 Intervention Convention and the 1973 Protocol.

20.25   COASTGUARD may "intervene" to prevent a pollution incident without invoking the statutory powers. For example it may formally recommend, on behalf of the Government, that the Master of a casualty should take a tow. Since the *BRAER* incident, instructions to HM Coastguard have been revised to make it clear that the six Regional Controllers and 21 District Controllers should exercise this function at their discretion in the absence of specific orders from the Chief Executive or Chief Coastguard, but with the advice of MPCU if that can be obtained. We return to the role of HM Coastguard in pollution emergencies at the end of this chapter.

20.26   The need to prevent pollution may coincide with a salvor's or owner's judgement that commercial salvage would be worthwhile. But if it does not COASTGUARD may have to get tug assistance to the casualty with the minimum of delay and decide whether to intervene in the commercial transactions between salvor and owner or Master. The decisions will often be difficult ones needing to be taken in the heat of the moment.

20.27   The intervention powers have been used six times:

(a)   *ELENI V* 1978: inside territorial waters. To prevent salvors abandoning the forward section after towing the stern section away.

(b)   *CHRISTOS BITAS* 1978: outside territorial waters. To prevent salvors towing the leaking casualty to Milford Haven.

(c)   *PERINTIS* 1989: outside territorial waters. To enable the location, survey and recovery of marine pollutants from the seabed.

(d)   *CERRO COLORADO* 1992: inside territorial waters. To lighten the vessel which had suffered internal leakage. The ship's structure was in doubt.

(e)   *BRAER* 1993: inside territorial waters. To prevent owners from abandoning the wreck until all the oil had been recovered. This incident is described in Chapter 21 and Appendix L.

(f)   *ODIGITRIA B* 1993: inside territorial waters. To have the vessel removed from her breakdown position in a hazardous location. This incident is described in Appendix L.

20.28   In addition on 30 occasions between September 1989 and February 1994 the Department of Transport gave instructions without recourse to intervention powers.

20.29   In the *ODIGITRIA B* incident the DMEO followed a well established practice of putting an SGO (now MSA) Marine Surveyor on board by helicopter to assess the situation, to discuss remedial measures with the Master and to act as the Department's agent. After the incident the practice was confirmed within the Department, and it was agreed that in future cases the surveyor should stay on board if he had any doubts about the Master's or the owner's willingness to comply with instructions. It was also agreed that there should be no delay in issuing a Direction if that was thought necessary, and that the powers to call out a tug should also be used quickly when they were thought necessary.

20.30 We applaud this tough line. We hope that if in future incidents there is a case for a larger boarding party, perhaps including Royal Navy personnel, there will again be no hesitation in arranging for it straight away. We recommend that the Department of Transport should seek an understanding with the Ministry of Defence on the provision of suitable military and salvage personnel in principle and the way in which they would act on board a casualty.

The adequacy of the intervention powers

20.31   There have been some doubts expressed on whether the 1971 Act gives the Director of Marine Emergency Operations all the powers he needs. It is important both that the powers are fully adequate and that it is clear to everyone concerned just what they are. **The powers should:**

(a) **be as effective for potential pollution incidents as for actual ones;**

(b) **cover non-oil pollutants to the same extent as oil pollutants; and**

(c) **cover dangerous and particularly explosive cargoes.**

The powers appear to be adequate for these purposes, except that the test of causing pollution "on a large scale" (see paragraph 20.20) may be too onerous. Pollution on a small scale can in some circumstances cause unacceptable damage.

20.32   The Merchant Shipping (Salvage and Pollution) Bill (see paragraph 1.35) will extend the powers so that they apply to prevent pollution in an area equivalent to an EEZ, as envisaged in UNCLOS 1982[12]; and so that they apply within territorial waters or within an area equivalent to an EEZ in order to protect the interests of another State. We consider that the powers should also:

(a) **be amended to make the test for intervention less onerous;**

(b) **include a power to issue an enforceable direction within an area larger than the territorial sea in order to protect it; and**

(c) **include clear power to place an agent of the Secretary of State on board to inform him of the situation or to take action on his behalf: this might involve a Royal Navy boarding party.** While we believe that it is possible to put someone on board any ship in territorial waters using the Royal Prerogative – as was done in the case of the *ODIGITRIA B* (see Appendix L) – a clear and specific power is desirable to eliminate any scope for argument on powers in a crisis. Any new legislation should specifically put in a saver for the Prerogative power to prevent its extinction.

---

[12] Article 221.

20.33   We believe that the Intervention Convention 1969 and Article 221 of UNCLOS 1982 taken together allow these powers to be exercised in a reasonable and proportional manner, not just in territorial waters but also in an EEZ (or equivalent) and on the High Seas. **We recommend that suitable domestic legislation should be drawn up, after any necessary international consultation, in particular with neighbouring countries, to ensure consistency of approach.**

Lloyd's Open Forms

20.34   Salvage services have always been, and still are, capable of being rendered and remunerated without any agreement between ship and salvor, their respective rights and duties and the salvor's remuneration being determined by maritime law as interpreted by the courts with jurisdiction at the place where the salvage service ends. Despite this, since the 19th Century there has been a demand for some sort of salvage agreement regulating these matters, whilst still retaining the "no cure – no pay" basis. Lloyd's of London met this demand in 1892 with the publication of "Lloyd's Standard Form of Salvage Agreement – No Cure – No Pay". It has been progressively updated and for the purposes of this Inquiry it is only necessary to refer to LOF (Lloyd's Open Form) 80 published in 1980 and LOF 90 published in 1990, following the conclusion of the International Convention on Salvage, 1989.

20.35   The Forms are known as "Open" because they are drafted in general terms which are applicable to any salvage situation and therefore leave nothing which need be specifically agreed between the parties. Whilst the Forms contemplate that they will be signed by the parties, this can be done at any time, it being sufficient that the ship and salvor shall in fact have agreed, possibly orally on the radio, that the salvage service shall be rendered on the basis of Lloyd's Open Form. Once agreed, it also applies to services rendered before the agreement was reached and which otherwise would be regulated by general maritime law.

LOF 80 and LOF 90

20.36   Both Forms detail the rights and obligations of each party and the performance of the salvage service, make provision for security for the salvor's remuneration, for arbitration by an arbitrator from a panel of specialist salvage arbitrators with a right of appeal to an appeal arbitrator in the event of a dispute and for the payment of salvage remuneration and other sums as agreed between the parties or, in default of agreement, awarded by arbitration.

20.37   Both Forms, like their predecessors, are based upon the traditional principle of "no cure – no pay". However LOF 80 departs from this principle in the case of salvage services rendered to a tanker laden or partly laden with a cargo of oil to the extent that if the services are not successful, are only partially successful or the salvor was prevented from completing the salvage services, the salvor can recover his reasonably incurred expenses together with an increment not exceeding 15 per cent if, but only to the extent that, this would exceed what would otherwise be recoverable on a "no cure – no pay" basis.

20.38   LOF 90 (which is reproduced as Appendix M) takes this process considerably further by incorporating various provisions of the International Convention on Salvage, 1989, and, in particular, Article 14 entitled "Special Compensation". This applies if the salvor:

> "has carried out salvage operations in respect of a vessel which by itself or its cargo threatened damage to the environment and has failed to earn a reward under Article 13 [the general criteria for fixing the reward] at least equivalent to the special compensation assessable in accordance with this Article".

The special compensation, which is payable by the ship and not by the cargo, is equivalent to the expenses of the salvor. However if:

> "the salvor by his salvage operations has prevented or minimised damage to the environment",

it may be:

> "increased up to a maximum of 30 per cent of those expenses".

However:

> "the tribunal, if it deems it fair and just to do so ... may increase such compensation further, but in no event shall the total increase be more than 100 per cent of the expenses".

This somewhat surprising formula conceals starkly differing views amongst those drafting the Convention on whether the ceiling for special compensation should be 30 per cent or 100 per cent in excess of the salvor's expenses.

20.39   The Forms differ in other respects which are less relevant to this Inquiry and both are in use today. It is said[13] that in terms of threatened pollution in mid-ocean far from coastal waters some professional salvors prefer LOF 80 to LOF 90.

20.40   A LOF 90 contract was in place in the case of the *BRAER* and we understand that the salvor is making a claim under the Convention, as incorporated in LOF 90, to cover his expenses even though in the event his efforts did not prevent or minimise pollution. Without LOF 90 it is highly unlikely that the salvor would have been prepared to persist in his efforts long after the prospect of saving property had passed.

---

[13] *Maritime Law of Salvage* by Geoffrey Brice QC (2nd edition) para 6-01.

20.41   Ship-to-shore communications are so sophisticated that a Master can normally get in touch with the shipowner very quickly. Nevertheless delays are likely, particularly if the owner or his agent is in a different time zone and, perhaps, asleep or unavailable at the crucial moment. At best, communication, explanation and decision are likely to take half an hour or so. Establishing communication with cargo owners or demonstrating that it cannot be done is even more time consuming. Even a short delay may prove critical to the ability of the salvor to prevent pollution.

20.42   When the *UNION STAR* was lost in 1981, and the Penlee lifeboat was also lost with all hands trying to save her crew, delay while the Master obtained the owner's permission to sign Lloyd's Open Form arguably contributed to the loss of life. The report of the Formal Investigation[14] also commented adversely on the Master's reluctance to announce a distress situation. It is also interesting to note that the report[15] suggested to the Department of Trade (which was then responsible for marine safety) that HM Coastguard should have powers to engage tug assistance.

20.43   **Shipowners and Masters should make the fullest use of LOF 90. We recommend that the Department of Transport should seek to persuade them to do so through insurers, through the Chamber of Shipping and through IMO.**

The Salvage Convention 1989

20.44   United Kingdom legal and insurance interests played a key role in the development of the 1989 Salvage Convention which substantially revises and updates salvage law and its adoption was strongly supported by the Government. The United Kingdom has signed the Convention but ratification depends on primary legislation being enacted: the necessary legislation is currently before Parliament. By the end of 1993 the Convention had obtained eight of the 15 ratifications needed for it to enter into force internationally. It will come into force one year after the fifteenth State ratifies. When the Convention is in force internationally or applied through national law its terms will apply, in the absence of a specific salvage contract, to all acts of salvage affected by United Kingdom law.

20.45   Even though it is not yet in force internationally, the 1989 Convention has already proved its worth through its partial incorporation into LOF 90 and the awards subsequently made by Lloyd's salvage arbitrators. There have been six Arbitral Awards since 1990 under LOF 90 in which Article 14 Special Compensation has been awarded. In all cases save one the increment on the salvor's expenses has been 30 per cent or less. In one, involving a fire on a large tanker, it was 65 per cent. The cases have ranged from threatened environmental pollution from bunkers to pollution from crude oil cargoes, and have been located geographically on the coasts of the Baltic, the UK, Spain, Kenya and Malaysia. Two of these cases are subject to appeal. In addition there are four pending part-heard Article 14 arbitrations.

---

[14] HMSO 1983: ISBN 0 11 513722 X.
[15] paragraph 15.5.2.

20.46   Article 6(2) of the 1989 Convention provides that:

> "The Master shall have the authority to conclude contracts for salvage operations on behalf of the owner of the vessel. The Master or the owner of the vessel shall have the authority to conclude such contracts on behalf of the owner of the property on board the vessel."

These provisions are of vital importance in the context of saving time when an emergency threatens and change the law in two respects. First, although the Master had implied authority to bind his owners, this authority could be circumscribed by instructions from them that, for example, he should not accept salvage services without first consulting them. The Convention prevents this happening as a matter of law, if not of fact. Second, neither the owners nor the Master had any authority to bind the cargo, save where it could be shown that they could not communicate with the cargo owners and obtain express authority. Bearing in mind that the different parts of the cargo may well have different owners, the problem is obvious.

20.47   We gave the Secretary of State advance warning on 10 June 1993 that we believe that **it is essential in the interests of reducing the chances of future pollution that the Government ratifies the Salvage Convention as quickly as possible.** The letter is reproduced at Appendix P. As we said in paragraph 1.35, we are delighted at the introduction in Parliament of the Merchant Shipping (Salvage and Pollution) Bill which will enable the Convention to be ratified.

Peril at Sea and Salvage

20.48   *Peril at Sea and Salvage – A Guide for Masters*[16], produced jointly by the International Chamber of Shipping and the Oil Companies International Marine Forum, emphasises not only that early communication with all those who might be concerned is vital, but that requests for assistance should never be delayed merely to negotiate a particular form of agreement or contract terms. The guide makes it clear that engaging salvors does not affect the Master's authority or overriding responsibility for the safety of the ship, its cargo and those on board. It stresses that the Master must also make every effort to prevent or minimise damage to the environment.

20.49   We were interested to note that the Liberian report into the *BRAER* incident recommended that *Peril at Sea and Salvage* should be carried aboard all Liberian vessels: the recommendation is reproduced in Appendix Q.

20.50   **Although the guide was prepared mainly for oil tankers and gas carriers, much of its advice applies to other types of ships and we recommend its universal adoption by shipowners as part of their company rulebooks. This would be the clearest endorsement for charterers and managers of the principle that the Master has the authority to take any action necessary for the safety of the ship.**

---

[16] 4th edition, 1992—ISBN 1 85609 032 9.

Salvage and insurance

20.51 The cost of salvage, and thus payment for the salvor on the terms agreed, is normally included in hull and cargo insurances. However the special compensation under LOF 90 and the Salvage Convention[17] (paragraph 20.38) is payable only by the vessel owner, not the cargo owner, and is insured by the P & I Clubs. The cost of a salvage award will thus often be split three ways between the hull insurers, the cargo insurers and the P & I Club.

20.52 The insurers are aware of the advantages of salvors or other assistance being called out, even if they are not in the end used. **We welcome any pressure they put on owners and Masters to ensure that assistance is called for at an early stage.**

20.53 When the Salvage Convention was being drafted (1981 – 1989) it was assumed both that there would continue to be an effective salvage industry and that there would be universal P & I cover. In fact, the salvage industry is in decline and, as we have discussed in the previous three chapters, some ships have neither hull nor P & I cover.

20.54 If there is no insurance the public purse may have to bear any cost of assistance to prevent pollution. An owner who is irresponsible enough – or impoverished enough – not to have insurance cover is unlikely to be sufficiently public spirited to incur the cost of saving a worthless vessel to prevent pollution. In the *BORODINSKOYE POLYE* incident described in Chapter 17 and Appendix L, MPCU spent over £500,000 in recovering over 400 tonnes of bunker oil from the wreck. The vessel was not insured and at the time of writing MPCU was still seeking payment by the owners of its costs and costs incurred by other authorities during the incident.

Salvage and compensation claims

20.55 There have been a number of instances where salvage operations undertaken after an oil pollution incident have led to claims under the 1969 Civil Liability and 1971 International Fund Conventions. The Executive Committee of the International Oil Pollution Compensation Fund has agreed that salvage operations could be considered as falling under the definition of "preventive measures" in the Conventions only if the primary purpose was to prevent pollution damage; if the operations primarily had another purpose, such as salvaging hull or cargo, the operations would not be covered by the Conventions. **We believe that this distinction is mistaken. There is no necessary antithesis between saving the ship and cargo and preventing pollution. So long as *a* purpose of the operation is to prevent pollution, it is wholly or in part a "preventive measure" and should be treated by the Fund as such. As we said in paragraph 19.9, in the context of standing costs incurred by national and local authorities in maintaining a pollution response capability, we hope that the Fund will reconsider, and we recommend that the UK Government should press it to do so.**

[17] Article 14.

The salvage industry

What salvors do

20.56 Most salvage and emergency assistance work is carried out by members of the International Salvage Union (ISU), which has over 40 member companies in 27 countries. In recent years ISU salvors have performed over 2,000 salvage operations, more than 250 of them involving oil tankers and chemical carriers. In the last four years, they have salved 36 laden tankers which threatened major pollution and prevented over 4.5 million tonnes of cargo entering the marine environment.[18]

20.57 Salvage action may involve extinguishing a major tanker fire, making the vessel safe and carrying out a ship-to-ship transfer of the cargo. Salvage is sometimes impossible: in that case the best strategy may be to pump out the contents of intact cargo tanks. If the ship sinks, it may still be possible to rig special pumping systems and recover cargo, or even lift the entire vessel and her contents. Even where a casualty spills oil, subsequent salvage can prevent further pollution. The same can be said for vessels carrying chemicals and other hazardous cargoes.

20.58 In 1990 the tanker *MEGA BORG* suffered a huge stern fire while 60 miles off Galveston, Texas. A professional salvage team brought the fire under control, extinguished it and redelivered the vessel and remaining cargo. The small percentage of oil lost was almost entirely consumed in the flames. The rest of the cargo was saved, and major pollution was avoided.

Salvage teams

20.59 Salvage and towing assistance are complex tasks requiring highly trained and expert teams, usually under the direction of skilled Salvage Masters – the "Red Adairs" of the sea. Non-specialist teams, or those not accustomed to working together, may prove incapable of dealing with a real emergency. The crews of harbour and off-shore support tugs, though highly skilled at their normal tasks, may well not have the training and experience necessary for a successful salvage or other emergency operation.

20.60 It would be possible to train special incident teams to be airlifted onto a tug in an emergency, but they would inevitably be unfamiliar with the tug itself. Comprehensive training of all relevant crews is probably more effective.

Salvage equipment

20.61 Essential salvage equipment is bulky: it includes pumps, generators, compressors, lighting kits, towing gear and fenders. But much of this can be made up into 3 tonne loads which can be airlifted, including by helicopter, if necessary. MPCU maintains a stockpile

---

[18] evidence from Smit Tak BV, Rotterdam.

of salvage equipment in air-transportable loads. So do some professional salvors. Normal tugs and support vessels are unlikely to carry this equipment and airlifting it from a central stockpile would take several hours. Salvage vessels often employ teams of divers to assess underwater damage and perhaps carry out emergency repairs. Again, divers and their equipment could be airlifted to a salvage vessel but this also would take several hours.

Tugs for emergency towing

20.62   Tugs vary enormously in their purposes and capacity. For our purposes, the most significant measure is "bollard pull": the rating given to a towing craft measured in tonnes force. The maximum bollard pull is the force that can be exerted over a short pull and the continuous bollard pull is the force exerted by a tug over a long period. Under reasonable weather conditions a tug or supply ship with a rated bollard pull of 100 tonnes would be capable of towing a fully laden VLCC, but a tug with a bollard pull of 150 tonnes would be needed to control a VLCC successfully in bad weather[19]. It was suggested to us in oral evidence[20] that a bollard pull of about 125 tonnes should be enough in most circumstances for a ship to be held in position.

Harbour or berthing tugs

20.63   Most harbours have tugs to escort and manoeuvre vessels into their berths: all areas of the UK except north west Scotland are within reasonably easy reach of a harbour tug[21]. Most harbour authorities would be willing to release at least one tug immediately for emergencies (leaving another to deal with any problems arising within the port itself) but their capacity for emergency use is limited. Berthing tugs generally operate in sheltered waters and are not designed for sea-keeping. Even the newest of these tugs have a bollard pull of only about 60 tonnes: some have bollard pulls of 6 tonnes or less.

20.64   Some harbour tugs are fitted with fairly basic salvage equipment, but they could not routinely carry the full range needed for a major operation. They may be very useful as a first response while a stronger tug is on its way: but without major upgrading they could not provide a full emergency towing service. Harbour tugs use different towing gear from that employed for ocean towing.

Off-shore anchor-handling tugs

20.65   Tugs used by the off-shore industry for supply and anchor handling are stronger, typically with a bollard pull of about 90 tonnes. They are used to ferry supplies to and from off-shore installations, and to lift and manoeuvre rig chains and anchors. Both of these tasks require clear deck space. They may also tow rigs. They can operate in bad weather but they steam slowly in it.

---

[19] Recommendation to Department of Transport in Murray Fenton report.
[20] 29 June 1993: Mr M J Lacey.
[21] evidence from British Tugowners' Association.

20.66   There is a large and modern fleet of off-shore support vessels operating in some areas around the United Kingdom, but the number of craft available worldwide at any one time varies considerably. Off-shore tugs often cannot practicably abandon their current task immediately to help in an emergency. Even when they can do so, they may have to return to port to deposit unnecessary personnel and equipment before being able to take on towing duties. And of course there will often be contractual problems, as support vessels usually operate under fixed medium-term contracts.

20.67   Like harbour tugs, off-shore support vessels do not and could not routinely carry equipment for salvage and assistance.

Salvage tugs

20.68   Salvage tugs are, not surprisingly, by far the most effective at the job for which they were designed. They can operate in virtually all weathers, and can normally reach a casualty far faster than a non-purpose built tug. They can have a bollard pull of up to about 250 tonnes. There are now very few such tugs worldwide, and those that exist are getting old, but a salvage tug is normally to be found on station in the Falmouth/Western Approaches area during the winter months, as salvage is still a commercial prospect there. There are otherwise no dedicated commercial salvage tugs based in the UK.

20.69   Salvage tugs alone are inadequate for our purposes: they must be supported by the personnel, equipment and skills inherent in an experienced salvage organisation.

Ministry of Defence tugs

20.70   The Ministry of Defence (Royal Navy) has tugs of up to 50 tonnes bollard pull stationed at bases around the UK coast. They are available to assist in maritime emergencies, particularly when life is at risk or serious pollution is threatened. When life is not at risk, and when pollution is not threatened, they would not be used in competition with commercial salvors. When tugs are in harbour outside normal working hours they are at a maximum of 8 hours' notice.

20.71   Ministry of Defence (Royal Navy and Royal Air Force) helicopters are regularly used for search and rescue under formal arrangements between the Department of Transport and the Ministry of Defence. There is no similar arrangement for the use of Royal Navy tugs but their availability and readiness are known to the Coastguard stations adjacent to their bases and their use would be considered by COASTGUARD for incidents requiring towing assistance.

Availability of tugs by area

20.72   The Department of Transport estimates[22] that:

(a)   there is still a good chance of being able to get a tug to a casualty in the English Channel within 12 hours, and often within 6 hours. It remains a matter of probability, not certainty;

(b)   off the East Coast and particularly to the north east of Scotland and Shetland there is a good chance of getting an anchor handler or off-shore support vessel to a casualty within 12 hours. Again this is a matter of probability; and

(c)   in the Bristol Channel, Irish Sea and on the west coast of Scotland the probability of getting a powerful tug within 12 hours is less, although with the off-shore developments in Morecambe Bay and the "Celtic Sea" the chance of obtaining a support vessel is increasing; the chances of a tow in the area from the North Channel to Cape Wrath are particularly poor.

The problem of salvage capacity

20.73   The professional salvage industry has been in decline for some 20 years. There are fundamental uncertainties associated with the business of salvage, including low remuneration which deters investment in new salvage vessels, equipment and personnel. The traditional family owned companies have disappeared. Many now exist as lone divisions within diversified marine services groups which are preoccupied with other, more lucrative markets and which expect salvage enterprises to yield a satisfactory return on capital employed. As a result, tugs are no longer on salvage station and the salvage fleet is much reduced. Experienced salvage personnel within many companies have been redeployed or have left the industry.

20.74   Ironically the reduction in the casualty rate has made a major contribution to the decline in salvage capacity, and thus to an increase in the risks to safety and the environment from vessels which get into worse difficulties than necessary because salvage tugs are not close enough. Further reductions in the number of casualties will inevitably reduce still more the capacity of the salvage industry to respond. The problem has been much discussed in IMO, by the EC and by Governments, but no consensus has emerged.

20.75   Salvage awards have always taken some account of standby facilities, and the Salvage Convention[23] specifically states that awards should take account of the availability and use of vessels or other equipment intended for salvage operations, and the state of readiness and efficiency of the salvor's equipment and the value thereof. These provisions already apply to arbitrators under LOF 90 and will apply to the courts once the Salvage Convention is fully incorporated into UK law. **We believe that in future the courts and salvage arbitrators should take greater account of the cost of maintaining standby facilities in fixing salvage awards, and we entirely agree with the recommendation of the Salvage Working Group** (see the next paragraph) **to that effect.**

---

[22] Written evidence, annex 7.
[23] Article 13.1 (i) and (j).

The Salvage Working Group

20.76   In 1990, shipowners and insurers joined salvors in establishing a Salvage Working Group which reported in February 1993[24]. Its recommendations relevant to our study were:

(a)   "Tribunals involved in the assessment of remuneration for salvage services under the terms of international salvage conventions and 'no cure, no pay' contracts incorporating the terms of such conventions should, when assessing the award, take particular account of the decline of the salvage industry ... and ensure they give sufficient encouragement to the dedicated professional salvor."

(b)   "When contracting salvage services, the shipping and insurance industries should give more weight to salvors who have a major investment in salvage equipment and expertise, and have the capacity to deal with very large salvage incidents. This implies that users would, when taking immediate commercial decisions concerning salvage contracts, bear in mind their long term interest in ensuring the continued availability of essential expertise."

(c)   "The dialogue be maintained between users and the salvage industry, to further strengthen the positive relationship between salvors and their clients and promote a greater understanding of each other's problems."

The Salvage Working Group considered that these recommendations would at best only stabilise the current situation in the short term. It concluded that:

(d)   "there is a need for investment in salvage vessels, equipment and personnel which cannot be funded from present commercial returns on salvage activities. The maritime and insurance industries therefore need to work together to seek a solution to the reduction and ageing of the salvage fleet."

The Working Group pointed out that:

(e)   "All nations benefit from the ready availability of salvage resources. The saving of life and property and the prevention of pollution are matters of public interest. Increasingly, salvage is taking on a public service dimension. This has been recognised by some Governments ... who have made arrangements to provide stand-by salvage capability on a local basis which are only partly funded through commercial salvage awards and contracts."

It went on to recommend that:

(f)   "Such arrangements could be extended on a multinational, regional basis. States should cooperate in order to maximise the benefits of any salvage capacity which

---

[24] The Report was endorsed by American Institute of Underwriters, USA; Associazione Nazionale fra le Imprese Assicuratrici, Italy; The Baltic and International Maritime Council; The Central Union of Marine Underwriters, Oslo; Deutscher Transport-Versicherungs-Verband EV, Germany; European Chemical Industry Council, Belgium; Intercargo (International Association of Dry Cargo Shipowners); International Chamber of Shipping; International Group of P & I Clubs; International Salvage Union; Intertanko (International Association of Independent Tanker Owners); International Association of Marine Assurance; The Institute of London Underwriters; Lloyd's Underwriters' Association; The Marine and Fire Insurance Association of Japan; The Salvage Association; Shell International Marine Ltd; The Swedish Club.

is available. By such cooperation, salvage cover worldwide could be substantially improved."

We very much welcome this initiative and commend the Working Group's recommendations.

Action taken by some other countries

France

20.77 Since the *AMOCO CADIZ* disaster in 1978, when 220,000 tonnes of crude oil spilled into the sea, the French Government has paid for two tugs of some 160 tonnes bollard pull to be permanently stationed, one at Cherbourg and one at Brest. The tugs, which are capable of operating in the worst weather, are on 40 minutes' notice when in port: in specified unfavourable weather conditions they proceed to sea so that they are ready to respond immediately to incidents. The Préfecture Maritime may dispatch a tug either at the request of a ship's Master or on its own initiative. A solution can be imposed upon a Master, but only as a last resort.

20.78 The tugs' sole task is to tow ships in danger to a place of safety. Since 1978 they have been involved in providing assistance to over 400 vessels. They can accept salvage and towage contracts, on either a day rate basis or LOF. Unlike some other countries, the French do not forbid other salvors to operate. The net salvage proceeds from the contracted tugs are shared equally between the salvage company and the French Government. We understand that salvage proceeds normally cover only a fairly small proportion of the French Government's costs.

20.79 The French Government also shares the cost of a 33 tonne bollard pull harbour tug at Dunkirk.

Spain

20.80 A comprehensive agency, Sociedad Estatal de Salvamento y Seguridad Marítima (SASEMA), was established in November 1992 to coordinate search and rescue, monitoring, salvage and anti-pollution measures. SASEMA has contracts with salvage companies to maintain 11 tugs, among other resources, on permanent station at designated ports, in return for a fixed annual fee. When a ship is identified as being a potential problem, SASEMA will direct a tug (or an aircraft) to attend it.

Italy

20.81 The Italian Government requires that each port has one tug on permanent standby to be available to assist in any marine emergency. The costs of this service are met by the State.

South Africa

20.82 South Africa was the first State to appreciate the extent to which its coastline was exposed to the threat of pollution following the closure of the Suez Canal in 1967, and the development of the VLCC.

20.83   Since 1976 there has been a cost and profit sharing scheme under which two 160 tonne bollard pull tugs remain on station, one in Cape Town and the other in Port Elizabeth, during the four winter months: in the rest of the year one tug remains on the South African coast and the other trades internationally. They provide emergency towing, usually as a response to a casualty report through the normal channels but occasionally as a reaction to reports from aircraft surveillance.

20.84   Over the last 17 years these tugs have carried out some of the most spectacular salvage services to laden oil tankers of up to 350,000 dwt. They claim to have salvaged some 6.7 million tonnes of tanker tonnage in a total of 42 successful tanker salvages. They have made 59 other ocean or coastal ship salvages.

The future of outside assistance in UK waters

20.85   Outside assistance should be recognised as an essential part of the prevention of incidents which may lead to pollution. **The primary duty must be on the owner and Master to make sure, by calling for assistance when needed, that they do not risk safety or pollution directly or indirectly.** The system which we recommend in Chapter 15 whereby faults must be reported to HM Coastguard should reinforce this responsibility: it most certainly should not replace it. **The polluter pays principle should apply to potential pollution as much as to actual pollution. Costs of pollution prevention should be met by potential polluters rather than by the Government.**

20.86   **Salvage is, and should remain, a primarily private sector service. It would not be sensible for the Government to buy its own salvage capacity: this would be an inefficient use of taxpayers' money and an intrusion into a limited market.**

20.87   Nevertheless, the Government has a strong interest in preventing vessels in difficulties from going aground. **There is not sufficient salvage capacity in UK waters at the moment, nor is it coherently organised. The market will not provide enough capacity. Action needs to be taken to achieve the ends of the action taken by other Governments, though we suggest a rather different approach.**

20.88   **We believe that the Government should set up a system to ensure that tugs with adequate salvage capacity are available at key points around UK shores. The tugs concerned would normally be provided commercially, but where the Royal Navy – or other public sector bodies – have tugs available it might make more sense for them, or if necessary stronger replacements, to be used. Where adequate capacity cannot be provided in any other way, the Government should arrange for the funding of the difference between what is needed and what the private sector can provide.**

20.89   We have considered whether there would be a case for positioning emergency tugs only in the winter months, when the risks are greater. The cost would be less, but the risk of a catastrophe during the summer months would remain. We do not think that this would be acceptable.

Equal sectors – a flawed solution

20.90   One possible approach is to divide the coast into several sectors, each of roughly the same size, and station a full power salvage tug in each of them. When we first considered this problem we thought that up to ten areas, each with a strong tug, might be justifiable in terms of distance and thus steaming time[25] to a possible casualty, but we dismissed this as impracticable. The cost would be substantial and very difficult to justify: but even more important, most of the tugs and their crew would have virtually nothing to do for much of the time. That is not merely wasteful of high quality scarce resources in terms of the tugs themselves and their skilled crews: it also means that the crews would have no chance to practice their skills and would inevitably find it hard to maintain them. After a while it would become very difficult, perhaps impossible, to recruit and retain the necessary crews: the type of people needed for salvage are unlikely to tolerate such a tediously uneventful existence.

20.91   One suggestion put to us[26] on a similar basis was for four tugs of about 125 tonnes bollard pull, to be stationed off the Isle of Wight, off the Tees, in the Fair Isle Channel and between Anglesey and the Isle of Man. As these stations are some 400 miles apart, the maximum distance to any part of the coast would be some 200 miles. Assuming an average speed of about 12 knots, the **maximum** steaming time to a casualty would be about 17 hours: actual times would of course depend on many factors, including distances and the weather.

20.92   The Department of Transport's consultants took the sensible approach that if a vessel is broken down and drifting, the time available for a tug to get to her will depend, among other things, on her distance from land. They concluded that it makes most sense for tugs to be stationed where shipping routes pass closest to land: that is in straits. On that basis they suggested that there should be five sectors, covering the Dover Strait; the Western Approaches; the Western Isles and North Channel; Orkney and Shetland; and the East Coast.

20.93   We see considerable problems with this approach. While we believe that it is sensible to base calculations on the assumption that help should be available to reach vessels around UK coasts within a maximum of about 12 hours in normal conditions, we have two important qualifications. One is that in some areas, such as the Dover Strait, assistance, if needed, will have to be provided in much less than 12 hours. The other is that we do not believe that, for the reasons set out above, it is realistic to set up a system whereby a tug of 150 tonnes bollard pull could reach all areas around the UK coast within 12 hours in all weathers.

A mix of sectors – the pragmatic solution

20.94   **We believe that the problem needs to be tackled pragmatically, with a mixture of a very few full capacity tugs with smaller tugs which can administer**

---

[25] The time elapsed from a tug leaving port or its permanent station to arriving at a casualty.
[26] Written evidence from Mr M J Lacey.

first aid to a ship in difficulties, minimising her drift while a stronger tug is on her way. Decisions on the mix of tugs and the areas to be covered should take into account such matters as the type and density of traffic, particular hazards, the prevailing weather, the risk of grounding on a dangerous shore and the sensitivity of the coasts as well as commercial practicalities. It is also crucially important to consider what facilities are already available, or could be made available, to ensure good coverage at the least cost.

Sharing with other countries

20.95   The first point to consider is whether neighbouring countries are willing to cooperate to ensure sensible provision. We are encouraged to learn that the French Government has made it clear that its dedicated tugs are available for use in UK waters in an emergency, assuming that they are not otherwise engaged: this is typical of the excellent cooperation between Bonn Agreement countries (see paragraphs 5.60 and 21.7) in dealing with emergencies. **We recommend that the Government should consider with the Governments of neighbouring countries – the Republic of Ireland, France, Belgium and the Netherlands – whether combined salvage capacity in adjacent waters is practicable. The Government might also want to approach the EC Commission to investigate the possibility of a joint approach.** But while we would welcome international cooperation, we recognise the difficulties and the inevitable delays which negotiation will require.

Sharing with other users

20.96   **There is no case for either full power salvage tugs or smaller "first aid" tugs on permanent standby duty with no other tasks.** The cost would be formidable and could not be justified without offsetting savings. Equally important is the waste and blunting of skills that would arise from highly trained and highly skilled crews hanging around for most of the year with nothing to do, as would inevitably be the case.

20.97   **What is needed is multi-use vessels which can earn much of their keep by doing other jobs:** "first aid" tugs might do so for perhaps three-quarters of their time, the full power salvage tugs probably for less. **Salvage tugs** may be able to take on extra tasks including:

(a)   commercial salvage and towing work;

(b)   rescue: this forms an important part of the Spanish system, where tugs also serve as rescue vessels. We accept that most SAR is best carried out by lifeboats and helicopters, but that in the Dover Strait there may be a case for equipping tugs for a dual use in rescuing large numbers of people from ferries, the high sides of which create special problems; and

(c)   Royal Navy salvage: alternatively, Royal Navy salvage might be entrusted to commercial salvors.

20.98 **Smaller tugs** may be able to take on extra tasks including:

(a) off-shore support vessels, including modern multi-purpose vessels such as anchor handling tug supply vessels – an owner of a fleet of these might conclude that he can so organise his fleet that one will always be available; and

(b) harbour or terminal tugs – a harbour or terminal operator or a fleet operator might again decide that it would be practicable to organise a fleet of tugs so that one, with the necessary bollard pull, can always be made available.

In all cases it would be necessary for other tasks to be abandoned or curtailed in an emergency.

20.99 There may also be a case for equipping and using tugs for at-sea recovery of pollutants, surveillance, dispersant spraying, fisheries protection, customs duties or fire fighting, or any combination of these uses. We hope that discussions between the Department of Transport, other Government Departments and the industry will generate further ideas, but it must be made clear that the prime role of the tugs is emergency towing.

20.100 When carrying out other tasks, dual use vessels may not be able to carry dedicated salvage gear, and may indeed have to offload other equipment before taking it on. In these cases there may be a case for keeping salvage gear at strategic places to be taken out to the tugs at short notice.

The criteria for stationing tugs

20.101 On this basis of a mix of large and small tugs, all of them with other potential uses, the first thing to do is to establish the areas where need is greatest. **There should be two alternative criteria for this: density and type of traffic, and whether any tug assistance at all is now available.**

Traffic density

20.102 As Plate 1 shows, the densest traffic flows in the UK are along the southern and eastern coasts, with a particular concentration in the Dover Strait. The eastern coast of the UK is reasonably well served by off-shore support vessels and tugs based in other North Sea countries. The southern coast of England and the Western Approaches can be reached by the French tugs stationed at Cherbourg and Brest, and a commercial tug is normally stationed in Falmouth during the winter months. In both areas, the potential demand for towage assistance is high, but as the supply is reasonable there is no urgent need for a major tug in either area.

20.103 The exception to this is the key point where traffic is densest: the Dover Strait itself, where there is some of the most concentrated sea traffic in the world. We do not understand why there is no tug on regular station: there should be one as a high priority.

20.104   Traffic is far less dense on the northern and north western coasts of Great Britain, but, largely because of the lack of traffic, there is less tug provision. All major ports, including those in Orkney and Shetland, have tugs available, and in most cases harbour tugs could provide the necessary "first aid". There are also Royal Navy tugs in some areas which could also be called out to provide first aid in an emergency.

20.105   The one significant exception is north western Scotland – the area of the Minch and the DWR to the west of the Western Isles, the only area of great environmental sensitivity around UK coasts where there is no emergency assistance of any sort now available. Although traffic is sparse, the potential dangers of a failure to the west of the islands are considerable, as we point out in Chapter 14.

The way forward

20.106   **We believe that the way forward is to consider first how the two key areas – the Dover Strait and north western Scotland – can best be provided with strong tugs. The Western Approaches should be considered next. After that, ways should be found to fill in the gaps between those areas in a sensible, pragmatic and cost-effective fashion.**

Contracts for shared use

Defining the sectors and criteria

20.107   **On this approach, the "sectors" will vary substantially in size and nature. Some will be comparatively small, covered by existing tugs which could probably do little more than apply "first aid". Others may be larger, covered by larger tugs which could cope with some incidents themselves and provide "first aid" for the remainder. Others will be covered by full scale salvage tugs, which will both provide direct help in their own areas and go to the aid of ships in other sectors.** These supertugs will be a bit like archbishops, who are directly responsible for their own dioceses as well as superintending the dioceses of their bishops.

20.108   There already exist clear boundaries between countries for search and rescue and counter-pollution purposes, which should obviously remain. The sensible boundaries of sectors within the UK area will to a large extent become apparent in the course of the necessary discussions with other countries and with operators: availability of tugs in other countries or under arrangements reached with contractors are likely to prove a key factor in determining what the sectors within UK waters should be. The basic principles should be that tugs are stationed at points close to the busiest shipping routes and to other areas where vessels are likely to get into difficulties.

20.109   Discussions will also be needed with the industry and other interested parties on the criteria needed in each sector and on minimum standards for crew, including training. Consideration should be given to the possibility of trained crews, and possibly a minimum of essential equipment, being airlifted onto suitable vessels. Clear guidance on all these points will be needed.

20.110   Where shared use with other countries is practicable, an agreed means of contracting for the use of tugs and financing them will need to be established. Agreement will also be needed on which country's law should apply in given circumstances, and on who would be in charge. If, as we hope, it proves practicable and acceptable to the French Government for the UK to share the use of the tug stationed at Cherbourg, and perhaps that stationed at Brest, it might not be reasonable to expect significant changes in the existing organisation for the financing and use of those tugs.

Franchises

20.111   In other cases, there should be a franchise for each sector. The franchises will be specially negotiated flexible contracts, designed to balance commercial benefits against the broader needs of the community: a compromise which maximises total benefits. Bids should be invited to provide the service, with stated minimum criteria in terms of availability and bollard pull of tugs, and of crewing (including training and qualifications) and equipment. We expect these criteria to establish a high minimum standard.

20.112   Tugs will normally be owned, managed and manned by commercial operators. The Department of Transport will not be involved in their ownership or in their operation but will have the authority as part of franchising arrangements to call out these tugs in an emergency or potential emergency.

20.113   The bids will be for a retainer, to bridge the gap between the cost of providing a service to the standard required and the net benefit – including other uses – to the provider. Assuming that the minimum criteria are met, the organisation requiring the smallest figure for this retainer to provide the service will normally get the franchise. In some areas, particularly the Dover Strait, there is unlikely to be a case for a large retainer, in which case the bids could be judged by the quality of service provided. A decision will need to be taken on whether the franchisee should get the whole value of any salvage awards or whether this should be shared: the decision would of course affect the value of the franchises.

20.114   The franchisee will then be obliged, by the terms of his franchise, to provide a service to the level stated on the instructions of the Department of Transport. How he does it is his concern. This system allows the franchisee much greater flexibility than any alternative, and thus greater efficiency and lower costs. Administrative costs to the Department of Transport are also reduced to a minimum. We were pleased to see that the Department of Transport's consultants concluded that a similar system, which they described as a "turnkey" operation, represented the best value for money.

20.115   Consideration will also need to be given to the problem of whether non-franchised tugs can be discouraged or even excluded in a particular incident. Because of the scarcity of tugs this situation is unlikely to arise very often. The key point is that the best available assets should be used to deal with a marine emergency whether they are already contracted to COASTGUARD or whether they simply happen to be there. If a Master wishes to contract with a tug which is as good as or better than a franchised one, in terms of either strength or nearness, there should be no impediment. But if he prefers to strike a deal with a tug which is less suitable for any reason, we believe that COASTGUARD should use the intervention powers to override the Master's preference.

Dual uses within the public sector

20.116   **We believe that the same principles of franchising should apply if more than one use is envisaged within the public sector.** If, say, the Royal Navy or a publicly owned harbour authority wishes to bid for franchises it should do so on the same terms as the private sector.

20.117   **Where a dual use is contemplated which would be for the benefit of the public sector, the relevant part of the public sector should consider a similar franchising operation.** Where Department of Transport interests such as search and rescue, at-sea recovery of pollutants, surveillance or dispersant spraying are concerned, the Department can franchise two or more uses at the same time if that is desirable. It would be for discussion whether the Department should pay for any equipment or dispersant (including the replacement of dispersant past its expiry date) or whether this should be covered by the franchise. We discuss how pollutants should be dealt with in the next chapter.

20.118   Where another Department is concerned – for instance, the Scottish Office Agriculture and Fisheries Department (SOAFD) for fisheries protection – the position will be more complicated. There is no reason in principle why, for instance, the Royal Navy should not add an emergency towing franchise to existing fisheries protection duties for SOAFD, so long as both the Navy and SOAFD are content with the arrangements. Equally we can see no reason why a private sector salvage company should not carry out both tasks – and perhaps salvage of Royal Navy vessels as well.

The costs and benefits of franchising

20.119   The Department of Transport's consultants considered both the costs and the benefits of establishing the system described in paragraph 20.92. They concluded that the cost of buying a new tug of 150 – 170 tonnes bollard pull is some £12 million – £15 million: second hand prices are about £4 million – £6 million. A new tug of 100 – 120 tonnes bollard pull might cost some £12 million and a second hand one some £4 million. For a 70 tonne bollard pull tug the figures might be £5 million to £8 million and £2 million respectively. Chartering costs for a 150 – 170 tonne bollard pull tug might be between £2.5 million and £3.3 million a year. Buying or chartering more than one vessel, or chartering for a lengthy period, would be likely to make a substantial difference to prices. The consultants' own suggestion of five large tugs might thus cost something in the region of £10 million to £15 million a year gross, before taking into account sharing with other countries and with other uses, and any salvage awards.

20.120   We cannot assess either the pattern of sectors and tugs which will be required under our proposals, or the scope for dual use, and thus what the cost to the Department of the franchise retainer will be. We believe however that the cost will vary widely between areas: in particular the retainer for north west Scotland is likely to be larger than elsewhere. We will not hazard any guesses: to do so would be misleading and could undermine the Department's negotiating position.

20.121   Given these uncertainties, in considering costs we have taken the Department of Transport's consultants' assumptions as the best available. We believe that it is reasonable to assume that dual use will recoup half to two-thirds of the gross cost, leaving some £5 million to be met by other means. We must stress that this figure can only be a rough estimate, which might prove too high or too low.

20.122   We explained in Chapter 4 some of the difficulties of predicting catastrophes, including pollution catastrophes. Because of these difficulties we were not surprised that the Department's consultants found that assessing the benefits of increased availability of tug assistance was extremely difficult. They did not attempt to establish a benefit figure in money terms: they concluded that most of the benefits either accrued, eventually, to owners, insurers and the IOPC Fund or were non-quantifiable. It is because the benefits mostly accrue to commercial interests that we believe that the costs should not be met by the UK taxpayer; our proposals for meeting them are in Chapter 22.

20.123   We have considered the likely benefits and the likely range of costs carefully. We are convinced that the benefits of tug assistance on the basis we recommend do justify the substantial costs: but we cannot demonstrate it. One never can demonstrate the worth of an insurance premium. All we can say is that we believe that the UK cannot risk **not** having the insurance against disaster that facilities for emergency assistance will provide. It appears that some other countries at similar risk have reached the same conclusion.

20.124   That is not to say that it will never be possible to use quantification in assessing the value of capacity for emergency assistance: as we explain in Chapter 4, techniques do exist and are developing, but a great deal of work would be needed before any conclusions could be reached, and a great deal would still be based on value judgements. **We do not believe that it is sensible to wait for such a study, which could take several years: the tugs need to be in place quickly.**

Backchecks

20.125   Because of the substantial resources required and the changes in practices needed, the franchises should be for a fairly long period – at least five years. Before the first franchises expire, we expect that the Government will carry out backchecks to consider how actual use of the franchised tugs related to expected use, and to consider again the boundaries of sectors and the criteria for franchises. We anticipate that by that time it will be possible for a more formalised study of costs and benefits to be carried out.

Timing

20.126   We appreciate that there will be a great deal of work to do in deciding, after the essential wide consultation, just what tug assistance is needed and how best to provide it. There will also be a great deal of work to be done in setting up the new funding arrangements we propose in Chapter 22. While we would very much like to see the entire system in place before the winter of 1994–95, we appreciate that this may not be practicable.

20.127   **We therefore propose that there should be interim arrangements during the winter months until the new system is fully operational, and that the UK Government should be prepared to bear the full cost of such interim arrangements.** We cannot specify just what interim arrangements will be needed, but they should concentrate on the three key areas we identified: north western Scotland, the Dover Strait and the Western Approaches.

Manning and training of tug crews

20.128   We wholly accept a point which was stressed to us in evidence: that salvage and emergency towing are skilled jobs, very different from the normal tasks of the crews of harbour tugs or off-shore support vessels. There is a need for skilled, specialised and above all experienced crew; and they are currently in short supply.

20.129   The key member of a salvage team is the Salvage Master. Salvage Masters are specialised and rare. Various options may need to be considered, including the use of consultant Salvage Masters and Salvage Masters from a different company from that supplying a tug: in either case the Salvage Master is likely to need to be flown in to the tug.

20.130   The new arrangements we recommend will create a market and thus create a demand for training. **We recommend that COASTGUARD should ensure that the terms of contracts encourage initial and repeat training, to ensure smooth handling of a crisis.**

Calling out franchised tugs

20.131   We envisage that, as in other countries, either Masters or the shore-based authorities should be able to call out franchised tugs, and that salvage awards, including awards and special compensation made under LOF 90 and the Salvage Convention, should be awarded in the usual way.

Callout by a Master

20.132   The franchised tugs will be available for normal commercial use, and thus (unless otherwise occupied) available to any Master who needs their services. Whenever a Master is concerned about the safety of his ship he should seek at least first line protection – possibly alerting the nearest tug to the possibility of a problem.

20.133 We recommend in Chapter 15 a system whereby Masters must report immediately any specified failures, as an addition to the existing MARPOL requirement for Masters to report if they are in any difficulty when carrying oil cargoes. Shipowners' standing instructions to Masters should reinforce this system and should also give Masters clear authority to summon salvage assistance without prior approval or delay.

Callout by COASTGUARD

20.134 Masters and owners should not fear that the Department of Transport will call out expensive assistance whenever it is told of any potential problems. We recommend in Chapter 15 that ships should notify HM Coastguard immediately of any problems which are arising or might arise. If the Master and Coastguard are both satisfied that there is no risk, the only reaction to a report of a vessel with mechanical difficulties will be that the Coastguard will contact the vessel after, say, half an hour to find out what is happening.

20.135 The Chief Coastguard issued revised instructions in January 1994 which will ensure that all Coastguard stations have detailed, up-to-date and readily accessible information on tugs which may be available in an incident. The instructions make it clear that tugs can and should be summoned for both safety and pollution prevention reasons, using Lloyd's of London Press Intelligence and suitable tug brokers, and that if necessary tugs can be called out without the agreement of the Master concerned. This will only be done if HM Coastguard is convinced that it is necessary, the Master has not taken action himself despite being advised to do so, and the Master has been warned that suitable tugs will be despatched and that his owner will be expected to bear the cost. The Chief Coastguard or the Chief Executive of COASTGUARD will be informed immediately if this is done by a Coastguard station. Lloyd's of London Press told us in February 1994 that this faster "hot line" early warning system had already enabled them to place a tug alongside a crippled ship in the North Sea before a formal request was passed for salvage assistance.

20.136 If the Master refuses to accept a tow he can be directed to do so by HM Coastguard. If he still refuses, COASTGUARD on behalf of the Secretary of State can take whatever action appears necessary and proportionate to prevent pollution. We hope and expect that it will do so.

20.137 Amendments to the instructions will no doubt be needed in the light of experience: a review of effectiveness will be required. Changes will also be needed once the system of franchised tugs which we recommend is set up. We would expect the Coastguard to call out the most appropriate vessels available, giving preference to franchised tugs or franchised operators only in the rare situation where two tugs or operators are equally suitable.

20.138 We believe that an additional power should be taken. Once this assistance has been ordered, the ship should be deemed by statute to be in peril and to have summoned salvage assistance. The effect of that would be that the owner would be obliged to pay for the cost of callout even if the ship gets under way before assistance arrives: clearly the Master should have summoned assistance and accepted financial responsibility. The scale of payment should be on a salvage basis. The quantum should be determined by the courts and the ship should, if necessary, be arrested as security.

20.139   Such a power should clearly only be used very sparingly and in cases of real need. But we believe that the very existence of the power would act as a spur to ships to summon assistance early, on the much cheaper towage scale. It would **not** be an incitement to refrain from reporting a breakdown because of the fleet sanctions which would then be attracted (see paragraph 15.77).

The role of HM Coastguard in pollution emergencies

20.140   We discuss in Chapter 16 a new role for HM Coastguard in the monitoring and surveillance of shipping. Before considering the way in which franchised tugs should be called out, we need to consider its role in relation to developing emergencies.

20.141   HM Coastguard is part of the Coastguard Agency or COASTGUARD along with the Marine Pollution Control Unit (MPCU) and an administrative division which supports both MPCU and HM Coastguard. Their functions are described in Appendix I.

20.142   Given the very close organisational links between HM Coastguard and MPCU, we were surprised to discover that HM Coastguard takes a comparatively minor role in pollution emergencies. It is the Coastguard Watch Officers, who are on duty at 21 stations around the coast day and night throughout the year, who first hear of a potential or actual emergency. The senior Coastguard Watch Officer on duty has the authority to initiate search and rescue, and in doing so can mobilise lifeboatmen and helicopter winch-men whose lives may be put at risk, as well as mobilising their extremely expensive equipment. A Coastguard does not, however, have authority to mobilise counter-pollution equipment. Instead he immediately notifies MPCU: all MPCU staff are on-call 24 hours a day by telephone or pager. Only if a Coastguard has been unable to get in touch with MPCU within 30 minutes does he initiate action himself.

20.143   One consequence of this is the apparently bizarre one that the Chief Executive of COASTGUARD may be actively involved in the pollution response to an incident while his deputy, the Chief Coastguard, relies on his staff to respond and may not even be aware of the incident concerned. There are in fact good reasons for this situation. First, any HM Coastguard coordinating officer with a major incident to deal with will be fully occupied in mobilising search and rescue. It helps him enormously if he can make a single telephone call to MPCU and leave it to deal with the anti-pollution side of the operation, leaving him to concentrate on search and rescue. We know of no cases where MPCU has not been available within a very few minutes.

20.144   Another reason is that Coastguards undergo intensive training to enable them to react correctly to a search and rescue incident. That training is reinforced by comparatively frequent SAR incidents: an average of 9,000 incidents a year, a high proportion of them involving pleasure craft.

20.145   Pollution incidents where a response may be needed are far rarer and potentially far more complicated, involving a very wide range of polluting chemicals (see the Annex to Appendix J) and a surprisingly wide range of types of oil. Not only training but scientific knowledge is necessary for dealing properly with these incidents. The range of contacts and actions to be taken has little in common with the list for SAR incidents. An enormous amount of training would be needed before MPCU's responsibility in response to spills could be devolved to Coastguard stations. It should also be borne in mind that there are far fewer polluting incidents than SAR incidents and that frequent repeat training would be needed to keep Coastguards' skills properly honed. It is perfectly possible that the vast majority of Coastguard staff would be intensively trained for an activity which never happened. **We accept that this would be a wasteful use of resources.**

20.146   These arguments do not, however, apply with similar force to the summoning of emergency assistance to a vessel which is or may be getting into difficulties. There are clear advantages in terms of both SAR and pollution prevention that emergency assistance should be got to such a vessel as fast as possible. The range of information, contacts and actions does not differentiate between SAR and pollution prevention. **We consider that the Coastguard Watch Officers should be fully trained and equipped to call out emergency assistance to any vessel in difficulties.** We are pleased to record that the Chief Executive of COASTGUARD has come independently to the same conclusion following the relevant observations on the Coastguard's actions in the MAIB report on the *BRAER*, which is recorded in Appendix Q, and has already taken steps to implement his decision.

20.147   **Any review of the legislation under which HM Coastguard and MPCU operate** (see paragraph 20.23) **should ensure that any new legislation is framed in broad terms and that any limitations on the use of the powers should be managerial rather than legislative.** Absolute clarity is of course needed on who should do what: but that is best covered in guidance for staff and users.

Contingency planning

20.148   While we broadly endorse the fairly detailed new responsibilities envisaged for HM Coastguard set out in Government evidence to us, which include arrangements for Coastguard Watch Officers to call out tugs when they consider them to be necessary, our proposals for franchised tugs mean that changes to those arrangements are needed. **Detailed plans for the use of this system need to be drawn up, with wide consultation.**

20.149   There should also be contingency plans for the use of franchised tugs and powers of intervention, bearing in mind the variety of possible situations. The plan should recognise that in extreme cases several tugs may have to be used and should provide contingency arrangements for that.

Chapter 21

Cleaning Up Spills

21.1   Our recommendations so far will go a long way towards reducing the chances of oil or other pollutants spilling into our seas, but we must accept that the risks cannot be eliminated. There must be good contingency planning for dealing with spills, to enable a very quick reaction in an emergency to prevent, so far as practicable, oil reaching the shore.

Responsibility for clean-up in the United Kingdom

21.2   The first grounding of a large tanker, the *TORREY CANYON* in 1967, (described later in this chapter) caught the United Kingdom Government unawares. The Government subsequently recognised that it was not reasonably practicable for owners of deep sea tankers, which voyage worldwide, to make contingency arrangements for dealing with oil spills wherever they may occur. It was this which led the Government to accept responsibility for dealing with spillages of oil and other hazardous substances at sea from ships which threatened UK interests. The Government's stated aim in any counter-pollution activities is to minimise damage to people, wildlife, fisheries, ecologically sensitive areas and amenity beaches. This responsibility is exercised by the Marine Pollution Control Unit (MPCU), part of the Coastguard Agency (COASTGUARD). The functions and operations of COASTGUARD are described in Appendix I.

21.3   Coastal local authorities in England, Scotland and Wales have accepted responsibility for dealing with pollution of the shoreline, and harbour authorities have accepted the responsibility for dealing with pollution within port or harbour limits. Their roles are discussed later in this chapter. Shoreline clean-up in Northern Ireland is the responsibility of the Department of the Environment for Northern Ireland.

21.4   As well as dealing itself with major spills at sea the Government, through MPCU, helps local and harbour authorities to coordinate the shoreline clean-up response and provides equipment. MPCU directs off-shore operations and assists in the coordination of the shoreline clean-up response and equipment supply. MPCU also advises local authorities on local plans; arranges courses for training of their staff in shoreline clean-up management and techniques; and manages a programme of research relating to both at-sea and shoreline response.

21.5   Under the 1983 regulations giving effect to MARPOL in the UK, all reports of spillages of oil or other hazardous substances from ships in or near UK waters are – or ought to be – reported immediately to HM Coastguard, which also receives reports of potentially polluting incidents. We discuss this reporting system in paragraphs 15.72 –

15.83. In either case HM Coastguard alerts MPCU. If for any reason the Watch Officer cannot get hold of MPCU staff within 30 minutes, he (or she) can commit first line resources and initiate counter-pollution action. Our recommendations on the relationships between HM Coastguard and MPCU are in paragraphs 20.140 – 20.147.

21.6   The response to a chemical spillage will be tailored to deal with the chemical or chemicals involved. If necessary it will extend to salvage of the vessel and retrieval of lost chemical packages or containers. Chemical Strike Teams[1] on contract to MPCU are available at short notice to go to the scene of an accident which involves, or may involve, a chemical spillage to advise or take action as necessary. MPCU maintains a stockpile of equipment for the use of this team including chemical suits, breathing apparatus and transfer pumps. MPCU can consult a Chemical Hazards Advisory Group of experts in the handling and transport of chemicals. It also has access to various standard national databases on the hazards presented by spills of different chemicals and the means of dealing with them.

International cooperation

21.7   Eight European States (Belgium, Denmark, France, Germany, The Netherlands, Norway, Sweden and the United Kingdom) together with the European Community, are parties to the Bonn Agreement for Cooperation in dealing with Pollution of the North Sea by Oil and Other Harmful Substances 1983. Despite its title, this Agreement also applies to the English Channel. Bonn Agreement members notify each other of any pollution or risk of pollution which may threaten the coasts of other States. They also assist one another to the best of their ability, if asked, on a cost reimburseable basis.

21.8   The UK and French Governments have joint responsibility under the Agreement for the English Channel, and their jointly produced *Mancheplan* sets out detailed arrangements. A similar agreement between the UK and Norway for a hundred mile wide zone between the countries is called *Norbritplan*. The UK and Irish Governments are negotiating similar arrangements.

The International Convention on Oil Pollution Preparedness, Response and Cooperation (OPRC Convention) 1990

21.9   This Convention was developed by the Marine Environment Protection Committee (MEPC) of IMO and adopted in November 1990. It has been signed by the United Kingdom, and will be ratified once the Merchant Shipping (Salvage and Pollution) Bill (see paragraph 1.35) has been enacted. So far as practicable, the UK already complies with its provisions.

21.10   The Convention provides a framework for international cooperation for combatting major oil pollution incidents. Amongst other things, it requires:

---

[1] A Chemical Strike Team consists of six Masters, Mates, Chief Engineers or Engineers with recent chemical tanker experience and the appropriate in-date endorsements who are available under contract at short notice. The teams receive briefing and training by MPCU twice a year.

(a) ships, ports and oil handling facilities to have oil pollution emergency plans;

(b) ships, off-shore installations, sea ports, oil handling facilities and aircraft to report all actual or observed oil spills;

(c) a basic framework for preparation for and response to oil pollution incidents, including detailed contingency planning; the placing of equipment in strategic positions; and exercises and training;

(d) when practicable, the provision of advice, technical support, and equipment when requested by another country; and

(e) cooperative research and development.

The United Kingdom approach

21.11   The UK Government has stockpiles of inflatable booms for containment and other counter-pollution equipment, including beach cleaning and ship-to-ship transfer equipment, strategically located to respond to incidents anywhere around the coast of the UK. It has also developed low-toxicity dispersants, designed effective dispersant spraying systems and established comprehensive contingency plans with guidelines for action. The emergency organisation is tested by regular exercises and major pollution incidents are carefully studied so that lessons can be learned. There is no doubt that MPCU's emergency organisation has worked very fast and effectively in dealing with recent spills, thanks to its good contingency planning.

The "do nothing" option

21.12   In spite of the existence of this organisational structure, the value of the "do nothing" option must be recognised. Oil will evaporate and break down in the sea by physical and chemical processes; it will disperse and be diluted by water movements; above all, since it is a natural substance, it will biodegrade, leaving only inert tarry residues. Thus, if a spill is being carried out to sea, and unless bird flocks are likely to encounter it, then it may be best left alone. The *ARGO MERCHANT* spilled 29,000 tonnes when she grounded on the Nantucket Shoals off the east coast of the United States in 1976, but off-shore winds carried the oil out to sea and it was lost in the North Atlantic. None of it reached the shoreline, there was no coastal impact and no damage was detected in the ocean.

Containment

21.13   However, experience from many spills has shown that oil washed ashore can cause extensive environmental damage to the coast and result in very high clean-up costs. Costs for clean-up of the *EXXON VALDEZ* spill exceeded $2 billion. Action must therefore be considered if oil is threatening the shore. The most environmentally-friendly response is to contain and recover it. In this context, sophisticated equipment has been developed over the years, including transportable systems of booms, oil recovery systems and absorbent materials. Unfortunately the efficiency of these systems is low. In calm weather there can be some success but in general only a small percentage of the oil is recovered and in anything more than moderately choppy seas they are ineffective. The International Tanker Owners Pollution Federation Ltd (ITOPF) commented in evidence that even countries such as Norway and the USA which had invested large amounts of money in off-shore recovery equipment are still unable to recover more than about 10 per cent of the original spill volume from the surface of the sea in a major incident in open waters.

21.14   Containment at sea as a first response would require huge amounts of equipment to be quickly available at points all round the UK coast. The necessary booms and recovery systems would have to be on permanent standby, with suitable vessels for deploying them, coastal tankers and barges to receive recovered oil and aircraft and communication systems to coordinate the whole operation. At the end of the day the results would be disappointing.

Chemical dispersants

21.15   The one approach that can be seen to produce results is the application of chemical dispersants. Dispersants act by breaking up the oil into small droplets which mix and move downwards into the water column. This dilution enhances the rate of biological breakdown. At the *TORREY CANYON* spill, industrial detergents were applied which when used on-shore caused more damage to the environment than the oil itself. Since then low toxicity dispersants have been developed. For approval these must produce a mixture with oil which is no more toxic to marine life than the oil alone, and their use is carefully controlled. The physical effectiveness of dispersants is tested by the National Environmental Technology Centre (formerly Warren Spring Laboratory) and their toxicity to marine life by the Ministry of Agriculture, Fisheries and Food (MAFF), which is, as we record in paragraph 1.29, currently reviewing the testing and approval procedures.

21.16   Some countries do not favour the use of dispersants, but the UK relies heavily on them, because of the nature and length of its coastline (nearly 12,500 km) and the frequency of rough seas, which prevent recovery of oil from the sea by mechanical means but increase the effectiveness of dispersants by providing the energy to break up the oil into small droplets. Norway and France, also with long rocky coastlines, have dispersant options. The Republic of Ireland was the first country to undertake a large-scale aerial dispersant spraying operation, after the *BETELGEUSE* incident in 1979, described in paragraph 8.75.

21.17   Dispersants were at first applied from boats and were mixed into the slick by the vessels' own propellers and by towed breaker-boards. However, to be effective, dispersants must be applied to fresh oil. Depending on their composition, many crudes become too viscous for effective use of dispersants within hours of a spill.

21.18   The window of opportunity for spraying dispersants begins when the oil emerges from the vessel. If all the oil escapes over a short period the window of opportunity can be very small, especially in bad weather. If the oil seeps out over several days, the opportunities for spraying may be greater. In either case the spraying must stop when the oil becomes too viscous to be amenable to dispersant.

21.19   Given the small window of opportunity, the slow speed of deployment of surface vessels and the low rate of application, the UK turned largely to aerial spraying, and since 1983 has had a permanent standby facility for aerial spraying of oil dispersants. Its capacity has been increased twice, in 1987 and again in 1990 when it was decided to increase the capacity from 10,000 tonnes to 14,000 tonnes. In circumstances where it is necessary to take action to protect economic or environmental resources, the United Kingdom's first response to a major oil spill is now aerial spraying of dispersants, assuming that conditions are suitable. The conditions which may be unsuitable include unsafe flying conditions and oil lying in shallow waters or in the proximity of fish farms.

Methods of clean-up used in actual incidents

21.20   The UK's aerial spraying capacity has been used on five occasions. We briefly describe below the worst oil spill in the United Kingdom's history, the *TORREY CANYON*, when aerial spraying was not available, and three incidents when aerial spraying was used.

The *TORREY CANYON*

21.21   In March 1967 the *TORREY CANYON* hit the Seven Stones rocks, between the Isles of Scilly and Lands End. She was carrying 117,000 tonnes of Kuwait crude oil. Some 30,000 tonnes escaped straightaway and some 20,000 tonnes more escaped over the next seven days. After the failure of an attempt by salvors to drag her off the rocks, some 50,000 more tonnes escaped. She was then bombed to burn the 20,000 tonnes or so still on board. The burning attempt was largely successful.

21.22   Oil slicks at sea were sprayed with industrial detergent from naval and civilian vessels for a period of 18 days, starting immediately after the grounding. 3,500 tonnes of detergent were used and this was estimated to have dispersed at least 15,000 tonnes of oil. Some 20,000 tonnes reached the Cornish coast, starting five days after the accident. The Brittany and Channel Islands coasts were also affected.

21.23   Although large numbers of pilchard eggs were killed, there was no detectable effect on the population of adult fish in the years following the spill. On the other hand, the Breton oyster industry was significantly affected.

21.24   The Cornish shores were cleaned by three methods: spraying with detergent; burning, either *in situ* or in heaps; and mechanical removal of oil or oil-contaminated sand. A huge operation was required. The costs of the clean-up and other damage to both the United Kingdom and France was estimated at the time to have been £6.5 million, equivalent to £52 million in 1993-94 prices.

21.25   It is impossible to estimate with any accuracy how much of the *TORREY CANYON*'s oil could have been dispersed if the current aerial spraying fleet had been in existence. However, the weather was calm for the week after the accident, the hours of daylight were enough for spraying to have been intense, and the oil did not reach the coast for five days. It is reasonable to assume that a substantial proportion of the oil, probably at least half, would have been dispersed.

The *PHILLIPS OKLAHOMA*[2]

21.26   In the early hours of a Sunday morning in September 1989 the tanker *PHILLIPS OKLAHOMA*, laden with 52,000 tonnes of North Sea crude oil, collided with the tanker *FIONA*, carrying 46,400 tonnes of low sulphur fuel oil, some 9.5 nautical miles off Spurn Head on the approach to the Humber. One of the *PHILLIPS OKLAHOMA*'s tanks was breached: the *FIONA*'s remained intact. It was estimated that a total of over 800 tonnes of oil was spilled from the *PHILLIPS OKLAHOMA* during the collision and afterwards, spreading into a slick five nautical miles long and up to one nautical mile wide. Plate 14 shows the *PHILLIPS OKLAHOMA* shortly after the collision.

21.27   Within 70 minutes of the collision, all the MPCU counter-pollution aircraft and two commercial tugs, fitted with MPCU spray gear and dispersant, were under orders to go to the scene. Other emergency services reacted equally quickly. Over the following three days MPCU aircraft sprayed 74 tonnes of dispersant and the tugs sprayed a further 12 tonnes. The remainder of the *PHILLIPS OKLAHOMA*'s cargo was transferred to another vessel. The *FIONA* moved into port and discharged all her own cargo there.

21.28   The spraying of dispersants was wholly successful: all the oil was dispersed. The marginal costs of the exercise to MPCU and to HM Coastguard together were some £183,000, or £230 per tonne of oil dispersed, of which all but £11,000 was recovered.

21.29   It is arguable – it has been argued in evidence before us – that all the oil from the *PHILLIPS OKLAHOMA* would have dispersed naturally without intervention. That may be so, but it must not be forgotten that winds and weather can change quickly – they did in fact worsen during the incident. Had the wind had an easterly component the shoreline to the north and south of the Humber could have been oiled. This area contains some very important Sites of Special Scientific Interest including (to the north) Spurn Head to Salt End Flats, an internationally important site for birds. The intertidal flats are locally rich in invertebrates and support large numbers of estuarine birds, including dunlin, knot, red-shank, curlew, bar-tailed godwit and grey plover which occur in nationally important numbers. The knot population is internationally significant.

21.30   To the south the North Lincolnshire coast is a breeding site for both grey and common seals. There are breeding colonies of little terns and ringed plover, both of which are of national importance. The site is host to many species of wintering waders and wild-fowl, some of which represent internationally significant populations. The moral is that it is

---

[2] *Report by the Marine Pollution Control Unit into the PHILLIPS OKLAHOMA incident,* Department of Transport 1992.

never possible to be sure, either at the time or later, what would have happened if different action had been taken, but that inaction could be disastrous.

The ROSEBAY[3]

21.31   In May 1990 the tanker *ROSEBAY*, laden with 130,000 tonnes of Iranian Heavy Crude and a similar amount of Iranian Light Crude, was struck by the trawler *DIONNE MARIE* some 14 nautical miles south of Start Point in Devon. 1,100 tonnes of heavy crude escaped, which by the following day had formed a slick 10 by 8 nautical miles. Plate 16 shows some of the effects of the spill.

21.32   MPCU aircraft were called out within half an hour of the collision. Only five of the seven planes were used: one was undergoing routine maintenance and a second suffered engine failure. Over the following three days the aircraft and a tug (fitted with Shell spraying equipment) between them sprayed 112 tonnes of dispersant. It was estimated that more than half of the total oil spilled – about 600 tonnes – was dispersed through spraying, another 300 tonnes evaporated, and the remaining 200 tonnes emulsified with seawater into 600 tonnes of "mousse". 70 tonnes of this "mousse" was recovered at sea and the remaining 530 tonnes landed on the coasts of Devon and Cornwall.

21.33   The at-sea recovery process was very difficult and it is unlikely that more oil could have been recovered in this way if there had been no dispersant spraying. MPCU has calculated that dispersant spraying reduced the amount of "mousse" landing on the coast by more than three-quarters. The figures, which are inevitably estimates, are:

oil spilled	actual	without dispersant
spilled	1,100 tonnes	1,100 tonnes
evaporated and naturally dispersed	300 tonnes	300 tonnes
chemically dispersed	600 tonnes	—
remaining oil	200 tonnes	800 tonnes

mousse (oil spilled x3)	actual	without dispersant
emulsification	600 tonnes	2,400 tonnes
recovered at sea	70 tonnes	70 tonnes
impact SW England	530 tonnes	2,330 tonnes

21.34   A major clean-up exercise was needed. The total costs of the entire exercise to MPCU was some £824,000 (in 1990 prices) of which just under half (£369,000) was due

---

[3] *Report by the Marine Pollution Control Unit into the ROSEBAY incident,* Department of Transport 1992.

to shoreline clean-up. In addition the cost of clean-up to local authorities was some £191,000. The totals were:

Aerial spraying	£212,000
At-sea recovery	£243,000
Shoreline clean-up (MPCU and local authorities)	£560,000

So the marginal cost of dealing with the oil per tonne of oil spilled (or per three tonnes of mousse) was:

Aerial spraying	£353
At-sea recovery	£10,414
Shoreline clean-up	£3,170

The high cost of dealing with oil per tonne for at-sea recovery in comparison with aerial spraying and shoreline clean-up was due to a combination of factors. The high cost of chartering the types of vessel required from the spot market, a high sea state, an on-shore wind, and later, the westward migration of oil remaining close inshore and the relatively small amount of oil recovered all combined to inflate the cost per tonne recovered.

21.35   It is impossible to assess whether the costs per tonne of clean-up would have been the same if aerial spraying had not been carried out. The increase in the costs of clean-up of a larger quantity of oil is not necessarily in the same ratio as the increase of the volume of oil – the cost per tonne could be higher or lower depending on the length and type of polluted shoreline.

21.36   Broadly speaking, the total cost of cleaning a thick layer of oil from a beach is little more than the cost of cleaning a thin layer. The cost per tonne of cleaning a thick layer is therefore much less than the cost per tonne of cleaning a thin layer. So if the total amount of oil needing to be cleaned up had been greater, the unit cost of cleaning that extra oil would have depended on whether it was widely spread in a thin layer or concentrated in a thick layer in the areas which actually were polluted.

21.37   It is therefore misleading to quote a cost per tonne for shoreline clean-up of oil: the characteristics of each spill are quite different and the cost per tonne of oil will vary widely between spills. Nevertheless it is worth recording that if there had been no dispersant sprayed in the *ROSEBAY* incident, and if the cost of clean-up per tonne of oil had been about the same as the cost per tonne of the actual clean-up, the total additional cost of shoreline clean-up would have been over £1.5 million. All this would, of course, have been reclaimable from the IOPC Fund. The less quantifiable losses to amenity and the general local economy of oil on the coasts might have been substantially greater.

21.38   In speculating what might have happened had circumstances been different, it is worth remembering that only a very small proportion of the *ROSEBAY*'s cargo was spilled – less than half of one per cent.

The BRAER[4]

21.39   The *BRAER* was fully laden with 84,700 tonnes of Norwegian "Gullfaks" light crude oil when she went aground off Shetland on 5 January 1993, some six hours after losing power. She also had some 1,600 tonnes heavy fuel oil bunkers. Immediately oil began to escape in large quantities. The vessel broke up a week later and all her remaining cargo and bunkers then spilled.

21.40   Severe weather hampered the clean-up operation but helped to disperse the oil naturally. Spraying was impossible on the day of the wreck because of the weather. MPCU's six DC3s (one DC3 was undergoing routine maintenance at Coventry) sprayed some 100 tonnes of dispersant on the second day, all that was possible in the short daylight hours. On the third day a small quantity of dispersant was also sprayed by helicopter on fuel oil inshore close to the wreck. This was ineffective due to adverse weather conditions. Spraying was impossible on the following two days. On the fifth day, once local fears on the effects of spraying had been alleviated, a further 20 tonnes of dispersant were sprayed. The ferocious on-shore winds and the location of the wreck very close to land meant that very careful control of spraying was essential.

21.41   Most of the oil dispersed naturally because of the combination of harsh weather and the lightness of the oil. Some of it fell on land as a polluting airborne oil spray. No mousse was formed, but light "sheen" was seen at a maximum of 20 nautical miles north of the incident site. Very little oil was washed ashore. Nine beaches and other sites merited cleaning: a further 11 sites were lightly oiled with foam or sheen but did not require cleaning. Inshore fisheries in the south of Shetland were threatened, as were all the salmon farms in that area – one-fifth of all those in Shetland (a Shetland fish farm affected by oil sheen from the *BRAER* is shown at Plate 15). A fishing exclusion zone was established in the area by the Scottish Office. Salmon from affected fish farms, although healthy, were tainted and had to be destroyed.

21.42   1,500 seabirds were found dead. Some may have died from causes other than oil, but there will have been others that were not found. 218 birds, 34 seals and three otters were treated for oil contamination. No seal or otter deaths have so far been shown to have been caused by the oil[5].

21.43   MPCU's and HM Coastguard's costs together amounted to some £2 million, of which some £460,000 related to aerial spraying. These costs form part of the total claim we discuss in paragraph 19.4.

21.44   The effectiveness of the aerial spraying undertaken was particularly difficult to assess, because much of the light oil might have dispersed naturally in the heavy weather. MPCU accepts, with hindsight, that this is probably true though it could not have been predicted at the time the spraying was undertaken. The oil did not in fact disperse immediately and some oil and oily debris polluted beaches. The oil which was selected for spraying was lying on the surface in danger of being carried ashore in the immediate vicinity of

---

[4] *Report by the Marine Pollution Control Unit into the BRAER incident,* (HMSO 1994)—ISBN 0 11 55 1208 X.

[5] *Interim report of the Ecological Steering Group on the Oil Spill in Shetland,* published by the Scottish Office 1993—ISBN 0 7480 0767 9.

the wreck. The 120 tonnes of dispersant sprayed probably dealt with at most 2,000 tonnes out of the total cargo of 84,700 tonnes, at a very approximate cost of £200 per tonne of oil dispersed.

Comparing incidents

21.45 These four incidents were very different from each other, and it is difficult to compare them or to draw general conclusions from them. The UK was unprepared for a disaster on the scale of the *TORREY CANYON*, and the spraying of industrial detergent on-shore to minimise pollution of the coasts created more problems than it solved. With both the *TORREY CANYON* and the *ROSEBAY* there was no possibility of all the oil dispersing naturally. Coastlines were polluted but, at least in the United Kingdom, commercial fisheries were not much affected.

21.46 The *PHILLIPS OKLAHOMA* and the *BRAER* incidents were quite different as lighter oils were involved. The *BRAER*, like the *TORREY CANYON*, was a total loss, but the effects were very different. The oil from the *BRAER* disappeared from the surface of the sea and from beaches remarkably quickly, but it had very significant effects on farmed fish.

21.47 The only sensible conclusion that can be drawn is that oil spills vary enormously and that contingency planning must take into account as many variables as possible. We have imagined, with horror, a spill involving a total loss, as with the *TORREY CANYON* or *BRAER*, with a heavy crude such as on the *TORREY CANYON* or *ROSEBAY*, a ship as large as the *ROSEBAY* as close to land as the *BRAER*, in an area with particular ecological distinction, vulnerable fish farms, high amenity value and a local economy geared to tourism. Such a catastrophe may never happen – but it could.

21.48 The *AMOCO CADIZ*, which grounded on the coast of Brittany in 1978, was close to such a catastrophe. It was a near-shore spill with an on-shore wind, and over a period of four weeks the entire 220,000 tonnes of crude oil cargo, and several thousand tonnes of bunkers, were released into the sea. About 300 km of coast were oiled in an area with a valuable oyster culture industry and an important tourist industry. The UK may continue to be comparatively lucky, but a similar catastrophe will happen again somewhere and sometime.

The United Kingdom dispersant spraying capacity

21.49 MPCU's aerial spraying capacity has been used on five occasions, including the *PHILLIPS OKLAHOMA*, *ROSEBAY* and *BRAER* incidents. It has since 1990 consisted of seven DC3s (Dakotas) on contract. This means that, allowing for maintenance, at least six are available at any time. Five are based at Coventry and two at Inverness. They are permanently fitted with spraying equipment and dispersant tanks. Plate 13 shows one of them in action. The DC3s are supported by – and cannot be used without – two small aircraft equipped with remote sensing equipment. These are also used for routine surveillance. In addition, the "spotter" plane used in conjunction with CNIS for identifying breaches of the Dover Strait TSS (see paragraph 16.10) may also be used for surveillance of pollution within the CNIS area. Dispersants are held at 21 stockpiles around the coast.

21.50   The total cost of the standby spraying capacity is some £3.5 million a year. The aerial surveillance capacity, which is essential for dispersant spraying, costs some £1.2 million a year. Routine purchase and storage of dispersant (which can deteriorate with age and may need to be replaced) costs some £70,000 a year. The Department of Transport claims from the insurer or the IOPC Fund for the costs of dealing with an actual spill, but this covers only a small proportion of the standby costs.

Technical limits on spraying

21.51   Dispersant spraying is effective only until the oil emulsifies with seawater and turns into "mousse". This may be any period between two and 48 hours. Some heavy oils cannot be dispersed at all and some light oils can take longer to emulsify and even then only form unstable emulsions. The period is also dependent on weather conditions. In the case of the *ROSEBAY* the oil emulsified in just over 24 hours.

21.52   The dispersant spraying aircraft can operate only during daylight hours where there is visibility of at least one nautical mile with a cloudbase of more than 500 ft. These figures are not absolute: it is ultimately a matter for the pilot's discretion. Spraying was impossible for much of the *BRAER* operation because the very high cross-winds made take-off and landing unsafe. These conditions also produced the turbulent seas which left little oil on the surface to be sprayed.

Spraying from the air and from vessels

21.53   A DC3 can typically spray 11 square kilometres in a ten hour day. The aircraft are required to take off within half an hour of callout during daylight hours and can be on the scene of any incident around the UK coast within 3.5 hours of daytime callout. The callout period at night is two hours and in appropriate weather conditions, there is sufficient light to start a spraying operation half an hour before sunrise.

Spraying from helicopters

21.54   MPCU does not have any facility for spraying from helicopters. It is estimated that one helicopter can typically spray 0.6 square kilometres in a day – one-eighteenth of the capacity of a single DC3. Each helicopter needs two tank spray systems, so 18 helicopters and 36 tank spray systems would be needed to equal the spraying capacity of one DC3, and 126 helicopters and 252 tank spray systems would be needed to equal the theoretical spraying capacity of the DC3 fleet. Using dedicated helicopters would be very much more expensive than the existing DC3s and is obviously not an option.

21.55   Aerial spraying by helicopter would thus depend on using whatever helicopters could be quickly chartered or otherwise made available. Only twin-engined helicopters can be used over the sea for safety reasons. Although contingency plans could obviously include emergency arrangements for quick access to such helicopters, they and their crews would have to stop what they were doing and get to the scene. The spray tanks would also have to be got to the scene and attached to the helicopters. The process would take significantly longer than deploying the DC3s, and the window of opportunity for spraying might be partly or wholly missed. Clearly, helicopters cannot provide a service as good as the DC3 fleet.

Spraying from vessels

21.56   Several MOD harbour service and fishery protection vessels are equipped with dispersant spraying capacity. In addition, MPCU has provided equipment which is fitted in some 25 tugs, Scottish Office Agriculture and Fisheries Department (SOAFD) and Northern Lighthouse Board vessels in ports around the coast. Supplies of dispersant are kept on the vessels or the dockside. These vessels have to be chartered if needed, so apart from the cost of equipment and dispersants there are no standing costs. The cost of spraying equipment for tugs is of the order of £6,000 and dispersant costs approximately £1,000 per tonne. The cost of charter vessels will vary enormously depending on the spot charter market, but will certainly run into tens of thousands of pounds for vessels chartered for several days.

21.57   Unless a spill is close to a harbour where a tug equipped for spraying is based, she is likely to take longer to reach the site of an incident than a DC3 would. Typically a tug will spray about three square kilometres in a day – five times as much as a helicopter but still not much over a quarter of the spraying capacity of a DC3. The oil is far less visible from the sea than the air, so direction from the air is highly desirable in the same way that surveillance aircraft are used to guide aerial spraying. Small vessels may be limited by rough seas but are less limited by fog and low cloud than aircraft. Vessels are more limited by weather conditions than aircraft. Like aircraft, they cannot spray at night, because their crew cannot see the oil clearly enough. One advantage they have over aircraft is that in very calm conditions they can mix the oil and dispersant with their own propellers.

Environmental effects of spraying

21.58   Removing oil from the sea surface and dispersing it as fine particles throughout the water column protects birds and reduces contamination of coastal sites. However, it makes the oil more available to organisms below the sea surface and could taint species of commercial importance, so needs to be used with caution in shallow water where dilution is low. If a slick is drifting towards a fish farm the decision must be made whether to disperse it and thereby possibly enhance tainting, or to leave it and risk the fouling of farm structures if they cannot be protected by booms.

Restrictions on the use of dispersants

21.59   As we record in paragraph 1.29, in April 1993 the Minister of Agriculture, Fisheries and Food announced a comprehensive review of the standards by which dispersants are assessed for toxicity, efficiency and other aspects of performance. The review will include consideration of whether any changes are needed in the procedure for issuing approval; the adequacy of information made publicly available about the composition of dispersants; and in addition will take account of the circumstances in which the use of chemical dispersants is likely to remain the most effective way to protect the environment from oil spilled at sea. It will also cover the effects of dispersants on humans through inhalation.

21.60   Oil dispersants cannot be used in waters less than 20 metres deep, or within one mile of such an area, without the specific approval of the licensing authority (MAFF, SOAFD or DoENI – the Department of the Environment for Northern Ireland)[6]. Outside these shallow areas dispersants may be used without prior authorisation, but only in accordance with the terms of the approval and the instructions for use issued by the manufacturer.

21.61   MPCU consults the relevant Fisheries and Environment Departments before using dispersants. Full scale spraying operations are authorised only following a carefully controlled test spray and spraying operations are monitored to ensure that dispersant is applied only where there is a sufficient quantity of amenable oil.

21.62   All these procedures take time. Probably the most significant advantage of aerial spraying over tug spraying is the speed with which aircraft can reach the oil and start work. To use this advantage to the full, contingency plans should, where possible, identify in advance where spraying could take place, environmentally sensitive areas where spraying would not be appropriate, and areas where particular consideration would need to be given in the light of the circumstances of the incident.

21.63   Planning in advance, though vital, is difficult to do in practice because bird populations and their breeding grounds, fisheries and other environmental sensitivities change with the seasons. Weather conditions and the type of the oil spill will also influence the approach to a particular incident. Consultation on contingency plans is needed with all bodies with relevant expertise, including the Fisheries Departments, the Nature Conservation agencies and bodies such as the Royal Society for the Protection of Birds.

Information on dispersants

21.64   During the *BRAER* incident one of the spraying aircraft turned on its sprays by mistake just after it had taken off and dispersant was blown over the land. This understandably gave rise to public concern and representatives of the public asked for information about the chemical composition of the dispersants. MPCU's report on the incident[7] accepted that information on chemical composition of dispersants should be immediately available through MPCU to local people who might be affected, but

---

[6] Part II of the Food and Environment Protection Act 1985 and the Deposits in the Sea (Exemption) Order 1985.
[7] *Report by the Marine Pollution Control Unit into the BRAER incident*, (HMSO 1994)—ISBN 0 11 55 1208 X.

explained that it would have been a breach of commercial confidentiality to have made the manufacturer's "trade secret" public.

21.65   There should be nothing secret about the composition of dispersants. Information should be readily available through a database, accessible by MPCU, MAFF, SOAFD, the National Environmental Technology Centre and anyone else with a relevant interest. Even so, very few of the general public are likely to understand the full implications of the chemical composition. This is illustrated in the report on the *BRAER* which relates how an environmental pressure group believed that a particular dispersant was "toxic" because it was not on the current list of approved dispersants for technical reasons[8]. So any release of information would need to be accompanied by an explanation. We were pleased to learn that the MAFF review will address the question of the public availability of the make-up of oil dispersants.

The future of dispersant spraying

Alternatives to dispersant spraying

21.66   A first line of defence to deal with oil at sea is essential. The question is whether dispersant spraying is the best way of achieving this.

At-sea recovery

21.67   As we have commented, the collection of oil from the surface by mechanical means is the most environmentally-friendly option, but it is of limited effectiveness in practice. As the figures from the *ROSEBAY* incident illustrate, it can also be expensive even as a backup to aerial spraying of dispersant: the equipment which would be needed for at-sea recovery as a first line of defence would add substantially to the cost.

21.68   We therefore reject the possibility of at-sea recovery as the first line of defence. Recovery can, however, be a very useful part of defences in some circumstances, and should be included within contingency plans. It should be noted that only a limited stock of the necessary equipment is held by MPCU, but the oil industry has a very good stock of the necessary equipment available for use in the United Kingdom: in addition to Government stockpiles, the oil industry has an international stockpile in Southampton for use in a major spill, and other industry stockpiles intended for use on a local or regional scale could be made available.

21.69   **We recommend that MPCU should keep a database, for use by all concerned including harbour authorities, of all equipment which could be used in the**

---

[8] Paragraph 129 of that report reads "It was alleged by one environmental group during the *BRAER* incident that some dispersant was "toxic" in that it had not passed a toxicity test, and that some was no longer on the approved list. One of the dispersants used (Dispolene 34S) no longer featured on the approved list because the manufacturer had not sought to have its approval renewed after 5 years as is required. This is because they had reformulated their product and no longer sold the product in question—the current approval applies to the new formulation. MPCU tests its dispersant stocks for effectiveness periodically and withdraws batches which are less than 60 per cent of their original effectiveness (in terms of volume of oil dispersed by a given amount of dispersant). There is no reason to suppose that stocks become more toxic with storage and periodic repeats of toxicity tests are not carried out. The fact that one of the *BRAER* dispersants was not on the current approved list did not mean that it was not approved by MAFF for use. The environmental group subsequently acknowledged their mistake but not before dispersants had received unfavourable publicity".

UK owned by themselves, other Governments, harbour authorities and terminals, and the oil industry.

21.70   If at-sea recovery is not to be the first line of defence, we do not think that there is a case for dedicated vessels on standby. We do, however, consider that MPCU should continue to keep in touch with developments of portable machinery for at-sea recovery to be used from non-dedicated vessels. **Franchised tugs, recommended in Chapter 20, might sensibly be fitted with spraying equipment.**

Burning

21.71   In some circumstances oil on the sea surface can be removed by burning, and continuing research is providing increased understanding of the burning process and rate; the emission, composition and dispersal of the smoke; and the nature of the residue. The problems are practical. The slick must be at least 2-3 millimetres thick for ignition, and the combustion must be controlled sufficiently to prevent danger to the oil source and to people involved. Following the grounding of the *EXXON VALDEZ*, some 15,000 to 30,000 gallons of the floating oil were collected within a fire-proof boom and ignited. Over a period of 75 minutes the oil was reduced to approximately 300 gallons of a viscous residue which was easily picked up[9].

21.72   Opportunities for burning will remain limited and it can never be regarded as the first line of defence. However, since it can eliminate large amounts of oil quickly and obviate the need for expensive recovery, at the cost of some short-term reduction in local air quality, it may be seen as an attractive backup occasionally for mechanical pick up techniques. **We recommend that MPCU should continue to review the work done elsewhere on the possibility of burning oil at sea.**

Bioremediation

21.73   The eventual disappearance of spilled oil from the marine environment is largely due to its breakdown by micro organisms. Much work is being done, particularly in the USA, on ways of speeding up this process of biodegradation and many commercial products claiming to do so are on the market. It may be done by bioenhancement, which involves encouraging the indigenous microbes already present at the polluted site, or by bioaugmentation which implies the addition of new microbes. Bioremediation – the common term for the two techniques – is thought to be effective particularly in the final stages of coastline clean-up. But little convincing evidence is available and further research is required.

21.74   **We recommend that MPCU should commission or share in long-term research and development of bioremediation.**

---

[9] ALLEN, A. A. *Controlled burning of crude oil on water following the grounding of the EXXON VALDEZ.* pp 213–216 in Proceedings: 1991 International Oil Spill Conference. American Petroleum Institute Publication 4529.

Demulsifiers

21.75   Demulsifiers are chemicals which can inhibit or reverse water-in-oil emulsion formation. The possibility of using aerially applied demulsifier to inhibit emulsion formation and therefore extend the window of opportunity for dispersant use has been recognised. If demulsifiers were added after an emulsion had formed the process could be reversed, thus lowering the viscosity and permitting natural dispersion at a greatly enhanced rate.

21.76   Research carried out by Warren Spring Laboratory for MPCU sought to provide further information on the possible use of demulsifiers in dealing with oil spills. The results confirm that aerial application of certain demulsifiers would be an effective technique to combat persistent oil slicks. Sea trials have indicated, but not proved, that combined demulsifier and dispersant application is effective. It might therefore be possible to treat slicks effectively that are too viscous to be successfully treated with dispersants alone. The window of opportunity for chemical treatment would also be significantly enlarged for some oils.

21.77   Further work is required to examine the effects of demulsifiers on oils of a range of viscosities and to identify other factors which might affect the use of demulsifiers. Checks need to be made that demulsifiers do not reduce the effectiveness of dispersants and more work needs to be done on the best combination of demulsifier and dispersant and the best way of applying them. Clearly, demulsifiers hold out the promise of making aerial spraying more effective and **we recommend that MPCU should continue its research programme on this as a matter of high priority.**

Do nothing

21.78   If at-sea recovery is dismissed as the first line of defence, on the grounds of cost and limited effectiveness, there remains a stark choice between dispersant spraying, burning where practicable and doing nothing. Doing nothing, is, as we explain in paragraph 21.12, in some circumstances the best option: but it is rarely an acceptable option if it allows oil to reach beaches, cliffs, commercial fish farms and wildlife habitats. Do nothing can never become the first line of defence. It is not a defence at all. It is, however, an option which should always be borne in mind.

The value of dispersing

21.79   Dispersing can be seen as insurance against damage to wildlife and to the coast including the cost of shore clean-up. It can benefit local businesses such as tourism, as well as amenity and wildlife. There is also the understandable desire of the authorities to do anything possible. It is worth pointing out that we have received evidence which shows a powerful belief that dispersants are vital – and have had complaints that dispersant stocks are not widely enough spread.

21.80   The decision to disperse oil must always be taken with an explicit understanding of the effects and not for cosmetic purposes. There are, and must remain, clear limitations on when the spraying of dispersants is the best practicable environmental option. We hope that the MAFF review will help to clarify the issues and to establish, in advance, just which areas are likely to be suitable for spraying and which are not. But despite the limitations, the spraying of dispersants remains the best first line option for the foreseeable future.

Aerial or surface spraying

21.81 If a dispersant spraying capacity is valuable and should be retained, the next question is whether dispersants should be sprayed from the air or from the surface or both. Aerial spraying is much more effective. The point is whether the cost of the standby capacity can be justified given the rare occasions on which a potentially damaging spill occurs.

21.82 One witness[10] questioned the practice of aerial spraying as expensive and ineffective. It was pointed out that flying operations are limited to daylight hours; that pilots must see the oil and fly very low for effective spraying; that spraying is effective only against oils of low viscosity; that if the sea is calm there is not enough mixing energy and that if it is rough there is not enough contact time. Other witnesses disagreed: for instance, the International Tanker Owners Pollution Federation Ltd commented that

> "We believe that the strategy adopted by the UK Government of enhancing the natural dispersion of oil through the use of dispersants applied from aircraft is sensible given the length of the coastline and the sea conditions likely to be encountered."

21.83 There is no doubt that aerial spraying is expensive. Costs are constant and benefits variable. There will be many years when benefits are less than costs, but there may be a catastrophe when benefits outweigh costs by a very large margin. As with any insurance in an area with few precedents, whether the premiums are justified is essentially a value judgement.

21.84 We have concluded, after much discussion and careful consideration of the costs, that **it is right to retain an aerial spraying capacity for dispersants as the front line of defence for the United Kingdom against pollution by oil.**

21.85 We must stress that what is right for the United Kingdom is not necessarily right for other countries, and that what is right for other countries is not necessarily right for the United Kingdom. Different geographical features and meteorological conditions, not to mention different lengths of coastline, can make a substantial difference to practicalities.

Reducing the costs of aerial spraying

21.86 We are, however, keen to find means by which the current large cost of the aerial spraying capacity could be reduced.

21.87 Firstly, economies should be actively sought by sharing capacity wherever practicable. We have considered whether the spraying capacity might be shared with another

---

[10] Captain A J Corner.

country, with shared standing costs. We note that under the Bonn Agreement the North Sea countries already consult closely on contingency plans and remedial measures, and accept that any country which wants to borrow part of the UK aerial spraying fleet has only to ask. Marginal costs would be charged to the relevant country which would reclaim them from the IOPC Fund.

21.88   We doubt whether it is worth investigating whether any neighbouring country would be interested in sharing the aerial spraying capacity on a more formal basis, with the right to use an agreed part of the MPCU capacity in defined circumstances in return for payment of a share of fixed as well as marginal costs. In practice they would gain little if anything which they do not have already: and seeking contributions might damage the cooperative basis of the Bonn Agreement, risking the UK's reciprocal ability to use other countries' facilities. There would also be disadvantages for the UK, as some dilution of MPCU control of the aircraft might be unavoidable. There might also be problems with distances: no country can afford to denude itself of its own protection.

21.89   We see far more future in the idea of sharing uses for the aircraft within the United Kingdom. This could work by finding another use for the DC3s or by using aircraft with a different main purpose for spraying.

Alternative uses for existing aircraft

21.90   There appear to be few economic alternative uses for the DC3s. We have considered crop (or forest) spraying or firefighting. The existing aircraft do not appear to be well adapted for either, but this might be a possibility when the contract comes up for renewal. The short callout times which are essential for effective dispersant spraying limit the options.

21.91   We considered the possibility of using the DC3s for routine surveillance, replacing or supplementing not only COASTGUARD's existing surveillance aircraft but also those used by other authorities, such as the Fisheries Departments or HM Customs and Excise. We concluded that this was impracticable: the operational cost of the DC3s is substantially higher than those of the small aircraft used for surveillance, so their use for this purpose is uneconomic. We also considered equipping the surveillance aircraft for spraying. Again this would not work: the small surveillance aircraft cannot carry dispersant as well as remote sensing equipment.

21.92   A better solution is close cooperation, and duplication of equipment, between the various surveillance organisations. A fisheries surveillance aircraft, for instance, might be equipped so that it can detect oil on the water, while a COASTGUARD surveillance aircraft might look out for illicit fishing or smuggling. Coordinated surveillance of all illicit activities is likely to benefit all the authorities, not least because wrongdoers would be unable to tell whether a particular surveillance aircraft was looking out for their activity.

We recommend that the Department of Transport explores the possibilities with other Government Departments.

Use of other aircraft

21.93 We have also considered the possibility of wholly or partly replacing COAST-GUARD's contract spraying aircraft with other Government owned or leased aircraft. The first point is that we have seen no reason to suppose that it is possible to hire aircraft upon an incident occurring – in the way vessels can be hired for booming oil. There does not appear to be a market for fairly large, slow and manoeuvrable aircraft, with pilots trained in the specialised art of spraying dispersant. So without a contract, the capacity for spraying would not exist.

21.94 The most promising possibility is an arrangement for the emergency use of Her-cules C130 aircraft, of which there are several, both military and civil, in the UK, for aerial spraying. A self contained unit, the Aerial Dispersant Spraying Package (ADS Pack), can be quickly loaded into a Hercules C130 aircraft. Unfortunately C130 aircraft on the UK register are not licensed for aerial spraying by the Civil Aviation Authority and so cannot be considered as an alternative to the DC3 until clearance can be obtained. We recognise that clearance would take time and cost money, and we also recognise that the C130 may be less well suited to spraying than a DC3 and less effective at putting down the right density of dispersant spray accurately on the oil. We nevertheless believe that this option is well worth pursuing. **We therefore recommend that COASTGUARD should investi-gate the emergency use of either civil or military C130 aircraft with ADS Packs to replace or supplement their present arrangements for aerial spraying.**

Dispersant stocks

21.95 We have considered the possibility of reducing costs by reducing the number of stockpiles of dispersant. As we note in paragraph 21.79, there appears to be a widespread belief that the number of stockpiles should, if anything, be increased. We believe that any savings would be fairly small and we see no point in pursuing the idea.

Paying for standby dispersant spraying capacity

21.96 Even with the recommendations we make for economies fully implemented, the standing costs of the aerial spraying capacity will remain considerable. The capacity is a form of insurance, but it is an insurance from which neither the UK Government nor UK citizens benefit financially. This is because the costs of pollution by attributable tanker oil spills are reimbursed by the IOPC Fund, up to the limit mentioned in paragraph 19.4. The higher costs which would result from a big spill without aerial spraying would also be met from the Fund.

21.97 We recommend in paragraph 19.9 that the UK Government should seek to per-suade the IOPC Fund to contribute to the insurance premium for which it is the chief beneficiary. In the next chapter we make recommendations for a new fund which would, amongst other things, cover the cost of the remaining part of the fixed costs of UK preparedness: or for all of it if the IOPC Fund remains adamant.

Planning for emergencies

21.98   Clear, detailed and precise contingency planning is essential for any successful emergency response or clean-up. The UK National Contingency Plan produced by the Department of Transport covers both the immediate emergency phase and any necessary clean-up. It links with local contingency plans produced by local authorities and harbour authorities. The national plan deals in considerable detail with a wide variety of problems likely to arise.

21.99   The national and local contingency plans will need amending to take into account our recommendations on emergency assistance. Insofar as they do not do so already, they should cover, in as much detail as practicable:

(a)   **the areas and circumstances in which dispersant spraying is or is not likely to be acceptable;**

(b)   **at-sea recovery, including the database mentioned above** (paragraph 21.69); **and**

(c)   **on-shore cleaning with a similar database of equipment.**

The national plan should include a section on the organisation for a long-running response operation: a spill the size of that in the *BRAER* incident could in other circumstances have taken months to deal with, and more staff would have been necessary to cope. No one can work flat out for weeks at a time.

Command and control

21.100   It is essential that it should be entirely clear from the outset just who does what in any emergency. We agree that COASTGUARD should be in clear command during a pollution incident and that no one (except the Ministers on whose behalf it acts) should be able overrule it. COASTGUARD staff should discuss their proposed action with anyone with relevant expert or local knowledge, but must take their own decisions in the light of the advice given to them.

21.101   It is also essential to be clear on responsibilities between HM Coastguard and MPCU within COASTGUARD. We have noted the changes recorded in paragraph 20.146 put in place since the *BRAER* incident. The changes discussed in Chapter 19 should make the relationship between the two parts of COASTGUARD clearer and more effective. We support the long standing clear instruction to HM Coastguard that if for any reason it cannot get in touch with MPCU staff within 30 minutes it should commit first line resources and initiate counter-pollution action itself. We consider that this represents a sensible compromise between the need for a swift response and the need to avoid overreaction.

A pollutant database

21.102 Different types of oil behave differently – for instance, the very light Norwegian Gullfaks crude spilled from the *BRAER* behaved very differently from the Iranian Heavy Crude which spilled from the *ROSEBAY*. MPCU already has a database on different types of oil and on chemicals. **We recommend that this database should be expanded as much as possible. Information ought to be collected from and disseminated to all member countries by IMO. Oil and other companies ought to cooperate as a matter of public duty. We expect that they will do so – but if not, powers to compel cooperation may be needed.**

Land contamination

21.103 Land contamination from oil was a problem which had not been encountered on the scale seen in the *BRAER* incident. The question of possible effects of dispersants on human health is being considered in the context of the MAFF review of dispersants. The possibility of land contamination ought to be taken into account in contingency planning, but we do not agree with the view put forward by MPCU in its report on the *BRAER* incident that MPCU should provide face masks for the general population. Stockpiles adequate for the population of a large town would be needed. We believe that the likelihood of a recurrence of this phenomenon is so remote that it would not be justifiable for MPCU to invest in such stockpiles.

Dealing with the media

21.104 The contingency plan also needs to include ways of meeting the legitimate needs of the media and of ensuring that they do not inadvertently interfere with either search and rescue or pollution containment and clean-up. Analysis of the transcript of one search and rescue incident showed that the HM Coastguard rescue centre concerned took 62 media enquiries in 64 minutes. Not surprisingly, this caused considerable disruption. During the *ROSEBAY* incident all lines into Brixham Coastguard were jammed with press queues. The public has a legitimate interest in events, but the media must realise that in a crisis, when immediate action needs to be taken, newsgathering must take second place.

Exclusion zones

21.105 A restricted area was established around the wreck of the *BRAER* under the Protection of Wrecks Act 1973, but this is not suitable for all occasions: in particular it applies only when there is a wreck. Exclusion zones were established around the *PHILLIPS OKLAHOMA* and the *ROSEBAY* for safety reasons. While the procedure has proved effective in practice, it is complex for an emergency situation. The London Air Traffic Control Centre has to be asked to issue and broadcast a Notice to Airmen, and the Hydrographer of the Navy has to be asked to place a sea exclusion zone on the specified area. The Hydrographer issues a Notice to Mariners and HM Coastguard broadcasts the information.

21.106 The procedure could be simplified if HM Coastguard had the power to establish sea exclusion zones: we would not want to alter the system for aviation. We consider that such a power is required. It should be selective, so that some vessels can be asked to assist while others are told to stay away, and it should apply both to wrecks and to vessels in difficulties.

21.107 We envisage that the new power might be exercised in two stages. HM Coast-guard Watch Officers should be allowed through their standing instructions to **advise** vessels to follow a particular course of action in an emergency. **Instruction** would be given only very rarely, only on the authority of senior staff (perhaps the Regional Controller) and only if advice had not been heeded. **We recommend that such powers should be taken.**

21.108 There are also powers in the Food and Environment Protection Act 1985 enabling the Government to make emergency orders prohibiting the taking of food from designated areas likely to be affected by a pollution incident. Such an order was made by SOAFD banning certain fishing operations after the loss of the *BRAER*.

On-shore clean-up

21.109 Once oil has come ashore, the question of treatment again arises. Plates 17 and 18 illustrate some of the problems which may be encountered. Oil can be picked up manually, sucked up, collected by absorbent material, washed back into the sea, dispersed by chemicals or left to weather naturally. On amenity beaches active clean-up will be favoured, but aggressive operations can damage the ecosystem. Hosing and flushing, especially using high pressure hot water, can effectively remove the oil but do great damage to the fauna and flora. Pumping and the use of earth-moving equipment to lift contaminated sand generates disposal problems. Also over-active cleaning may retard recovery. After the *AMOCO CADIZ* spill, badly oiled marshes were restored within five years by natural processes, but those that had been artificially cleaned took two years longer to recover. Similarly, after the *ESSO BERNICIA* spill at Sullom Voe, biological communities on intertidal rocky shores returned to near normal within the first year, but on shores cleaned manually, recovery was not complete after almost nine years[11].

The role of the National Rivers Authority (NRA)

21.110 The NRA has powers under the Water Resources Act 1991 to deal with pollution of the sea up to three nautical miles from the baselines of internal waters. Its interest is, however, essentially confined to the control of pollution from land-based sources, and does not extend to discharges from vessels. It has powers only in relation to England and Wales.

21.111 The duplication of powers, though both necessary and deliberate in order to provide both authorities with the necessary freedom to act in appropriate circumstances, could lead to confusion. We are pleased to note that MPCU and the NRA have agreed a

---

[11] Rolan, R C and Gallacher R. *Recovery of intertidal biotic commals at Sullom Voe following the ESSO BERNICIA spill of 1978.* pp 461–465 1991 International Oil Spill Conference American Petroleum Institute Publication No. 4529 Library of Congress Catalogue No. 75–4161.

Memorandum of Understanding which sets out their roles and responsibilities in dealing with oil and chemical pollution in estuarine and coastal waters. This is reproduced in Appendix K.

The role of local authorities

21.112   When the Government accepted overall responsibility for dealing with pollution from shipping, coastal local authorities at both county and district level accepted the responsibility for both contingency planning and clean-up of on-shore pollution arising from oil spills.

21.113   The Government appreciates that local authorities cannot cope with a major incident causing exceptional coastal pollution without specialised equipment. It would be wasteful for each authority to acquire equipment which would rarely be required. The Government has therefore set up stockpiles of such equipment in strategic locations to be drawn on by authorities as need be. The Government also provides scientific and technical advice to local authorities on beach cleaning management and techniques and organises advance training of local authority staff.

21.114   Although local authorities have accepted responsibility for clean-up, and have power to spend money on it, they do not have a formal statutory responsibility. When it comes to deciding priorities in expenditure and staffing, it would not be surprising if they favoured statutory responsibilities over non-statutory ones. **We believe that they should be given a formal statutory responsibility to clean-up beaches and for drawing up contingency plans for doing so.**

21.115   In the event of an oil spill which exceeds a local authority's capacity to respond, the authority can request that a Joint Response Centre (JRC) is set up. If MPCU agrees to this it commits central Government resources: manpower, equipment and finance, at no cost to the local authority. The JRC is a management structure which enables all the various bodies to come together as a single team to mount an effective shoreline clean-up operation. The local authority remains in overall charge of the shoreline response, setting priorities and defining the response strategy. MPCU advises, coordinates and leads in some areas such as the selection of appropriate clean-up methods.

The role of harbour authorities

21.116   Most harbour authorities have no specific statutory responsibility to prepare contingency plans or to clean-up pollution within their areas, though their powers are wide enough to enable them to do so. The implementation of the OPRC Convention (which will be achieved under the provisions of the Merchant Shipping (Salvage and Pollution) Bill) will place an obligation on them to prepare contingency plans. Like local authorities, harbour authorities have accepted responsibility to prepare such plans for their areas, in consultation as necessary with local authorities and others who may be affected by contamination from a spillage. The plans identify responsibilities and lines of communication;

reporting arrangements; availability of resources; command and control arrangements; and priority areas for clean-up.

21.117 We recommend that harbour authorities should have similar statutory obligations to local authorities to take the major responsibility for cleaning up their areas in addition to the obligation they will have under the OPRC Convention to draw up contingency plans.

Local contingency plans and action

21.118 Local contingency plans, prepared by local authorities and harbour authorities alike, need to be consistent with the national contingency plan. MPCU needs to be able to vet them: not in order to give formal approval, but so as to check that they cover all necessary points and mesh properly with the national plan. **We recommend that local authorities and harbour authorities should be under a duty to submit their contingency plans to the Secretary of State for this checking process, but not for formal approval. MPCU should discuss any problems with the authority concerned.**

21.119 There needs to be a fairly standard pattern of local authority contingency plans, not least to avoid confusion and to make sure that all necessary points are covered. Harbour authorities similarly need a pattern for their contingency plans, but as those plans will normally cover rather different matters from those of local authorities, the two patterns may well be different. In particular, harbour authorities will want to pay special attention to oil, chemical and bunkering terminals.

21.120 Local contingency plans should be informed by consultations with relevant local interests such as fish farmers and marina operators. They should include detailed local maps, including sensitive areas. They should also include particulars of national and local stockpiles of equipment such as booms or dispersants held by public or private sector interests. The plans should also contemplate pollution by substances other than oil, to the extent which the authority and MPCU jointly consider this to be necessary.

21.121 Harbour authorities and local authorities also need to keep closely in touch with MPCU in dealing with actual spills, just in case the spill becomes more difficult to deal with than they had expected. **We recommend that as a matter of routine all spills which they decide to act on should be notified immediately to MPCU by the harbour or local authority. The authority would also give MPCU an indication of what they were doing about the spill in question. MPCU should offer advice and assistance: it should also have a reserve power – which we would expect to be used very infrequently – to direct the authority to take different action. Local or harbour authorities should also inform MPCU of any incident which has the potential to cause a significant marine spill, even if at that stage nothing has actually been spilt.**

21.122   In unfavourable conditions it will be almost impossible to stop oil at sea coming ashore. An important line of defence then would be protective booming of sensitive areas, particularly vulnerable estuaries. **Local contingency plans should contain plans for booming sensitive areas, specifying the lengths and type of boom needed. Local authorities and harbour authorities should also give careful consideration to installing permanent anchorage points for booms,** as has been done in some locations in Shetland. MPCU should give advice and encouragement.

Checking and testing contingency plans

21.123   Checking, discussing and assisting in the drawing up of local contingency plans is a major job for the very small MPCU. **We recommend that MPCU should encourage secondment (or loan) of staff from oil companies and harbour authorities to MPCU.** This would provide temporary increases of capacity in MPCU, to allow for the checking and discussion of local contingency plans; provide a bank of staff who might be called upon to help in a lengthy crisis; and foster mutual understanding and cross-fertilisation of ideas.

21.124   Exercises to test contingency plans are an essential part of the planning and training process. MPCU carries out a major exercise every year, simulating a real incident. In 1993 the exercise was on the coast of County Antrim and involved the Department of Transport and the Department of the Environment for Northern Ireland. The exercise was in part a paper one but also involved the physical movement of equipment from MPCU's stockpiles and mock aerial spraying and at-sea recovery. Wholly paper exercises are also used.

21.125   Local contingency plans also need testing through exercises. We welcome the fact that many local authorities are active in testing contingency plans and frequently get together with other authorities and oil companies in joint exercises. **It is obviously valuable if MPCU can play its part in local exercises where the exercise incident would be expected to trigger off the National Contingency Plan. This may place an additional burden on MPCU, but it is clearly an important function and we recommend that it should be undertaken whenever possible.**

Contingency planning by private sector interests

21.126   It will never be possible for the Government to provide all the emergency equipment such as booms in the quantities or in all the locations which some interests might like it to. Nor should it: it is up to the Government to decide what is reasonable protection in the national interest. Where a private interest might be adversely affected by pollution and the owners are not happy with the level of public provision, they can and should consider what they could do to help themselves.

21.127   In particular, fish farmers might want to bear in mind the possibility of spills and should be in a position to take precautions against them – to deal with small spills completely and to buy time for MPCU to deal with large ones. Probably the most important precaution they can take is to install permanent fixing points for booms at key locations such as the entrance to sea lochs: they might also want to consider buying booms themselves, as individuals or as a cooperative, for possible emergency use.

21.128 We note that one of the lessons of the *BRAER* incident was that effective methods of protecting Fish Farms from oil spills in bad weather do not exist. **We recommend that MPCU and the Fisheries Departments, with representatives of fish farmers, should investigate and develop possible methods of protecting fish farms and should publish advice to fish farmers.**

Chapter 22

Paying for Pollution Prevention

22.1 We set out in this chapter our recommendations for a new system of financing an expansion of Port State Control (Chapter 11); emergency assistance (Chapter 20); and MPCU's counter-pollution capability (Chapter 21). We believe that it is better for the potential polluter to pay, so that costs are correctly attributed: but we accept that payment by the taxpayer is a valid, if less satisfactory, alternative. **The crucial point is that enhanced Port State Control, tug assistance and a counter-pollution capacity are all vitally important and that payment, from whatever source, must be made in order to provide UK coasts with essential protection.**

Taxpayer or polluter?

Taxpayer

22.2 The Government, with its responsibility for the defence of the realm, already pays for Port State Control at a cost of about £1 million a year. It also pays – and is inadequately compensated – for the standing costs of MPCU's counter-pollution capacity, including surveillance, the dispersant spraying capacity, the associated stockpiles of dispersant and equipment, at-sea oil recovery and cargo transfer capabilities and beach cleaning stockpiles, at a cost of over £5 million a year.

22.3 The Government is, of course, funded by the general taxpayer, and the existing arrangements are a breach of both the polluter pays principle and the user pays principle. While it would obviously be possible for the taxpayer to pay also for enhanced Port State Control and the tug assistance we recommend in Chapter 20, constraints in public expenditure are an obvious difficulty.

Potential polluter

22.4 Irrespective of that consideration, we believe that the case for payment by the potential polluter is stronger. The principle that the polluter should pay is well established and, as we point out in paragraph 1.15, has been a cornerstone of Government policy for many years. In this case we believe that the application of the principle would not only ensure that costs are correctly attributed but also act as an incentive to reducing those costs, and thus reducing the risks of pollution. It is also manifestly fairer.

22.5 We appreciate that payments by potential polluters may be passed on, and that this application of the (potential) polluter pays principle may, at least in part, transfer the burden from the taxpayer to the consumer of goods transported by sea – and that in practice there may be little difference between them. This applies to virtually any application of the polluter pays principle: but it does not make it any less valid.

22.6   We are also well aware of the many competing claims upon public expenditure, not only in the UK but in other countries which we hope will agree to share in the approach we advocate. While we must accept that it is ultimately for Governments to decide whether a particular item of public expenditure is worthwhile, we believe that it would be wrong for our proposals to be rejected or watered down because of difficulties in financing that expenditure. It would cripple our proposals for Port State Control, and perhaps for shared tug assistance, if States were reluctant to endorse our views wholeheartedly because of considerations of cost.

22.7   We discuss in this chapter whether our proposals should be funded by a flat charge on shipping, which would be comparatively easy to collect, or by levies on individual ships which can be more closely related to their **individual** capacity to pollute, and can thus have a deterrent effect. **We prefer the first for tug assistance and counter-pollution capacity and the second for Port State Control; but we do not rule out a simpler flat rate for Port State Control.**

Existing charges on shipping

22.8   Although the Paris MOU ensures a reasonably even-handed approach to Port State Control in the relevant countries, and the Bonn Agreement ensures cooperation in reaction to pollution emergencies, different countries adopt different approaches on the levels of provision needed to deal with emergencies and on the means of financing them. Expenditure seems mostly to be met by the Governments concerned.

The Australian Maritime Safety Authority (AMSA)

22.9   The Australian Government has already adopted the principles which we advocate. AMSA (see Appendix N) funds its Port State Control (among other things) from a charge on ships visiting Australian ports or operating on the Australian coast. In 1993-94 this charge was expected to amount to A$7 million (£3.3 million). AMSA's contingency plan is funded by a charge made quarterly on all ships carrying 10 tonnes or more of oil. In 1993-94 the charge was expected to raise $A3.5 million (£1.7 million). While this is significantly less than the cost of maintaining MPCU's standby capacity, AMSA has acquired through this charge equipment worth over $A13 million (£6.2 million) to respond to oil spills from ships.

Existing UK charges – port dues

22.10   All merchant shipping calling at UK ports has to pay dues to the port concerned. These are simply the commercial charges made by the harbour authority for the services it provides: they are not in any sense a tax or levy. The structure of charges varies from port to port: some are inclusive, while others include separate charges for items such as pilotage and docking. There are wide variations in charges even within a port for the same type of vessel and cargo. The British Ports Association has given us some reasonably typical port costs, which include both handling and conservancy charges, based on reasonable assumptions on the length of time spent in port. The figures are:

Coastal tanker – 1,871 grt	£1,730
Coastal tanker – 30,000 grt	£50,000
Tanker – 49,809 grt	£48,683
Tanker – 76,149 grt	£69,111
General Cargo – 999 grt	£4,070
General Cargo – 7,300 grt	£47,000
Container – 1,000 grt	£8,500
Off-shore Supply Vessel – 1,010 grt	£1,599

Existing UK charges – light dues

22.11   As we explain in paragraph 13.43, the three General Lighthouse Authorities (GLAs – Trinity House, the Northern Lighthouse Board and the Commissioners for Irish Lights) are responsible for providing and maintaining aids to general navigation in UK and Irish waters. The cost is met from the General Lighthouse Fund, which is administered by the Department of Transport and which comprises light dues paid by ships calling at UK and Irish ports, together with contributions from the Irish Government and the Ministry of Defence. We discuss here only light dues paid by merchant shipping, which amount to some £60 million a year. We calculate[1] that approximately 95 per cent of this, or £57 million, is attributable to shipping calling at UK ports.

22.12   Light dues are charged on arrivals at UK and Irish ports. They are tonnage related, with the due set at 43 pence per net registered tonne. Only the first seven calls by an individual vessel at a UK or Irish port in a year are liable for light dues.

22.13   Light dues do not attempt any correlation between the use made of navigational aids by a particular vessel and the charges made on that vessel. The smaller pleasure craft are exempt from dues, largely because of the difficulties of collection, as are passing vessels which do not call at UK ports. Both may rely on navigational aids provided by the GLAs.

Effects of light dues on trade

22.14   Most other EC States fund marine navigational aids not through light dues but by other means, such as general taxation. The European Commission, in its communication *A Common Policy on Safe Seas*, recognised that different approaches lead to some ports operating at a competitive disadvantage. It therefore agreed that there should be a study of the funding of navigational aids with a view to achieving a consistent basis throughout the Community, based on the "user pays" principle.

22.15   It is reasonable to assume that light dues must affect the prices of goods and the competitiveness of ports. However, we know of no studies which have demonstrated that the effects are significant. We conclude that either light dues are absorbed into general costs or, more probably, that their effect is so small as to be imperceptible.

---

[1] Source: the 1992–93 General Lighthouse Fund accounts.

Funding Port State Control

22.16 Although we consider that the issues of principle are the same for funding Port State Control on the one hand and tug assistance and dispersant spraying on the other, there are substantial practical differences. We therefore discuss them separately.

Should owners be charged?

22.17 We have already acknowledged the importance of the principle that the polluter – or potential polluter – should pay. The first question that must be answered is whether Port State Control, which is a safety measure quite as much as a pollution prevention one, is so exceptional that the principle should be waived. We believe it is not.

22.18 Under current UK legislation, the carrying out of Flag State Control surveys, for which charges are made, is a statutory duty upon MSA. The carrying out of first inspection of either UK or non-UK ships, for which no charges are made, is not. We do not consider this distinction between the statutory and non-statutory functions to be relevant to the question of charging: the crucial point is that Port State Control is clearly within the MSA's *vires* or powers and functions. **But if there is any doubt, the statutory position should be changed.**

22.19 It can be argued that "policing" inspections should not be paid for by those policed. Even within the UK, some types of "policing" functions are charged for while others are not. Examples of the first include charges by the police to football clubs for policing football matches, and to airports for police work done there: railway services pay directly for policing. We also understand that the Civil Aviation Authority recovers its costs in enforcing safety standards from aircraft operators through the fees it charges them. We believe that the numbers of such charges are likely to increase rather than decrease, for reasons of accountability and efficiency. We can see no reason why Port State Control should be any different.

22.20 Another argument is that it could be unfair, and send the wrong messages, if charges were to be levied irrespective of whether ships were in good or bad condition. This is recognised by the present system, which imposes penalties in terms of charges both for repeat inspections and, more importantly, delay. But charges under the present system are designed primarily as penalties, not for cost recovery: we want to see a system which both recovers costs in an equitable fashion and imposes penalties where these are deserved.

22.21 The most important point is that there should, so far as is practicable, be equal treatment within the Paris MOU club, and for ships of all nations. Clearly UK flagged ships should be treated the same as foreign flagged ones, and charges for similar inspections should be levied equally on both. We can see difficulties if one country within the Paris MOU charges for Port State Control inspections while others do not, and we would like to see charging on a similar basis throughout the Paris MOU, though we recognise that this may take time to achieve.

A charging regime for Port State Control

22.22   We have no doubt that the best solution is to charge shipowners for inspections on the basis of rates which would produce a full cost recovery. The need for Port State Control stems from the conduct of the industry as a whole in putting substandard ships to sea. The polluter, or potential polluter, should pay.

22.23   Whilst the resource cost would in aggregate be significant – more than the net cost of some £1 million (see paragraph 11.36) to the UK taxpayer of current arrangements – the burden upon each shipowner for any individual inspection would normally be small. We understand that the resource cost of a routine inspection in the UK is about £350, assuming that no deficiencies are found. This is small compared to the port charges listed in paragraph 22.10.

22.24   We have in this Report, and particularly in Chapter 4, stressed the commercial difficulties which good shipowners face because of the unfair advantages which fly-by-night operators have over them. It is very much in the interests of good shipowners that improvements in the effectiveness of Port State Control, which are crucial to dealing with the problem of poor shipowners, are not hampered by a lack of funds. A modest extra charge for Port State Control is a small price to pay for the potential benefits. To use the analogy of football in paragraph 22.19, all football supporters pay for policing a match in the price of a ticket, even though policing may be needed to deal with only a small minority: it is the peaceable majority who arguably benefit most.

22.25   There remains the question of whether there should be a scale of charges, so that the more extensive or frequent inspection a ship needed the higher the charge would be, or a single flat rate, perhaps added to port dues. There are advantages in both. The Australian Marine Safety Authority, whose system is described in Appendix N, has adopted a flat rate system, which has the merit of simplicity. Nevertheless, we believe that a scale of charges has the considerable advantage that the heaviest charges fall on the worst ships. We recognise that owners would have to pay fees for inspections which found no faults, though there would be advantages for them in that inspections finding no faults would discourage their ships from being targeted for Port State inspection. It is also relevant that an average charge would inevitably be heavier.

22.26   We recommend that a new fund is set up to pay for all Port State Control inspections, funded by the shipping industry through a charge. The UK Government should consult widely, not least with its partners in the Paris MOU, on the system of charging for Port State Control to be adopted. The aim should be full cost recovery, and the system should ensure so far as practicable that ships found to be seriously deficient incur higher charges than those found to be free of or with only minor deficiencies. The long-term aim should be for a similar system of charging to be applied by all Paris MOU States. The principles to be followed should be that the charges should be sufficient, but not more than is required, to meet the costs taking one year with another; that clear, separate accounts should be published; and that economy, effectiveness and efficiency should be demonstrated.

Paying for tug assistance and the counter-pollution capacity

Why new funding arrangements are needed

22.27 As we explain in Chapter 19, the International Oil Pollution Compensation (IOPC) Fund pays compensation to those who suffer a measurable loss from oil pollution from a tanker, and to the public authorities concerned for the marginal costs of the action they take to prevent pollution reaching the shore and to clean up pollution which does reach the shore. The limit for compensation is a total of about £57 million per incident.

22.28 The IOPC Fund pays only for the cost of operations during an incident with only a small degree of "uplift" towards the standing costs of the arrangements needed to minimise pollution and to clear it up, even though the existence of these arrangements reduces the costs of clean-up and thus the charges to the Fund. As we explain in paragraphs 19.8 – 19.9, we believe that this is misguided, and an active disincentive to States to plan properly for emergencies.

22.29 While we very much hope that the IOPC Fund will change its mind and fund a greater part of the standing charges of necessary preventive measures, we have to accept that as an international body funded by the oil industry it may prove resistant to pressure. We must also recognise that if the IOPC Fund agreed to pay towards one country's standing charges, it would be expected to pay towards the costs of them all: and that the levels of response, and thus the charges, may vary widely from one country to another. We have therefore considered alternative means of covering existing costs (including the dispersant spraying capacity and other major standing costs such as the cost of maintaining equipment stockpiles) and the new emergency assistance plan.

Who should pay?

22.30 We have already discussed the principles of payment by the taxpayer or the polluter at the beginning of this chapter. Again, we accept that there is a case for the taxpayer to pay but think that the burden properly lies with those whose activities give rise to the need. There are however other interests which might bear part of the cost, and these are discussed here.

Local authorities

22.31 Coastal local authorities have an interest in preventing pollutants reaching the shore, but we do not think it sensible to ask them to pay for prevention. They would need to raise local taxes or give up other functions, either of which would mean that local people had to pay for their own protection. There would be no point in their receiving extra payments from the Government for this purpose: this would be no better than the Government itself paying.

Local interests

22.32 Similar arguments apply to local businesses which would be adversely affected by pollution, such as tourism and fish farming: though they often should have a role in contingency planning as we point out in paragraphs 21.126 – 21.128. They may also wish to invest in some special local protection beyond that provided nationally, as we suggest in Chapter 21.

Harbour authorities

22.33 There is an argument that harbour authorities should pay: the effect would be an increase in charges to users which would be largely paid by the potential polluters. We would not necessarily dismiss harbour authorities as an instrument for collecting contributions to the new fund – for either Port State Control or emergency assistance and counter-pollution capacity – but it should be clear that it is the polluter, not the harbour authority, who has the responsibility to pay. If this approach was adopted, the harbour authority would act simply as the agent of the Department of Transport in collecting the charges.

The potential polluter

22.34 That leaves the potential polluters themselves: the owners, operators and users of those vessels which carry significant amounts of oil or other pollutants. Some of these already subscribe to the IOPC Fund and to TOVALOP or CRISTAL. Even though they already contribute in this way, we believe it is right that they should also contribute to the costs of prevention, including standby costs, not met by the IOPC Fund, in accordance with both the user pays principle and the (potential) polluter pays principle.

22.35 We also believe, however, that the costs should be borne by the shipping industry rather than by the oil industry, and that all those whose activities contribute towards the need for threat-removal measures should contribute towards their financing. As we have said in this Report, bunker oil can cause significant damage to the environment. We believe that it is particularly important that the polluting potential of bunker oil is recognised and that the carriers of bunker oil as well as cargo oil should contribute towards the costs of standby arrangements for dealing with pollution. We recognise however that the relationship of each vessel to the need for preventative measures is less clear cut than is the case with Port State Control, and that different arrangements may be needed.

A new emergency assistance and counter-pollution fund

22.36 A new fund should be set up to pay for the subvention for emergency assistance and for MPCU's standby response capacity. It should be funded by the shipping industry through a charge.

22.37 We expect some resistance to a new fund from the shipping industry, which already pays port and light dues and which is, as we have explained, suffering from overcapacity and cut-throat competition. The oil companies (which already fund the IOPC Fund) and various commercial response centres may also dislike the idea of a second fund, even though they would not contribute directly. Our comments on that are as follows. First, by our calculations the effect of the charge will be very small – see paragraph 22.47 below. Second, at least two industry witnesses suggested that a charge on the industry was a solution to some of the problems. Third, the user pays and polluter pays principles are important: there is no reason why the taxpayer should have to pay directly for measures which are required solely as a result of the activities of the shipping and oil industries. Fourth, our proposal is much less onerous than requiring shipowners to provide their own spill response capability as in the USA.

What the fund should cover

Emergency towing

22.38 **The fund should pay for the provision of emergency standby towing capacity, as described in Chapter 20.** We estimate – see paragraph 20.121 – that about £5 million a year will be needed for this, though it must be stressed that this figure might prove to be an over or under estimate. Emergency towing assistance will benefit all types of merchant shipping. It is therefore right in principle that all types of merchant shipping should pay for the standby capacity for emergency towing, in proportion to the amounts of potential pollutants carried.

Counter-pollution capacity

22.39 **The fund should also pay for the counter-pollution capacity and other essential clean-up equipment, as described in Chapter 21.** It should cover:

	1994-95 budget
aerial spraying capability	£3,500,000
aerial surveillance capability	£1,200,000
routine aerial surveillance	£230,000
ship spraying capability	£62,000
dispersant stockpiles	£70,000
beach cleaning and at-sea equipment stockpiles	£199,000
cargo transfer and salvage equipment stockpiles	£130,000
total	£5,391,000

22.40 We have included the £1.2 million cost of the aerial surveillance capability because, as we point out in paragraph 21.49, the spraying aircraft cannot be used without them. It is less clear whether the £230,000 for routine surveillance of shipping lanes (to look for signs of pollution) should be included, but by analogy with Port State Control we believe it should.

22.41 Our recommendations in the previous chapter ought to reduce the standing costs of aerial spraying, but we believe that it would be imprudent to hazard a guess at the amounts, or at when any savings can be made. We therefore assume for the purposes of our discussion in this chapter that the figures will remain at about £5.4 million, though we believe that it should be less.

22.42   There is a case for oil spill response preparations by local authorities, such as the installation of fixing points for booms, to be financed from a charge. We have considered this carefully. MPCU's counter-pollution capacity consists entirely of commercial contracts with the private sector for the supply of equipment and for the necessary manning for that equipment, including training costs. This is easily separable from other tasks, including the management of the contracts themselves. We have concluded that it would be difficult to reconcile inclusion of any of MPCU's general costs with simplicity of administration and accountability. For similar reasons we do not think that the charge should finance training, contingency planning or exercises, or any other local authority costs.

22.43   The total amount to be met from the new fund is therefore something in the region of £10 million a year, split roughly equally between emergency assistance on the one hand and counter-pollution (including surveillance) capacity on the other.

Contributions to the fund

22.44   It is important to stress that the new fund – like the similar fund for Port State Control – would be based on charges, not taxes, for specific and limited purposes. As such, it ought in principle to be related directly to the risk for which the facilities are provided, for instance by relating the charges to tonne-kilometres. It can be argued that the more polluting oils should lead to higher payments than less polluting oils. The risk of pollution from a particular vessel relates to the length of time she spends within polluting distance from shore – and that distance can vary not only with geography but also with changing weather conditions. It would be very burdensome to attempt to assess the degree of risk in any detail. Simplification and approximation are essential.

22.45   As with the Port State Control fund, we want to see the simplest organisation compatible with reasonable equity and accountability. We do not want to set out a system in detail, because consultation will be needed with affected parties and agreement reached on the most effective way of establishing the fund.

22.46   Dispersant spraying is only useable for oil spills[2]. It is irrelevant to other forms of pollution such as chemicals. There is a case for setting up two funds, one (fund A) for emergency assistance and one (fund B) for counter-pollution capacity. On this basis, all vessels above a certain size would pay into both funds in respect of their bunker oils, and all vessels would pay into fund A in respect of emergency assistance. Only vessels carrying oil would also make a further payment into fund B in respect of their cargoes.

22.47   Such a system would be difficult to set up and administer, and the costs of administration would therefore be high. If the charge was likely to be large, and its effects on competitiveness and the prices of finished goods significant, it might be worth the complexity in the interests of fairness. But, as we point out in paragraph 22.15 above, the effect of light dues on the ultimate prices of goods is likely to be very small. The charge we

---

[2] Generally only crude oil spills, although some medium fuel oils and some petroleum products may also be amenable.

advocate, at approximately £10 million a year, is likely to be just over one-sixth of the light dues payable at UK ports (£57 million a year). The additional charge is likely to be less than a fifth of light dues, or the equivalent of an addition to light dues of about 8 pence per net registered tonne. Given the smallness of this figure, we do not believe that such an elaborate two fund system is justifiable.

Principles of collection

22.48   Although we have taken light dues as a comparison, we do not believe that the charge should simply be added on to light dues. The light dues system is complex, and the complexities would not necessarily serve our purposes.

A simple charge on ports

22.49   There are various ways of levying and collecting charges for the fund. One is for Government to put a simple charge on ports, related to tonnage, and leave it to each port to decide how to fund it. Despite its simplicity, we do not think that this is the right answer. We do not think it would be right to ask ports to impose a charge without specifying how the charge should be structured: otherwise there would be nothing to ensure that the potential polluter did actually pay. A simple charge would thus negate the principle we set out in paragraph 22.33 that the polluter, not the harbour authority, should clearly be responsible for payment.

A tonnage charge on ports

22.50   A variant of this idea would be to put a charge on each port:

(a)   in relation to total tonnage in respect of an emergency towing fund; and

(b)   in relation to tonnage of oil handled, including bunkers, in respect of a dispersant fund.

While this has considerable attractions, charges would inevitably be only roughly in line with the potential for pollution. It would be important to avoid any significant increase in the price of bunker fuel in UK ports, to avoid encouraging vessels to take on cheaper bunker fuel elsewhere: this would not only reduce the income from the charge but also encourage vessels to carry more potentially polluting bunkers than is necessary. It would also put those who sell bunkers in the UK at an unfair disadvantage, unless similar arrangements were in place in other European ports.

22.51   A potential problem with charging through harbour authorities by either of the methods outlined in the last two paragraphs is that it would be essential to have a single basis for charging at each port. We appreciate that it has for some years been UK Government policy that harbour authorities should set their own dues, but, as we point out in paragraph 7.61, Ministers have already accepted that changes may be needed in the context of segregated ballast tankers. We recommend in paragraph 9.65 (in the context of MARPOL reception facilities) that harbour authorities should, if necessary, be obliged when setting their dues to take certain principles into account for the benefit of the wider environment, although we would, of course, prefer it if a satisfactory voluntary agreement could be reached. The same principle would have to apply to a charge of the type we are discussing here.

A charge on individual vessels

22.52   A third way of charging is to assess an amount for each vessel above a certain size, taking into account both bunkers and cargo. For the sake of practicality charges would need to be assessed by capacity rather than actual pollutants carried per voyage. It might be best to establish a series of bands for bunkers, perhaps based on an assumed ratio between bunker capacity and cargo capacity. Some allowance would be needed for ships with segregated ballast tanks – see paragraphs 7.54 – 7.62.

22.53   On this basis, decisions would need to be taken on a number of issues. The more detailed the relationship between actual polluting capacity and the charges levied, the more complex the scheme and the greater the administration costs.

22.54   The first decision to be made is the threshold above which charges should be levied. We believe that this should be fairly low, probably 50 tonnes capacity for the carriage of oil or other polluting liquids as cargo; and also 50 tonnes bunker capacity. 50 tonnes of a heavy crude oil could lead to quite serious pollution: we appreciate that 50 tonnes of some fuels or pollutants would not have serious effects but think it best to have a single threshold. A similar system will need to be devised for non-liquid pollutants.

22.55   The second question is whether mixed cargo and container ships (which can carry pollutants), bulk carriers of solids (including powders) and gas and chemical carriers should have charges levied on them at the same rate as oil tankers. We believe that, for the sake of simplicity, there should be two levels of charge. The lower level should be in respect of bunkers only, above the 50 tonne capacity threshold, and should be levelled on all passenger vessels and all mixed cargo ships, and on those carrying non-polluting bulk cargoes such as ores. The higher level of charges should be in respect of both bunkers and polluting cargoes, in both cases above the threshold, and should be levied against all vessels whose sole or main cargo is potentially polluting in the broadest sense. In this we include:

(a)   tankers carrying non-persistent oils as well as persistent ones. Non-persistent oils represent a hazard to people by fire or explosion and can be highly toxic; and

(b)   bulk carriers of other pollutants[3], in liquid, solid (including powder) or gaseous form.

---

[3] As defined in the schedule to the Merchant Shipping (Prevention of Pollution) (Intervention) Order 1980, SI 1980 No. 1093. The list of pollutants is reproduced in the Annex to Appendix J.

22.56 We appreciate that some carriers of pollutants will thus be paying for a facility which will be of limited use to them, but it must be remembered that their need for emergency assistance can be considerably greater than some other polluting vessels. The cargoes of gas carriers in particular would not pollute the sea or the coastline in the conventional sense but, like some non-persistent oils, could create enormous damage through explosion or pollution of the atmosphere. Emergency assistance would be required as quickly as possible for a gas carrier in difficulties. We therefore believe that evenhandedness is the best solution.

22.57 Other points which need to be resolved are:

(a) whether charges should be levied on all voyages, laden or unladen; and if laden only, whether they should be levied on voyages from UK ports, to UK ports or both. For the higher charge levied on vessels with polluting cargoes we favour a charge based on each laden trip beginning or ending at a UK port (though a laden trip between two UK ports should count only once) and for the lower charge in respect of bunker capacity a charge per visit to a UK port;

(b) whether there should be special measures for ferries and coastal shipping which visit ports frequently but pose no more of a risk than vessels travelling a long way past our shores but calling only at one port. We believe that there should be some sort of annual "season ticket" for the lower charge, and perhaps for the higher charge as well, which would apply to all calls by a single vessel to any UK port; and

(c) how the charges would be assessed and collected. The best course might be for harbour authorities or perhaps terminal operators to act as agents for the Department of Transport in imposing the charges alongside port dues. If that was the arrangement, it might be sensible for the same authorities to check and perhaps issue season tickets as well, also on behalf of the Department of Transport.

The way forward

22.58 Despite its potential complexity, we believe that the third system outlined in paragraphs 22.52 – 22.57 is the best, because it is much the most closely aligned to actual pollution potential. However, we do see considerable attractions in the much simpler tonnage charge on ports, though this would depend on an equitable system of charging being agreed by, or if unavoidable imposed upon, the harbour authorities. **We recommend that the Department of Transport should consult with the shipping industry, harbour authorities and other interested parties on both these alternatives: it might prove that the industry would prefer the simpler version, with its lower administrative costs, to the more precise one.**

Organisation of the fund

22.59 The aims and limits of the fund need to be carefully defined. Contributors to the fund, and the cargo owners and end users who ultimately bear the charges, must be clear that their money is being used sensibly and efficiently. **The principles to be followed should be the same as those set out in paragraph 22.26: that the charges should be sufficient, but not more than is required, to meet the costs taking one year with another; that clear, separate accounts should be published; and that economy, effectiveness and efficiency should be demonstrated.**

22.60   We believe that the levies ought to be charged against the owner of the ship rather than against the charterer or cargo owner, with a power of arrest of the ship (to be used with discretion) against defaulters.

22.61   We do not anticipate funds being brought up to a predetermined level and subsequently topped up as and when necessary. Instead we envisage a fairly constant level of expenditure each year on the emergency assistance subvention and on MPCU's standing costs. The charges would thus be fairly regular from year to year. We would expect, after initial primary legislation, that the scale of charges would be set every year by the Secretary of State by a Statutory Instrument.

22.62   We would like to see broadly similar arrangements for the Port State Control fund.

Control of the funds

22.63   Both funds would need to be clearly under the control of the relevant Agency Chief Executive: the Chief Executive of the Marine Safety Agency for the Port State Control fund and the Chief Executive of the Coastguard Agency for the emergency assistance and counter-pollution fund. Both would be accountable to the Secretary of State. The Chief Executives should be under a duty to use the funds efficiently. We have considered the merits of some sort of controlling board of major contributors, but rejected this on the grounds that the Chief Executives must have clear responsibility for deciding what is required, and negotiating freedom to devise the best way of achieving this. Nevertheless, regular consultation is clearly necessary and a mechanism for this needs to be devised. It might be best to include in the necessary legislation a duty on MSA and on COASTGUARD to consult representatives of contributors and to take account of representations received.

Effects of charges on shipping and trade

22.64   As we have made clear, we are not able to reach a final judgement on the best method of charging: consultation is needed on the two bases we set out in paragraph 22.58. We cannot therefore predict what the charges will be, still less what their effects will be. The best guide we can give is that our recommendations on emergency assistance and counter-pollution capacity are likely to lead to the **equivalent of** an increase in light dues of about 8 pence per net registered tonne or 18 per cent, although we do not suggest that there should be a straight addition to light dues. The effects of the much smaller charge which we recommend will obviously be even less than that of light dues. We are unable to assess the extra costs of our proposals for Port State Control, but the current cost is about £1 million a year, or one-tenth of the estimated cost of emergency assistance and counter-pollution capacity.

22.65 When we discussed with some industry witnesses the possibility of charging, their reaction was that very small increases of this nature would in practice be absorbed into Worldscale prices without noticeable effect. That has been the experience of the fund raised in the United States of America by the imposition of a 5 cent charge on every barrel of oil processed. Whether all the charges are absorbed or part of them is passed on is immaterial: the effect will be negligible on either basis.

22.66 We therefore conclude that the charge we recommend to raise roughly £10 million a year for emergency assistance and the counter-pollution capacity is likely to have little or no perceptible effect on the ultimate prices of goods, and equally little effect on the competitiveness of UK ports. The much smaller charges for Port State Control are very unlikely to have any perceptible economic effect at all.

Interim arrangements

22.67 We recommend in paragraph 20.127 that there should be interim arrangements for the provision of emergency assistance around the UK coast, and that the UK Government should be prepared to pay the full cost if necessary. We hope that it will be possible to complete the setting up of the fund we recommend reasonably quickly, but **we consider that the UK Government should be prepared to pay the full cost until it has been set up. Some phasing in of the new charging regime may be needed: if so, again, the UK Government should bear the full cost in the meantime.**

A single fund?

22.68 There would be obvious advantages in a single fund for Port State Control, emergency assistance and the counter-pollution capacity, but we suspect that they are outweighed by the disadvantages. A single fund could not incorporate the incentives to good behaviour that graduated charges for Port State Control would introduce. A single fund would also have to be shared between the two Agencies, MSA and COASTGUARD, and this could give rise to accounting problems. Most importantly, a single fund would make international cooperation difficult, because the groups of countries in the Paris MOU and Bonn Agreement are different, despite a substantial overlap. We therefore see no merit in pursuing this idea.

A European approach

22.69 A consistent European approach towards charging for Port State Control inspections is clearly sensible and we recommend this in paragraph 22.26. We would also welcome a European approach to charging for emergency assistance and counter-pollution capacity. A major disadvantage of charging solely on a UK basis is that the UK Government alone can impose a charge only on ships visiting its ports, not on ships such as the

ROSEBAY and *BRAER* which were passing by. We hope that a broader strategy will help to cover passing traffic as well.

22.70   Our concern in the United Kingdom, with this as with many other issues discussed in this Report, is with the waters around our shores and with the waters adjoining, such as the North Sea and perhaps the Baltic. Whilst we obviously would not want to decry the importance of the Mediterranean, we have no direct interest in it, though our proposals may offer useful precedents to Mediterranean authorities. So for our purposes it would be more important to set up common arrangements with Bonn Agreement countries including Norway and Sweden than with all EC countries, useful though common EC arrangements undoubtedly would be.

22.71   Apart from the geographical problem, even neighbouring countries often take a different approach on their first line of clean-up defences. Those countries which do not rely on dispersants to the extent that we do might understandably object to an international charge funding the United Kingdom's aerial spraying capacity: equally the United Kingdom might be reluctant to accept an international charge funding other countries' different approaches.

22.72   That does not rule out cooperation in funding: a common approach to charging does not necessarily mean a complete pooling of resources. It would be much fairer to shipping if all Bonn Agreement (or EC) countries charged for their emergency assistance capacity and for their clean-up standby capacity on a common basis, even though the charges would be likely to be different. The arguments are very similar to those for a common approach to navigational aids where, as we record in paragraph 22.14, the EC Commission is considering concerted action.

22.73   While we very much hope that there will be concerted European action here, it must not be allowed to delay the setting up of a UK fund for emergency assistance and counter-pollution. **We therefore recommend that the UK Government consults its European partners on the general principles of charging while proceeding with consultation with the shipping and ports industries which we recommend in paragraph 22.58.** It will, of course, need to consult neighbouring countries, particularly the Republic of Ireland, France, Belgium and The Netherlands, on the possibility of shared arrangements for ensuring the availability of salvage tugs for emergency assistance in the interests of pollution prevention, as we recommend in Chapter 20. Common arrangements for funding would make a great deal of sense if they can be arranged in an equitable and cost-effective manner.

Chapter 23

Principal Conclusions and Recommendations

23.1   In the Overview we outline the main problems to be overcome in reducing the risks of pollution to our coasts and mention some of our most important conclusions. In summarising our recommendations in this chapter, we would have liked to have included a self-contained summary of the arguments and conclusions which have led us to those recommendations. We have reluctantly decided that to do so would unduly lengthen what is already a long Report and we have included only a very brief summary of key points. We wish however to emphasise that the recommendations cannot be fully understood without reference to those arguments and conclusions which are to be found in the paragraphs of the Report to which reference is made.

23.2   All our recommendations are addressed to either the UK Government as a whole or to a particular Government Department or Departments. In some cases the main action is for other organisations, but we believe that the Government is best placed to ensure that action is taken.

Flag State Control

23.3   Flag States have a responsibility to ensure that ships flying their flag meet the internationally agreed standards (paragraphs 6.1 – 6.3). There is clear evidence that some Flag States are failing in their responsibilities and international action is needed to improve compliance (paragraphs 6.4 – 6.13 and 6.18 – 6.29).

23.4   <u>Recommendation 1</u> **The UK Government should encourage the improvement of Flag State performance generally by giving IMO's Sub-Committee on Flag State Implementation its full support** (paragraph 6.26). **It should press IMO to:**

(a) **publish information on deficiencies and detentions for each Flag State based on data provided by Port States; and**

(b) **if that proves unsuccessful, amend Regulation 17 of Chapter I of SOLAS, and similar provisions in other Conventions, to remove the requirement to recognise certificates issued under the authority of a Contracting Government if the record of the Government concerned is held by IMO, or by a Port State without dissent by IMO, to justify such a course** (paragraph 6.28); **and**

(c) **remove the ban on publication of accident investigation results in SOLAS (Chapter I Regulation 21) which not only limits proper investigation of**

363

**underlying causes of accidents but prevents full appreciation of the vary-
ing record of different Flag States** (paragraph 12.40).

23.5   We believe that the UK's performance as a Flag State (paragraphs 6.15 – 6.17)
compares very favourably with that of most other Flag States but there is no room for
complacency (paragraphs 6.30 – 6.32).

23.6   **Recommendation 2** **The UK Government should reinforce its commitment
to quality and to better Flag State implementation by monitoring its own performance as a Flag State even more closely. To facilitate this, it should ensure
that, as far as possible, it has complete and immediate information as to deficiencies in UK ships found on inspection under foreign Port State Control** (paragraph 6.32).

23.7   Whatever the future of the Marine Safety Agency the delegation of additional survey and certification work to classification societies must not be allowed to compromise
maritime safety in the UK (paragraphs 6.35 – 6.46).

23.8   **Recommendation 3** **The UK Government should ensure that the Marine
Safety Agency has sufficient resources to enable it to audit properly the increasing
amount of survey and certification work which the UK is delegating to classification societies** (paragraph 6.45).

Ship design, construction, maintenance, equipment and reliability

23.9   In paragraphs 7.1 – 7.26 we discuss some of the problems and requirements of the
construction of vessels.

MARPOL requirements

23.10   We support the recent amendment to MARPOL which requires that, from July
1995, oil tankers over five years old should carry a survey history file (paragraphs 7.22 –
7.25). **Recommendation 4** **The UK Government should:**

(a)   **monitor the effectiveness of the MARPOL survey history file requirement once it is in force;**

(b)   **urge other Flag States, Port States and IMO, to do the same;**

(c)   **urge IMO to introduce any changes which monitoring shows to be
necessary** (paragraph 7.24); **and**

(d)   **encourage IMO to consider extending the requirement to carry a survey
history file to vessels other than oil tankers** (paragraph 7.25).

Classification societies

23.11   More needs to be done to ensure that classification societies (paragraphs 6.34 and 7.27 – 7.37) operate to acceptable standards. IMO has developed guidelines for the authorisation of organisations acting on behalf of administrations (paragraph 7.36). The EC is developing a draft Directive to ensure that classification societies are both professionally reliable and able to maintain proper control of compliance with standards (paragraph 7.36). The UK Government supports the EC's proposals: so do we (paragraph 7.37).

23.12   <u>Recommendation 5</u> **The UK Government should work through IMO to press for:**

(a)   **a review of the IMO guidelines and minimum standards for classification societies; and**

(b)   **swift implementation of minimum standards for all work delegated by Flag States to classification societies. Classification societies which do not meet these international standards should not be granted international recognition** (paragraph 7.37).

23.13   We are encouraged by the work of the International Association of Classification Societies (IACS) in attempting to harmonise the standards of its members and in introducing a mandatory Quality System Certification Scheme (QSCS) (paragraph 7.32). IMO is participating in QSCS but insurance interests have so far refused to take part. **<u>Rec</u><u>ommendation 6</u> The UK Government should ask insurance underwriters to reconsider their decision not to participate in QSCS** (paragraph 7.33).

Double hulls

23.14   We have some doubts on the merits of double hulls and consider that there is scope for discussion (paragraphs 7.38 – 7.50). We accept the line that IMO has taken in promoting double hulled tankers or equivalents but believe that there is a need for further research (paragraph 7.44).

23.15   <u>Recommendation 7</u> **The UK Government should seek to ensure through IMO that:**

(a)   **classification societies, ship designers and others ensure that the design of double hulled tankers incorporates proper access facilities. Additional requirements should be introduced if necessary** (paragraph 7.49); and

(b)   **the effectiveness of the design of double hulled tankers is monitored with a view to introducing changes to design, construction, maintenance or inspection if necessary** (paragraph 7.50).

High tensile steel (HTS)

23.16   <u>Recommendation 8</u> **The UK Government should press IMO, the classification societies, ship designers and others concerned with the structure and** maintenance of vessels to give careful consideration to the survey requirements for vessels whose construction includes a significant proportion of HTS (paragraphs 7.51 – 7.53).

Segregated ballast tankers (SBTs)

23.17 We believe that SBTs have considerable environmental advantages over conventional tankers. We support the aim of IMO Resolution A.747(18) and the need for EC action (paragraphs 7.54 – 7.62).

23.18 <u>Recommendation 9</u> **The UK Government should:**

(a) encourage the EC to apply Resolution A.747(18) in an appropriate manner to all Community ports on the basis that:

   i. any increased costs should be borne by the tanker industry and not by shipping in general; and that

   ii. there should be differential charging between SBTs and conventional tankers taking into account the different charging regimes of different ports;

but if EC efforts fail the UK Government should:

(b) encourage IMO to reconsider and redraft Resolution A.747(18) so that it can be applied in practice along the lines we suggest (paragraph 7.62).

Maintenance

23.19 Proper maintenance is fundamental to ship safety (paragraphs 7.63 – 7.65). <u>Recommendation 10</u> **The UK Government should:**

(a) consider with the classification societies and others engaged in the survey and inspection of ships whether procedures can be improved to probe maintenance standards fully; and

(b) encourage discussion of this issue at IMO (paragraph 7.65).

Age limits

23.20 The age of ships alone is not likely to be the most significant factor in casualties. We do not agree with the suggestion that ships should be subject to arbitrary age limits after which they should be scrapped (paragraphs 7.66 – 7.69). **Recommendation 11 The UK Government should resist any attempts to introduce arbitrary age limits** (paragraph 7.69).

Contaminated fuel oil

23.21 Contaminated fuel oil can disable a ship, increasing the risk of an accident which may result in serious pollution (paragraphs 7.73 – 7.79). **Recommendation 12 The UK Government should:**

(a) **ensure that bunker oil suppliers review their quality control systems with a view to the identification of substandard fuel oil before it is sold** (paragraph 7.77)**; and**

(b) **encourage IMO to develop a system to eliminate the problem of contaminated fuel oil based on:**

  i. **a certificate of quality which all suppliers would be required to issue on delivery; and**

  ii. **on-board testing of the fuel supplied – most merchant ships should be required to carry a simple test kit; and**

  iii. **on-shore laboratory testing of a sample of the fuel oil** (paragraph 7.78)**.**

Stress monitoring and voyage data recorders

23.22 We support the broad principle that the fitting of hull stress monitoring systems and voyage data recorders to certain vessels is beneficial and should be extended (paragraphs 7.81 – 7.84). **Recommendation 13 The UK Government should pursue this issue within IMO with a view to extending present international requirements** (paragraph 7.84).

Anchoring systems

23.23 We note the concern that present standards for anchoring systems are inadequate (paragraph 7.90). In the short term it must be for shipowners to decide whether or not to invest in new equipment (paragraphs 7.86 – 7.88). Research is important to find longer term solutions, and the UK Government has already agreed to evaluate worldwide research on equipment to allow anchors to be lowered if a ship is without power. We support this, subject to an assessment of the cost and benefits of any feasible systems (paragraph 7.89).

23.24 **Recommendation 14 The UK Government should:**

(a) **widen its review of research on anchoring systems to include the adequacy of conventional anchoring systems in slowing and stopping drifting vessels;**

(b) **work with IMO to commission any further research which may be needed; and**

(c) **support the upgrading of present international requirements if the benefits of doing so clearly justify the costs** (paragraph 7.90).

Emergency towing arrangements

23.25   If a vessel, particularly a large laden oil tanker, is disabled, it is essential that a secure tow can be established (paragraphs 7.91 – 7.92). We support IMO's proposed amendment to SOLAS – Regulation 15-1 – which requires all tankers over 20,000 dwt to be fitted with emergency towing arrangements at both ends by 1 January 1999 (paragraph 7.93). **Recommendation 15 The UK Government should press IMO to ensure that this timetable is adhered to** (paragraph 7.93).

23.26   We are concerned that the draft specification for emergency towing arrangements specifies pick-up gear and a towing pennant for the aft arrangement but makes these optional for the forward arrangement. **Recommendation 16 The UK Government should ask IMO to reconsider the specification for the forward emergency towing arrangements for tankers laid down in the draft revision to Resolution A.535(13) to include pick-up gear and a towing pennant** (paragraph 7.94).

23.27   Both the MAIB and Liberian reports into the *BRAER* accident made recommendations about safe access to the bow from the aft superstructure of tankers to enable handling of forward towing arrangements and anchors in an emergency (paragraphs 7.95 – 7.96). **Recommendation 17 The UK Government should support IMO's commitment to give further consideration to the matter of safe access from aft. The Load Line Convention should be amended if necessary** (paragraph 7.96).

23.28   We considered a number of suggestions for emergency valves and pipelines but concluded that the problems involved outweighed the advantages (paragraphs 7.97 – 7.99).

Ship operation

Encouraging a safety culture

23.29   Most maritime casualties are caused, or aggravated, by human error. Human error can never be eliminated, but reducing it must be a major priority (paragraphs 8.1 – 8.5). The position has been made worse by changes in relationships between owners, managers and Masters over the last few decades (paragraphs 8.6 – 8.8): we believe that bad owners and managers are behind most substandard ships (paragraph 8.14). Encouraging a safety culture is vital (paragraphs 8.9 – 8.12), but this is virtually impossible for regulators (paragraph 8.5). We believe that it should be made abundantly clear that it is against the long-term commercial interest of shipowners for them to ignore safety considerations, as a few evidently do (paragraph 8.12). Charterers could exercise more influence on standards than they do (paragraph 8.13). The responsibility of the Master (paragraphs 8.15 – 8.16) and the competence and motivation of the crew (paragraph 8.17) are particularly important.

23.30   **Recommendation 18 The Department of Transport should take action nationally by continuing to develop up-to-date training and manning structures with a strong emphasis on safety, on human factors and on recent advances in technology** (paragraph 8.68). **In particular, it should urge the shipping industry and, where appropriate, charterers and insurers to:**

(a) encourage widespread use of the IMO International Safety Management Code (before it becomes mandatory in 1998) (paragraph 8.10) **and of the ISO 9002 standard** (paragraph 8.11);

(b) **consider carefully whether demands being placed upon Masters are reasonable** (paragraph 8.16);

(c) **ensure that all crew receive basic craft, safety and survival training as well as higher technical training** (paragraphs 8.18 – 8.22);

(d) **consider carefully human factors such as stress, alertness and psychology when considering safe manning scales** (paragraphs 8.29 – 8.30);

(e) **be extremely cautious in the introduction of the potentially dangerous One Man Bridge Operation** (paragraphs 8.34 – 8.36); **and**

(f) **ensure that living, welfare and employment conditions do not fall below those needed to ensure good morale and motivation** (paragraphs 8.53 – 8.54).

23.31 <u>Recommendation 19</u> The UK Government should take action internationally by pressing IMO to deal speedily and forcefully with the problems (paragraph 8.68) **and in particular:**

(a) to work towards early completion of the current overhaul of the Convention on Standards of Training, Certification and Watchkeeping (STCW), taking account of requirements for modern training, audit and on-board communication (paragraphs 8.24 – 8.26);

(b) to increase pressure on lax administrations to ensure that the standards agreed are adhered to in practice (paragraph 8.26);

(c) to consider the requirements for better training related directly to jobs on board (paragraphs 8.18 – 8.22);

(d) to bring pressure to bear on Flag States on training certification (paragraphs 8.27 – 8.28);

(e) to institute an international system of validation for both certificates and training courses which would involve regular inspections by someone acting on behalf of, and reporting direct to, IMO (paragraph 8.28);

(f) to redefine the circumstances in which Flag States can give dispensations on crewing levels (paragraphs 8.37 – 8.39); **and**

(g) to review urgently manning standards and reconsider the extent to which they should remain open to interpretation by the Flag State (paragraph 8.39).

Language

23.32   When officers and crew speak different languages or come from different cultures there is a danger that they will fail to communicate properly with each other, and may put the ship in danger as a result (paragraphs 8.40 – 8.43). Language difficulties can also make ship-to-ship and ship-to-shore communication difficult (paragraphs 8.44 – 8.45). Communication in a crisis is particularly difficult: everyone tends to panic in their own language. A list of mutually comprehensible words is not enough (paragraph 8.46) and no single person should provide the link between groups speaking different languages (paragraphs 8.47 – 8.49).

23.33   <u>Recommendation 20</u> **The UK Government should press IMO to:**

(a)   **include the general issue of communication in the revision of STCW** (paragraph 8.50);

(b)   **seek international agreement on new standards which should make it plain that:**

  i.   **the Master and officers must be able to communicate properly with each other;**

  ii.   *some of them* **must be able to communicate properly with the crew;**

  iii.   **the senior petty officers must always be able to communicate properly with both officers and crew; and**

  iv.   **there should be sufficient overlap so that orders given by those in command can be understood by the crew** (paragraph 8.49);

(c)   **to adopt English formally as the international language of the sea with minimum standards of comprehension and ability to communicate** (paragraphs 8.51 – 8.52).

UK seafarers

23.34   Although exploitation undoubtedly exists (paragraphs 8.53 – 8.54) and, even where exploitation does not exist pay differentials may cause difficulties (paragraphs 8.55 – 8.57), we see no automatic link between exploitation and flagging out (paragraph 8.55). We also accept that a flagged out owner may be able to employ non-western European officers and crew without any loss of standards (paragraphs 8.58 – 8.61). But a reduction in the numbers of experienced UK officers may affect shore-based authorities (paragraphs 8.61 – 8.62). The Government Assistance For Training scheme should ease the problems (paragraphs 8.63 – 8.66).

Port operations

23.35   Poor port operations can lead to damaging pollution and to loss of life (paragraphs 8.71 – 8.75). Port and terminal operators need to have proper procedures in place (paragraph 8.74). <u>Recommendation 21</u> **The Department of Transport should discuss with IMO, the International Chamber of Shipping and any other relevant bodies how best to remind all shipowners of the need to ensure that their crews:**

    (a)   follow loading and unloading procedures which are appropriate to the design of their particular ship (paragraph 8.75);

    (b)   are familiar with the bunkering procedures and characteristics of their ship (paragraph 8.76); **and**

    (c)   are made aware of advice on pollution prevention (paragraphs 8.77 – 8.79).

Non-accidental discharges

Oily wastes, garbage and noxious liquid substances

23.36   Substantial quantities of oily waste and garbage are still discarded in the sea. Oil from bilges and fuel discharges is estimated to be the biggest source of oil entering the sea from marine transportation (paragraphs 3.4 and 9.17). Controls over both oily wastes and garbage are more stringent in Special Areas (paragraphs 9.2 and 9.26). There are no Special Areas for oily wastes in the seas around the UK (paragraphs 9.2 and 9.7 – 9.9). There are disadvantages in Special Area status (paragraph 9.8) which need to be carefully assessed, but we believe that <u>Recommendation 22</u> **The UK Government should, subject to that assessment, regard the adoption of the North Sea, the English Channel and the Irish Sea as Special Areas for oily wastes as a long-term aim.** Waste reception facilities will need to be improved first (paragraph 9.9).

23.37   Automatic oil discharge monitoring and control systems are already required for some discharges (paragraphs 9.20 – 9.23). <u>Recommendation 23</u> **The UK Government should seek improvements in the reliability of monitors** (paragraph 9.24).

23.38   The North Sea and the English Channel form a Special Area for garbage disposal purposes (paragraphs 9.25 – 9.29), but it is not known how much garbage is dumped there. <u>Recommendation 24</u> **The UK Government should:**

    (a)   sponsor surveys, preferably in conjunction with IMO or with other European States, of the amounts of garbage generated on a representative sample of different types of vessel;

    (b)   seek through IMO a requirement that an entry should be made in the ship's log when garbage is discharged ashore, and that the entries should be subject to checking; and

    (c)   when good estimates of average amounts of garbage generated are available, ask IMO to consider how a Port State Control regime could best ensure compliance with garbage disposal regulations (paragraphs 9.45 – 9.52).

23.39   The controls over noxious liquid substances (paragraphs 9.30 – 9.33) are out of date. We welcome the current IMO review and recommend that **Recommendation 25 The UK Government should seek to ensure that revised regulations reflect the need for more stringent and effective controls on discharges** (paragraph 9.32).

Reception facilities

23.40   Regulations on the disposal of garbage at sea are difficult to enforce (paragraph 9.28) and the key to improvements in the disposal of both oily wastes and garbage is better reception facilities at ports (paragraphs 9.3, 9.9 and 9.34 – 9.37). We conclude, from a study carried out for the Department of Transport and evidence given to us, that reception facilities for oily wastes (paragraphs 9.38 – 9.44 and 9.57) and garbage (paragraphs 9.45 – 9.52 and 9.57) are inadequate and that there are disincentives to their use. The Department of Transport is planning a survey of reception facilities. **Recommendation 26 Once the level of reception facilities is established, the Department of Transport should initiate a further publicity campaign on their use and monitor its effects** (paragraph 9.58).

23.41   There need to be more waste oil and garbage reception facilities and they need to be easier to use (paragraphs 9.53 – 9.62) without the disincentive of specific charges (paragraphs 9.63 – 9.67). **Recommendation 27 The UK Government should:**

(a)   **place a statutory obligation on port and terminal operators to provide reception facilities which:**

   i.   **are fully adequate;**

   ii.   **are geared to ease of use; and**

   iii.   **avoid disincentives such as a requirement for ships to pre-sort waste** (paragraph 9.59);

(b)   **encourage port and terminal operators to consider carefully, in consultation with shipping interests and waste disposal contractors:**

   i.   **what level of provision is needed;**

   ii.   **how disincentives to use the facilities can be avoided; and**

   iii.   **what scope there is for alternative means of waste collection, such as the use of barges rather than fixed points** (paragraph 9.60);

(c)   **set up a system of certification to ensure that facilities are adequate, involving the Department of Transport as experts on what is required and waste regulation authorities as experts on how it should be handled. Policing of the use of reception facilities must be part of such a scheme** (paragraph 9.61);

(d) **consider with other North Sea and North East Atlantic States whether reception facilities need improving on a wider scale** (paragraph 9.62);

(e) **ensure, preferably through agreement, that the cost of reception facilities in the UK is subsumed into standard port dues rather than through additional charges, and that the reception facilities element of port dues is proportional to the size and type of vessel** (paragraph 9.65);

(f) **pursue vigorously a North Sea agreement designed to ensure that, so far as practicable, all European ports take a similar approach** (paragraph 9.66); **and**

(g) **consider whether the customs duty raised on the import of oil as waste justifies the disincentive to an orderly and legal discharge of oily wastes** (paragraph 9.44).

Ballast water contamination

23.42   The taking on and discharge of ballast water is an essential part of shipping operations, but on voyages between areas with significantly different ecosystems alien species can be imported in ballast water. Control is difficult. The UK so far appears not to have been seriously affected by ballast water releases but it is important that the threat is recognised (paragraphs 9.69 – 9.77). **Recommendation 28 The UK Government should encourage relevant studies and should support the IMO working group on this topic** (paragraph 9.77).

Anti-fouling paints

23.43   Ships' hulls are treated with tributyl tin (TBT) to keep down the growth of organisms. This benefits the atmosphere by reducing fuel consumption but TBT can leach into the water and affect a wide range of marine organisms (paragraphs 9.78 – 9.81). **Recommendation 29 The UK Government should ensure that monitoring of TBT continues and that any substitutes are carefully evaluated** (paragraph 9.81).

Hazardous and noxious substances

23.44   There are detailed rules for the carriage of hazardous and noxious substances, both non-nuclear (paragraphs 10.3 – 10.18) and nuclear (paragraphs 10.19 – 10.34). We are broadly satisfied with these arrangements and with how they work in practice (paragraph 10.36). The safety record for the transport of nuclear materials is excellent (paragraphs 10.35 and 19.42).

23.45   We have not considered the problem of containers whose contents include hazardous substances which have been lost overboard and subsequently broken up: it was not raised in evidence. We hope that the UK Government will feel able to cooperate with the French Government in taking forward measures emerging from the current Senatorial investigation into recent incidents (paragraph 10.12).

23.46   At present, no satisfactory arrangements exist for the electronic "tagging" of containers. **Recommendation 30 The UK Government, with its European partners, should encourage the development of a workable system** (paragraph 10.13).

23.47   Port State Control inspections in 1992 showed a higher than average detention rate for chemical tankers and for oil tankers and combination carriers. **Recommendation 31 The UK Government should investigate, with its European partners, the reason for this worse than average detention rate and consider remedial measures** (paragraph 10.5).

Port State Control

23.48   Port State Control ought to be unnecessary, because the prime responsibility for ensuring the safety of ships lies with Flag States (and the classification societies to which they delegate work) and not with Port States (paragraph 6.1). We have no doubt that Port State Control is an inferior substitute for Flag State Control, because the scope for inspection is so much less (paragraphs 11.23 – 11.27). But it is an essential substitute for as long as the control exercised by some Flag States is patently unsatisfactory (paragraphs 11.1 – 11.4). The existing cooperative system has achieved a great deal, but it needs to evolve further (paragraph 11.5).

23.49   The system of Port State Control exercised by the European "club" of nations (paragraphs 2.19 and 11.15 – 11.22) can and should be improved (paragraphs 11.6 – 11.32). We are glad that the European Commission agrees (we saw its draft Directive a few days before our Report was submitted) but we believe that its approach, which seeks to consolidate and formalise existing practices rather than develop new ones, to be less effective than our own. **Recommendation 32 The UK Government should take all necessary steps to persuade the EC Commission and Member States to include consideration of our recommendations in developing proposals for Community action** (paragraphs 11.89 – 11.90).

The conclusiveness of Flag State certificates

23.50   Regulation 19(b) of SOLAS and similar provisions in other Conventions limit Port State Control inspection to checking certificates unless there are clear grounds for believing that the condition of a ship does not correspond with her certificates. **Recommendation 33 The UK Government should press IMO to consider amending the Conventions if the experience of Port States suggests that these provisions are unreasonably inhibitory to Port State Control inspection** (paragraphs 11.24 – 11.26).

A strategy for the future

23.51   The system of Port State Control operated by the Paris MOU needs to be strengthened to improve the apparent and the actual chances of a ship being inspected, improve the detection rate amongst ships inspected and increase the disincentives to being found to be operating a substandard vessel (paragraphs 11.37 – 11.38).

Self-targeting

23.52   <u>Recommendation 34</u> **The UK Government, together with its Paris MOU partners, should introduce a system of self-targeting (*not* self-regulation) for Port State Control inspection** (paragraphs 11.39 – 11.41) **based on:**

(a)   **a Paris MOU log book** (paragraphs 11.42 – 11.44) **which would:**

   i.   **be issued to each ship on her first visit to a Paris MOU port** (paragraph 11.42);

   ii.   **include details of the extent and nature of the inspection carried out or a detailed description of any deficiencies** (paragraph 11.44); **and**

   iii.   **include the names of the ship's owners and managers** (paragraph 11.50);

(b)   **a notice requirement** (paragraphs 11.45 – 11.52) **under which certain ships would have to give 48 hours notice of their arrival at a Paris MOU port** (paragraph 11.45). **The notice requirement should include disclosure of the names of the ship's owners and managers** (paragraph 11.50) **and would apply to:**

   i.   **every ship on her first visit to a Paris MOU port and on each subsequent visit until she was inspected for the first time and issued with a log book** (paragraph 11.46);

   ii.   **every ship which had not been inspected or been required to give notice during the previous 12 months or other appropriate period** (paragraph 11.48);

   iii.   **every ship with recorded deficiencies.** Such ships would be required to give notice at each Paris MOU port visited until an inspection resulted in a report that no deficiencies were detected (paragraph 11.48);

   iv.   **every ship with deficiencies which would have resulted in detention but for the fact that the owners have agreed to effect repairs at a subsequent port of call.** She would be required to give notice at her next visit to a Paris MOU port where she would be inspected to confirm that the deficiencies had been rectified. If they had not, she would be detained. If they had, she would be required to continue giving notice at each Paris MOU port visited until on a subsequent inspection she emerged with a clean bill of health (paragraph 11.48);

   v.   **every ship following detention.** The notice requirement would apply to each visit to a Paris MOU port for the following 12 months. Such a ship would be liable to inspection on every visit to a Paris MOU port (paragraph 11.48); **and**

vi. **every ship in the same ownership or management if more than one of their ships was found to be substandard.** The notice requirement would be removed ship by ship as each achieved a clean sheet on inspection (paragraph 11.49).

23.53   Advance notice of arrival should be capable of being combined with any other reports required by MAREP, the EC Directive on vessels carrying dangerous goods or any other scheme (paragraph 11.53). Self-reporting would not apply to cross-Channel and other short-sea ferries which call at Paris MOU ports several times a day but special attention should be paid to such vessels because of the risk to passengers (paragraph 11.54).

23.54   Self-reporting would render quotas, whereby each Paris MOU member undertakes to inspect 25 per cent of foreign ships calling at its ports, inappropriate and irrelevant – the work would be demand led (paragraphs 11.57 – 11.59).

23.55   Self-reporting would place a greater emphasis on the current Paris MOU aim of inspecting ships with recent recorded deficiencies but the other targeted categories would remain both as a guide to use of resources not committed to other inspections as a result of self-targeting and to provide a check on the effectiveness of self-targeting in high risk categories (paragraph 11.57).

Additional information

23.56   Port State inspectors need access to the widest possible sources of information (paragraphs 11.60 – 11.64). In addition to self-targeting and the Paris MOU log book there is the SIRENAC database. **Recommendation 35 The UK Government should work with its Paris MOU partners to revise this database so that it can record:**

(a)   **the fact that a Paris MOU log book has been issued to a particular ship** (paragraph 11.43)**; and**

(b)   **the names of managers as well as the names of owners of ships** (paragraph 11.50)**.**

23.57   Information from harbour authorities is vital to Port State Control inspection in the UK. If it becomes clear that harbour authorities are not providing this information as required, **Recommendation 36 The UK Government should consider imposing a statutory obligation to ensure that they do** (paragraph 11.61).

23.58   The major oil companies, insurers, classification societies and others have a great deal of information on shipping. **Recommendation 37 The Department of Transport should foster close links with these sources to facilitate the informal exchange of information** (paragraph 11.63) **and should urge all those involved, particularly marine insurers,** (paragraph 18.39) **to cooperate. The UK Government should encourage other Paris MOU countries to take a similar approach** (paragraph 11.63). We believe that the wider dissemination of information will not only benefit Port State Control but will also be of value to Flag States and the shipping industry generally in improving performance.

23.59 The Salvage Association has information on worldwide marine casualties and incidents which it used to make publicly available on a daily basis. Such information is of great value to a wide range of shipping interests. We regret the Salvage Association's decision in March 1994 to halt this practice. **Recommendation 38 The UK Government should ask the Association to reconsider** (paragraph 11.62).

23.60 **Recommendation 39 The UK Government should ensure that the information logged on MSA's database, which could be made available to insurers and potential charterers, should include ships whose crews have ignored routeing advice. The UK Government should also seek the agreement of its Paris MOU partners to include similar information on the SIRENAC database** (paragraph 16.56).

Saturation inspections

23.61 To reinforce Port State Control, both before and after the introduction of self-targeting, **Recommendation 40 The UK Government should:**

(a) **establish occasional inspections of *all* ships entering a particular port in a particular period** (paragraphs 11.65 – 11.66)**; and**

(b) **encourage its Paris MOU partners to cooperate in extending the policy to the whole Paris MOU region** (paragraph 11.67).

Publicity

23.62 Publicity can help to raise the profile of inspection and the perceived risk. **Recommendation 41 The UK Government should highlight serious cases more frequently and persuade its Paris MOU partners to do so as well** (paragraph 11.68).

Enforcement

23.63 A flexible sanction is needed to deal with those who fail to operate the self-targeting system or who persistently operate substandard ships (paragraphs 11.69 – 11.71). It might be ineffective to deny a right to enter ports (paragraph 11.72). **Recommendation 42 The UK Government, with its Paris MOU partners, should take powers to allow a ban or a delay on the discharging or loading of cargo to be imposed on such ships** (paragraphs 11.73 – 11.81). Similar sanctions are proposed in Recommendations 43(c), 60 and 71(e).

Coastal shipping

23.64 A significant number of foreign flagged ships are engaged solely in UK coastal trade. **Recommendation 43 The UK Government should consider imposing a spe-**

cial inspection regime in relation to ships engaged primarily in UK coastal waters based upon:

(a) self-targeting;

(b) either a Paris MOU log book or a UK log book; and

(c) enforcement using the discharging or loading sanction in Recommendation 42 (paragraphs 11.83 – 11.85).

General

23.65 Given the likely expansion of the Paris MOU, **Recommendation 44 The UK Government and other members should reassess standards of inspection to ensure consistency between Member States** (paragraph 11.22).

23.66 **Recommendation 45 The UK Government should seek to agree with its partners in the Paris MOU that routine Port State Control inspections should include:**

(a) **the validity of training certificates** (paragraphs 8.27 – 8.28);

(b) **actual dispensations on crewing levels, which should be reported to IMO for checking against the records held by Flag States** (paragraphs 8.37 – 8.39);

(c) **cross checks between the Oil Record Books and print-outs** (paragraphs 9.20 – 9.24);

(d) **active and frequent checks on whether vessels have the right charts** (paragraphs 13.22 – 13.24);

(e) **checks on the continuous function of transponders, once they become a requirement** (paragraphs 15.27 – 15.29);

(f) **a requirement that Masters and navigators should demonstrate by reference to log books and charts the routes followed on the inward voyage, with confirmation by the Master or Watch Officer that the route indicated has indeed been taken** (paragraphs 16.52 – 16.53); and

(g) **"clear grounds" for a careful Port State inspection should include cases where there is little evidence available on board to trace the voyage of the ship** (paragraph 16.53).

Accident investigation

23.67 The investigation and analysis of accidents is essential to enable a realistic assessment of likely risks to be made and effective preventative measures to be taken (paragraphs 12.1 – 12.7). While it is essential that individuals who may be criticised should have a chance to defend themselves, (paragraphs 12.8 – 12.10), the procedure needs to be as quick as possible so that lessons may be learnt (paragraph 12.11). **Recommendation 46 The Department of Transport should ensure that:**

(a)   the Chief Inspector of Marine Accidents adopts, in appropriate cases, a shorter procedure for consulting those who may be criticised in his reports (paragraphs 12.12 – 12.16);

(b)   any new regulations enable the Chief Inspector of Marine Accidents to publish an interim report without making recommendations (paragraph 12.17); and

(c)   the Chief Inspector of Marine Accidents does not hesitate to make interim recommendations, even when he cannot publish findings of fact (paragraph 12.18).

23.68   A more forward looking approach is needed (paragraphs 12.19 – 12.36), including analysis of the causes of accidents and near accidents. **Recommendation 47** **The Department of Transport should ensure that:**

(a)   **accident themes are selected for analysis** (paragraph 12.33);

(b)   **there is a dialogue between the Marine Accident Investigation Branch (MAIB), MSA, COASTGUARD and shipping interests on technical and human matters** (paragraph 12.34); **and**

(c)   **MAIB continues to consider the areas which may be suitable for further research and that accident reports make recommendations accordingly** (paragraph 12.36).

23.69   International cooperation is very valuable in accident analysis (paragraphs 12.37 – 12.40). This analysis, both national and international, is particularly important in considering duplication of equipment. There is no need for across-the-board duplication of steering, propulsion and other ship systems (paragraph 7.71), but analysis of incidents and accidents might identify trends indicating that further duplication is justified (paragraph 7.72). **Recommendation 48** **The UK Government should urge IMO to take a more active role in examining accident and incident information, identifying themes for investigation and considering the adequacy of current requirements** (paragraph 12.40).

Scientific safety regulation

23.70   The "safety case" approach would provide a forward rather than backward looking approach to safety regulation (paragraphs 12.41 – 12.45) but it presents substantial difficulties (paragraphs 12.46 – 12.49). We support the UK Government's Formal Safety Assessment approach and its efforts in pursuing this through IMO (paragraphs 12.51 – 12.55). **Recommendation 49** **The UK Government should continue to assess the current state of ship science in this country and consider what further action is needed to ensure that there is sufficient capacity to support the UK's work in IMO** (paragraph 12.50).

Navigation

Advice to mariners

23.71 A great deal of advice and information is available to mariners using UK waters, but some of it is unclear, particularly to non-native English speakers (paragraphs 13.1 – 13.4). There is also too much guidance in total, so much of it is likely to remain unread.

23.72 **Recommendation 50 The Department of Transport should draw up a concise outline of a *Seaway Code*, a brief, clear, simple guidance note which should cover the main points which Masters of vessels are expected to observe in UK waters (paragraphs 13.5 – 13.12). The Department of Transport should then consult widely with shipping, maritime and navigational interests on matters to be covered and the best means of publication (paragraph 13.12). The *Seaway Code* should include:**

(a) **the more important legal requirements, both national and international (paragraph 13.6);**

(b) **information on facilities and services, including MARPOL facilities, pilotage, emergency communications channels and rescue services (paragraphs 9.57 and 13.8);**

(c) **advice, including routeing advice (paragraph 13.9);**

(d) **information on where to find more detailed advice (paragraph 13.10); and**

(e) **reference to the publication *A Guide to the Planning and Conduct of Sea Passages,* which should be revised and reissued (paragraph 13.13).**

23.73 **Recommendation 51 The UK Government should seek to ensure that safety margins are respected by:**

(a) **issuing advice and reminders to the effect that everyone with a financial interest in a voyage should expect the Master to adhere to guidance issued (paragraph 13.37);**

(b) **seeking the updating, perhaps by the International Chamber of Shipping, of the BP distance tables to take account of all routeing measures (paragraphs 13.38 – 13.39); and**

(c) **seeking, through international bodies, to persuade all shipowners to issue guidance on safety margins and to monitor regularly Masters' compliance with it (paragraphs 13.40 – 13.42).**

Charts and hydrographic surveying

23.74 Clear, accurate and up-to-date charts are essential to navigation (paragraphs 13.14 – 13.32). **Recommendation 52 The UK Government should:**

(a) **preserve the current civil hydrography programme in real terms at least until all the remaining priority areas have been surveyed** (paragraphs 13.16 – 13.19);

(b) **ensure that defence cuts do not affect the part of the Hydrographer's work which is essential for civil purposes** (paragraph 13.20); **and**

(c) **examine critically the wording on charts to make it as comprehensible as possible to a non-native speaker of English** (paragraph 13.27).

Navigational equipment and emergency backup

23.75   No one system of navigational aids should be used in isolation (paragraphs 13.43 – 13.48). **Recommendation 53 The UK Government should seek the agreement of the relevant international organisations to:**

(a) **the compulsory carriage of an electronic positioning system** (paragraphs 13.49 – 13.50) **with emergency battery power supplies** (paragraph 13.51); **and**

(b) **cooperative reassessment of the requirements for emergency electrical systems** (paragraphs 13.52 – 13.54).

Pilotage

23.76   Deep sea pilotage can be very useful for a Master who is unfamiliar with a particular area. We hope that owners will encourage Masters to take pilots whenever they feel they would benefit (paragraphs 13.60 – 13.62), but there is no case for making deep sea pilotage compulsory (paragraphs 13.63 – 13.70). Nor is there a case for changing the existing clear responsibilities of Master and pilot (paragraph 13.55). **Recommendation 54 The UK Government should:**

(a) **examine the wording on charts to see whether the advantages of pilotage can be more clearly stated** (paragraph 13.65); **and**

(b) **consider the lessons to be learned from recent accidents in relation to each UK pilot station** (paragraphs 13.73 – 13.74).

Escort tugs

23.77   We do not believe that there is any justification for large vessels with potentially polluting cargoes to be accompanied by tugs whenever they are within a set distance from land (paragraphs 13.77 – 13.81).

Routeing

23.78   Routeing measures, including advice, are essential for safety in busy waters such as the Dover Strait, but they are also valuable in protecting environmentally sensitive areas (paragraphs 14.1 – 14.8). There are a wide range of routeing measures in place in UK waters (paragraphs 14.15 – 14.90). The main problems are lack of knowledge: with a few exceptions, the UK Government does not know either precisely where ships go within its waters (paragraphs 14.9 – 14.14) or the extent to which routeing advice is followed (paragraphs 14.91 – 14.95). Masters, owners and insurers may not appreciate the importance of following routeing advice and probably do not know which areas are both environmentally sensitive and at risk (paragraph 14.119). The first step is to improve knowledge.

23.79 **Recommendation 55 The UK Government should:**

(a) **consider with its European partners the extent to which further information is necessary and jointly or individually commission any necessary studies** (paragraphs 14.9 – 14.11);

(b) **ask IMO to consider the extent to which Masters accept IMO endorsed advice** (paragraphs 14.91 – 14.93); **and**

(c) **if it is found that Masters are not accepting IMO endorsed advice:**

    i. **ask IMO to consider the reasons** (paragraph 14.93); **and**

    ii. **press IMO to speed up and resolve its consideration of ways in which existing voluntary measures can be made mandatory on all vessels** (paragraph 14.94).

23.80 **Recommendation 56 The Department of Transport should consider the scope for routine checks on the routes taken by vessels into and out of particular ports** (paragraph 16.55).

23.81 Several routeing and reporting measures are directed primarily at laden tankers. Unladen tankers and other vessels with large bunker carrying capacity can also create a significant pollution hazard (paragraph 3.8). **Recommendation 57 The UK Government should press IMO to ensure that all vessels with a large bunker capacity are subject to the same routeing and reporting requirements and recommendations as laden tankers** (paragraph 14.108).

23.82 Cruise ships should not be banned from entering unusually environmentally sensitive areas, but they need to take great care (paragraphs 14.109 – 14.111). **Recommendation 58 The Department of Transport should:**

(a) **ensure that the sponsors and organisers of such cruises are aware of the importance of strict observance of IMO rules;**

(b) **ensure that all cruise ships report to HM Coastguard on entering an Area To Be Avoided; and**

(c)   consider, with other interested bodies, the case for a code of practice (paragraph 14.111).

Marine Environmental High Risk Areas (MEHRAs)

23.83   We do not believe that blanket bans are appropriate (paragraphs 14.114 – 14.116): only limited areas can be singled out for special status (paragraphs 14.117 – 14.118). Existing routeing measures advise or require a Master to take a particular route or avoid a particular area: they do not explain to him **why** he should do so. Any new measure should **inform** Masters of areas of great sensitivity: this prime purpose is separate from any consequential defensive measures (paragraph 14.119).

23.84   <u>Recommendation 59</u> The UK Government should establish *Marine Environmental High Risk Areas* or MEHRAs: a few small areas of high sensitivity which are also at risk from shipping (paragraphs 14.120 – 14.144):

(a)   the Department of the Environment, with its Northern Irish, Scottish and Welsh counterparts and their statutory advisors, should work jointly with the Department of Transport to identify MEHRAs on the criteria we suggest (paragraphs 14.120 – 14.126 and 14.143);

(b)   the UK Government should urge IMO and the EC to adopt and promote MEHRAs, but should not wait for international agreement before promulgating UK MEHRAs (paragraph 14.121);

(c)   the Department of Transport should monitor MEHRAs to see whether Masters' behaviour has changed (paragraphs 14.127 – 14.128);

(d)   if further steps are needed, the UK Government should consider options with IMO (paragraph 14.129). Possibilities include compulsory Areas To Be Avoided, compulsory routes and protected headlands (paragraphs 14.130 – 14.137 and 14.139); **and**

(e)   the UK Government should consider with IMO, the EC and other interested parties how best to publicise and monitor MEHRAs (paragraph 14.144).

23.85   <u>Recommendation 60</u> The UK Government should seek to ensure through IMO and the EC that any new routeing measures are enforced through special entry reporting conditions, similar to those in Recommendation 34. Repeated breach of the conditions should lead to a ban on loading and unloading as in Recommendation 42 (paragraph 14.140).

The problems of particular areas

23.86   All areas of sensitivity will benefit from our general recommendations. Several of the areas with particular problems which we discuss in Chapter 14 will be candidates for

MEHRA status (paragraphs 14.70, 14.74 and 14.126). Others, despite their high sensitivity, will not qualify for such status because they are not significantly at risk from merchant shipping (paragraph 14.122).

Fair Isle Channel

23.87 The Fair Isle Channel is a wide strait with low traffic density. The coasts around it now have the highest degree of protection in UK waters (paragraphs 14.23 – 14.27). We do not consider that it would be useful to contemplate excluding traffic from the Channel (paragraphs 14.28 – 14.30) or setting up a Traffic Separation Scheme (paragraphs 14.31 – 14.33).

Pentland Firth

23.88 The Pentland Firth is narrow, busy and presents problems of navigation (paragraphs 14.34 – 14.37). The possibility of pilotage in the Firth is covered by Recommendation 61(f).

North western Scotland

23.89 The Minch is generally wide and presents no particular navigational problems, but there are strong local objections to the passage of oil tankers through it (paragraphs 14.38 – 14.49). Large merchant ships of all types, laden as well as unladen, should use the Deep Water Route to the west of Harris and Lewis as a matter of routine (paragraphs 14.50 – 14.59) but they should retain the option of using the Minch when **exceptional** weather or other conditions make it safer for them to do so (paragraph 14.60). There is no case for moving the Deep Water Route to the west of St Kilda (paragraphs 14.53 – 14.54).

23.90 **Recommendation 61 The UK Government, with the agreement of IMO where necessary, should:**

    (a) **issue advice that merchant ships should keep well to seaward of the Flannan Islands and St Kilda in bad weather** (paragraph 14.55);

    (b) **advise vessels to keep several miles off the western coast of Barra, the Uists, Harris and Lewis and the intervening islands, preferably by an extension both north and south of the Deep Water Route to the west of Harris and Lewis** (paragraph 14.56);

    (c) **continue cooperative monitoring arrangements in the Minch and continue to seek explanations from the owners or Masters of vessels using the Minch** (paragraphs 14.43 – 14.44 and 14.60);

    (d) **continue to monitor large vessels using the Minch. If there is no improvement within a reasonable period, the UK Government should raise the problem with IMO** (paragraph 14.61);

(e) **build on the early success of informal reporting of tankers in the Minch by:**

   i. **checking any discrepancies between local reports and MAREP; and**

   ii. **discussing the effectiveness of the scheme with those concerned** (paragraph 16.45); **and**

(f) **seek to establish whether demand exists for a regular, fully commercial deep sea pilotage system in northern and north western Scotland** (paragraph 13.72).

The North Channel and south west Wales

23.91   The North Channel has a greater density of traffic than the Fair Isle Channel or the Minch (paragraphs 14.62 – 14.64). There is potential for conflict between the use of Milford Haven by tankers and the important bird site nearby (paragraphs 14.66 – 14.70). <u>Recommendation 62</u> **The Department of Transport should:**

(a) **survey traffic in the Traffic Separation Schemes in the North Channel and off south west Wales and consider voluntary reporting** (paragraphs 14.64 and 14.69);

(b) **survey traffic using the Grassholme Channel off south west Wales and consider whether there is a case for an Area To Be Avoided to be established to protect Skomer Island and Skokholm Island** (paragraph 14.70);

(c) **ensure that the Masters of tankers arriving at and leaving Milford Haven are always asked to confirm that they use the approved route between Grassholme Island and The Smalls to and from St Brides Bay** (paragraph 16.55); **and**

(d) **consider with local interests the possibility of setting up a voluntary system for reporting tankers, similar to that in the Minch** (paragraph 16.45).

The Isles of Scilly

23.92   The ecologically sensitive Isles of Scilly are at a busy shipping crossroads (paragraphs 14.71 – 14.74). <u>Recommendation 63</u> **The Department of Transport should:**

(a) **review the case for Areas To Be Avoided or other means of enhanced protection around the Isles of Scilly** (paragraph 14.74); **and**

(b) **consider with the Council of the Isles of Scilly the possibility of setting up a voluntary system for the reporting of tankers, similar to that in the Minch** (paragraph 16.45).

Lyme Bay

23.93   Although Lyme Bay is large, it is used both as a significant anchorage and by fishing vessels and numerous pleasure craft (paragraphs 14.75 – 14.78). Lyme Bay should be covered by Recommendation 54(b): beyond that we do not believe that any form of overall control of traffic in Lyme Bay is desirable (paragraphs 14.79 – 14.82). Lyme Bay is also occasionally used for transshipments of oil (paragraphs 8.80 – 8.85 and 14.83 – 14.85). **Recommendation 64 The Department of Transport should change the transshipment areas in Lyme Bay from four small points to a single large area well away from shore** (paragraph 14.85) **and bring new Regulations into force to control transshipments as quickly as possible** (paragraph 8.85).

The Dover Strait

23.94   The Dover Strait is one of the busiest international straits in the world. At one point one of its shipping lanes is narrower than those going through the Fair Isle Channel, the Pentland Firth, the Minch or the North Channel (paragraphs 14.86 – 14.90 and 16.6 – 16.13). **Recommendation 65 The Department of Transport should:**

(a)   **speed up the system of reporting infringements of the Dover Strait Traffic Separation Scheme seen on radar, so that Masters of ships *en route* to UK ports can be admonished immediately;**

(b)   **ask the French Government to adopt a similar approach** (paragraph 16.12)**; and**

(c)   **ensure that Masters in the Dover Strait are encouraged to keep watch on VHF Channel 11 as well as on Channel 16** (paragraph 15.52)**.**

Identification

23.95   We were surprised to discover how difficult it can be to identify ships. This matters a great deal: it may make rescue more difficult; it may endanger ships by making it difficult for them to communicate with each other; it makes it difficult to apply sanctions; and it can encourage Masters in the belief that if they break the rules they are unlikely to be caught. Better means of identification are needed (paragraphs 15.2 – 15.11).

23.96   **Recommendation 66 The UK Government should work through IMO to ensure that all vessels bear prominently painted unique recognition signs. There is no good reason why this should not be implemented quickly** (paragraphs 15.13 – 15.19).

23.97   Useful though they will be, more visible recognition signs are not a complete answer. Transponders, which can identify a vessel automatically and give additional useful information, are the long-term solution (paragraphs 15.20 – 15.37). **Recommendation 67 The UK Government should press for the introduction of a worldwide system of transponders. Any opposition on commercial grounds should be resisted** (paragraph 15.26)**. To implement this recommendation, the UK Government should:**

(a)   **seek as soon as possible to amend the International Electrotechnical Commission specification for transponders** (paragraphs 15.27 – 15.30)**;**

(b) **seek through IMO to ensure that once a transponder system is fully operational:**

    i.   **it will be an offence to have a non-functioning transponder;**

    ii.   **ships carrying dangerous and polluting goods must report to coastal authorities when a transponder is malfunctioning;**

    iii.   **records must be kept available for Flag State and Port State inspection (paragraph 15.29);**

(c) **press through IMO for a rigid timetable for agreeing carriage requirements for both transponders themselves and for an associated accurate position finding system (paragraphs 15.31 – 15.32 and 13.50);**

(d) **press for international agreement on a timetable for the introduction of transponders on fishing vessels and larger sea-going pleasure vessels (paragraphs 15.33 – 15.34);**

(e) **press for international agreement on a specification for interrogation equipment (paragraph 15.36); and**

(f) **equip the Department of Transport with it (paragraph 15.35).**

Reporting

Routine reporting

23.98 Voluntary arrangements for routine reporting for certain types of vessels (MAREP) have existed for some years in the English Channel and are observed by a reasonable proportion of affected vessels (paragraphs 15.39 – 15.40). The aim is precautionary: the ship reports at a convenient moment details which would be of considerable assistance to COASTGUARD if something went wrong (paragraph 15.47). The system has recently been extended to some other areas (paragraph 15.41), but only for larger ships.

23.99 **Recommendation 68 The Department of Transport should improve this system by seeking IMO agreement to an extension of MAREP reporting to include all vessels over 300 grt and any vessels below that level carrying dangerous or polluting materials (paragraph 15.65).**

23.100 A recent EC Directive, agreed but not yet in force, takes a different approach by requiring dangerous and polluting goods carried to or from Community ports to be notified before the ship sails (paragraphs 15.43 – 15.44). The information will be available to HM Coastguard. **Recommendation 69 The UK Government should ensure that HM Coastguard is alerted to any vessels whose planned routes would ignore advice, so that remedial action can be taken (paragraph 15.44).**

23.101   A recent draft Directive, which is at an early stage of discussion, would require ships carrying dangerous and polluting goods not covered by the existing Directive to report on arrival in European waters (paragraph 15.45). We were initially attracted by the idea of universal reporting by ships to shore-based authorities (paragraphs 15.56 – 15.59). Advantages would include human contact between Masters and HM Coastguard, which would encourage the early reporting of problems (paragraphs 15.51 – 15.53). We concluded that the likely benefits are too small to justify such a system (paragraph 15.60), particularly as reporting will largely be superseded by transponders. Reporting arrangements will need to be retained only to the extent that ships will need to identify themselves on first entry to the reporting area and as a backup in case of equipment failure (paragraphs 15.29 and 15.71).

23.102   **Recommendation 70 The UK Government should:**

(a)   **resist any attempts to introduce a system of universal reporting by ships to shore-based authorities** (paragraphs 15.56 – 15.60);

(b)   **seek to modify the draft EC Directive on ship reporting** (paragraphs 15.67 – 15.69) **to bring it into line with our proposals that the compulsory reporting system should:**

  i.   **operate only in specified areas of high traffic density or particular environmental sensitivity, such as those now covered by the voluntary MAREP scheme;**

  ii.   **cover all large vessels and all those, whatever their size, that carry dangerous and polluting goods;**

  iii.   **be enforced only through Port State Control or through Vessel Traffic Services and surveillance planes where those are justified for other reasons;**

  iv.   **be brought into operation only after the existing Directive has been implemented and its effects assessed** (paragraph 15.70); **and**

(c)   **press the EC Commission to concentrate its efforts on transponders rather than on the reporting systems which they will largely supersede** (paragraph 15.71).

Reporting of failures in ships' equipment

23.103   The existing requirement under MARPOL to report potentially dangerous or polluting incidents, including the failure of equipment, to land-based authorities (paragraphs 15.73 – 15.74) does not appear to be as effective as it should be. **Recommendation 71 The UK Government should:**

(a)   **explore with its partners in the EC and the Paris MOU the possibilities for research to establish how widespread is the failure to report promptly, and whether the reactions of coastal authorities could be improved** (paragraph 15.75);

(b) if standards of reporting are not good enough, seek to establish a system of mandatory *immediate* reporting to coastal authorities of any specified problems or failures within a set area (paragraphs 15.76 – 15.77);

(c) press IMO, the EC and North Sea States to develop their thinking on mandatory reporting to include mandatory reporting of failures as they arise and regardless of whether the Master considers that there is any risk in terms of safety or pollution (paragraph 15.77);

(d) discuss with its partners the difficulties of enforcement (paragraph 15.78);

(e) seek to agree with its partners that the sanction should be a notification condition, as in Recommendation 34(b), for all ships in the same owner-ship or management, and, in extreme cases, a ban on loading and unloading as in Recommendation 42 (paragraph 15.77); and

(f) ensure that all reports of failures are entered on the Port State Control computer record. In serious cases, the authorities at the port of desti-nation should be alerted to the fault by telephone (paragraph 15.83). Reports should also be copied to MAIB as a matter of routine (paragraph 12.32).

Improving the effectiveness of reporting systems

23.104   <u>Recommendation 72</u> The Department of Transport should:

(a) consider carefully whether existing means of publicising and promoting changes to reporting schemes could be improved (paragraph 15.42);

(b) ensure that when vessels which are contravening any routeing measures report to shore-based authorities, they are asked to explain their actions and refrain from repeating them. The requests should be reinforced by letters to owners (paragraphs 15.61 – 15.62);

(c) ensure that when HM Coastguard receives a routine report, it checks whether the ship is experiencing any problems, and gives warnings of hazards and any weather warning which might be appropriate (paragraphs 15.51 – 15.53 and 15.63 – 15.64); and

(d) ensure, with international agreement if necessary, that all reports made by ships in or planning to enter specified areas should include the rea-sons why the route in question has been chosen (paragraph 15.61).

Vessel surveillance and tracking

Radar surveillance

23.105   The UK Government tracks sea traffic by fixed radar only in the Dover Strait (paragraphs 16.6 – 16.13). Radar has its limitations (paragraphs 16.15 – 16.18). A major expansion of radar surveillance would be very expensive (paragraph 16.19) and it is essential to consider what ends it could usefully serve and whether it would represent value for money. Any attempt at "Sea Traffic Control", by analogy with Air Traffic Control, would be unwise (paragraphs 16.23 – 16.24). We conclude that coverage of all the UK coastline would not be justified (paragraph 16.24). Radar is useful for "policing" traffic in busy areas (paragraphs 16.26 – 16.28), and for occasional "policing" in rather less busy areas (paragraphs 16.31 – 16.32). Unless it is required for other reasons, it is **not** justified to detect navigational problems (paragraphs 16.33 – 16.41) or to overlook environmentally sensitive areas (paragraph 16.42).

23.106 **Recommendation 73 The UK Government should resist any pressure for permanent radar coverage of shipping except in areas where the density and conflicting movements of traffic in restricted areas make "policing" desirable** (paragraph 16.28). **In those areas where permanent radar coverage is needed for "policing" according to our criteria** (paragraph 16.28), **the Department of Transport should first consider whether an existing radar could be used** (paragraph 16.29).

23.107 **Recommendation 74 The Department of Transport should make more use of mobile radar in order to keep informed of ship movements during an emergency (when practicable)** (paragraph 16.22) **and should set up a few sites for temporary radars for the second and third aims, with any necessary publicity** (paragraphs 16.31 – 16.32), **so as to:**

(a) **carry out traffic counts to establish whether routeing measures or permanent radar would be useful; and**

(b) **monitor traffic from time to time, as part of a surveillance bluff** (paragraphs 16.20 – 16.22).

Non-radar surveillance

23.108 **Recommendation 75 The UK Government should encourage:**

(a) **close cooperation between Government Departments and agencies so that all their surveillance aircraft can be used to observe several potential forms of unlawful or antisocial behaviour** (paragraph 21.92);

(b) **full use of the three surveillance aircraft the Department of Transport already has on contract. After a trial period the Department should assess whether a higher level of aerial surveillance would be sensible** (paragraphs 16.48 – 16.50);

(c) **the use of satellite surveillance where practicable by the Department of Transport, with the cooperation of the Ministry of Defence. The Department of Transport should also keep track of developments** (paragraph 16.51);

(d) **voluntary systems for the reporting of tankers similar to that in the Minch** (paragraphs 16.43 – 16.46) – see also Recommendations 62(d) and 63(b);

(e) **ships' Masters, the crews of pleasure craft and the general public to report pollution and potential pollution incidents to HM Coastguard** (paragraph 16.47); **and**

(f) **aircraft operators to report any vessels in areas ships are asked to avoid** (paragraphs 16.48 – 16.49).

The use of information from surveillance

23.109   <u>Recommendation 76</u> **The Department of Transport should:**

(a) **ensure that any cases where routeing advice is ignored are taken up with owners and Flag States** (paragraph 16.56); **and**

(b) **set up systems to ensure that it receives any relevant information on the behaviour of civil shipping outside harbour authority areas which other authorities may obtain. It is important that there is no doubt in anyone's mind that COASTGUARD is responsible for any short-term action and that MSA is responsible for any long-term action** (paragraphs 16.63 – 16.65).

Fish factory ships

23.110   In the autumn of 1993 there were about 90 fish factory ships off Shetland, some of which were in a very poor condition. There were three serious incidents (paragraphs 17.2 – 17.13). There is no doubt that fish factory ships are important for the economy of the UK as a whole and of the areas where they operate (paragraph 17.24), but events during 1993 showed that safety and pollution prevention standards were not good enough (paragraphs 17.25 – 17.26). Although some effective action has been taken already (paragraphs 17.19 – 17.23), more needs to be done (paragraphs 17.27 – 17.29).

23.111   <u>Recommendation 77</u> **The UK Government should:**

(a) **require that transshipment of fish can take place in UK waters only if the ship concerned carries adequate insurance and if she meets clear, basic safety and pollution-prevention criteria. Permission for transshipment should be revokable if the conditions are subsequently breached** (paragraph 17.30);

(b) **seek to amend Section 4 of the Sea Fish (Conservation) Act 1967 so that transshipment licences** (paragraphs 17.14 – 17.16) **can be issued only to vessels which meet basic safety standards** (paragraph 17.31);

(c) limit the number of licences issued in relation to the quantities of fish available, for reasons of safety and to limit congestion (paragraph 17.31);

(d) ensure that the reasonable costs of checking the safety of the ship and her insurance, and of any inspection, are charged to the vessels concerned (paragraph 17.32);

(e) ensure that the Fisheries Departments agree transshipment areas with the Department of Transport and any harbour authorities affected (paragraph 17.32); and

(f) declare straight away that from a specified date, well before next winter, the Fisheries Departments will not consider any application for a transshipment licence unless the Master concerned produces evidence that his vessel is adequately insured and reaches minimum safety standards. Any licences issued under existing rules before that date should not run beyond that date (paragraph 17.33).

Insurance

23.112 Further unilateral regulation of the London marine insurance market would succeed only in making the London market uncompetitive. There would be little benefit for shipping safety if significant business were lost to overseas competitors operating without comparable restrictions (paragraphs 18.1 – 18.5). P & I Clubs already operate a sophisticated rating system and exert a good influence on shipping standards (paragraphs 18.19 – 18.23). The publication of insurance ratings or premiums would not act as an incentive to those paying higher premiums to improve quality, as no meaningful comparison between different rates can be made by an individual shipowner (paragraphs 18.28 – 18.29). Shipowners should continue to be allowed to insure against fines (paragraphs 18.24 – 18.25).

23.113 We support the efforts of hull insurers to take greater account of quality and actual risk in fixing premiums (paragraphs 18.7 – 18.11). Cargo insurers take account of a range of factors in determining premiums but we believe that too much emphasis is placed upon the age of a ship (paragraphs 18.14 – 18.18). **Recommendation 78 The UK Government should ask cargo underwriters to consider how they might improve their assessment of *actual* risk** (paragraph 18.18).

23.114 Agreed values should not tempt owners by providing an easy way out of financial difficulties. **Recommendation 79 The UK Government should ask hull insurers to examine the problem and do everything they can to solve it** (paragraphs 18.12 – 18.13).

Compensation and liability

Compensation and liability for oil pollution

Standing costs

23.115 In meeting claims for dealing with oil pollution, the International Oil Pollution Compensation (IOPC) Fund pays for the cost of operations during an incident with only a small degree of "uplift" towards the standing costs of maintaining a response capability. **Recommendation 80 The UK Government, in concert with other Governments if possible, should seek to agree with the IOPC Fund a formula for the uplift of marginal costs by a fixed percentage so as to reflect a reasonable proportion of fixed costs** (paragraphs 19.4 – 19.9).

Salvage Convention and 1992 Protocols to the 1969 Civil Liability Convention and 1971 Fund Convention

23.116   We informed the Secretary of State in June 1993 that we intended recommending that the UK Government should ratify the Salvage Convention 1989, the 1992 Protocols to the 1969 Civil Liability Convention and the 1971 Fund Convention as soon as possible. We welcome the introduction to Parliament in January 1994 of the Merchant Shipping (Salvage and Pollution) Bill, which will enable the UK Government to do so (paragraph 1.35). **Recommendation 81 The UK Government should complete its ratification of the Convention and Protocols as soon as possible and should urge other States to do the same** (paragraphs 19.10 – 19.20 and 20.44 – 20.47). We welcome improvements to and extensions of the CRISTAL and TOVALOP voluntary compensation schemes and support the industry view that the Protocols must be ratified before the voluntary schemes expire (paragraphs 19.22 – 19.27).

23.117   The 1992 Protocol to the Civil Liability Convention makes it more difficult to break a shipowner's right to limit his liability. The test is the same as that in the 1976 Limitation Convention. **Recommendation 82 The UK Government should take action with other States signatory to the Conventions to implement the necessary revisions should it become clear that the revised test is providing unreasonable protection for reckless shipowners** (paragraph 19.21).

The United States of America's Oil Pollution Act 1990 (OPA 90)

23.118   We believe that the United Kingdom should not adopt a liability and compensation regime similar to that operating in the United States. The regime established under OPA 90 is, as yet, untested and it has received no support internationally, even from those who have reservations about the 1992 Protocols (paragraphs 19.28 – 19.32).

Compensation and liability for other types of pollution

Nuclear materials

23.119   We have no reason to doubt that the Nuclear Installations Act 1965, as amended, provides adequate compensation in the event of a pollution incident involving a vessel carrying a nuclear cargo in UK waters (paragraphs 19.33 – 19.38), but **Recommendation 83 if the international community decides that limits need to be raised the UK Government should make the necessary changes to the 1965 Act** (paragraph 19.39).

Hazardous and noxious substances (HNS) and compulsory insurance for third party liability

23.120   Although the shipment of hazardous and noxious substances has a good safety record, a catastrophic incident could occur. The limits to compensation are inadequate (paragraphs 19.40 – 19.44). We strongly support IMO's efforts to negotiate a satisfactory international liability and compensation system for HNS and to revise the 1976 Limitation Convention. **Recommendation 84 The UK Government should:**

   (a)   continue to give IMO its full support in this work; but

   (b)   stick to its commitment to pursue regional agreement if IMO fails (paragraph 19.43);

   (c)   ensure that whichever system is adopted it:

      i.   covers claims in respect of spills of bunker fuel oil and oil-based pollutants not already covered by the oil pollution compensation regime; and

      ii.   allows for compensation in the event of pollution from an unidentified ship (paragraph 19.44); and

   (d)   press IMO to include a requirement for compulsory liability insurance in the revision of the 1976 Limitation Convention (paragraphs 18.32 – 18.37 and 19.44).

Punitive damages

23.121   We do not accept that punitive damages would make potential polluters more careful (paragraph 19.45).

Dealing with emergencies

23.122   Vessels which are in distress, or which have lost power and are in danger of grounding or being in a collision, need immediate assistance (paragraphs 20.2 – 20.18). Current arrangements for this are inadequate, because there is not enough capacity around UK shores for emergency towing (paragraphs 20.56 – 20.75 and 20.85 – 20.87). Some other countries have already taken action (paragraphs 20.77 – 20.84). Action is needed, but there is no case for equal sectors around the UK coast each with a full power salvage tug stationed in it (paragraphs 20.90 – 20.93), or for either full power salvage tugs or smaller "first aid" tugs on permanent standby duty with no other tasks (paragraphs 20.96 – 20.100).

23.123   **Recommendation 85 The UK Government should set up a system to ensure that tugs with adequate salvage capacity are available at key points around UK shores (paragraphs 20.85 – 20.89):**

   (a)   the tugs concerned should normally be owned, managed and manned by commercial operators (paragraphs 20.86 and 20.112), but where public sector bodies have tugs available they, or stronger replacements, could be used (paragraph 20.88);

(b) where adequate capacity cannot be provided in any other way, the UK Government should arrange for the funding of the difference between what is needed and what the private sector can provide (paragraph 20.88);

(c) there should be a mixture of a very few full capacity tugs with smaller tugs which can administer first aid to a ship in difficulties, minimising her drift while a stronger tug is on the way (paragraphs 20.94 – 20.97 and 20.107);

(d) decisions on the mix of tugs and the areas to be covered should take into account:

   i.   the type and density of traffic;

   ii. particular hazards;

   iii. the prevailing weather;

   iv. the risk of grounding on a dangerous shore;

   v.   the sensitivity of the coasts;

   vi. commercial practicalities; and

   vii. what facilities are already available, or could be made available (paragraphs 20.101 – 20.106);

(e) the UK Government should consider with the Governments of neighbouring countries whether combined salvage capacity in adjacent waters is practicable. The UK Government might also want to approach the EC Commission to investigate the possibility of a joint approach (paragraph 20.95). Agreement will be needed on the means of contracting for the use of tugs, for financing them, on which country's law should apply, and on who would be in charge (paragraph 20.110);

(f) there should be a system whereby multi-use vessels which spend much of their time on other tasks are available for emergency assistance on a sectoral basis (paragraphs 20.96 – 20.100): they might also be fitted with dispersant spraying equipment (paragraph 21.70);

(g) the sectors should be defined by considering first how two key areas – the Dover Strait and north western Scotland – can best be provided with strong tugs. The Western Approaches should be considered next. After that, ways should be found to fill in the gaps between those areas (paragraph 20.106). Tugs should be stationed at points close to the busiest shipping routes and to other areas where vessels are likely to get into difficulties (paragraphs 20.107 – 20.108);

(h) discussions should be initiated with the industry and other interested parties on the criteria needed in each sector and on minimum standards for crew. Decisions will be needed on whether trained crews, and possibly a minimum of essential equipment, could be airlifted onto suitable vessels (paragraph 20.109). Contracts should be structured so as to encourage crew training (paragraphs 20.128 – 20.130);

(i) there should be a franchise for each sector: specially negotiated flexible contracts, designed to balance commercial benefits against the broader needs of the community. Bids should be invited to provide the service, with stated minimum criteria which should establish a high minimum standard (paragraph 20.111);

(j) the bids will be for a retainer to bridge the gap between the cost of providing a service to the standard required and the net benefit to the provider (paragraphs 20.112 – 20.115);

(k) the same principles of franchising should apply if more than one use for tugs is envisaged within the public sector (paragraphs 20.116 – 20.118);

(l) there should be contingency plans for the use of franchised tugs, recognising that in extreme cases several tugs may have to be used (paragraph 20.148 – 20.149); and

(m) there should be interim arrangements during the winter months until the new system is fully operational: the UK Government should be prepared to bear the full cost of such interim arrangements (paragraphs 20.126 – 20.127 and 22.67).

23.124 We have considered the likely benefits and the likely range of costs of our proposals carefully. We are convinced that the benefits of tug assistance justify the substantial costs: but we cannot demonstrate it. While we would in principle like to see a proper economic appraisal carried out, it would be wrong to wait for it: the tugs need to be in place quickly. (paragraphs 20.119 – 20.124). We expect backchecks to be carried out before the first franchises expire (paragraph 20.125).

Reactions to emergencies and potential emergencies

Action to encourage others

23.125 **Recommendation 86 The UK Government should encourage shipowners and Masters to make the fullest use of emergency services on terms which are most likely to benefit the environment, and salvors to provide the assistance needed to protect the environment, by:**

(a) seeking to persuade shipowners that their standing instructions to Masters should give Masters clear authority to summon salvage assistance without prior approval or delay, and that Masters should do so (paragraphs 20.14 – 20.18, 20.48 – 20.50 and 20.132 – 20.133);

(b) seeking to persuade owners and Masters to make the fullest use of Lloyd's Open Form 90 (LOF 90) through insurers, through the Chamber of Shipping and through IMO (paragraphs 20.36 – 20.43);

(c) encouraging shipowners to adopt the publication *Peril at Sea and Salvage – A Guide for Masters* as part of their company rulebooks (paragraph 20.50);

(d) pressing the International Oil Pollution Compensation Fund to change its rules so as not to penalise some types of salvage work which benefit the environment (paragraph 20.55);

(e) urging the courts and salvage arbitrators to take greater account of the cost of maintaining standby facilities in fixing salvage awards (paragraphs 20.73 – 20.75); and

(f) taking powers to ensure that once tug assistance has been ordered, the ship is deemed to be in peril and to have summoned salvage assistance, ensuring that the owner would pay for the cost of callout whatever the outcome of the incident. Payment should be on a salvage basis determined by the courts and the ship should, if necessary, be arrested as security (paragraphs 20.134 – 20.139).

Action by COASTGUARD

23.126 **Recommendation 87** The UK Government should ensure that COAST-GUARD has the necessary authority, capacity and powers to intervene and board vessels when necessary (paragraphs 20.19 – 20.33):

(a) the Department of Transport should seek an understanding with the Ministry of Defence on contingency arrangements for the provision of suitable military and salvage personnel (paragraph 20.30);

(b) the powers of intervention should be amended (paragraphs 20.32 – 20.33); and

(c) any new legislation should be framed in broad terms and any limitations on the use of the powers should be managerial rather than legislative (paragraph 20.147).

23.127 **Recommendation 88** The UK Government should ensure that HM Coastguard Watch Officers are fully trained and equipped to call out emergency assistance to any vessel in difficulties (paragraphs 20.140 – 20.146).

23.128 **Recommendation 89** The UK Government should seek powers for the Coastguard Agency to establish sea exclusion zones (paragraphs 21.105 – 21.107).

Cleaning up spills

23.129   In some circumstances nothing should be done to spilled oil, but this is unacceptable when there is a risk of pollution to the coastline (paragraph 21.78). The UK relies on the spraying of dispersants, particularly aerial spraying, as its first line of defence against pollution of the coast by oil from spills (paragraphs 21.79 – 21.83). After considering the methods of clean-up used in four actual incidents (paragraphs 21.20 – 21.48), we conclude that it is right for the UK to retain the capacity for aerial spraying of dispersants, despite the cost of the standby capacity (paragraphs 21.84 – 21.85).

23.130   **Recommendation 90 The UK Government should seek to minimise the costs of the standby capacity for aerial spraying of dispersants** (paragraphs 21.86 – 21.95) **by investigating the use of alternative aircraft with Aerial Dispersant Spraying Packs to replace or supplement present arrangements** (paragraphs 21.93 – 21.94).

23.131   **Recommendation 91 The UK Government should also pursue other techniques for cleaning up spills by:**

(a)   **maintaining a database of all equipment for at-sea recovery which could be used in the UK** (paragraphs 21.67 – 21.69);

(b)   **continuing to review the work done elsewhere on the possibility of burning oil at sea** (paragraphs 21.71 – 21.72);

(c)   **commissioning or sharing in long-term research and development of bioremediation** (paragraphs 21.73 – 21.74); **and**

(d)   **continuing its research programme on demulsification as a matter of high priority** (paragraphs 21.75 – 21.77).

Responsibility for cleaning up

23.132   While we are content with the present division of responsibility for cleaning up between the Coastguard Agency, local authorities, harbour authorities and, in some circumstances, the Department of the Environment for Northern Ireland and the National Rivers Authority (paragraphs 21.2 – 21.6, 21.100 – 21.101 and 21.109 – 21.117), **Recommendation 92 The Department of Transport should ensure that:**

(a)   **local authorities and harbour authorities are given a statutory responsibility for the tasks which they have accepted** (paragraphs 21.112 – 21.117);

(b)   **local authorities and harbour authorities report to the Coastguard Agency as a matter of routine:**

i.   **all spills upon which they are taking action themselves;**

ii.   **the action they take; and**

iii.   **any incident which has the potential to cause a significant marine spill** (paragraphs 21.118 – 21.121); **and**

(c)   the Coastguard Agency is given a reserve power to direct local and har-
       bour authorities on the action they should take (paragraph 21.121).

Contingency planning

23.133   While contingency planning arrangements (paragraphs 21.98 – 21.128) are generally satisfactory, <u>**Recommendation 93**</u> **The UK Government should:**

(a)   **update the national contingency plan to take into account our rec-
       ommendations** (paragraphs 21.98 – 21.99);

(b)   **impose a duty upon local authorities and harbour authorities to produce
       contingency plans and to submit their contingency plans to the Secretary
       of State for checking, but not for formal approval** (paragraphs 21.118 –
       21.120);

(c)   **seek to ensure that local contingency plans take our recommendations
       fully into account** (paragraph 21.99);

(d)   **seek to ensure that local contingency plans include plans for booming
       sensitive areas** (paragraph 21.122);

(e)   **ensure that the Coastguard Agency takes part in relevant local exercises
       designed to test contingency plans** (paragraphs 21.123 – 21.125);

(f)   **expand its database on the characteristics of different pollutants as far as
       possible, taking powers to compel the sharing of information if necessary**
       (paragraph 21.102); **and**

(g)   **investigate improvements in methods of protecting fish farms** (paragraphs
       21.126 – 21.128).

The operational practices of COASTGUARD

23.134   <u>**Recommendation 94**</u> **The Department of Transport should:**

(a)   **reconsider whether HM Coastguard's existing arrangements for the
       advice of a qualified mariner to be made quickly available to Watch Offi-
       cers are adequate** (paragraphs 15.79 – 15.81), **or whether further advice
       needs to be made available by agreement with MSA** (paragraphs 15.81 –
       15.83);

(b)   **ensure that all Coastguards recognise that part of their job is to pass on
       to ships which report any navigational information which their Masters
       may not have and which may be useful to them** (paragraphs 15.51 – 15.53);

(c)   **issue instructions to ensure that when a Coastguard Watch Officer
       becomes aware of an impending infringement of the rules, from CNIS or**

any other source, he or she should inform the vessel that if she continues on her present course, she will break the rules. If the rules are already being broken, that should be stated quite clearly (paragraphs 16.57 – 16.60); and

(d) accept the principle that on rare occasions the senior Coastguard Watch Officer should give navigational advice to reduce unacceptable risks. The Department of Transport should accept any liability for advice given in good faith, but should be able to pursue disciplinary action if it has reason to believe a Coastguard officer acted recklessly (paragraphs 16.61 – 16.62).

Financing our proposals

23.135   We have at all stages considered whether our proposals represent good value for money. We are convinced that they do (paragraphs 4.7 – 4.23), but have not been able to demonstrate this (paragraph 4.29). We believe strongly that the polluter, or potential polluter (paragraphs 1.15, 11.86, 20.85, 22.1 – 22.7, 22.16 – 22.21 and 22.30 – 22.35), should pay for the costs of pollution and of pollution prevention, except in the few instances, such as the provision of waste reception facilities, where a different system will have a better effect (paragraphs 9.63 – 9.66).

23.136   We believe that new funding arrangements are needed for enhanced Port State Control, for tug assistance and for a counter-pollution capacity. The crucial point is that these are all vitally important and that payment, from whatever source, must be made in order to provide UK coasts with essential protection (paragraph 22.1). Although it would be possible to institute a single fund, we believe that it is better to have two separate funds, one for Port State Control and the other for emergency assistance and pollution response capacity (paragraph 22.68).

23.137   **Recommendation 95 The UK Government should take steps to set up a new fund to pay for all Port State Control inspections, funded by the shipping industry through a charge** (paragraphs 22.22 – 22.26). **Ideally this should be funded by levies on individual ships: these can be more closely related to their *individual* propensity to pollute, and can thus have a deterrent effect. We do not however rule out a simpler flat rate for Port State Control** (paragraph 22.7). **The UK Government should:**

(a) **consult widely, not least with its partners in the Paris MOU, on the system of charging to be adopted; and**

(b) **encourage its partners in other Paris MOU States to set up similar systems in the long term** (paragraph 22.26).

23.138   **Recommendation 96 The UK Government should also set up a second new fund to pay for emergency response** (paragraphs 21.96 – 21.97 and 22.27 –

22.29), **funded by the shipping industry through a charge** (paragraphs 22.34 – 22.37). **This fund should cover:**

(a) **the provision of emergency standby towing capacity, as in Recommendation 85** (paragraph 22.38). **We estimate that about £5 million a year will be needed for this** (paragraph 20.121); **and**

(b) **the existing counter-pollution capacity and other essential clean-up equipment, including aerial spraying capability, aerial surveillance capability, routine aerial surveillance, ship spraying capability, dispersant stockpiles, beach cleaning and at-sea equipment stockpiles, and cargo transfer and salvage equipment stockpiles, at an estimated cost in 1994-95 of £5.4 million** (paragraphs 22.39 – 22.41).

23.139 We believe that the best system for charging would be through assessed amounts for each vessel above a certain size, taking into account both bunkers and cargo (paragraphs 22.44 – 22.58), because it is much the most closely aligned to actual pollution potential. The alternative is a much simpler tonnage charge levied on ports (paragraphs 22.50 – 22.51). **Recommendation 97 The Department of Transport should consult with the shipping industry, harbour authorities and other interested parties on both these alternatives** (paragraph 22.58). **The UK Government should also consult its European partners on the general principles of charging, but this should not be allowed to delay the setting up of a UK fund** (paragraphs 22.69 – 22.73).

23.140 The two new funds will be financed by charges, not taxes, for specific and limited purposes (paragraph 22.44). The owner of the ship rather than the charterer or cargo owner should be charged, with a power of arrest against defaulters (paragraph 22.60). The funds should have the simplest organisation compatible with reasonable equity and accountability (paragraph 22.45). Their effects on shipping will be very small (paragraphs 22.9 – 22.15, 22.37 and 22.64 – 22.66) and we do not believe that elaborate systems are justifiable (paragraph 22.47). There may be a case for the two Chief Executives (MSA and COASTGUARD) to be under a duty to consult representatives of contributors and to take account of representations received (paragraph 22.63).

23.141 **Recommendation 98 The Department of Transport should ensure that both funds are based on principles of:**

(a) **full cost recovery, with charges sufficient, but not more than is required, to meet the costs taking one year with another;**

(b) **the publication of clear, separate accounts;**

(c) **evident economy, effectiveness and efficiency** (paragraphs 22.26 and 22.59); **and, in the case of the Port State Control fund,**

(d) **higher charges for ships found to be seriously deficient than for those found to be free of or with only minor deficiencies** (paragraph 22.26).

General

Annual report

23.142   **Recommendation 99** The UK Government should make an annual report to Parliament on the implementation of this Report (paragraphs 1.35 – 1.36).

Assessment and consultation

23.143   **Recommendation 100** The UK Government should set up mechanisms to ensure that, so far as practicable, proper consideration is given to the full costs, including the costs to third parties, of any new measures it agrees, either with other Governments or domestically, before they are finalised. Similar consideration needs to be given to compliance, enforcement and backchecks (paragraphs 4.24 – 4.28).

23.144   **Recommendation 101** The Department of Transport should review its mechanisms for consultation and the circulation of information to ensure as wide a coverage as practicable, both within the UK and internationally (paragraphs 14.96 – 14.99).

Legislation

23.145   Legislation will be needed to implement several of our recommendations. In addition, **Recommendation 102** The UK Government should:

(a)   take suitable powers to ensure that vessels not on passage can be required to move on (paragraphs 5.28 – 5.30);

(b)   use those powers to ensure that unlicensed fish factory ships are instructed to leave UK waters when that is in the best interests of safety or the prevention of pollution (paragraph 17.35);

(c)   take powers to extend UK jurisdiction to the maximum extent consistent with the UK's obligations under the Conventions (paragraphs 5.88 – 5.94);

(d)   take powers to enable regulations to be made covering those aspects of Port and Coastal State Jurisdiction which are recognised by international law but which are not covered by specific Conventions or other international agreements (paragraphs 5.88 – 5.94); **and**

(e)   specify the areas within which the power to detain ships can be applied, by defining in legislation a "port" for this purpose (paragraphs 17.36 – 17.43).

Broadening experience

23.146   **Recommendation 103** The Department of Transport should set up exchanges of secondees between:

(a) **MSA and the classification societies who carry out delegated work, so as to maintain direct experience of delegated functions and to promote mutual best practice** (paragraphs 6.40 – 6.46);

(b) **MPCU and oil companies and harbour authorities, so as to build up cooperation and expertise in dealing with emergencies** (paragraph 21.123); and

(c) **MSA and oil companies which carry out ship inspections if that proves practicable** (paragraphs 6.40 – 6.46).

Appendix A

Lord Donaldson's Inquiry

Members of the Inquiry

The Rt. Hon. The Lord Donaldson of Lymington was until 1992 the Master of the Rolls. In 1966 he became a Judge of the High Court, and from 1971-74 was President of the National Industrial Relations Court – in which capacity he sat in Scotland as well as England and Wales. In 1979 he became a Lord Justice of Appeal and in 1982 the Master of the Rolls. He was a Vice-President of the British Maritime Law Association from 1969-72 and has been President since 1979.

Professor Alasdair McIntyre is Emeritus Professor of Fisheries and Oceanography at Aberdeen University. He was the Director of the Fisheries Research Services for Scotland from 1983-86. He is a Vice-President of the Scottish Association for Marine Science having been President from 1988-93 and has served on many other national and international bodies concerned with the pollution of the seas.

Mr John Rendle CBE spent 38 years with Shell Tankers (UK) Ltd. After serving in command and gaining an Extra Masters Certificate, he was then responsible for the operations and navigational safety of Shell vessels and was Managing Director from 1981-88. He was, until recently, Chairman of the National Sea Training Trust and has been a member of the Council of the Marine Society, an advisor to Missions to Seamen, a Governor of the College of Maritime Studies at Warsash, and has served on committees of the General Council of British Shipping and Lloyd's Register of Shipping.

Secretariat to the Inquiry

Angela Moss *Secretary to the Inquiry*
(from January 1993 until submission of the Report)

John Parkinson *Assistant Secretary to the Inquiry*
(from February 1993 until submission of the Report)

Ian Scott
(from July 1993 until submission of the Report)

Charles Chappell
(from April 1993 until submission of the Report)

Dean Eatherton
(from January 1993 until submission of the Report)

Sue Cole
(from February 1993 until submission of the Report)

Jackie Alexander
(January 1993-February 1993)

Claire Briggs
(June 1993-July 1993)

Appendix B

Evidence submitted to Lord Donaldson's Inquiry

Written evidence and public hearings

B.1   The setting up of the Inquiry was announced by the Secretary of State for Transport in Parliament on 11 January 1993. At a preliminary hearing on 29 January 1993 interested parties were asked to submit written evidence. This request met with a tremendous response. The great volume of material received by the Inquiry ranged from letters from individuals making a single point to lengthy papers from major organisations. Below is a list of more than 250 individuals or organisations who contributed. The list includes individual Government Departments although some of the evidence submitted by some Departments was submitted jointly.

B.2   In addition to requesting written evidence, the Inquiry held 42 public hearings between 20 April and 1 July 1993. These hearings took place in London with the exception of four hearings held in Lerwick on 18 and 19 May and two hearings held in Inverness on 20 May.

List of those who submitted evidence

B.3   Almost one-third of the individuals or organisations who submitted written evidence also gave oral evidence. These are indicated *. Bodies which did not submit written evidence but gave oral evidence are indicated in *italics*.

The late Robert Adley MP
* Advisory Committee on Protection of the Sea
* Air Atlantique/Atlantic Air Transport Ltd
Alexandra Towing Co Ltd
Allworld Marine & Technical Ltd
Anderson and Goodlad
* Argyll and Bute District Council
Association of County Councils
Sir Robert Atkinson
Atomic Energy Authority (AEA)
Australian Maritime Safety Authority

J Baker and S Streatfeild
The Baltic Exchange
The Baltic and International Maritime Council (BIMCO)
R P Barston (London School of Economics)
The Bayswater Institute
S Bell
Vice Admiral Sir Stephen Berthon

K Best
Birkenhead & Associates Ltd
A Blackham
P M Bolton
* B P Shipping Ltd
G Brice QC
* British Maritime Technology Ltd (BMT)
* British Nuclear Fuels Ltd (BNFL)
* British Oil Spill Control Association (BOSCA)
British Ports Association
* British Tugowners Association
Broadgate Ltd
S D A Brogan
Bruce Anchor Ltd
B T International Networks
* Bureau Veritas
Burra & Trondra Community Council
Business Insurance

Cando Marine & Offshore Ltd
V Carey
G Carson
Field Marshal Lord Carver, GCB, MC
* Chamber of Shipping
Charles Hope & Co
Christchurch Borough Council
Clan Donald Lands Trust
Cleethorpes Borough Council
Cleveland County Council
P Clews
Clyde Marine Recruitment Ltd
A N Cockcroft (on behalf of the Marine Traffic Study Group of the Royal Institute of Navigation)
P Coleman
B Colles
Copeland Borough Council
Dr A G Corbet (University of Wales)
* Captain A J Corner
Cornwall County Council
* Cory Towage Ltd
Council for Nature Conservation and the Countryside (CNCC)
* Countryside Council for Wales
Cremer & Warner Ltd

* Deep Sea & Coastal Pilots Ltd
* Deep Sea Pilots Association
* Defence Research Agency, Ministry of Defence
* Department of the Environment

Department of the Environment for Northern Ireland
* Department of Transport
Det Norske Veritas Classification Association (DNV)
Devon Wildlife Trust Ltd
D Dixon MP
J Douglas OBE

Eagle Lyon Pope Associates
East Sussex County Council
Ecoboom Ltd
* EDS-Scicon Defence Ltd
* English Nature
S D Eriksen
Euronatur
K Evans
Exeter City Council
Exxon Chemical Ltd

Dr A Fitzgerald
Lord Flowers FRS
* Foreign and Commonwealth Office
French Embassy
Friends of the Earth International
* Friends of the Earth (Scotland)

T D George
Glasgow Chamber of Commerce
Global Authority for Ship Standards (GLASS)
Professor R Goss (University of Wales)
Greek Shipping Cooperation Committee
Greenpeace Ltd
P J Griffin

Hampshire County Council
Hampshire & Isle of Wight Wildlife Trust
J C Harbutt
O C Harbutt
K Harrison
The Hebridean Trust
Health & Safety Executive
Heritage Coast Forum
G Hicks
* Highland Regional Council
* Highlands & Islands Enterprise
L A Holder
* The Honourable Company of Master Mariners
J Hopper
* Howard Smith (UK) Ltd
* The Hydrographer of the Navy

* The Institute of London Underwriters (ILU)/Lloyd's Underwriters' Association (LUA) (including a joint submission from the Chairmen of ILU and LUA and submissions from their Joint Hull and Joint Cargo Committees)

The Institute of Petroleum

* International Association of Classification Societies (IACS)

International Association of Dry Cargo Shipowners (INTERCARGO)

* International Association of Independent Tanker Owners (INTERTANKO)

International Chamber of Shipping

International Federation of Shipmasters' Associations (IFSMA)

* International Group of P & I Clubs

International Logistics and Offsites Consultants (INTERLOC)

International Maritime Satellite Organisation (INMARSAT)

* International Oil Pollution Compensation Fund

International Petroleum Industry Environmental Conservation Association

* International Tanker Owners Pollution Federation Ltd (ITOPF)

Isle of Man Government

Council of the Isles of Scilly

The Isles of Scilly Environmental Trust

Italian Embassy

* Joint Nature Conservation Committee

G Keays

R Kelsall

Professor J F Kemp

J Kerr

H Knight

Professor C Kuo (University of Strathclyde)

* M J Lacey

R Lankester (Marine Ecology & Sailing/North Sea Work Group East Anglia)

The Law Society of Scotland

L H D Ltd

Lerwick Harbour Trust

Liberian Shipowners Council Ltd

* Lloyd's Register of Shipping

Vice Admiral Sir Roderick Macdonald

Vice Admiral Sir Ian McGeoch

Captain N McKie

A Mackinnon

Captain R Mackinnon

Captain D McNeill

Professor J S Malpas

Commander H Manners

M Mansfield

Marconi Radar and Control Systems Ltd

* The Marine Conservation Society Ltd

* The Marine Society

410

N R Messinger
* Meteorological Office
Midar Systems Ltd
* The Ministry of Agriculture, Fisheries and Food (MAFF)
* The Missions to Seamen

National Farmers Union of Scotland
National Medical Examination Network (Definitech Ltd)
National Rivers Authority (NRA)
The National Trust
* The National Trust for Scotland
The National Union of Civil and Public Servants (NUCPS)
* The National Union of Marine Aviation and Shipping Transport Officers (NUMAST)
Natural Environment Research Council
* The Nautical Institute
New Forest District Council
* Noble Denton Weather Services Ltd
Norges Naturvernforbund
* North Sea Pilots Association
North Wales Coastal Forum
Royal Norwegian Embassy

Oil Companies International Marine Forum (OCIMF)
Oil Spill Service Centre
* Orkney Fisheries Association
* Orkney Islands Council
* R Owen (Roil Global)

L Quilty

Captain T Parker
Penningtons
P/F Alma Maskinverkstaòur & Smiòja
Phillips Petroleum Company United Kingdom Ltd

Rees & Freres
* Dr K Ridgway (University of Sheffield)
Captain D M Robinson
L Ross
* Ross & Cromarty District Council
Royal Institute of Naval Architects
Royal National Lifeboat Institution
Royal Society for Nature Conservation (RSNC)
* The Royal Society for the Protection of Birds (RSPB)
Royal Yachting Association (RYA)

The Salvage Association
* Samuel Stewart & Co (London) Ltd

T J Sard (Multitrade)
* Save Our Seabirds Network
Scottish Campaign for Nuclear Disarmament (CND)
Scottish Confederation of Tourism
Scottish Council for Development and Industry
* Scottish Natural Heritage
Scottish Office
Scottish Salmon Growers Association Ltd
* The Scottish Scenic Trust
* Scottish Society for the Prevention of Cruelty to Animals
Scottish Trades Union Congress
* Scottish Wildlife Trust
* Sea Fish Industry Authority (National Federation of Fishermen's Organis-
ation/Scottish Fishermen's Federation/Northern Ireland Fishermen's Federation
(joint submission))
* Sea Safety Group (UK)
Seamartin Shipping Services Ltd
Seas at Risk
* Shell UK Ltd
The Shellfish Association of Great Britain
* Shetland Fishermen's Association
* Shetland Islands Council
* Shetland Labour Party
* The Shetland Movement
* Shetland Oil Disaster Petition (Ms I Mitchell)
* Shetland Salmon Farmers' Association
R L Shipp
* Smit International (UK) Ltd
* Smit Tak BV
W Smith
SNA Project Services
* South Hams District Council
South Wales Sea Fisheries Committee
Southern Seas Fisheries District
* Rear Admiral M Stacey
A H Stobbs
Strathkelvin District Council
Subsea Offshore Ltd
* Sutherland District Council

Tayside Regional Council
Thermodyne
J W Thomas
Tidy Britain Group (papers attached to evidence submitted by Advisory Com-
mittee on Protection of the Sea)
R Tomsett
* Borough of Torbay
* Torbay & Brixham Shipping Agents Ltd

Torridge District Council
Transport & General Workers Union (TGWU)
B Trott
Professor R Turvey

United Kingdom Offshore Operators' Association (UKOOA)
United Kingdom Petroleum Industry Association Ltd (UKPIA)
* United Kingdom Pilots Association (Marine)
United Towing Ltd

Captain E G Walford
Walker Wingsail Systems plc
* J Wallace MP
Ms J Walley MP
Professor T Wälde (University of Dundee)
* Warren Spring Laboratory
Captain F Weeks
Welsh Office
* Western Isles Islands Council
J Willmer QC
Dr J W G Wills (Shetland News Agency)
C Woods
* World Wide Fund for Nature (WWF)

Fact-finding visits

Orkney

B.4   The Inquiry visited Orkney on 22 February 1993. The itinerary included visits to the Harbour Authority building in Scapa, the oil terminal at Flotta and the Orkney Coastguard Marine Rescue Sub Centre (MRSC) in Kirkwall.

Shetland

B.5   The Inquiry visited Shetland on 22 and 23 February 1993. The itinerary included visits to the Shetland Coastguard MRSC in Lerwick and the oil terminal at Sullom Voe. The Inquiry team was flown from Sullom Voe to Sumburgh Airport over fish farms and the wreck of the *BRAER*.

B.6   The Inquiry visited Shetland again on 18 and 19 May 1993 for public hearings in Lerwick.

Inverness

B.7   The Inquiry visited Inverness on 20 May for public hearings.

Stornoway

B.8   The Inquiry visited Stornoway on 21 May. The visit included a helicopter flight over the Minch and the Deep Water Route west of the Isle of Lewis.

Dover

B.9 The Inquiry visited the Coastguard Marine Rescue Control Centre (MRCC) at Dover on 16 June 1993 to look at the Channel Navigation Information Service (CNIS).

Other visits

B.10 The Chairman also made informal visits to the Coastguard MRSCs at Lee-on-Solent and at Holyhead and to the Department of Transport Marine Office in Southampton.

Appendix C

Marine Safety Agency

C.1 The Marine Safety Agency (MSA) came into being on 1 April 1994. It is an executive agency of the Department of Transport. Until 31 March 1994 it was the Surveyor General's Organisation (SGO) which was part of the Marine Directorate of the Department of Transport. The title "Surveyor General" lapsed on 31 March 1994 and MSA is headed by a Chief Executive. The function of MSA remains broadly similar to that of SGO, although it has additionally taken on responsibility for the Register of Shipping and Seamen (RSS). MSA operates within a strategy for marine safety and prevention of pollution from shipping laid down by the Secretary of State for Transport on advice from the Department's Shipping Policy Directorate, following consultation with MSA.

C.2 Much of the work of MSA is explained in the body of our Report: for instance, in Chapter 6 we describe its work on statutory survey and certification work and its relationship with classification societies. Here we give a brief overview.

Aims and main tasks

C.3 MSA's aim is:

> "to develop, promote and enforce high standards of marine safety and to minimise the risk of pollution of the marine environment from ships, within the policy framework set by the Secretary of State."

MSA's main tasks are normally split into three main areas of activity: Marine Standards; Survey and Certification; and Inspection and Enforcement. There is no fundamental split between Flag State and Port State responsibility in its approach to its tasks.

Marine Standards

C.4 MSA sets standards and provides advice for:

(a) the safe navigation of shipping around the UK coast;

(b) the safety standards, construction and equipment of passenger ships, cargo ships and other vessels including fishing vessels and vessels on inland waters; and

(c) competency, training and health for seafarers, including safe manning levels for UK ships.

C.5 Reviewing and developing policies on ship safety and pollution control is a major concern. It is based on an examination of trends in all aspects of shipping safety to identify new developments; use of risk assessment techniques where appropriate to ensure that existing and proposed standards are adequate and cost effective; examination and analysis of MAIB reports, HM Coastguard reports, inquest and Fatal Accident Inquiry reports, inspection and survey results and international developments; and assessing and improving cost effectiveness of survey and inspection practices.

C.6 Most of the relevant standards are internationally agreed, though standards for vessels below the size covered by the international Conventions are largely a matter for the UK alone. MSA plays a major part in the negotiating of international agreements through IMO, the EC, the ILO and other international organisations.

C.7 A comparatively recent development is the setting up of eight District Marine Safety Committees following Mr John Hayes' report[1] on river safety. The Committees include representatives of a wide range of organisations, public and private. Their work is guided by a National Marine Safety Steering Committee.

Survey and Certification

C.8 The main task here is the Flag State one of managing the provision of statutory survey and certification services to meet the needs of the UK shipping industry, as described in Chapter 6. Tasks undertaken are:

(a) carrying out survey and certification work on a full cost recovery basis, including work on behalf of other flag administrations;

(b) ensuring through monitoring and audit procedures and any other appropriate measures that survey and certification work is carried out in accordance with statutory requirements and Departmental specifications: this task applies equally to work carried out by MSA's own surveyors and to work delegated to classification societies.

Inspection

C.9 As well as statutory surveys, MSA also carries out non-statutory inspections of domestic shipping including inspections of small passenger ships not covered by the international Conventions, inland waterway craft and fishing vessels.

C.10 The other main task is the carrying out of Port State Control inspections of foreign ships using UK ports, as described in Chapter 11.

Infringement of regulations

C.11 MSA also investigates incidents relating to infringements of regulations and misconduct, and instigates appropriate follow-up action to enforce safety, pollution prevention and operational standards.

---

[1] *Report of the Enquiry into River Safety* (HMSO 1992) Cm 1991—ISBN 0 10 119912 0.

Organisation and funding

C.12   In addition to its headquarters in Southampton, MSA has six districts each with a Marine Office located at or near a major sea port. The six districts are: London, based in Orpington; South and South West of England, based in Southampton; North West of England and Wales, based in Liverpool; West of Scotland and Northern Ireland, based in Glasgow; East of Scotland, based in Aberdeen; and North East and East of England, based in Newcastle. There are also sub-offices in busy smaller ports to provide a better service where the distance from the Marine Office would make daily travel impracticable or unduly expensive.

Staff

C.13   At 1 April 1994, MSA had a staff complement of 376.5. 198 of these posts are for professionals who concentrate on the technical aspects, including the survey and inspection of ships. The remaining posts cover administrative and executive functions. 67 of the professional posts and 101.5 of the administrative and executive posts are in headquarters with the rest split between the district offices.

C.14   Professional staff are recruited in three main disciplines:

(a) " **Nautical Surveyors**" are all ex-seafarers with either an Extra First Class Certificate of Competency or a Class 1 Master Mariner's Certificate of Competency plus a relevant BSc degree or equivalent. They have all previously served as Master or Chief Officer on foreign-going ships and have been responsible for the safe navigation, loading and discharge of ships of various types and managing the crew. Some have also had previous experience in companies or consultancies ashore;

(b) " **Engineer and Ship Surveyors**" are usually ex-seafarers, some with a Royal Navy background, and are generally chartered engineers. They must have either an Extra First Class Certificate of Competency (Marine Engineer) or a Class 1 (or First Class) Certificate of Competency (Marine Engineer) plus a degree or equivalent in engineering. They must also have at least three years' experience as a Watch Keeping Engineer; and

(c) "**Ship Surveyors**" have a degree or equivalent in naval architecture. They must have at least seven years' experience, following a suitable period of training, in an establishment concerned with ship building, design, operation or relevant research including at least three years in a position of responsibility.

The two latter terms are potentially confusing but the first is concerned with engineering and the second is concerned with naval architecture. Surveyors recruited into the three main disciplines are known as Grade 1 surveyors. MSA also employs Grade 2 surveyors to survey fishing vessels. The qualification requirements are lower than for Grade 1 posts.

C.15   Marine surveyors are expected to cover a wide range of duties, including the survey of hulls, main and auxiliary machinery, boilers and navigation equipment, and inspection of manning and cargo aspects such as overloading and passenger and crew accommodation. Surveyors also look at construction and stability aspects. Surveyors are not split into separate "Port State" or "Flag State" groups: the same surveyors carry out both Flag State and Port State functions depending on who is available to do the work.

Surveys of radio installations

C.16 Surveys of radio installations have been delegated to BT (British Telecommunications plc) and it charges shipowners directly for this service. MSA also has a contract with BT through which it pays BT to undertake inspections of radio installations in connection with Port State Control and other inspections and to provide MSA with specialist advice on radio matters generally.

Recruitment

C.17 Following a major recruitment campaign in 1993, MSA now has a full complement of **"Engineer and Ship Surveyors"** but there have been problems in recruiting enough **"Nautical Surveyors"** and **"Ship Surveyors"**. A further recruitment drive is planned for all three disciplines to cover existing and anticipated vacancies arising through natural wastage. There has also been a problem in filling professional posts in the grade senior to Grade 1, because there is no direct recruitment to that grade and not enough internal candidates have passed promotion boards. MSA is reviewing entry level qualifications and experience criteria with a view to ensuring that recruitment needs can be met in future. We refer to the general issue of the supply of ex-seafarers for land-based jobs in paragraphs 8.58 – 8.62.

Funding

C.18 SGO's budget for 1993-94 was about £26.4 million. Gross expenditure for the year to 31 March 1994 amounted to almost £26 million including about £13.4 million on running costs such as pay and accommodation, £11.9 million programme expenditure and about £0.6 million on capital investment. These costs were offset by receipts from industry which totalled almost £3.3 million. An ongoing major item of programme expenditure is the £6 million budget for civil hydrography in the UK, as described in paragraphs 13.16 – 13.21. The work is carried out by the Royal Navy, using either their own vessels or chartered commercial craft, and by the private sector under contract.

C.19 MSA is a vote-funded organisation, with cash limits imposed on its running and programme costs. As such it does not have flexibility in responding to unbudgeted demands other than by reducing spending elsewhere or requesting additional funding from the Department of Transport. Further budget details are included in the Annex to this Appendix.

Annex to Appendix C

SGO/MSA Expenditure and Income

SGO/MSA Expenditure (£k)

Running Costs	SGO Outturn 1993-94	MSA Budget 1994-95	RSS Budget 1994-95
Pay	9,739	10,388	449
Non pay	2,372	2,393	144
Accommodation	1,155	1,038	88
Total	**13,266**	**13,819**	**681**

Administrative Capital	SGO Outturn 1993-94	MSA Budget 1994-95	RSS Budget 1994-95
Information Systems	534	490	193
Accommodation (excluding headquarters)	97	20	—
Total	**631**	**510**	**193**

Programme Costs	SGO Outturn 1993-94	MSA Budget 1994-95	RSS Budget 1994-95
Civil Hydrography	6,150	6,158	—
Merchant Navy Training			
– Government Assistance for Training	2,700	2,827	—
– Development of Certified Seafarers	—	1,500	—
– Youth Training Scheme *	573	613	—
Merchant Navy Reserve Bounty Payments **	—	—	180
Crew Relief	—	—	2,000
Paid Publicity	—	100	—
Other Services	2,281	2,608	—
Total	**11,704**	**13,806**	**2,180**

* funded by the Department of Employment
** funded by the Ministry of Defence

SGO/MSA Income (£k)

Running Costs	SGO Outturn 1993-94	MSA Budget 1994-95	RSS Budget 1994-95
Survey Income	2,580	2,846	—
Other	641	579	965
Total	**3,221**	**3,425**	**965**

Programme	SGO Outturn 1993-94	MSA Budget 1994-95	RSS Budget 1994-95
Miscellaneous	76	78	2
Total	**76**	**78**	**2**

Appendix D

Certificates and Documents required to be carried on board ships

D.1   Throughout the Report we refer to the certificates which are required by the various international Conventions and agreements. This Appendix details the more significant certificates. All ships are required to carry certain certificates. Certain types of ship are required to carry additional certificates. All certificates carried on board ships must be originals.

D.2   We list here all the certificates required to be carried by all ships but we have restricted the list of other certificates to those most relevant to the Inquiry. We also list the Conventions and agreements under which they are issued. A full list of certificates can be found in Appendix 3 of the IMO publication *SOLAS, Consolidated Edition, 1992*[1] which has been of invaluable assistance in compiling this Appendix.

D.3   All ships must carry:

(a)	*Certificate of Registry*	Facilitation (FAL) Convention
(b)	*International Tonnage Certificate (1969)*	Tonnage Convention article 7
(c)	*International Load Line Certificate*	Load Line Convention 1966 article 16
	or	
	International Load Line Exemption Certificate	Load Line Convention 1966 article 6
(d)	*Intact Stability Booklet* for all ships over 24 metres in length	SOLAS 1974 regulation II-1/22
(e)	Minimum safe manning document	SOLAS 1974 (1989 amendments) regulation V/13(b)

---

[1] ISBN 92 801 1294 5.

(f)	*Certificates for Masters, officers or ratings*	STCW 1978 article VI
(g)	*Deratting Certificate*	FAL Convention
	or	
	Deratting Exemption Certificate	
(h)	*International Oil Pollution Prevention Certificate (IOPP)* for any oil tanker of 150 grt and above and any other ship of 400 grt and over engaged in international voyages. The certificate is supplemented as appropriate by either	MARPOL 73/78 annex I regulation 5
	Record of Construction and Equipment for Ships other than Oil Tankers (Form A)	
	or	
	Record of Construction and Equipment for Oil Tankers (Form B)	
(i)	*Oil Record Book* every oil tanker of 150 grt and above and every ship of 400 grt and above other than an oil tanker shall be provided with an Oil Record Book Part I (Machinery space operations). Every oil tanker of 150 grt and above shall also be provided with an Oil Record Book Part II (Cargo/ballast operations)	MARPOL 73/78 annex I regulation 20

D.4 In addition to the certificates listed in D.3 passenger ships must carry:

(a)	*Passenger Ship Safety Certificate* for ships complying with chapters II-1, II-2, III and IV and any other relevant requirements of SOLAS	SOLAS 1974 regulation I/12 as amended by GMDSS amendments
(b)	*Exemption Certificate* in addition to (a) if an exemption has been granted in accordance with SOLAS 1974	SOLAS 1974 regulation I/12
(c)	**Special trade passenger ships**	
	A form of safety certificate for special trade passenger ships issued under the provisions of the Special Trade Passenger Ships Agreement 1971	STP Agreement rule 5
	Special Trade Passenger Ships Space Certificate issued under the provisions of the Protocol on Space Requirements for Special Trade Passenger Ships 1973	SSTP 73 rule 5

D.5   In addition to the certificates listed in D.3 cargo ships must carry:

(a)	*Cargo Ship Safety Construction Certificate* issued after survey to cargo ships of 500 grt and above which satisfy the relevant requirements of SOLAS 1974	SOLAS 1974 regulation I/12 as amended by GMDSS amendments
(b)	*Cargo Ship Safety Equipment Certificate* issued after survey to cargo ships of 500 grt and above which satisfy the relevant requirements of SOLAS 1974	SOLAS 1974 regulation I/12 as amended by GMDSS amendments
(c)	*Cargo Ship Safety Radio Certificate* issued after survey to cargo ships of 300 grt and above fitted with a radio installation which complies with the relevant requirements of SOLAS 1974	SOLAS 1974 regulation I/12 as amended by GMDSS amendments
(d)	*Exemption Certificate* issued in addition to the above certificates if an exemption has been granted under and in accordance with the provisions of SOLAS 1974	SOLAS 1974 regulation I/12
(e)	*Document of compliance with the special requirements for ships carrying dangerous goods*	SOLAS 1974 regulation II-2/54.3
(f)	*Dangerous goods manifest or stowage plan*	SOLAS 1974 regulation VII/5(3) MARPOL 73/78 annex III regulation 4
(g)	*Document of authorization for the carriage of grain* issued to all ships loaded in accordance with SOLAS chapter VI	SOLAS 1974 regulation VI/10
(h)	*Certificate of insurance or other financial security in respect of civil liability for oil pollution damage* issued to ships carrying more than 2,000 tons of oil in bulk as cargo and complying with article VII of the CLC Convention	Civil Liability Convention 1969 article VII

D.6   In addition to the certificates listed in D.3 and D.5 above, where appropriate, any ship carrying noxious liquid chemical substances in bulk shall carry:

(a)	*International Pollution Prevention Certificate for the Carriage of Noxious Liquid Substances in Bulk (NLS Certificate)*	MARPOL 73/78 annex II regulations 12 and 12A
	In respect of chemical tankers the certificates listed in D.7 (a) below shall have the same force and receive the same recognition as the NLS Certificate	

(b) *Cargo Record Book* issued to every ship to which annex II of MARPOL 73/78 applies

MARPOL 73/78 annex II regulation 9

D.7 In addition to the certificates listed in sections D.3 and D.5 above, where applicable, any chemical tanker shall carry:

(a) *Certificate of Fitness for the Carriage of Dangerous Chemicals in Bulk*

Bulk Chemicals Code section 1.6

or

International Certificate of Fitness for the Carriage of Dangerous Chemicals in Bulk

International Bulk Chemicals Code section 1.5

D.8 In addition to the certificates listed in D.3 and D.5 above, where applicable, any gas carrier shall carry:

(a) *Certificate of Fitness for the Carriage of Liquified Gases in Bulk*

Gas Carrier Code section 1.6

or

International Certificate of Fitness for the Carriage of Liquified Gases in Bulk

International Gas Carrier Code section 1.5

Appendix E

Port State Control Inspection

E.1   In Chapter 11 we discuss Port State Control and our ideas on making it more effective. This Appendix explains what happens during a typical Port State Control inspection at a UK port and provides a couple of case histories. The first concerns the inspection of a ship at Southampton which was found to be in a seriously unseaworthy condition. The second describes the inspection of a Russian fish factory ship off Shetland.

UK Port State Control inspection

E.2   As we explain in Appendix C the UK is divided into six districts each of which is run from a Marine Office. In order to carry out Port State Control inspections each Marine Office depends upon reliable information on ship movements from the ports in its area. Some of the larger ports send a daily list of ships which are in, or due in, port but smaller ports may have only one arrival a day and the Marine Office contacts these for details. Once the ships in port have been identified the Paris MOU database (SIRENAC) is interrogated to determine which ships are suitable for inspection. When a number of ships is selected preference is given to those in targeted categories, including those with recent recorded deficiencies.

E.3   Once the Marine Office has established which ships are to be visited, the inspector assigned to a particular ship arrives unannounced to carry out his inspection. As we explain in Chapter 11, insofar as the requirements of safety are covered by the international Conventions the inspector is limited to ensuring that the ship has valid certificates unless he has "clear grounds" for further inspection.

E.4   Before going on board, the inspector takes a good look at the outside of the ship from the quayside to see if there are any obvious deficiencies. Once on board he makes his way to the Master's Cabin to look at the certificates. This gives him a chance to see at least part of the ship and gain an initial impression. Once the paperwork has been checked the inspector usually asks to be shown around the ship. Depending on what he then finds and his overall impression of the ship he decides if a more detailed inspection is justified. The inspection may cover any aspect of the ship's construction, equipment, manning, documentation or operation.

E.5   In selecting areas for particular attention the inspector relies not only upon the various guidelines available but also upon his professional experience. The inspection takes a very practical form. If he is on the bridge the inspector may look at the charts: if the first few are up to date he will look no further. On deck, if the first fire box opened has a fire hose and nozzle in good condition and clearly regularly maintained the inspector is unlikely to open more fire boxes.

E.6 If the inspector starts off finding very little wrong the inspection will normally be finished quite quickly. But if deficiencies are identified, the deeper the inspector looks the more he tends to find and the inspection may take a considerable time. Some deficiencies clearly indicate that there may be more serious problems. If, for instance, breathing apparatus is locked away and poorly maintained and crew members are unclear how to use it, questions must be raised about the general standard of maintenance of key safety items, training in their use and overall safety awareness.

E.7 Inspections may be carried out by a single inspector or a team of inspectors depending on the size and type of ship and the resources available on a particular day. If a single inspector finds that the state of a ship justifies a more thorough inspection he can call for assistance.

E.8 Once he has finished his inspection the inspector completes a Report of Inspection form listing any deficiencies found, the action which has to be taken to correct those deficiencies and the time within which corrections are to be made – for example before departure or at the next port. A copy of the report is left with the Master. If the deficiencies are very serious the ship may not be allowed to sail until they are rectified. The decision to detain a ship will take into account a number of factors and will be taken only after consultation with a senior surveyor at the Marine Office. If a ship is unduly detained the Port State Control authority is liable to pay compensation. No court has yet found the UK to have unduly detained a vessel.

E.9 Other sanctions available to a UK inspector are Improvement Notices and Prohibition Notices (Merchant Shipping Act 1894) which require that a particular defect is repaired within a stated period or that a particular activity ceases. These notices apply only to a foreign ship whilst she is in the UK and are therefore of limited effect except in the case of regular traders. Prosecution may also be considered but detention is thought to be the most effective sanction because of the loss of revenue it usually imposes and the cost of making swift repairs and of further inspection.

E.10 On his return to the Marine Office the inspector may complete a more detailed written report of the inspection if it has revealed significant deficiencies. If a ship has been allowed to sail on condition that deficiencies are rectified at the next port of call, the Marine Office notifies the next port. The main details on the Report of Inspection form are entered on the SIRENAC database.

Some case histories

MV STELLA

E.11 The *STELLA*, a general dry cargo carrier of 1,865 grt, built in 1965 and registered in St Vincent & Grenadines, arrived at Southampton in November 1993. In the previous two years she had been detained at various Paris MOU ports on three occasions and so was a prime target for inspection. On 15 November she was visited by two UK inspectors.

E.12 The hatch covers were open and were clearly visible from the quayside. The inspectors could see that the hatchside girders were very corroded and the hull was streaked with rust. Closer examination of the bow shell plating revealed three possible areas where cracks might be present.

E.13 When they came to go on board the inspectors found that the ship's gangway was clearly unsafe with a rail missing and no net provided. Once on board they noticed that the hatch covers were in poor condition and that some of the hatch-end girder supporting brackets were completely detached from the main deck (Plate 10). The inspectors then went in the direction of the bridge to find the Captain and to examine the ship's papers. The Captain was not available and the ship's papers were with the ship's agent. The Chief Officer was asked to have the ship's papers available for inspection as soon as possible. In the meantime, in the light of what they had already seen, the inspectors decided to carry out a more thorough investigation of the ship. The Chief Officer agreed and accompanied the inspectors around the vessel.

E.14 The inspectors could not investigate the possible hull cracks which they had seen from the quayside because this required access to a starboard ballast tank which had not yet been certified "safe" by a chemist. They therefore extended their inspection to other areas.

E.15 Their inspection revealed a number of deficiencies including:

(a) some of the cargo in the forward hold was contaminated by sea water which indicated that the hatch covers were not weathertight;

(b) closer examination of the interior of the forward hold revealed perforations between it and the main weatherdeck;

(c) the decks of the forecastle compartments were wet because the anchor had punctured a hole in the anchor recess;

(d) the emergency fire pump was a "portable" pump. Its portability was questionable and it could not be started for several hours;

(e) the main engine room air inlet fire dampers could not be fully closed; and

(f) there was fairly widespread use of a "Thistle-bond" type material, normally used for temporary repairs, on main engine cooling water pipes.

E.16 After consulting a senior surveyor at the Marine Office in Southampton, the inspectors decided to detain the STELLA citing at least one non-weathertight hatch cover and the inability to close the main engine room fire dampers. A detention form was delivered to the Captain on the evening of 15 November.

E.17   The next day access was gained to the ballast tank which had previously been unavailable for inspection. The internal structure of the tank was badly corroded and a crack in the side shell of the hull was confirmed.

E.18   On 17 November two of the port ballast tanks were found to be seriously corroded (Plates 11 and 12). The holds were also in poor condition with the two main transverse corrugated bulkheads completely detached from the main deck. Further inspection over the next few days revealed a number of other serious deficiencies including a crack in the side shell in the midship region.

E.19   It was clear from this more detailed inspection that the vessel was wholly unseaworthy and a new detention order was delivered to the Captain on 26 November stating that the conditions for release would be "extensive repairs" in Southampton or a "dead ship" tow to a port where repairs could be undertaken. Ultimately the latter option was chosen.

PREZIDENT PIK

E.20   As we discuss in Chapter 17 a number of incidents involving fish factory ships operating off Shetland in 1993 led to concern at the general standard of these vessels. As a result Port State Control inspections were carried out at sea on a number of ships. One of these was the *PREZIDENT PIK*, a 3,102 grt fishing vessel, built in 1976, and registered with the Russian Federation.

E.21   A team of inspectors boarded the ship on 30 November 1993. The certificates were in order apart from the International Oil Pollution Prevention Certificate which the Master claimed had not been returned by the ship's agent.

E.22   A more extensive inspection revealed that sanitary conditions were very poor. The toilets themselves were black with corrosion as were the toilet doors which were barely hanging on. When the ship was blacked out to test the emergency lights a cockroach walked over the Mate's table and more cockroaches were found in the galley. The rest of the accommodation was satisfactory.

E.23   A thorough inspection of the lifeboats and firefighting equipment revealed that although most of the necessary equipment was in place, much of it was poorly maintained. Five out of six fire hoses in the machinery space were broken. The inspectors also gained a clear impression that the crew did not practice safety drills because they appeared unfamiliar with the operational requirements of much of the equipment and items such as fire hoses and nozzles were not readily available.

E.24   The inspectors' report listed numerous deficiencies, mostly relating to safety equipment. The report concluded that the ship was a very serious fire hazard with almost no useable equipment for fighting a machinery space fire. If the ship had been in port she would have been detained. The inspectors left a copy of the report with the Master with instructions to rectify the deficiencies identified.

Appendix F

Guidelines for vessels engaged in fish processing activities anchoring within the limits of United Kingdom Territorial Waters

F.1   In Chapter 17 we refer to the Guidelines for vessels engaged in fish processing activities anchoring within the limits of United Kingdom territorial waters. These Guidelines were produced by MSA (then the Surveyor General's Organisation) and issued to the Masters of fish factory ships. The text is reproduced below.

Introduction

F.2   *These notes are guidelines for Masters, officers and owners of vessels engaged in fish processing activities anchoring within the limits of United Kingdom territorial waters.*

F.3   *It is essential that Masters, officers and owners appreciate that the efficient performance of their duties is necessary in the interests of the safety of life and property at sea and the prevention of pollution of the marine environment.*

F.4   *Every Master should at all times comply with the relevant international Conventions. Vessels not used for catching fish but exclusively used for fish processing or as fish carriers are cargo ships. Subject to the relevant tonnage limitations, Load Line, SOLAS and MARPOL Conventions apply to such ships.*

F.5   *The rules made by the appropriate authority for the anchorage, roadstead or harbour in which the vessel lies should be complied with at all times.*

Guidance for all conditions

The following guidance applies at all times

Nautical publications

F.6   *All vessels should carry adequate and up-to-date charts (including large scale charts of the anchorage), sailing directions (pilot books), lists of lights, notice to mariners and tide-tables and atlases.*

F.7   *The publications referred to in paragraph [F.6] should be published by the Hydrographer of the Navy or be an equivalent publication published by any authority exercising functions similar to those of the Hydrographer.*

F.8 *The publications referred to in paragraph [F.6] should be consulted for information on dangers to navigation within the environs of the port and its anchorage and should be kept readily available to the officer of the watch at all times.*

Watchkeeping

F.9 *The vessel's anchorage position should be plotted on the large scale chart of the harbour area.*

F.10 *A continuous navigational watch should be maintained at anchor.*

F.11 *A proper look-out should be maintained at all times.*

F.12 *VHF radio and radar should be operational and monitored continuously.*

F.13 *The vessel's position should be checked at frequent intervals by taking visual bearings of fixed marks and by radar ranges of conspicuous fixed targets.*

F.14 *A safe distance from other anchored vessels should be maintained.*

F.15 *Weather and tidal conditions and the state of the sea should be observed throughout.*

F.16 *Weather forecasts and navigational warnings should be monitored continuously.*

F.17 *Correct navigation lights and shapes should be exhibited at all times and sound signals made when necessary.*

F.18 *The officer of the watch should inform the Master if there is any doubt about the safety of the vessel at anchor.*

F.19 *The officer of the watch and the Master should take all necessary measures if the vessel is unable to remain securely at anchor.*

Anchor arrangements

F.20 *Vessels should at all times have two operational anchors.*

F.21 *The satisfactory operation of the anchoring arrangement and equipment, including windlasses and securing devices, should be checked at regular intervals whilst the vessel is at anchor.*

Engines

F.22   *Vessels should maintain sufficient useable bunkers for a minimum of 3 days operation of main engines and generators at full sea-going power. The Harbour Authorities should be informed if fuel levels fall below this level.*

F.23   *Engines should normally be fully operational. If it is necessary to disable the engines for any reason permission should be obtained from the Harbour Authorities.*

F.24   *An efficient engine room watch should be maintained. Measures should be taken to protect the environment from pollution by the vessel.*

F.25   *All damage control and fire-fighting systems should be in readiness.*

Manoeuvring

F.26   *Steering gear should be in efficient working order.*

Watertight integrity

F.27   *Every watertight door should be kept closed except when it is required to be open for the working of the ship.*

Health and safety

F.28   *All accommodation spaces should be maintained in a clean and healthy condition.*

F.29   *All necessary precautions should be taken to reduce fire hazards particularly in machinery spaces. Such precautions include the maintenance of clean conditions, the prevention of oil leakage and the removal of combustible materials from vulnerable positions.*

F.30   *Safety equipment, including life-saving appliances, should be maintained in working order and ready for immediate use.*

F.31   *Arrangements for boarding the vessel safely should be available.*

Guidance for severe conditions

During winter months (September – March) or when strong onshore winds or winds over force 7 are forecast the following guidance should be followed in addition to that contained in [paragraphs F.6 – F.31] of these notes.

F.32   *Main engines should be kept ready for immediate use at full power. If this becomes impossible the Harbour Authorities should be advised immediately.*

F.33   *Ballast water should be taken on board so as to reduce windage to a minimum (all ballast tanks full unless this would submerge the loadline mark) if the Master has any doubt over the manoeuvrability of the vessel in its existing condition. If this becomes impossible the Harbour Authorities should be advised immediately.*

F.34   *The Master should, when appropriate, take **EARLY** action to drop a second anchor and operate the main engines. If necessary the Master should take **EARLY** action to move to a more sheltered position or weigh anchor and proceed to sea.*

Licences

F.35   *The provisions of licences to receive pelagic sea fish should be complied with at all times.*

General

F.36   *The Master and crew should not neglect any precaution which may be required by the ordinary practice of seamen.*

Appendix G

Qualifications for "Red Ensign" Registers

G.1 Any ship registered with the UK Shipping Register or with one of the registers of a UK Crown Dependency or Dependent Territory[1] may be described as a "Red Ensign" ship. Not all of the Dependent Territories have registers.

The UK Shipping Register

G.2 A ship is eligible for the UK Shipping Register only if a majority of the shares in her – that is 33 out of 64 – is owned by qualified persons. A qualified person is a citizen, subject or Body Corporate as defined below:

(a) a British citizen;

(b) a British Dependent Territory citizen;

(c) a British Overseas citizen;

(d) a British citizen under the British Nationality Act 1981;

(e) a British National overseas (Overseas) as defined in the Hong Kong (British Nationality) Order 1986;

(f) a Body Corporate incorporated in the UK or any relevant overseas territory[2] and having its principal place of business there;

(g) a citizen of the Republic of Ireland.

This means that nearly half of the shares in a UK registered ship can be owned by non-qualified nationals.

G.3 Following a European Court judgement in what is known as the Factortame case[3] the UK is required to allow EC citizens and companies to be the registered owners of UK ships. So EC citizens and companies can have a majority shareholding and still qualify for

---

[1] The terms "Dependency" and "Dependent Territory" have no general technical meaning. They refer to a country, province or territory which, at least in respect of the conduct of its external affairs, is subject to the control of the Government of a State or country of which it is not an integral part. The Dependent Territories of the UK are: Anguilla; Bermuda; British Antarctic Territory; British Virgin Islands; Cayman Islands; Falkland Islands and Dependencies: Gibraltar; Hong Kong; Montserrat; Pitcairn; Henderson; Ducie and Oeno; St Helena and its Dependencies: South Georgia and South Sandwich Islands; Sovereign Base Areas of Akrotiri and Dhekelia; and the Turks and Caicos Islands. The Crown Dependencies are the Bailiwicks of Guernsey, Jersey and the Isle of Man. For the purposes of statutory interpretation the Dependent Territories are colonies of the UK: the Channel Islands and the Isle of Man are not.
[2] The relevant overseas territories are: Anguilla, Bermuda, British Antarctic Territory, British Indian Ocean Territory, Cayman Islands, Channel Islands, Falkland Islands and Dependencies, Gibraltar, Hong Kong, Isle of Man, Montserrat, Pitcairn Islands, St Helena and Dependencies, Turks and Caicos Islands, British Virgin Islands.
[3] European Court of Judgement C246/89.

the UK Shipping Register. It is therefore perfectly possible for a ship to qualify for the UK Shipping Register even though none of the shares in it are owned by a UK national.

G.4   While the Factortame judgement does not apply to the major UK Dependent Territory and Crown Dependency registers, some of them could in principle allow EC citizens and companies onto their registers. The Cayman Islands has already done so by incorporating Factortame into Caymanian law.

Major non-EC Crown Dependency and Dependent Territory registers

Bermuda

G.5   The majority of shares in a vessel must be owned by qualified persons as defined in G.2 above. EC citizens and companies do not count as qualified persons.

Cayman Islands

G.6   The majority of shares in a vessel must be owned by qualified persons as defined in G.2 above. EC citizens and companies also count as qualified persons.

Hong Kong

G.7   The majority of shares in a vessel must be owned by:

(a)   an individual who holds a valid Hong Kong identity card and who is normally resident in Hong Kong;

(b)   a Body Corporate incorporated in Hong Kong;

(c)   an overseas company registered under the Hong Kong Companies Ordinance.

Isle of Man

G.8   The majority of shares in a vessel must be owned by qualified persons as defined in G.2 above. EC citizens and companies do not count as qualified persons.

Red Ensign flags of convenience

G.9   We discuss the definition of a flag of convenience in Chapter 6. The International Transport Workers Federation (ITF) defines a flag of convenience as a register where "the nationality of beneficial ownership is different from the flag" (paragraph 6.22). Under this definition, the ITF includes three "Red Ensign" registers, namely Bermuda, the Cayman Islands and Gibraltar, on its list of flags of convenience. However, this definition is not universally accepted and the three registers are certainly not flags of convenience according to MSA's definition (paragraph 6.23) or the Inquiry's (paragraphs 6.24 – 6.25).

Appendix H

Routes taken by Shipping

H.1   Plate 1 showing the daily frequency of shipping movements was derived from data on the annual traffic on each of a number of identified shipping routes. These data resulted from two research projects undertaken for the Department of Transport by DNV Technica Ltd and are included in Annex H.1 (Tables H.1, H.2 and H.3).

Data

H.2   The data included in Annex H.1 were obtained during the 1980s from statistics for European ports which showed the port or off-shore location from which a ship arrived or to which she departed and included details of the tonnage (dwt) of the ships involved. They are now somewhat out of date. Whilst it is unlikely that shipping patterns will have changed significantly since the late 1980s there will have been some changes and the information should be regarded as illustrative rather than as providing a true picture of actual traffic in 1994.

H.3   The Tables in Annex H.1 show:

(a)   merchant vessels;

(b)   off-shore supply/support vessels; and

(c)   off-shore tanker vessels.

H.4   The Tables show the annual totals and the percentage of vessels in five size classes:

(a)   0-1,499 tonnes (dwt);

(b)   1,500-4,999 tonnes (dwt);

(c)   5,000-14,999 tonnes (dwt);

(d)   15,000-40,000 tonnes (dwt); and

(e)   Over 40,000 tonnes (dwt).

The data are presented by shipping lane (see H.6 below).

H.5   The data do not include warships, fishing vessels, off-shore supply vessels on irregular voyages and ferry traffic. The omission of ferry traffic is particularly significant as in

1992, the last year for which statistics are currently available, some 47 per cent of the total number of ship movements at UK ports involved roll-on, roll-off ferries. Ferry services operate on set routes, notably across the English Channel (an indication of ferry movements across the Dover Strait is shown on Plate 4), the North Sea and the Irish Sea.

Shipping Lanes

H.6   The shipping lanes illustrated on Plate 1 were developed in a number of ways including interviews with deep sea pilots, ships' Masters and navigators, and visual and radar observation at a limited number of locations. Ships do not in fact tend to follow set lanes, except on port approaches and when there are Traffic Separation Schemes or other routeing measures. So the further ships are from ports, straits or the coast the greater the possibility that they will travel some distance from the lanes shown in the maps at Annex H.2 (merchant vessels) and Annex H.3 (supply/support vessels and off-shore tankers). The lane numbers shown in Annexes H.2 and H.3 are those used in the Tables in Annex H.1. Traffic has been distributed between the lanes on the basis of interviews on the routes ships actually took but it must be borne in mind that there can be seasonal variations and that the data are presented on an annual basis which has then been turned into a daily frequency for inclusion on Plate 1.

Analysis

H.7   As Plate 1 shows, the highest daily frequency of traffic is found through the English Channel and on an approach to the Mersey. High frequencies are also found to the south east and south west of Great Britain, through the North Channel and the Pentland Firth and on the approaches to the east coast ports including the Forth. Plate 1 and Annex H.1 also illustrate the transit traffic passing the UK through the English Channel and north of Scotland.

H.8   Shipping is found all around the UK but examination of Annex H.1 shows that some 64 per cent of all the vessel traffic is in the two lowest size classes, 0 – 1,499 and 1,500 – 4,999 dwt. 63 per cent of the traffic through the Pentland Firth and 80 per cent of the traffic through the Minch was in these two classes. Recent observations suggest that the passage of large tankers through the Minch has been declining since last year and the reinforcement by the UK and IMO of the navigational advice applying to the area. The highest concentrations of tanker traffic, mainly ships in the larger size classes and particularly above 40,000 dwt, are on the approaches to the main oil exporting and importing ports. The lane shown to Sullom Voe on Plate 1, which is not included in Annexes H.1, H.2 or H.3, is derived from 1992 data.

Annex 1 to Appendix H

Shipping Traffic Data

TABLE H.1: Merchant Vessel Size Distribution by Lane

Lane Identifications	No. of Vessels (per year)	% Ships in Size Class (dwt metric tonnes)				
		0-1499	1500-4999	5000-14999	15000-40000	Over 40000
1	389	37	41	12	7	3
2	393	2	2	3	6	87
3	308	22	24	23	16	15
4	467	22	24	23	16	15
5.1	440	2	2	3	6	87
5.2	440	2	2	3	6	87
6	600	2	2	3	6	87
7	800	2	2	3	6	87
8	747	22	24	23	16	15
9	2190	27	36	12	14	11
10	815	43	35	12	6	4
11	1968	46	27	4	7	16
12	1597	18	20	28	24	10
13	402	46	27	4	7	16
14	575	46	27	4	7	16
15	489	46	27	4	7	16
16	767	46	27	4	7	16
17	2005	46	27	4	7	16
18	518	22	24	23	16	15
19	346	43	36	11	5	5
20	1239	43	36	11	5	5
21	553	43	36	11	5	5
22	566	43	36	11	5	5
23	1480	46	27	4	7	16
24	359	27	34	13	15	11
25	894	27	34	13	15	11
26	4490	27	34	13	15	11
27	760	43	36	11	5	5
28	2395	43	36	11	5	5
29	1541	43	36	11	5	5
30	694	22	24	23	16	15
31	222	22	24	23	16	15

Lane Identifications	No. of Vessels (per year)	% Ships in Size Class (dwt metric tonnes)				
		0-1499	1500-4999	5000-14999	15000-40000	Over 40000
32	814	43	36	11	5	5
33	394	27	34	13	15	11
34	622	27	34	13	15	11
35	625	27	34	13	15	11
36	1406	43	36	11	5	5
37	9661	43	36	11	5	5
38	371	40	28	11	12	9
39.1	2821	37	41	12	7	3
39.2	2821	37	41	12	7	3
40.1	7983	43	36	11	5	5
40.2	7983	43	36	11	5	5
41	333	37	41	12	7	3
42	2541	43	36	11	5	5
43	299	37	41	12	7	3
44	256	38	36	12	11	3
45	891	38	36	12	11	3
46	668	38	36	12	11	3
47	3227	38	36	12	11	3
48.1	495	37	41	12	7	3
48.2	495	37	41	12	7	3
49	8450	38	36	12	11	3
50	1099	37	41	12	7	3
51	4811	38	36	12	11	3
52	752	37	41	12	7	3
53	1059	37	41	12	7	3
54	15694	38	36	12	11	3
55	1657	37	41	12	7	3
56	1131	43	36	11	5	5
57.1	1146	2	2	3	6	87
57.2	1146	2	2	3	6	87
58	471	37	41	12	7	3
59	496	37	41	12	7	3
60	6633	38	36	12	11	3
61	7759	43	35	12	6	4
62	1308	43	35	12	6	4
63	7797	43	35	12	6	4
64	6645	38	36	12	11	3
65	14807	43	35	12	6	4

Lane Identifications	No. of Vessels (per year)	% Ships in Size Class (dwt metric tonnes)				
		0-1499	1500-4999	5000-14999	15000-40000	Over 40000
66	1154	43	35	12	6	4
67	14802	43	35	12	6	4
68	16952	43	35	12	6	4
69	479	43	35	12	6	4
70a	3363	43	35	12	6	4
70b	3078	43	35	12	6	4
71	5086	43	35	12	6	4
72	4326	38	36	12	11	3
73a	5810	27	34	13	15	11
73b	5716	27	34	13	15	11
74a	14625	27	34	13	15	11
74b	15982	27	34	13	15	11
75	1541	38	36	12	11	3
76	2293	38	36	12	11	3
77	1458	37	41	12	7	3
78	4882	38	36	12	11	3
79	1736	38	36	12	11	3
80	4213	27	34	13	15	11
81a	25100	27	34	13	15	11
81b	24604	23	37	20	15	5
82a	8591	23	37	20	15	5
82b	8781	23	37	20	15	5
83	5939	27	34	13	15	11
84a	41547	23	37	20	15	5
84b	39817	23	37	20	15	5
85	2153	27	34	13	15	11
86	568	27	34	13	15	11
87a	818	37	41	12	7	3
87b	860	37	41	12	7	3
88a	1455	23	37	20	15	5
88b	1530	23	37	20	15	5
89a	4879	23	37	20	15	5
89b	5811	23	37	20	15	5
90a	34502	23	37	20	15	5
90b	35032	23	37	20	15	5
91	4192	23	37	20	15	5
92a	448	22	24	23	16	15
92b	643	22	24	23	16	15

Lane Identifications	No. of Vessels (per year)	% Ships in Size Class (dwt metric tonnes)				
		0-1499	1500-4999	5000-14999	15000-40000	Over 40000
93	8937	23	37	20	15	5
94a	4812	23	37	20	15	5
94b	3955	23	37	20	15	5
95	1529	38	36	12	11	3
96	1757	38	36	12	11	3
97	2944	38	36	12	11	3
98	1185	38	36	12	11	3
99a	1676	23	37	20	15	5
99b	1690	23	37	20	15	5
100.1	580	38	36	12	11	3
100.2	580	38	36	12	11	3
101a	2365	38	36	12	11	3
101b	3145	38	36	12	11	3
102a	735	38	36	12	11	3
102b	668	27	36	12	14	11
103	2237	38	36	12	11	3
104a	14078	23	37	20	15	5
104b	13582	23	37	20	15	5
105a	24432	23	37	20	15	5
105b	23987	23	37	20	15	5
106	1142	38	36	12	11	3
107a	352	38	36	12	11	3
107b	326	38	36	12	11	3
108a	161	38	36	12	11	3
108b	303	23	37	20	15	5
109a	6650	15	39	24	16	6
109b	6113	15	39	24	16	6
110a	816	15	39	24	16	6
110b	992	15	39	24	16	6
111a	19211	15	39	24	16	6
111b	19727	15	39	24	16	6
112a	2013	25	53	12	7	3
112b	1390	25	53	12	7	3
113a	2807	14	22	20	29	15
113b	2876	14	22	20	29	15
114a	2064	14	22	20	29	15
114b	2525	14	22	20	29	15
115a	1390	15	39	24	16	6
115b	916	15	39	24	16	6
116a	4957	38	36	12	11	3
116b	5249	38	36	12	11	3

Lane Identifications	No. of Vessels (per year)	% Ships in Size Class (dwt metric tonnes)				
		0-1499	1500-4999	5000-14999	15000-40000	Over 40000
117	1669	2	2	3	6	87
118	944	15	39	24	16	6
119	6749	22	24	23	16	15
120	570	23	37	20	15	5
121	1895	33	52	7	4	4
122	638	37	41	12	7	3
123	630	22	24	23	16	15
124	800	22	24	23	16	15
125	2688	22	24	23	16	15
126	642	14	22	20	29	15
127	471	14	22	20	29	15
128	1430	22	24	23	16	15
129	885	14	22	20	29	15
130	1243	37	41	12	7	3
131a	3698	30	52	10	6	2
131b	3978	30	52	10	6	2
132	1495	30	52	10	6	2
133	2383	33	52	7	4	4
134a	2099	30	52	10	6	2
134b	2187	30	52	10	6	2
135a	2017	30	52	10	6	2
135b	2271	30	52	10	6	2
136	468	33	52	7	4	4
137	11636	30	52	10	6	2
138	1839	30	52	10	6	2
139	1839	30	52	10	6	2
140	4300	30	52	10	6	2
141	697	33	52	7	4	4
142	3344	15	39	24	16	6
143.1	662	33	52	7	4	4
143.2	662	33	52	7	4	4
144	861	15	39	24	16	6
145.1	1482	14	22	20	29	15
145.2	1482	14	22	20	29	15
146	2435	15	39	24	16	6
147	887	33	52	7	4	4
148	5537	33	52	7	4	4
149	372	18	20	28	24	10
150	280	18	20	28	24	10
151	3286	42	38	6	4	10
152	3247	42	38	6	4	10

Lane Identifications	No. of Vessels (per year)	% Ships in Size Class (dwt metric tonnes)				
		0-1499	1500-4999	5000-14999	15000-40000	Over 40000
153	3123	42	38	6	4	10
154	3297	42	38	6	4	10
155	700	15	39	24	16	6
156	3106	18	21	18	25	18
157	1912	18	21	18	25	18
158	4503	31	32	11	13	13
159	320	2	2	3	6	87
160	337	22	24	23	16	15
F	2870	23	37	20	15	5
G	560	23	37	20	15	5
H	4560	38	36	12	11	3
I	4780	38	36	12	11	3
J	8420	22	24	23	16	15
K(1)	1850	22	24	23	16	15
K(2)	1470	22	24	23	16	15
L	4760	30	52	10	6	2

TABLE H.2: Offshore Supply/Support Vessel Size Distribution by Lane

Lane Identifications	No. of Vessels (per year)	% Ships in Size Class (dwt metric tonnes)				
		0-1499	1500-4999	5000-14999	15000-40000	Over 40000
S.1	292	41	59	0	0	0
S.2	1440	33	67	0	0	0
S.3	900	87	13	0	0	0
S.4	860	30	70	0	0	0
S.5	928	74	26	0	0	0
S.6	172	100	0	0	0	0
S.7	104	100	0	0	0	0
S.8	208	100	0	0	0	0
S.9	156	100	0	0	0	0
S.10	172	100	0	0	0	0
S.11	636	100	0	0	0	0
S.12	516	30	70	0	0	0
S.13	172	100	0	0	0	0
S.14	756	68	32	0	0	0
S.15	240	0	100	0	0	0
S.16	360	68	32	0	0	0
S.17	344	30	70	0	0	0
S.18	240	50	50	0	0	0
S.19	960	100	0	0	0	0
S.20	480	50	50	0	0	0
S.21	120	0	100	0	0	0
S.22	240	100	0	0	0	0
S.23	568	37	63	0	0	0
S.24	104	100	0	0	0	0
S.25	180	100	0	0	0	0
S.26	180	100	0	0	0	0
S.27	980	45	55	0	0	0
S.27a	156	100	0	0	0	0
S.28	1548	77	23	0	0	0
S.29	2888	68	32	0	0	0
S.30	516	100	0	0	0	0
S.31	360	100	0	0	0	0
S.32	336	45	55	0	0	0
S.33	388	100	0	0	0	0
S.34	696	100	0	0	0	0
S.A	2060	68	0	0	0	0
S.B	1700	32	0	0	0	0

TABLE H.3: Offshore Tanker Vessel Size Distribution by Lane

Lane Identifications	No. of Vessels (per year)	% Ships in Size Class (dwt metric tonnes)				
		0-1499	1500-4999	5000-14999	15000-40000	Over 40000
T.1	180	0	0	0	0	100
T.2	50	0	0	0	0	100
T.3.1	230	0	0	0	0	100
T.3.2	230	0	0	0	0	100
T.4.1	240	0	0	0	0	100
T.4.2	240	0	0	0	0	100
T.5	90	0	0	0	0	100
T.6.1	100	0	0	0	0	100
T.6.2	100	0	0	0	0	100
T.7	50	0	0	0	0	100
T.8	40	0	0	0	0	100
T.9	50	0	0	0	0	100
T.10	40	0	0	0	0	100
T.11	40	0	0	0	0	100
T.12	40	0	0	0	0	100
T.13	40	0	0	0	0	100
T.14	40	0	0	0	0	100
T.15.1	100	0	0	0	0	100
T.15.2	100	0	0	0	0	100
T.15.3	100	0	0	0	0	100
T.15.4	100	0	0	0	0	100

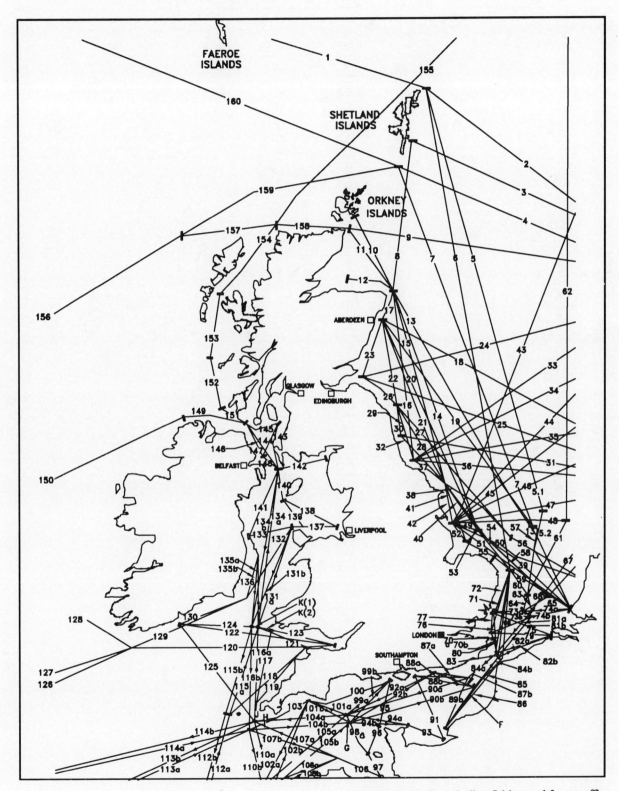

Merchant vessels excluding fishing and ferry traffic

Merchant Vessel Route Definition

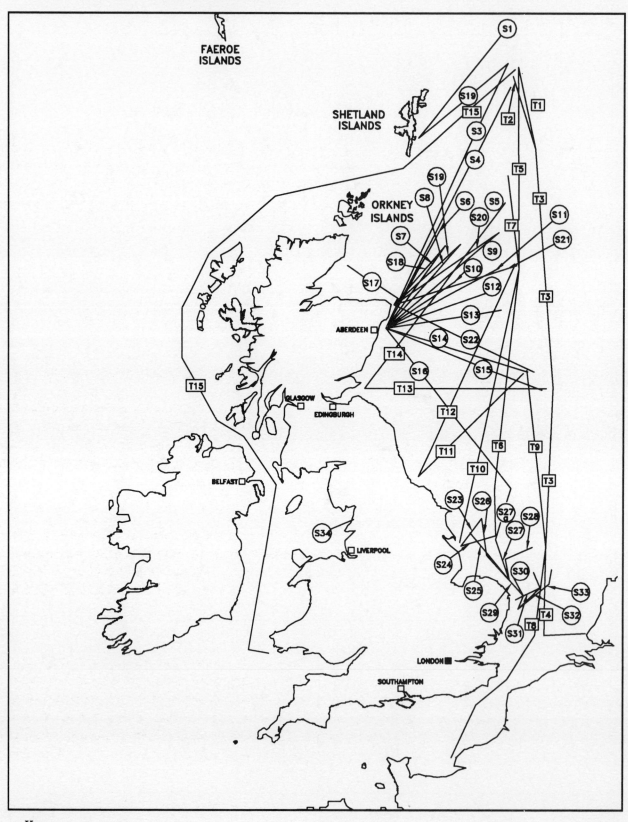

Key:
(S) Support vessel lane

[T] Tanker lane

Support/Supply Vessel & Offshore Tanker Route Definition

Appendix I

The Coastguard Agency

I.1   The Coastguard Agency or COASTGUARD is an executive agency of the Department of Transport. It came into being on 1 April 1994 when it replaced the Marine Emergencies Organisation (MEO). Under a Chief Executive, it consists of HM Coastguard (HMCG), headed by the Chief Coastguard, and the Marine Pollution Control Unit (MPCU) headed by the Director, MPCU.

I.2   The role of COASTGUARD is to minimise the loss of life amongst seafarers and coastal users and minimise pollution from ships to sea and coastline.

HM Coastguard (HMCG)

I.3   The task of HMCG has only recently been properly defined[1], as follows:

> "HM Coastguard is responsible for the initiation and co-ordination of civil maritime search and rescue within the United Kingdom Search and Rescue Region. This includes the mobilisation, organisation and tasking of adequate resources to respond to persons either in distress at sea or to persons at risk of injury or death on the cliffs or shoreline of the United Kingdom."

I.4   HMCG is primarily a search and rescue (SAR) organisation. HMCG partly fulfils the UK's responsibility for the establishment of a maritime search and rescue organisation under the International Convention on Maritime Search and Rescue 1979, the International Convention for Safety of Life at Sea 1974 and the Convention of the High Seas 1958.

I.5   HMCG's main task is to initiate and coordinate civil maritime search and rescue within the UK SAR region. 24 hour response to radio and satellite distress frequencies and monitoring the 999 emergency telephone network is carried out at 21 rescue coordination centres, each headed by a District Controller, and one hundred sector offices. The districts are grouped into six regions, each headed by a Regional Controller, at Aberdeen, Clyde, Great Yarmouth, Swansea, Dover and Falmouth.

I.6   HMCG relies upon the Royal National Lifeboat Institution to provide lifeboats. Most SAR helicopters are provided by the Ministry of Defence, but three are contracted directly by HMCG. HMCG also maintains up-to-date information on the availability,

---

[1] By the Minister for Aviation and Shipping in Parliament—Hansard 9 March 1992 col 413.

readiness, capability and limitations of all rescue assets and authorities which can provide assistance. In an incident HMCG organises and provides the main communication links between HMCG and other emergency services and shore-based authorities.

I.7   HMCG's other responsibilities include: cooperating with foreign SAR authorities in the coordination of civil maritime SAR outside the UK SAR region; acting as the UK operational authority for the Global Maritime Distress and Safety System (GMDSS); operating the Channel Navigation Information Service (CNIS) in the Dover Strait (described in Chapter 16), and assisting MPCU with counter-pollution reporting and operations.

I.8   HMCG is not, contrary to popular belief, responsible for spotting accidents visually, either with the naked eye or by radar. In this its role is analogous to the ambulance and fire services, which do not go out and look for incidents but rely on reports from others. In fact not all HMCG stations have a significant view of the sea and only one, at Dover, is equipped with radar. With the exception of distress, emergency and safety matters, HMCG is not, and should not become, an agency for solving problems for ships' Masters.

I.9   Perhaps surprisingly, HMCG is not responsible for policing routeing measures. The sole area where it has a picture of a routeing measure is the Dover Strait. Even in the Strait, where HMCG warn shipping of hazards caused by "rogues" infringing the traffic rules, and report identified "rogues" for prosecution, it does not instruct vessels to change their behaviour.

I.10   HMCG is not responsible for the prevention of accidents, for instance by routeing measures – that is the responsibility of the Marine Safety Agency. The two organisations share a headquarters building and help each other out when sensible: HMCG can and does act as agent for MSA, while MSA can provide COASTGUARD with expert assist-ance, as the *ODIGITRIA B* incident described in Appendix L shows.

I.11   HMCG has some 580 full-time staff, including administrative support, backed up by over 3,000 auxiliaries. All watchkeeping staff and auxiliaries are trained intensively to deal with search and rescue emergencies, but they are not all trained mariners and are thus not necessarily qualified to give navigational advice, let alone instruction, to Masters of vessels.

The Marine Pollution Control Unit (MPCU)

I.12   Following the *TORREY CANYON* incident off the Isles of Scilly in 1969, the UK Government recognised that it was not reasonably practical for owners of deep sea tankers, which voyage worldwide, to make contingency arrangements for dealing with oil spills wherever they may occur. Accordingly, central Government accepted the responsibility for dealing with spillages of oil at sea from shipping casualties which threatened UK waters. In

1978, after a series of major tanker incidents in western European waters, the UK Government set up MPCU as a dedicated contingency planning and response unit, with specific responsibilities for planning contingency arrangements and taking charge of operations to deal with pollution at sea.

I.13   In 1984, MPCU was transferred from the Department of the Environment to the Department of Transport. As a result of recommendations by the Royal Commission on Environmental Pollution in their Eighth Report *Oil Pollution of the Sea*, MPCU was given responsibilities previously exercised by the Department of the Environment in relation to on-shore clean-up so as to achieve a fully integrated at-sea and on-shore clean-up operation in the event of a major spill. In a major incident, MPCU is thus now responsible for coordinating the response on-shore as well as directing off-shore operations. The Secretary of State for the Environment still, however, retains a watching brief in view of his overall responsibility for coordinating Government policy on environmental pollution.

I.14   MPCU's main task is to monitor and follow up reports of spills of oil and other hazardous substances from ships in or near UK waters and to direct pollution response operations at sea. MPCU maintains the Government's National Contingency Plan for dealing with oil and chemical spills from ships at sea and provides guidance to authorities on local contingency plans and the establishment of Joint Response Centres.

I.15   As a first line of defence against oil pollution MPCU is responsible for procuring and maintaining adequate stocks of dispersants and managing the contract for aerial spraying. MPCU also ensures that there is adequate provision for shipborne spraying and equipment for the recovery or transfer of oil at sea and on the shoreline. MPCU maintains an airborne remote sensing capability and a computer system to aid assessment of the quantity, likely movement and characteristics of oil spills.

I.16   For chemical incidents MPCU maintains a contracted Chemical Strike Team, a stock of equipment for the team to use, a Chemicals Hazards Advisory Group to provide expert advice, and computer based risk assessment and response models.

I.17   MPCU also has a contracted capability to fly surveillance flights to detect and deter illegal operational discharges and submits evidence to Treasury Solicitors to enable prosecution of those responsible for such discharges when they can be identified.

I.18   MPCU consists of only 12 people. It was set up without any statutory backing, but that is being corrected by the Merchant Shipping (Salvage and Pollution) Bill currently before Parliament. The Chief Executive, the Chief Coastguard and the Director, MPCU can, however, exercise the "intervention" powers in the Prevention of Pollution Act 1971 (see Appendix J) on behalf of the Secretary of State for Transport. Any one of the three of them can also, if necessary, delegate the powers to a Regional Controller or Deputy Regional Controller to deal with a specific incident.

Finance

I.19 COASTGUARD's budget for 1994-95 is almost £50 million. Of this almost £24.5 million is expected to be spent on running costs including pay and accommodation. Capital spending on property and IT will total £3.2 million. Of the remaining £22 million, the largest single item of expenditure is SAR helicopters which will cost over £8.5 million. The next largest item is aerial spraying and surveillance, covered by a single contract at a cost in 1994-95 of some £4.7 million, divided approximately 75 per cent aerial spraying capacity – that is, the maintenance of the seven spraying aircraft, including training of crews and exercises – and 25 per cent surveillance – that is, the maintenance and operation of the surveillance aircraft which are also used for other purposes. In Chapters 21 (paragraph 21.50) and 22 (paragraph 22.40) we have assumed that the costs are £3.5 million for the dispersant spraying capacity and £1.2 million for the aerial surveillance capacity. The other major item of programme expenditure is communications which will cost about £3.9 million. About £540,000 will be spent on the operation and upkeep of CNIS, including some £130,000 on the replacement of equipment.

Appendix J

Statutory Powers of Intervention

Source: The Marine Pollution Control Unit's National Contingency Plan

The powers

J.1   The powers are set out in the Prevention of Oil Pollution Act 1971, sections 12 – 17; and the Merchant Shipping (Prevention of Pollution) (Intervention) Order 1980. Although they currently differ in important respects depending on whether the vessel is within UK territorial waters or not, the Declaration on the Coordinated Extension of Jurisdiction in the North Sea which was signed by North Sea Ministers on 22 September 1992 commits the UK to extend its jurisdiction either by establishing an EEZ or by designating an area adjacent to its territorial seas. When in place, such an extension of jurisdiction will establish a sound base for dealing with a serious pollution incident involving a foreign ship between 12 and 200 miles from the coast of the UK.

Within territorial waters

J.2   The powers are exercisable when three conditions have all been met:

(a)   an accident has occurred to or in a ship (this includes, but is not limited to, the loss, stranding, abandonment of, or damage to a ship);

(b)   in the opinion of the Secretary of State, or the person acting on his behalf, oil or some other harmful substance from the ship will or may cause pollution on a large scale in the United Kingdom or in the territorial waters thereof; and

(c)   in the opinion of the Secretary of State, or the person acting on his behalf, the use of the powers is urgently needed.

J.3   A list of the oils and other harmful substances mentioned in the legislation is at the Annex to this Appendix. It should be noted that the powers are not limited to accidents involving certain types of vessels, such as tankers, and are not limited to pollution from cargo oil as opposed to bunker fuel. The oil does not even need to be persistent, though there must be a risk of pollution on a large scale.

J.4   So far as harmful substances other than oil are concerned, those that give rise to the exercise of the powers are only partly set out in the Annex to this Appendix. As the Annex shows, the powers may also be used when dealing with any substance which is liable to create hazards to human health, to harm living resources and marine life, to damage amenities or to interfere with other legitimate uses of the sea.

451

J.5   When the three conditions mentioned in paragraph J.2 above have been met, there are powers which can be exercised to give directions in respect of the ship or its cargo. The direction can be given only to:

(a)   the owner of the ship or any person in possession of the ship (the owner of the ship means the person or persons registered as the owner of the ship or in the absence of registration, a person actually owning the ship. The person in possession of a ship means the person who has the power to give directions to the Master to take action in respect of the ship – the demise charterer or managing agent for example);

(b)   the Master of the ship (this means any person, except a pilot, having command or charge of a ship); or

(c)   any salvor in possession of the ship and who is in charge of the salvage operation (the salvor in possession means any person who is legitimately performing salvage operations on the ship, normally with the specific consent of the Master, but not necessarily – for example where a ship has been abandoned).

J.6   A direction can require the person to whom it is given to take or refrain from taking any action of any kind whatsoever, including, requiring the ship to be moved, or not to be moved to a specified place; the ship to be removed from a specified place or locality; the oil or other cargo to be or not to be unloaded or discharged; and specified salvage measures to be or not to be taken.

J.7   Directions should so far as possible be given in writing, but in extreme cases may be given orally to a person who is physically present or over a telephone or radio link. When an oral direction is given, it should be confirmed in writing.

J.8   When the three conditions mentioned in paragraph J.2 above have been met and the Secretary of State or the person acting on his behalf is of the opinion that the powers to give directions is inadequate or has proved to be inadequate, then he can take any action of any kind whatsoever extending to sinking or destroying the ship.

J.9   When action is to be taken under these powers, the Secretary of State or the person acting on his behalf, can arrange for other persons – such as commercial salvors or the Royal Navy – to act on his behalf.

Outside territorial waters

Ship registered in the UK

J.10   Where a ship outside UK territorial waters is registered in the UK, the statutory powers to give directions to take direct action can be applied in exactly the same way as they are applied to ships within UK territorial waters.

Foreign registered ships

J.11   Where the ship concerned is outside UK territorial waters and is not registered in the UK the statutory powers of the Secretary of State to give directions are more limited:

(a)   first, in addition to the three conditions mentioned in paragraph J2 above, the Secretary of State or the person acting on his behalf, also has to be satisfied that there is a need to protect the coast of the United Kingdom or the territorial waters thereof, against a grave and imminent danger of pollution; and

(b)   second, except in certain limited cases, the power to issue directions can be exercised only when the direction can be given to someone who not only comes within the group of people to whom such directions can be given when a vessel is within UK territorial waters but is also either a UK citizen or is a body corporate established under UK laws.

J.12   However, the power to take action continues to exist in exactly the same way as it applies to vessels, UK registered or otherwise, within UK territorial waters.

Consultation with Flag State

J.13   Although not expressly provided for in the UK legislation, the International Convention upon which the UK legislation is based, provides that when formal powers of intervention are to be used, the Flag State of the ship concerned should be consulted about or notified of the measures that it is proposed to take and interest must be taken of any views that it might express. This will normally be done either via the Foreign and Commonwealth Office or direct with the Embassy or Consulate of the country concerned. In cases of extreme urgency, requiring immediate measures to be taken, it is nevertheless permissable to give directions or take action without first notifying the Flag State.

Failure to comply and obstruction

J.14   The legislation makes it a criminal offence for a person to whom a direction is given not to comply unless he can show that he tried to do so with all due diligence or had reasonable cause to believe that there would have been a serious risk to human life. It is also a criminal offence for anyone to wilfully obstruct a person carrying out a direction given by the Secretary of State.

Liability for compensation

J.15   The legislation also provides for compensation to be paid by the Secretary of State where:

(a)   the action directed or taken was not reasonable to prevent or reduce pollution or the risk of pollution; or

(b)   the action taken or directed was such that the good that it did, or was likely to do, was disproportionately less than the expense incurred or the damage suffered as a result of the action.

Who can use the powers

J.16 The powers are vested in the Secretary of State who has agreed to other persons using them on his behalf. Whenever possible, MPCU should attempt to seek the agreement of the Minister responsible for shipping affairs or any other Minister carrying out those duties from time to time.

J.17 When none of the Ministers can be reached, the Chief Executive of the Coastguard Agency (formerly the Director of Marine Emergency Operations) has authority to use the powers without seeking any other person's consent. However, wherever practicable, the Chief Executive should seek legal and professional advice.

J.18 When the Chief Executive is not available, the Chief Coastguard and the Director, Marine Pollution Control Unit have authority to use the powers in the same way as the Chief Executive, except that if time allows they should first obtain the specific approval of senior officers within the Department, as well as legal and professional advice.

J.19 When events are moving fast in a complex situation and the person in overall command (the Chief Executive) does not have sufficient information to be able to decide how the intervention powers might best be used, he may delegate the powers to one of HM Coastguard's Regional Controllers or Deputy Controllers. In the Chief Executive's absence the Chief Coastguard or Director MPCU may make such a delegation. The central rule is that no direction should be given, or other intervention made, without a Minister or other senior officer's approval unless the circumstances require immediate action to be taken.

Annex to Appendix J

Secretary of State's powers of Intervention: List of Oils and other substances to which powers apply

Oils

Oil of any description including spirit produced from oil of any description, and also including coal tar.

Substances other than oil

Noxious substances

Acetic anhydride
Acetone
Acvetone cyanohydrin
Acrolein
Acrylonitrile
Aldrin
Allyl isothiocynate
Aluminium Phosphide
Ammonia (28% aqueous)
Ammonium Phosphate
Amyl mercaptan
Aniline
Aniline hydrochloride
Antimony compounds
Arsenic compounds
Atrazine
Azinphos methyl (Guthion)
Barium azide
Barium cyanide
Barium oxide
Benzene
Benzene hexachloride isomers (Lindane)
Benzidine
Beryllium powder
Bromine
Bromobenzyl cyanide
n-Butyl acrylate
Butyric acid
Cacodylic acid
Cadmium compounds

Carbaryl (Sevin)
Carbon disulphide
Carbontetrachloride
Chlordane
Chloroacetone
Chloroacetophenone
Chlorodinetrobenzene
Chloroform
Chlorhydrins (crude)
Chloropicrin
Chromic acid (Chromium trioxide)
Cooculus (solid)
Copper compounds
Cresols
Cupriethylene diamine
Cyanide compounds
Cyanogen bromide
Cyanogen chloride
DDT
Dichloroanilines
Dichlorobenzenes
Dieldrin
Dimethoate (Cygon)
Dimethyl amine (40% aqueous)
Dinitroanilines
4,6-Dinitroorthocresol
Dinitrophenols
Endosulphan (Thiodan)
Endrin
Epichlorohydrin

Ethyl bromoacetate
Ethylene chlorohydrin (2-Chloro Ethanol)
Ethylene dichloride
Ethyl parathion
Fentin acetate (dry)
Fluorosilicic acid
Heptachlor
Hexachlorobenzine
Hexaethyl tetraphosphate
Hydrocyanic acid
Hydrofluoric acid (40% aqueous)
Isoprene
Lead compounds
Lindane (gammexane, BHC)
Malathion
Mercuric compounds
Methyl alcohol
Methylene chloride

Molasses
Naphthalene (molten)
Naphthylthiourea
Nitric acid (90%)
Oleum
Parathion
Paraquat
Phenol
Phosphoric acid
Phosphorus (elemental)
Polyhalogenated biphenyls
Sodium pentachlorophenate (solution)
Styrene monomer
Toluene
Toluene diisocyanate
Toxaphene
Tritolyl phosphate (Tricresyl phosphate)
2,4,5-T

Liquified gases (when carried in bulk)

Acetaldehyde
Anhydrous Ammonia
Anhydrous Hydrogen Chloride
Anhydrous Hydrogen Fluoride
Butadiene
Butane
Butane/Propane Mixtures
Butylenes
Chlorine
Dimethylamine
Ethyl Chloride

Ethane
Ethylene
Ethylene Oxide
Methane (LNG)
Methyl Acetylene Propadiene mixture
Methyl Bromide
Methyl Chloride
Propane
Propylene
Sulphur Dioxide
Vinyl Chloride Monomer

Radioactive substances

Radioactive substances, including consignments of such substances which are required to be notified to competent authorities under paragraph 835 in Section VIII of the IAEA Regulations (The Regulations for the Safe Transport of Radioactive Materials, 1973 Revised Edition – published by the International Atomic Energy Agency in Vienna).

Other substances

Those other substances which are liable to create hazards to human health, to harm living resources and marine life, to damage amenities or to interfere with other legitimate uses of the sea.

Appendix K

Memorandum of Understanding between the National Rivers Authority and the Marine Pollution Control Unit

DEALING WITH OIL AND CHEMICAL POLLUTION IN ESTUARINE AND MARINE WATERS

K.1   As we mention in Chapter 21, representatives of the Marine Pollution Control Unit and the National Rivers Authority have signed a joint memorandum of understanding making clear the division of responsibility between the two organisations in the event of oil and chemical pollution in estuarine and marine waters. The memorandum was signed on 7 April 1993 and the text is reproduced in paragraphs K.2 – K.39 below.

Introduction

K.2   *The Government response to the Second Report of the Environment Select Committee (1991-92 Session) on Coastal Zone Protection and Planning recognised the necessary duplication of powers between those exercised by the Marine Pollution Control Unit (MPCU) under the Prevention of Oil Pollution Act 1971, and by the National Rivers Authority (NRA) under the Water Resources Act 1991 and the potential for confusion about command and control in an emergency.*

K.3   *This Memorandum of Understanding seeks to clarify the role and responsibilities of the NRA and MPCU in dealing with oil and chemical pollution in estuarine and coastal waters.*

The Duties and Powers of the NRA

K.4   *The NRA has specific responsibilities relating to water quality under the Water Act 1989 (WA '89) which have since been consolidated into the Water Resources Act 1991 (WRA '91); they apply to controlled waters which are defined by the Acts as including relevant territorial waters plus coastal waters. The Acts define relevant territorial waters as being those which extend seaward for three nautical miles from the baselines from which the breadth of the territorial sea adjacent to England and Wales is measured. Coastal waters are any waters which are within the area which extends landward from these baselines as far as the limit of the highest tide or, in the case of the waters of any relevant river or watercourse, as far as the freshwater limit of the river or watercourse, together with the waters of any enclosed dock which adjoins waters within that area.*

K.5   *The NRA has powers under Sections 86 to 88 of the WRA '91 to control pollution at source in order to protect the quality of controlled waters. Such powers include those necessary to consent to or prohibit discharges from land-based sources, even if discharged from pipes which extend beyond the three nautical mile limit. The NRA does not, however, have powers to consent to discharges from vessels outside such waters. (Within controlled waters, the NRA does have powers to control certain discharges from vessels by making relevant byelaws). The NRA also has powers under Section 161 of the WRA '91 to remedy or mitigate the effects of pollution in controlled waters, and to remove or dispose of polluting matter in them. These powers relate only to the pollution of water.*

The Duties and Powers of the MPCU

K.6 *Regulations to prevent pollution from ships are made by Statutory Instrument in compliance with international Conventions drawn up by the International Maritime Organization and to which the UK is a signatory. These Statutory Instruments are drawn up and enforced by the Department of Transport (DoT). The MPCU was set up in 1979 within the DoT to exercise the responsibility accepted by central Government for counter-pollution operations at sea when oil, or other dangerous substances, spilled from **ships** threatened major pollution of the UK coast, or harm to important fisheries or important concentrations of sea birds.*

K.7 *The MPCU maintains a national contingency plan and resources to cover its "at sea" clean-up responsibilities. In particular, at the request of a Local Authority, it will set up a Joint Response Centre (JRC) to control the shore clean-up of a major marine oil spill. It also provides advice and assistance to Local Authorities, who are primarily responsible for clean-up operations ashore and to Port Authorities are responsible for clean-up operations within their port areas; stockpiles of specialist beach cleaning equipment are maintained for deployment as agreed with Local Authorities. A research programme relating to both at-sea and onshore clean-up is funded and its results disseminated to interested parties. Local Authorities, Port Authorities and offshore operators are advised on their contingency plans. Assistance is given in the training of Local and Port Authority staff in beach cleaning management and techniques.*

K.8 *The Secretary of State for Transport has powers under the 1971 Act to intervene in shipping accidents and give directions or take other action to prevent or reduce oil or chemical pollution, or the risk of such pollution, which threatens the UK on a large scale. These powers are delegated to and exercised by the Director of Marine Emergency Operations as the head of the Marine Pollution Control Unit.*

K.9 *As well as fulfilling its primary role of responding to and planning the response to pollution incidents, the MPCU compiles and processes the Government's claims for compensation from polluters or their insurers. It has responsibility for following up reports of possible illegal discharges of oil at sea with a view to initiating prosecutions under the Merchant Shipping (Prevention of Oil Pollution) Regulations 1983.*

K.10 *In the event of an oil pollution, the MPCU has rapid response targets for mobilisation of aircraft for both aerial reconnaissance and dispersant spraying, and which are on thirty minute standby during the day and at two hours readiness at night.*

K.11   *In major pollution incidents from ships in UK waters, the NRA will act in support of the MPCU who will take the lead role in any remedial work and subsequent prosecution. Where ship to shore operations are being undertaken, however, both the NRA and the Harbour Authority also have responsibilities.*

The Duties and Powers of Other Bodies

K.12   *A number of organisations have responsibilities in both an operational and an advisory capacity in response to incidents or emergencies involving oil pollution in tidal waters. They have varying degrees of involvement, largely dependent upon statutory obligations which can be summarised as follows.*

Ministry of Agriculture, Fisheries and Food

K.13   *The Ministry of Agriculture, Fisheries and Food (MAFF) has responsibilities which essentially relate to:*

    (a)   *the protection of the marine environment;*

    (b)   *the protection of public health from contamination of the food chain (including that by fish); and*

    (c)   *the protection of fisheries, including liaison with the fishing industry.*

K.14   *In cases where the response to an incident might involve a deposit in the sea, MAFF's role has a statutory basis under Part II of the Food and Environment Protection Act 1985 (FEPA '85). Under the Act, deposits in the sea require a licence from MAFF (with certain exceptions specified in the Deposits in the Sea (Exemptions) Order 1985). This requirement covers activities such as the spraying of dispersants on oil. Under the Exemptions Order MAFF can approve the use of specific dispersants subject to conditions, provided that they are not used in an area of sea under 20 metres in depth or within 1 mile of such an area. MAFF can authorise derogations from this rule in cases of overriding need. Powers under this Act cover the Entirety of the sea, **including estuaries and other tidal waters.** In cases where the MPCU wishes to use dispersant, it is formally exempt from these requirements by virtue of Crown immunity. In practice, however, the MPCU will always consult MAFF if it is considering the use of a dispersant. The NRA does not qualify for Crown immunity, and cannot therefore use dispersants, or authorise their use, without MAFF approval in estuarine, coastal or territorial waters as defined in the Water Resources Act 1991.*

K.15   *Under Part 1 of FEPA '85, MAFF also has powers to make emergency orders imposing prohibitions to protect the public from contaminated food. These powers are not often used in relation to marine incidents, but they have been used where highly toxic chemicals have been involved.*

K.16   *MAFF also has an advisory scientific role in relation to the Government's response to incidents, particularly in relation to chemical analyses in support of decisions such as the recovery of containers lost at sea.*

Local Authorities

K.17 *Local Authorities have accepted the non statutory responsibility of dealing with pollution that impacts on the coast in line with DoE circular 29/81; however, Section 138 of the Local Government Act 1972 empowers both County and District Councils to deal with emergencies and disasters. Oil emergencies are thus included and Councils have the power to incur expenditure on the amelioration of the effects of such pollutions. The allocation of responsibilities between District and County Councils is clearly defined in local authority contingency plans. In general, the most common arrangement is for District Councils to be responsible for activities involved in beach clean-up; with the County Council undertaking inshore spraying of oil dispersants and coordinating operations which involve the efforts of more than one District. The County Councils generally exercise this responsibility up to a limit of one mile to seaward from the high water mark but there is no statutory provision supporting this.*

Port and Harbour Authorities

K.18 *The Port and Harbour Authorities do not generally have statutory duties to undertake oil clean-up operations when a spillage occurs in waters under their control, but will deal with spills as necessary to allow safe operation of the port. They do, however, have powers to prosecute a discharger under the Prevention of Oil Pollution Act 1971 (POPA '71). They may also call upon the support of the District Councils as required.*

Joint Nature Conservation Committee

K.19 *The UK Joint Nature Conservation Committee (JNCC) is a statutory body constituted by the Environmental Protection Act 1990 (EPA '90) to be responsible for research and advice on nature conservation at both UK and international levels. It was established by English Nature, Scottish National Heritage, and the Countryside Council for Wales, together with independent members and representatives from the Countryside Commission and Northern Ireland. It is supported by specialist staff.*

K.20 *The Seabirds at Sea Team is a unit of JNCC which specialises in research into seabird distribution at sea. The results of this research are used to give advice on the potential impacts of oil pollution at sea on seabirds. The Seabirds at Sea Team is funded externally.*

Responsibility for Dealing with Oil Spills

K.21 *Oil spills affecting the marine environment fall into the following categories:*

Offshore Fixed Installations

K.22 *Under regulations made by the Department of Trade and Industry (DTI) the operator of the installation is responsible for drawing up contingency plans and the provision of resources. MPCU vets these contingency plans and recommends acceptance or otherwise to DTI.*

K.23 *Oil spilt from an offshore installation must be reported to the Coastguard. It is a statutory duty for owners of offshore installations to contact the Offshore Safety Division (OSD) of the Health and Safety Executive to advise of a major incident offshore. A major oil spill emergency is one which causes pollution which cannot be brought under control in a relatively short period of time (hours). The Director of Operations OSD, or his Deputy will decide whether to call out the Offshore Emergency Team (OET). In the event of a spill which calls for a response beyond that available from the industry the MPCU's resources will be made available. The Head of the MPCU or his Deputy is a member of the OET for oil spills.*

K.24 *For the purposes of this MOU an offshore oil spill should be treated as a spill from a ship. The actions of the NRA in relation to an offshore spill should be the same as if that spill had originated from a ship.*

Major Spills from Ships

K.25 *The MPCU is responsible for dealing with major oil spills from ships where these threaten to cause pollution in UK waters or on the UK shoreline. The Unit will set up command and control arrangements, normally with an Overall Commander in the Marine Emergencies Operations Room (MEOR) and an Local Commander at the most convenient Coastguard Rescue Centre. It will call upon its own resources, or commission extra resources from within the UK, as necessary. It has agreements with foreign States to call upon their resources and may seek coordinated assistance from the EC or IMO.*

K.26 *In harbour areas the initial responsibility for dealing with smaller spills rests with the Harbour or Port Authority. These authorities should have contingency plans in accordance with MPCU guidelines. They submit these plans to MPCU to check, among other things, for consistency with the National Contingency Plan and Local Authorities contingency plans.*

K.27 *Although the Coastal Local Authorities and Port and Harbour Authorities in England, Scotland and Wales have accepted responsibility for dealing with pollution on the coastline and to ports and harbours respectively, HM Government accepts that they may not be able to cope with a major incident causing exceptional pollution without some assistance from central Government. In such circumstances, the MPCU will not only direct offshore operations but will also, when so agreed, set up a Joint Response Centre (JRC) with one or more local authorities and then provide beach clean-up equipment and other resources free of charge. If so requested, the MPCU Land Coordinator in the JRC would coordinate and lead the coastal clean-up response.*

K.28 *The NRA may be involved in assisting Local Authorities in clean-up operations or in working with other environmental protection groups in discharging its recreational and conservation duties. The NRA have a responsibility to prevent the spread of oil inland from estuaries on incoming tides. To do this, each NRA Region will prepare action plans, in consultation with the Local Authorities, MAFF, and English Nature or the Countryside Council for Wales, to protect wherever feasible, sensitive areas of coastline and estuaries.*

Discharges Entering Tidal Waters from either a Riverine Source or a Land Based Discharge

K.29   The NRA is responsible for the monitoring of and remedial action resulting from all oil and chemical discharges from land based sources in England and Wales. Under these circumstances, the NRA will take the lead role using the powers vested in it under Section 161 of the WRA '91.

K.30   The NRA will locate the source of the pollution and ensure the discharge is stopped as soon as is practicable. After establishing the extent of the pollution and the severity of the incident, appropriate remedial action will be instigated by the NRA, taking into consideration the views of other bodies, such as MAFF and English Nature, who have an environmental interest.

K.31   The NRA will set up command and control arrangements and will act as the coordinators in commissioning resources from both within the NRA and other bodies such as the Police, Fire Services, Harbour and Local Authorities. In the case of major incidents, the MPCU may be called in to assist with remedial operations.

Reporting Procedures

K.32   All reports of spillages of oil or chemicals into the sea are reported to HM Coastguard who maintain a 24 hour a day radio watch and can also be contacted by 999 telephone calls. HM Coastguard will alert the MPCU, whose staff are on call 24 hours a day.

K.33   All reports of spillages of oil or chemicals onto land or into rivers, estuaries and the sea are reported to the relevant NRA Regional Offices in England and Wales whose staff are on call 24 hours a day. The Regional Office will inform the NRA Head Office directly during normal office hours (0830-1700 hours Monday – Friday) and via the NRA Thames Barrier Control outside these hours.

K.34   Confirmed pollution reports (POLREPS) will be sent to the relevant NRA Regional Office and copied to NRA Head Office. In addition, the MPCU and NRA have undertaken to provide each other with up-to-date details of their respective call-out arrangements.

K.35   The NRA Regional Office will inform the MAFF District Inspector of Fisheries or, if unavailable, the Sea Fisheries Inspectorate Headquarters, of oil and chemical spillages.

Prosecution of Offenders

K.36   The relevant legislation is Section 2 of POPA '71 and Section 85 of the WRA '91.

K.37   Action under POPA '71 can be brought only:

   (a)   by or with the consent of the Attorney General;

(b)   *by the Harbour Authority; or*

(c)   *by the Secretary of State, or with his authorisation.*

K.38   *The organisation responsible for taking the lead role in any remedial operations will be the one responsible for any subsequent prosecution. Thus, for offences from offshore installations and discharges from ships, it should be left to the Harbour Authority or the MPCU to instigate any legal proceedings; whereas for discharges from land based operations or from a riverine source, any prosecution should be brought by the NRA.*

Joint Review Committee

K.39   *A Joint Review Committee will meet, whenever the need arises, to review the working of the Memorandum. Special meetings may be called by either party to resolve any immediate operational difficulties. The chair will be taken alternately by the two parties to this Memorandum. Committee membership will comprise at least two officials from each party.*

Appendix L

Incidents risking or causing pollution during the life of the inquiry

L.1   The Department of Transport kindly kept us informed of the more significant maritime incidents which took place during the course of the Inquiry, usually by showing us copies of their working papers. We were shocked to discover just how many potentially serious incidents there were.

L.2   In 1993 HM Coastguard dealt with 67 incidents involving merchant ships: 19 strandings, 17 collisions, 24 machinery failures and 7 fires. HM Coastguard also dealt with a large number of incidents involving pleasure craft. All those merchant ships carried bunkers: some also carried major polluting cargoes. All of these incidents could in other circumstances have led to pollution.

L.3   We describe here, in chronological order, groundings and near misses which were reported to HM Coastguard and which led, or could have led, to significant pollution during 1993 and the first nine weeks of 1994. We have included those incidents or accidents to ships carrying oil or other hazardous cargoes, or carrying sufficient bunkers to be a threat to the marine environment, which did not result in major pollution due to action taken or to luck. The locations of the incidents are generally shown on the map at Appendix R.

L.4   We also describe two incidents outside UK waters, the collision between the *BRITISH TRENT* and the *WESTERN WINNER* and the electrical failure of the *OLYMPIC BREEZE*, which influenced our thinking, and a third, the collision between the *HOO ROBIN* and the *BONNY*, which illustrates a very serious potential problem.

L.5   The incidents took place before the Coastguard Agency had been set up. The then Director of Marine Emergency Operations (DMEO – now the Chief Executive of the Agency) took charge of several of them.

Incidents during 1993

BRAER

L.6   On 3 January 1993 the Liberian registered tanker *BRAER* left Mongstad in Norway for Quebec in Canada on a course designed to take her through the northern Fair Isle Channel. She was fully laden with 84,700 tonnes of Norwegian "Gullfaks" light crude oil. The weather was adverse, with strong southerly gales. On the morning of 4 January four spare steel pipe sections broke loose from their housing on deck. They rolled around and damaged the air pipes from the diesel oil tanks. This damage led to contamination of the diesel oil supply by seawater.

L.7 By the early morning of 5 January the *BRAER* was suffering severe problems with her engines because of the contaminated fuel supply. At 04 40 the main engine stopped when she was ten miles to the south of the southern tip of Shetland, roughly in the middle of the northern Fair Isle Channel. Towage assistance was requested, but the tug/supply vessel *STAR SIRIUS* did not arrive until after the crew had been evacuated (this evacuation had taken place because *BRAER* was close to Shetland and thought to be in imminent danger of grounding). Volunteers, including the Master of the *BRAER*, were landed on her stern (and were later safely evacuated) but were unable to attach a messenger rope from *STAR SIRIUS*, and were thus unable to prevent *BRAER* from grounding on Garths Ness at 11 19 on 5 January, some six hours after she lost power.

L.8 The clean-up operation is described in paragraphs 21.39 – 21.44.

TROMSO ENDEAVOR

L.9 On 16 January 1993 the Liberian registered tanker *TROMSO ENDEAVOR*, laden with 139,737 tonnes of crude oil, suffered steering problems some 870 nautical miles off Lands End whilst on passage from Mexico to Rotterdam. She continued under her own power, escorted by two salvage tugs, to a position some 100 miles southwest of the Isles of Scilly. *TROMSO ENDEAVOR* was then taken under tow and boarded by a Department of Transport surveyor flown out by helicopter.

L.10 *TROMSO ENDEAVOR* proceeded to Falmouth Bay to anchor and effect repairs. These repairs and subsequent sea trials were monitored by the Department. On 6 February she was allowed to resume passage to Rotterdam under certain conditions imposed by DMEO after consultation with his French counterparts.

HAVKONG

L.11 The Bermuda registered liquified petroleum gas carrier *HAVKONG* (34,892 grt) broke adrift from her moorings in Braefoot Bay, Firth of Forth, on 23 January, in very strong winds with squalls gusting to about 80 knots. The vessel was loading at the time, but the emergency shut-off and disconnection arrangements operated correctly and there was no escape of cargo. The ship drifted downwind and by a combination of good fortune and good seamanship was successfully anchored, though she came close to colliding with the *TEVIOT*, another tanker lying at an adjacent berth and loading ethylene. No serious injury or damage was caused and there was no pollution.

BETTINA DANICA

L.12 The Danish dry cargo vessel *BETTINA DANICA* (1,354 grt) grounded on the reef to the south west of Stroma in the Pentland Firth at 03 50 on 13 February. The vessel was in ballast from Ireland to Norway. During the following days the *BETTINA DANICA* was driven by the sea further onto the rocks, finally to the extent that attempts to save the ship were given up. The owners arranged for a UK salvage company to recover the bunkers.

L.13   The grounding was primarily due to the First Mate realising too late the need to alter course for the passage between Stroma and the mainland. He compounded this error by failing to disengage the auto pilot, thus limiting the rate of turn.

FREJA SVEA

L.14   *FREJA SVEA*, a 52,500 grt Bahamas registered and Danish owned tanker, arrived in Tees Bay on 19 February; she was bound in ballast from Wilhelmshaven for Teesport where she was scheduled to load a full cargo of crude oil for New York. She was carrying 30,000 tonnes of water ballast in segregated ballast tanks, 1,664 tonnes of heavy fuel oil and 134 tonnes of diesel oil. The vessel reported to the Marine Operations Centre on arrival and anchored in a recognised waiting area. On 20 February the Master decided to shift *FREJA SVEA* to an anchorage further away from the pipeline and rocks off the coast of Redcar.

L.15   During the night of 20/21 February the weather deteriorated, with winds of gale – gusting to storm – force, resulting in the Master deciding to proceed to sea. However, during the course of the day, whilst attempting to weigh anchor, both the port and starboard windlass motors successively failed. Both motors were beyond repair on board, so replacements were ordered. During the night of 21/22 February the weather improved and remained moderate until 27 February. During this time *FREJA SVEA's* owners located two new windlass motors in Japan. These were flown to the United Kingdom with the intention of fitting them as soon as possible.

L.16   During the evening of 27 February the weather once again became severe, resulting in the replacement windlass motors not being fitted. *FREJA SVEA* dragged her anchor despite her engine running at full power.

L.17   At 06 00 on 28 February *FREJA SVEA* was about 1 nautical mile due north of the western end of the West Scar rocks off Redcar. This position was held until 13 00 by use of the main engines. The weather at this time was wind northerly, force 8/9 occasionally gusting to force 11, visibility was poor with snow showers. *FREJA SVEA* was labouring violently due to a heavy swell made worse by the shallow water.

L.18   Some time after 13 00 the vessel began to drag her anchor again. At 13 50 the Master reported to the harbour authority that the windlass was broken, and that although the *FREJA SVEA* was on full power, she was still moving astern. He requested tug assistance.

L.19   At 15 30 *FREJA SVEA* grounded about four hours before high water. The engines were run at full ahead and later emergency full astern in an effort to free the vessel with the rising tide. They were stopped at 16 05 due to the rudder being jammed 21° to starboard. Soon after grounding, on the advice of the Salvage Master, the Master began to take on further water ballast in her cargo and ballast tanks to prevent further pounding damage and to hold the vessel's position on the rising tide. At this time the vessel was holed in a number of tanks.

L.20 Harbour tugs *ESTON CROSS* and *ROSEBERRY CROSS* attempted to leave the Tees but were forced back by the severe weather conditions. By 15 52 the Teesmouth lifeboat, an RAF helicopter and the Hartlepool lifeboat had reached the scene. Both lifeboats experienced a capsize, resulting in a crew member from the Hartlepool lifeboat being swept overboard. He was recovered 30 minutes later by the RAF helicopter.

L.21 At 15 54 the RAF helicopter began evacuating nine non-essential crew from the vessel. The Technical Manager of Freja Tankers Ltd organised a joint salvage contract under Lloyd's Open Form 90 with Cory Towage Ltd and United Towing Ltd engaging the tugs *SOLJONN* and *NORTHERN EXPLORER*.

L.22 An MPCU air survey of the *FREJA SVEA* on 28 February found no evidence of oil pollution from the vessel. Only insignificant amounts of oil were found on the beach and these were quickly dealt with.

L.23 Unsuccessful attempts were made to refloat the vessel on 1 and 2 March. The majority of the heavy fuel oil was transferred to a contractor's oil recovery vessel, the *FORTH EXPLORER*, on 3 and 4 March. Holed tanks were pressurised and the vessel was refloated in the early hours of the following day. The vessel was then towed to Rotterdam for repairs.

FANNY

L.24 Another incident which happened in the Tees Bay in late February involved the *FANNY*, a 50,895 grt Bahamas registered tanker. At 00 50 on 27 February she lost an anchor while waiting to berth. At the time there was a heavy swell. The weather became severe later in the day.

L.25 *FANNY* then loaded a cargo of crude oil for Immingham from where she returned to the Tees. This voyage was made with one serviceable anchor as the spare anchor could not be connected because most of the cable had been lost as well. If *FANNY* had had to anchor again and the weather had deteriorated further, it is doubtful if one anchor would have held her and she could have suffered a fate similar to *FREJA SVEA*.

CERVANTES

L.26 On 29 March the Spanish registered LPG tanker *CERVANTES* suffered engine failure in the Dover Strait, drifted clear of the shipping lanes and anchored 8 nautical miles off Dungeness. The tanker was on passage to Houston, Texas with 2,707 tonnes of butadiene, a liquified gas which is a suspected carcinogen and extremely flammable. It can form an explosive mixture with air.

L.27 The vessel effected repairs and resumed passage the following day. She had full generating power throughout. At the time of the incident the weather was good.

APACHE/BIRTHE WEHR

L.28   At 14 00 on 1 May the 1,600 grt German owned and Liberian registered tanker *APACHE*, loaded with lubricating oil, was in collision with the 1,000 grt *BIRTHE WEHR* which was loaded with steel products, 22 nautical miles south of Shoreham. Visibility was less than 400 yards at the time and the collision resulted in *APACHE* being holed in her number one cargo tank and empty double bottom tank below it. She lost 255 cubic metres of "Solvent Neutral 150". The *BIRTHE WEHR* sustained minor damage to her forecastle and was diverted to Rotterdam for repair.

L.29   MPCU was alerted by MRSC Solent at 14 55 and immediately scrambled the remote sensing aircraft, Cessna 404. This aircraft was deployed to track and report on the spilled oil until the morning of 5 May when no oil was detected.

L.30   The owners of the vessel chartered the salvage tug *ATLANTIC* to assess the damage and to attempt to patch the holed tank if possible. A Department of Transport surveyor was airlifted onto *APACHE* during the late evening of 1 May to survey the extent of the damage.

L.31   Throughout the weekend of 1 – 3 May, DMEO and the Chief Operations Officer of MPCU were in regular contact with the Master, owners, agents, and other authorities and agencies involved. They also worked on contingency plans for offloading the remaining cargo. The arrangements for the transfer were the responsibility of the *APACHE*'s owners, Atlantic Rederei of Hamburg, who provided the lightening tanker *UNKAS*.

L.32   Conditions imposed on the transfer included the provision of a tug equipped with counter-pollution facilities, approval by MPCU of the discharge plan and an MPCU officer being on board during the transfer. On the morning of 3 May *APACHE* was authorised by DMEO to shift anchorage to more sheltered waters 6 nautical miles south west of Shoreham.

L.33   At 07 30 on 5 May *UNKAS* secured alongside *APACHE*. The transfer commenced at 09 20 and was completed successfully at 17 45 without incident.

L.34   MPCU gave careful consideration to aerial spraying of dispersant on the spilt oil. MAFF were consulted and agreed in principle to the use of dispersant. The oil was assessed as amenable to spraying, but was expected to emulsify within 12 hours. The wind was off-shore, (northerly), and successive surveillance flights showed that the oil was dispersing naturally. The emulsion proved to be unstable as by 5 May the slick had disappeared completely. Throughout the entire operation the French authorities were kept informed.

L.35   Following inspections by the classification society surveyor, the Salvage Master and the MPCU Operations Officer, DMEO (after consulting the District Chief Surveyor of the

Surveyor General's Organisation, now MSA) authorised the vessel to proceed towards Germany for repair.

ODIGITRIA B

L.36   The *ODIGITRIA B*, a Greek owned and Vanuatu registered vessel in transit from Germany to Turkey, suffered a generator failure leading to complete loss of power in the Dover Strait on the evening of Saturday 8 May 1993. She was carrying a cargo of scrap iron and also had 700 tonnes of heavy fuel oil bunkers.

L.37   The *ODIGITRIA B* anchored on the edge of the south west lane of the Traffic Separation Scheme at about 10 00 that night, and was reported as having only one very dim light showing. Dover Coastguard had her on radar, but from the time she anchored they were unable to raise her on VHF. Her owners in Greece could not be contacted by telephone.

L.38   The following day, DMEO arranged for a Marine Surveyor (from SGO, now MSA) to go out to the ship by RAF helicopter. After a short time on board the surveyor reported that the ship was unlikely to be able to move under her own power before nightfall. During that afternoon, contact was established with the owners who were persuaded to take the services of a tug which happened to be nearby. With assistance from the tug, the *ODIGITRIA B* showed lights that night but was still narrowly missed by another vessel.

L.39   At 14 00 on the following day, Monday 10 May, DMEO issued a Direction under Section 12 of the Prevention of Oil Pollution Act 1971 and sent it by facsimile to the owners in Greece. This Direction was to move the ship before 18 00 on Monday 10 May, either to continue her passage or to go to a safer anchorage, using a tow if necessary. During the four hours from the issue of the Direction to the deadline the owners gave repeated telephone assurances that the vessel would move soon, but they made no arrangements for a tow. The *ODIGITRIA B* finally left under her own power late on the evening of Monday 10 May, nearly five hours after the deadline.

L.40   DMEO had planned, if the ship had not moved herself, to order a tug to the scene at Government expense, and to try to recover the costs from the owners or their insurers.

L.41   The basic problem was that it is unsafe and unacceptable to have a vessel broken down and anchored in the Traffic Separation Scheme in the Dover Strait, particularly by night or in poor visibility. The risk of collision and subsequent risks to safety and the environment are too great: even when, as in this case, a broken down vessel is not a tanker the one which collides with her may be. In any event her bunkers were a pollution risk.

L.42   Communication with both the Master and the owners was at all times extremely difficult. Even when electrical power was restored to the ship the Master did not maintain a listening watch on VHF: indeed he appears to have gone to some trouble to contact his owner in such a way as to make it difficult for HM Coastguard to find out what was happening.

GRAN PIEDRA

L.43   The Cuban registered cargo ship *GRAN PIEDRA* was on passage from Riga to Cuba on 16 May 1993 when main diesel propulsion power was lost, leaving the vessel to drift in an area relatively near to the Isles of Scilly. She was carrying 587 tonnes of heavy fuel oil as bunkers and, although she was not in immediate danger of grounding, a tow to Falmouth was necessary in order to repair the engine.

L.44   The breakdown was due to poor quality fuel. Laboratory tests on the fuel indicated a disproportionate quantity of water and sodium associated with seawater contamination. The contaminated fuel caused rapid wear in the main engine, to such an extent that a major overhaul was necessary before the vessel could go back into service. The source of contamination was uncertain. Fuel tank air pipes were found to be in good condition and were of a standard type approved by classification societies. Water contamination from the sea during the voyage is a possibility, but the Master indicated that the deck area in the way of the air pipes had not shipped seas since the fuel was taken on board. Another possibility is that sea water was present in the fuel at the time of bunkering; this has been known or suspected on a number of occasions in the past.

L.45   *GRAN PIEDRA* was a classic example of a near miss. She drifted dangerously close to the Isles of Scilly, which was a lee shore, whilst trying to effect repairs. MPCU requested the Master to anchor immediately. Once she was anchored, the owners were reluctant to take a tug and MPCU had to pressure them into engaging one to tow the vessel into a safe haven for repair.

DANICA GREEN

L.46   On 18 May 1993 the *DANICA GREEN*, a small cargo ship registered in Denmark, was off Tiree when she listed 30° to port due to movement of cargo. Listing increased, reportedly to 60°, and the crew were taken off by helicopter. The vessel was bound from Bilbao towards Lerwick with a cargo of 466 tonnes of anchor cable and carried some 40 tonnes of diesel bunkers.

L.47   The vessel drifted for several hours with engines running slowly ahead in a south-easterly gale before the MOD salvage vessel *SALMOOR* was able to take her in tow off the island of Muck. The *DANICA GREEN* was taken to the shelter of Ockle Bay roughly 6 nautical miles to the east of Ardnamurchan Point where she was anchored overnight.

L.48   The following morning the Royal Navy took the vessel to the safe haven of Loch Na Beiste where her list was corrected and the vessel was handed back to her owners *in situ.*

ELOISA

L.49 On 8 July 1993, the *ELOISA*, a Spanish flagged chemical tanker, on passage from Algeciras in southern Spain to Purfleet on the Thames Estuary, suffered engine failure caused by a damaged crankshaft bearing. The vessel began to drift when she was 34 nautical miles south of Worthing. The 4,084 tonnes of liquid chemicals (toluene, xylene, cyclohexane and solvent naphtha) she was carrying were highly inflammable.

L.50 The vessel was anchored overnight whilst efforts were made to repair the engine. These were only partially successful and as she continued to remain a threat to other vessels the tug *FAIRPLAY XIV* towed her to a safe anchorage south of Shoreham, until repairs were carried out to enable her to complete her voyage successfully.

AVON

L.51 The *AVON*, a 78,943 dwt tanker owned by Wijsmullers and registered in St Vincent and Grenadines, was on passage under her own power from Southampton to the Far East for scrapping when she ran aground on 21 July at Browndown Beach within the limits of Portsmouth Harbour. She was in ballast but was carrying 1,800 tonnes of heavy fuel oil.

L.52 Grounding occurred owing to failure of the propeller pitch control system while the ship was weighing anchor; in addition, the pitch indicator was defective so that the failure was not immediately detected and there was a breakdown in communications between bridge and engine room. The problems were exacerbated by the fact that the vessel, having just been sold, had a completely new crew on board who had only just joined and were therefore not fully familiar with the ship.

L.53 The *AVON* was successfully refloated at 23 54 on 21 July with the assistance of five tugs and reanchored off Portsmouth. The vessel was surveyed before being allowed to proceed on her voyage.

PACIFIC MARCHIONESS

L.54 The *PACIFIC MARCHIONESS*, a 2,689 grt refrigerated cargo vessel registered in Cyprus and carrying a crew of 13, was carrying frozen fish from The Netherlands to West Africa when she suffered a complete electrical failure to the south west of the Needles (Isle of Wight) in the late evening of 29 May, resulting in the Coastguard losing all contact with the vessel.

L.55 The main engine shaft alternator tripped out possibly due to extreme voltage frequency variation. Subsequently, a main alternator was lost because of damage to its rectifiers. This was caused by placing a second alternator onto the switchboard with the main circuit breaker of the first still mistakenly closed. Further problems arose due to failure of the emergency first start arrangement.

L.56 There was considerable delay before the ship's managers in Hong Kong arranged tug assistance; eventually the tug *ANGLIAN WARRIOR* was sent and secured the tow at about 17 50 on 30 May. By this time the *PACIFIC MARCHIONESS* was 11 nautical miles to the south of Anvil Point. Both vessels arrived at Southampton at 10 41 on 31 May 1993.

ICE STAR

L.57 The *ICE STAR*, a 3,625 grt Danish registered refrigerated cargo vessel, fouled her propeller at 16 00 on 2 September. Weather conditions were wind force 6, northerly with good visibility.

L.58 *ICE STAR* passed within 1 nautical mile of the BP Magnus platform soon after starting to drift. If notified immediately the Coastguard could have organised towing arrangements during daylight hours but this was not done.

L.59 At 01 40 the following day HM Coastguard was first notified of the incident when the Marine Coordinator at Cormorant Alpha platform reported *ICE STAR* 120 nautical miles north east of Sumburgh, drifting towards the Eider platform. Sumburgh Coastguard helicopter was scrambled. At 03 30 *ICE STAR* passed 2 nautical miles west of the Eider platform, drifting towards the Shell Tern and North Cormorant platforms. Anchor handling tug *VIKING QUEEN* secured a line aboard *ICE STAR* at 04 35.

L.60 *ICE STAR*'s Master did not consider his vessel to be in distress. He did inform the platforms he passed of his situation, but he considered that it was not necessary to inform HM Coastguard. It did not agree.

L.61 Following this incident BP reiterated its procedure outlining action required in similar circumstances to the *ICE STAR* to all of their installations and standby vessels. The Danish Casualty Investigation and Supervision Board judged the Master to have had the situation under full control.

SAVA STAR

L.62 The Panamanian registered *SAVA STAR*, a 2,026 grt general cargo vessel, was bound from Norway to Immingham with a cargo of composite fertiliser. During the passage the cargo overheated and on Friday 8 October 1993, with the vessel approaching the Humber, a great deal of smoke was seen to be coming from the hold. Fumes were being blown towards the shore, and local inhabitants were advised by police to remain indoors with the doors and windows shut. The Master ordered his crew to remain in the ship's accommodation and navigated the ship from the bridge wearing breathing apparatus.

L.63 The tug *LADY STEPHANIE* proceeded to the vessel with salvage and fire crews and a chemist from the cargo consignees. The ship was brought to anchor off Spurn Head where the salvage team brought the incident under control by the afternoon of 9 October. The ship then berthed alongside at Immingham.

MATHRAKI

L.64   The Greek registered tanker *MATHRAKI*, with a cargo of some 24,500 tonnes of fuel oil, stranded in Larne Lough, Northern Ireland, at about 0400 on 23 August 1993. The ship was approaching her berth and was to be assisted by two tugs; however, the after tug was not made fast according to plan and the other tug was unable to control the ship on her own. The vessel grounded gently, was refloated on the afternoon tide and proceeded to her berth.

KANDALAKSHA

L.65   The *KANDALAKSHA*, a 2,581 grt Russian fish factory ship, grounded near Peterhead on 30 August 1993. She was inward bound, intending to anchor off the harbour entrance; the grounding was due to navigational error. The vessel had some 230 tonnes of bunkers (mainly diesel oil) on board some of which escaped into the sea as a result of damage caused by the grounding. She subsequently entered dry dock on the Tyne for repair and a small amount of pollution was caused by a further escape of oil during the operation of settling her in the dock. The dry dock owners claimed that they had not been informed of the pollution hazard. The incident ran for several weeks because the owners would not or could not pay for shoreside assistance and a diving survey.

NORMANDIE BRIDGE/EUROPEAN TIDEWAY

L.66   The *NORMANDIE BRIDGE*, a 48,235 grt Japanese owned and Liberian registered container ship, and the *EUROPEAN TIDEWAY*, a 8,583 grt British passenger and cargo roll-on, roll-off ferry, almost collided at 06 05 on 24 September within Harwich Harbour.

L.67   There was thick fog at the time and the vessels met on the eastern, in-bound, side of the fairway off the Landguard container terminal. The ferry was inward bound and the container ship was outward bound from a berth further up the harbour. *NORMANDIE BRIDGE*, with a pilot on board, had to make a turn to starboard off a shoal called The Shelf and failed to do so in time to keep position on the correct (western) side of the channel. There was no fault with the navigation of the ferry.

L.68   The pilot of the *NORMANDIE BRIDGE* was relatively inexperienced in handling large vessels in fog; in addition, evidence was given that she was rather sluggish and slow to turn, especially to starboard. To guard against a recurrence, it has been proposed that in fog, when there are in-bound vessels in the fairway, an out-bound vessel should not be given clearance to leave her berth without the authority of the Duty Senior VTS Officer; and that further training in "blind" pilotage should be given to pilots.

AZTEK/STELLAR HOPE

L.69 The *AZTEK*, a 1,599 grt Liberian oil/chemical tanker and the *STELLAR HOPE*, a 4,987 grt Panamanian chemical tanker, were in collision near the Channel Light-vessel on 31 October 1993. Damage was slight and both ships were able to proceed on passage.

L.70 Both vessels were west bound, *STELLAR HOPE* overtaking *AZTEK* and it is probable that the former failed to allow sufficient sea room. There was no pollution caused as a result of the incident.

AVERITY

L.71 The Bahamas registered *AVERITY*, a 1,144 grt motor tanker, carrying 1,690 tonnes of gas oil and 23 tonnes of heavy fuel bunkers, collided with a mooring dolphin after leaving the wharf at Coryton near Canvey Island on 5 November 1993. She was holed above the waterline in the vicinity of the engine room. Weather conditions were wind north easterly force 3, sea calm with visibility of half a mile.

L.72 Thames Coastguard alerted the Southend lifeboat and despatched a Coastguard response team to the area but SAR services were not required. *AVERITY* moored at Coryton without any evidence of pollution.

LUNOHODS-1

L.73 At 02 30 on 9 November the *LUNOHODS-1*, a 2,774 grt Latvian fish factory ship with 60 people on board, went aground on the south west coast of Bressay at the entrance to Lerwick Harbour, after weighing anchor and trying to clear the land in a southerly force 10 gale in heavy sea and swell. The fundamental cause of the foundering was the Master's delay in leaving the vessel's anchorage and proceeding to sea to ride out a period of severe weather. This delay was, in turn, a consequence of the vessel being very low on fuel oil. At the time of her loss she had sufficient fuel for only a few hours of main engine operation.

L.74 A major SAR operation was put into effect involving the Coastguard helicopter, a Sea-King helicopter from RAF Lossiemouth, a Norwegian helicopter from the Frigg Field and the local lifeboat. 56 people were winched from the vessel with considerable difficulty due to the atrocious weather conditions, a further three were rescued by the RNLI from life rafts and one from the base of the cliff by the Auxiliary Coastguard rescue team using cliff rescue gear. The helicopter crew which carried out the bulk of the rescue subsequently received the *Helicopter Aviation International* Crew of the Year Award 1992-93.

L.75 There were reports of limited pollution as the vessel was carrying an estimated 22 tonnes of diesel fuel oil, though only two tonnes were recovered. An MPCU aircraft surveyed the scene at first light and found no evidence of pollution.

BORODINSKOYE POLYE

L.76 On 15 November 1993 the *BORODINSKOYE POLYE*, a 3,983 grt Russian-flag fish factory vessel with 73 persons on board, anchored off the entrance to Dales Voe to the north of Lerwick Harbour. She was waiting to process fish from the local mackerel catch. At 22 00 hours on 17 November when the wind was from the south, force 9 (41 – 47 knots) the port anchor cable began to run out. The Master decided to weigh anchor and make for the open sea to ride out the storm. Whilst attempting to turn to starboard away from other vessels anchored on the port side, the vessel ran aground on The Unicorn shoal. She was pounded on the rocks by the heavy seas and sustained severe bottom damage.

L.77   All those on board were successfully taken off by the local lifeboat and Coastguard helicopter; there were no injuries. The coxswain of the lifeboat subsequently received the RNLI's bronze medal, and the other lifeboat men received bravery certificates. The ship had 968 tonnes of oil fuel on board, 575 tonnes of which were recovered in an operation carried out by the Marine Pollution Control Unit. There was some pollution but it was not considered to be serious.

L.78   By 2 February 1994 *BORODINSKOYE POLYE* was listing to 90° on her starboard side with most of the vessel under water. The vessel had broken up and was a total loss.

CRAIGMORE

L.79   Another incident involving contaminated fuel occurred on 28 November 1993 when the small British cargo ship *CRAIGMORE* bound from Arklow to London lost power in the English Channel. The vessel was not in immediate danger but had to be towed into Southampton by the anchor handling tug *ARCTIC NUTSUKPOK*.

GRAPE ONE

L.80   On 9 December 1993 the Italian registered chemical tanker *GRAPE ONE* broadcast a distress call. The vessel, with a cargo of 3,041 tonnes of xylene, had developed a severe list. All fifteen crew were rescued by helicopter.

L.81   The vessel capsized and sank in French waters, very close to the median line. No pollution was detected from the wreck.

SHERBRO

L.82   On 9 December 1993 the French registered vessel *SHERBRO* lost 88 containers in the vicinity of the Channel Islands. 10 containers contained hazardous materials, of which four posed a threat to the environment. The contents of these containers, a pesticide called Apron Plus, were washed ashore from Seine Bay to Germany over a three month period. No cargo was found on the UK coastline.

L.83   The total quantities of hazardous goods lost were; 7.2 tonnes of carbamate pesticide, 23 tonnes of nitrocellulose, 11 tonnes of sulphur and 19 tonnes of flammable liquid.

SEIKO

L.84 Whilst on passage to Ghent, Belgium from the North Sea on 9 December 1993, the *SEIKO* a 995 grt Greek owned and Panamanian registered tanker called Dover Coastguard with MAREP details. Due to suspension of pilotage because of weather conditions off the Belgian coast she had been unable to take on a pilot. The Master of *SEIKO*, whose command of English was almost non-existent, for some reason had elected to proceed along the south west traffic lane of the Dover Strait TSS. When he reached the vicinity of the South Falls Buoy, approximately 15 minutes after his initial call, the Master called Dover Coastguard again to state his intention to anchor.

L.85 The Master was advised not to anchor in the south west lane, particularly in the bottleneck of the South Falls area, and after saying that he held no chart for the area was given the coordinates for a recognised safe anchorage in The Downs (off Deal). The CNIS operator was then concerned to observe that *SEIKO* altered course directly to the coordinates given, which would probably have resulted in grounding on Goodwin Sands.

L.86 The Master was quickly advised to resume his previous course along the south west lane. The Coastguard thought it inadvisable to attempt to pilot the vessel "blind" into the Downs anchorage. The Master's lack of English hampered communications: extreme difficulty was experienced in trying to establish the identity of the owner of the vessel. In view of *SEIKO*'s unpredictability Dover Coastguard had decided that the best course of action was to persuade the Master to take a local pilot, through his owners/agents, in order to seek a safe anchorage.

L.87 Further negotiations by radio and telephone with the Master, the owners, and Wandelaar pilot station resulted in agreement that the Master would proceed to Wandelaar pilots who would find *SEIKO* a safe anchorage, even though the pilotage was still suspended. The Master was instructed to this effect by his owners via a link call through North Foreland Radio.

L.88 Dover Coastguard then advised the *SEIKO*'s Master of an appropriate course to steer from his position from the south west lane into the north east lane where he continued his passage to Wandelaar pilot station. His progress was continuously monitored through CNIS at Dover Coastguard.

L.89 This case illustrates how little knowledge some Masters have both of the hazards of the waters in which they sail and of the English needed for communication with the shore. The language difficulty would have made communications very difficult if Search and Rescue activity had been needed. This was a case where the Coastguard did give instructions in the way we recommend they should in Chapter 16: without those instructions, the incident could have had serious effects.

KAPITAN DZURASHEVICH

L.90 On 15 December the Russian registered general cargo vessel *KAPITAN DZURASHEVICH* anchored off Falmouth to correct a heavy list. The vessel had a cargo of

7,743 tonnes of rice bran and 4,467 tonnes of fluorospar in addition to 934 tonnes of bunkers. The list was eventually corrected by use of ship and shoreside labour and the vessel resumed passage to Avonmouth.

KONSTANTINE SAVALYEV

L.91 On 20 December the Russian registered general cargo vessel *KONSTANTINE SAVALYEV* anchored off the Island of Muck with steering failure. The vessel started to drag her anchor in severe gales and requested assistance. A tug was despatched from Londonderry to assist the rescue services. Following problems encountered in connecting and maintaining the tow, a second tug was despatched to replace the first. The tow eventually arrived in Belfast on 25 December.

Incidents during 1994

UNITED MIGHT/THALIA

L.92 At 04 18 on 25 January 1994, *UNITED MIGHT*, a general cargo ship of 10,204 grt registered in Malta, collided with the bulk carrier *THALIA* south west of Barry in the Bristol Channel. *UNITED MIGHT*, which was in ballast carrying 199 tonnes of heavy fuel oil and 44 tonnes of diesel oil, was manoeuvring out of her anchorage. *THALIA*, which was carrying a cargo of 27,500 tonnes of coal with 590 tonnes of heavy fuel oil and 71 tonnes of diesel oil on board, was at anchor. Weather conditions were wind west south west force 6-7 with poor visibility.

L.93 Both vessels reported slight damage to their bows above the waterline with no injuries to either crew and no sign of pollution.

SWAN ROCK

L.94 The Bahamas registered bulk carrier *SWAN ROCK*, in transit from Liverpool to Greece carrying a cargo of steel and scrap metal and with 513 tonnes of heavy fuel oil on board, reported a total engine failure at 03 35 on 26 January 1994 in weather conditions of wind force 8. This resulted in her drifting across the lanes of the Traffic Separation Scheme to the west of the Isles of Scilly. At 05 18 the same day the vessel reported that she was resuming passage as her main engines were now operational. This is a good case of the MARPOL requirement to report working satisfactorily.

VISHVA PARAG

L.95 At 02 46 on 28 January 1994 *VISHVA PARAG* a 12,810 grt Indian vessel with 56 crew and bunkers of 300 tonnes plus 100 tonnes of diesel, sent a distress signal south of Mumbles Head. This was because the cargo of steel plates had shifted and the vessel had apparently been holed on the starboard side below the waterline. Weather conditions were wind northerly force 5, moderate sea and swell with good visibility.

L.96 It was subsequently found that *VISHVA PARAG* was not holed externally. The shifted cargo breached a ballast tank which leaked internally. It was ballast water which the crew pumped out, and not sea water coming through the hull as they believed. This created a very dangerous situation in which the ship was unstable and could have capsized. It is relevant to note that a sister ship was lost with all hands in unexplained circumstances.

L.97 At 06 02 all but essential crew were evacuated by helicopter. A Swansea Port Pilot was placed on board the vessel which was then beached under controlled conditions approximately 1 mile north of Mumbles Head.

CORAL ACROPORA/NORSE LAGAN

L.98 At approximately 10 00 on 3 February the Netherlands Antilles registered roll-on, roll-off vessel *NORSE LAGAN*, carrying 84 passengers and 33 crew, attempted to berth at Victoria Terminal 2, Belfast on a journey from Liverpool. The weather conditions were wind east south east force 10. The *NORSE LAGAN* was blown into the gas carrier *CORAL ACROPORA* which was in the process of discharging her cargo of 2,100 tonnes of ammonia.

L.99 Tugs separated the two vessels. Neither vessel had suffered any damage and there was no evidence of pollution from either gas or bunker fuels.

L.100 This is another classic near miss. Had the ammonia tanks been breached a very dangerous situation would have been created, and not only for the crews involved. The easterly wind would have carried the resulting gas cloud into the centre of Belfast. An MPCU database model classes this incident as a potential disaster, which could have affected 42 square kilometres with a substance which is toxic to humans on inhalation.

ETILICO

L.101 At 16 35 on 23 February the Spanish registered container vessel *OOCL BRAVERY*, which was crossing the south west bound traffic lane of the Dover Strait, called Dover Coastguard to complain about the behaviour of the Spanish registered *ETILICO*, a 1,215 grt chemical tanker on passage from Hamburg to Spain. It is believed that she had a full cargo of acetone, a chemical with a low flash point. *ETILICO* had not given way as advised by the *COLREGS* and *OOCL BRAVERY* had to turn a complete circle to avoid a collision.

L.102 Around 16 45 *ETILICO* was identified and tagged on CNIS. It soon became clear that she was heading towards the Sandettié Bank and that if she continued on her course she would be in breach of the rules of the Deep Water Route and in some danger. HM Coastguard called *ETILICO* on VHF radio to establish whether her Watch Officer was aware of this fact. Though VHF communications were good, the standard of English of the Watch Officer on the ship was very poor. Basic nautical expressions such as "What is your position?" were not understood.

L.103　At 17 20 *ETILICO*'s radar echo merged with that of an unidentified vessel which was north east bound in the Deep Water Route. Although the Coastguards watching on CNIS were wrong in their initial fear that the vessels had collided, they estimated that the two vessels must have been less than 400 metres apart and the distance may have been less than 100 metres. The north east bound vessel did not report to the Coastguards, and they did not hear any call made to *ETILICO*.

L.104　Shortly afterwards the Master of *ETILICO* took over communications. It became clear that he was not where he thought he was. One possible explanation for this was that the ship's charts were out of date and that the Master mistook the "Inter Bank Buoy" for the Falls Light-vessel. Buoyage in this area was changed over two years ago when the Falls Light-vessel was removed.

L.105　Eventually the Master was persuaded that he was in the wrong lane of the Traffic Separation Scheme. He moved into the south west bound lane, nearly colliding with the F1 Buoy on the way. The Master subsequently crossed the Varne Bank, two hours before High Water.

L.106　MSA have taken up the case of the *ETILICO* with the Spanish authorities.

CITY OF LIMASSOL

L.107　On 2 March 1994, the Antiguan registered container ship *CITY OF LIMASSOL* (7,500 grt), carrying dangerous goods, was *en route* from Liverpool to Dublin when she broke down in the Off Skerries Traffic Separation Scheme. Her Master informed the Holyhead Coastguard, which informed a tug broker who in turn identified a tug which could go to her aid.

L.108　The Master subsequently informed HM Coastguard that he expected to be able to continue his voyage in about an hour. After that period the Coastguard called on VHF to check that all was well. It got no response, but obtained the ship's satellite telephone number from her agents and contacted the Master in that way, to discover that the ship had not moved because she was having difficulties in raising her anchor. The Coastguard remained in touch until the *CITY OF LIMASSOL* resumed her passage. It also notified the Irish Marine Emergency Service in Dublin in case of future problems with the vessel in their area.

L.109　In this incident the local Coastguard displayed good sense and initiative along precisely the lines we commend in this report.

Incidents outside UK waters

BRITISH TRENT/WESTERN WINNER

L.110　On the morning of 3 June 1993 the 25,100 dwt Bermudan registered tanker *BRITISH TRENT* and the 30,400 dwt Panamanian registered bulk carrier *WESTERN*

WINNER were in collision. The accident happened 9 miles off Ostend in Belgian waters where the visibility was severely reduced by fog. WESTERN WINNER, inward bound, was approaching the Pilot Station; BRITISH TRENT, outward bound, had just disembarked her pilot. BRITISH TRENT's tanks were ruptured and the escaping cargo set on fire; during the ensuing abandonment of the ship nine of the crew died. The tanker lost 3,600 tonnes of her cargo of unleaded petrol but there was no pollution. WESTERN WINNER suffered hull damage but no loss of life or injuries to her crew.

HOO ROBIN/BONNY

L.111   On 2 November 1993 HOO ROBIN, a 794 grt United Kingdom registered general cargo vessel, collided with BONNY, a 49,898 grt Bahamanian registered oil tanker, which was at anchor outside the port of Rotterdam. Fortunately, there were no injuries to personnel and no oil pollution. However, the accident had potentially very serious consequences.

L.112   The immediate cause of the collision was that the watchkeeper of HOO ROBIN, being the sole person on watch, fell asleep in the wheelhouse chair. HOO ROBIN's work pattern had allowed him little sleep in the previous two days and inadequate rest was a major contributory factor. However neither the Master nor the watchkeeper himself appreciated the extent to which the latter was fatigued and consequently the extent to which the safety of the vessel was jeopardised in allowing him to take the watch at that time.

OLYMPIC BREEZE

L.113   On 15 November 1993, while on passage from Kharg Island to Brofjorden in Sweden, the Greek oil tanker OLYMPIC BREEZE, laden with 260,000 tonnes of crude oil, suffered total electrical failure when some 170 miles north east of Great Yarmouth. The immediate cause of the failure was trivial: a fuse failed when crewman used a lift to the bridge. The lift motor failed as a result, and the main and emergency switchboards were shorted out. The weather was good and there was no immediate danger either to the vessel or the environment. Several tugs proceeded to stand by, but repairs were effected and the ship was able to proceed on passage though with escort vessels in company as a precaution.

L.114   This incident was, in the event, of no particular significance: but the vessel concerned was huge, her cargo large (nearly three times that of the BRAER) and her capacity to damage the environment was enormous. In another place, or in different weather conditions, a total electrical failure could have been disastrous.

LOF 1990

Appendix M

LLOYD'S

STANDARD FORM OF

SALVAGE AGREEMENT

(APPROVED AND PUBLISHED BY THE COUNCIL OF LLOYD'S)

NO CURE - NO PAY

On board the...

Dated......................................

+ See Note 1 above

IT IS HEREBY AGREED between Captain+...
for and on behalf of the Owners of the "..." her
cargo freight bunkers stores and any other property thereon (hereinafter collectively called "the Owners")
and...for and on behalf of...

* See Note 2 above

....(hereinafter called "the Contractor"*) that:-

1. (a) The Contractor shall use his best endeavours:-

See Note 3 above

    (i)   to salve the"..."and/or her cargo freight
    bunkers stores and any other property thereon and take them to #...or
    to such other place as may hereafter be agreed either place to be deemed a place of safety or if no
    such place is named or agreed to a place of safety and
    (ii) while performing the salvage services to prevent or minimize damage to the environment.

    (b) Subject to clause 2 incorporating Convention Article 14 the services shall be rendered and
    accepted as salvage services upon the principle of "no cure - no pay."

    (c) The Contractor's remuneration shall be fixed by Arbitration in London in the manner hereinafter
    prescribed and any other difference arising out of this Agreement or the operations thereunder shall
    be referred to Arbitration in the same way.

    (d) In the event of the services referred to in this Agreement or any part of such services having been
    already rendered at the date of this Agreement by the Contractor to the said vessel and/or her cargo
    freight bunkers stores and any other property thereon the provisions of this Agreement shall apply
    to such services.

    (e) The security to be provided to the Council of Lloyd's (hereinafter called "the Council") the Salved
    Value(s) the Award and/or any Interim Award(s) and/or any Award on Appeal shall be in

See Note 3 above

    #..currency.

    (f) If clause 1(e) is not completed then the security to be provided and the Salved Value(s) the Award
    and/or Interim Award(s) and/or Award on Appeal shall be in Pounds Sterling.

15.1.08
3.12.24
13.10.26
12.4.50
10.6.53
20.12.67
23.2.72
21.5.80
5.9.90

    (g) This Agreement and Arbitration thereunder shall except as otherwise expressly provided be
    governed by the law of England, including the English law of salvage.

PROVISIONS AS TO THE SERVICES

2. Articles 1(a) to (e), 8, 13.1, 13.2 first sentence, 13.3 and 14 of the International Convention on Salvage 1989 ("the Convention Articles") set out hereafter are hereby incorporated into this Agreement. The terms "Contractor" and "services"/"salvage services" in this Agreement shall have the same meanings as the terms "salvor(s)" and "salvage operation (s)" in the Convention Articles.

3. The Owners their Servants and Agents shall co-operate fully with the Contractor in and about the salvage including obtaining entry to the place named or the place of safety as defined in clause 1. The Contractor may make reasonable use of the vessel's machinery gear equipment anchors chains stores and other appurtenances during and for the purpose of the salvage services free of expense but shall not unnecessarily damage abandon or sacrifice the same or any property the subject of this Agreement.

PROVISIONS AS TO SECURITY

4. (a) The Contractor shall immediately after the termination of the services or sooner notify the Council and where practicable the Owners of the amount for which he demands security (inclusive of costs expenses and interest) from each of the respective Owners.

(b) Where the exception to the principle of "no cure - no pay" under Convention Article 14 becomes likely to be applicable the owners of the vessel shall on the demand of the Contractor provide security for the Contractor's special compensation.

(c) The amount of any such security shall be reasonable in the light of the knowledge available to the Contractor at the time when the demand is made. Unless otherwise agreed such security shall be provided (i) to the Council (ii) in a form approved by the Council and (iii) by persons firms or corporations either acceptable to the Contractor or resident in the United Kingdom and acceptable to the Council. The Council shall not be responsible for the sufficiency (whether in amount or otherwise) of any security which shall be provided nor for the default or insolvency of any person firm or corporation providing the same.

(d) The owners of the vessel their Servants and Agents shall use their best endeavours to ensure that the cargo owners provide their proportion of security before the cargo is released.

5. (a) Until security has been provided as aforesaid the Contractor shall have a maritime lien on the property salved for his remuneration. The property salved shall not without the consent in writing of the Contractor (which shall not be unreasonably withheld) be removed from the place to which it has been taken by the Contractor under clause 1(a).

(b) The Contractor shall not arrest or detain the property salved unless:-

(i) security is not provided within 14 days (exclusive of Saturdays and Sundays or other days observed as general holidays at Lloyd's) after the date of the termination of the services or

(ii) he has reason to believe that the removal of the property salved is contemplated contrary to clause 5(a) or

(iii) any attempt is made to remove the property salved contrary to clause 5(a).

(c) The Arbitrator appointed under clause 6 or the Appeal Arbitrator(s) appointed under clause 11(d) shall have power in their absolute discretion to include in the amount awarded to the Contractor the whole or part of any expenses reasonably incurred by the Contractor in:-

(i) ascertaining demanding and obtaining the amount of security reasonably required in accordance with clause 4

(ii) enforcing and/or protecting by insurance or otherwise or taking reasonable steps to enforce and/or protect his lien.

PROVISIONS AS TO ARBITRATION

6. (a) Where security is provided to the Council in whole or in part the Council shall appoint an Arbitrator in respect of the property covered by such security.

(b) Whether security has been provided or not the Council shall appoint an Arbitrator upon receipt of a written request made by letter telex facsimile or in any other permanent form provided that any party requesting such appointment shall if required by the Council undertake to pay the reasonable fees and expenses of the Council and/or any Arbitrator or Appeal Arbitrator(s).

(c) Where an Arbitrator has been appointed and the parties do not proceed to arbitration the Council may recover any fees costs and/or expenses which are outstanding and thereupon terminate the appointment of such Arbitrator.

7. The Contractor's remuneration shall be fixed by the Arbitrator appointed under clause 6. Such remuneration shall not be diminished by reason of the exception to the principle of 'no cure - no pay' under Convention Article 14.

REPRESENTATION

8. Any party to this Agreement who wishes to be heard or to adduce evidence shall nominate a person in the United Kingdom to represent him failing which the Arbitrator or Appeal Arbitrator(s) may proceed as if such party had renounced his right to be heard or adduce evidence.

CONDUCT OF THE ARBITRATION

9. (a) The Arbitrator shall have power to :-

    (i) admit such oral or documentary evidence or information as he may think fit

    (ii) conduct the Arbitration in such manner in all respects as he may think fit subject to such procedural rules as the Council may approve

    (iii) condemn the Contractor in his absolute discretion in the whole or part of the expense of providing excessive security and deduct the amount in which the Contractor is so condemned from the salvage remuneration and/or special compensation

    (iv) make Interim Award(s) on such terms as may be fair and just

    (v) make such orders as to costs fees and expenses including those of the Council charged under clauses 9(b) and 12(b) as may be fair and just.

(b) The Arbitrator and the Council may charge reasonable fees and expenses for their services whether the Arbitration proceeds to a hearing or not and all such fees and expenses shall be treated as part of the costs of the Arbitration.

(c) Any Award shall (subject to Appeal as provided in this Agreement) be final and binding on all the parties concerned whether they were represented at the Arbitration or not.

INTEREST

10. Interest at rates per annum to be fixed by the Arbitrator shall (subject to Appeal as provided in this Agreement) be payable on any sum awarded taking into account any sums already paid:-

    (i) from the date of termination of the services unless the Arbitrator shall in his absolute discretion otherwise decide until the date of publication by the Council of the Award and/or Interim Award(s) and

    (ii) from the expiration of 21 days (exclusive of Saturdays and Sundays or other days observed as general holidays at Lloyd's) after the date of publication by the Council of the Award and/or Interim Award(s) until the date payment is received by the Contractor or the Council both dates inclusive.

PROVISIONS AS TO APPEAL

11. (a) Notice of Appeal if any shall be given to the Council within 14 days (exclusive of Saturdays and Sundays or other days observed as general holidays at Lloyd's) after the date of the publication by the Council of the Award and/or Interim Award(s).

(b) Notice of Cross-Appeal if any shall be given to the Council within 14 days (exclusive of Saturdays and Sundays or other days observed as general holidays at Lloyd's) after notification by the Council to the parties of any Notice of Appeal. Such notification if sent by post shall be deemed received on the working day following the day of posting.

(c) Notice of Appeal or Cross-Appeal shall be given to the Council by letter telex facsimile or in any other permanent form.

(d) Upon receipt of Notice of Appeal the Council shall refer the Appeal to the hearing and determination of the Appeal Arbitrator(s) selected by it.

(e) If any Notice of Appeal or Cross-Appeal is withdrawn the Appeal hearing shall nevertheless proceed in respect of such Notice of Appeal or Cross-Appeal as may remain.

(f) Any Award on Appeal shall be final and binding on all the parties to that Appeal Arbitration whether they were represented either at the Arbitration or at the Appeal Arbitration or not.

CONDUCT OF THE APPEAL

12. (a) The Appeal Arbitrator(s) in addition to the powers of the Arbitrator under clauses 9(a) and 10 shall have power to :-

    (i)   admit the evidence which was before the Arbitrator together with the Arbitrator's notes and reasons for his Award and/or Interim Award(s) and any transcript of evidence and such additional evidence as he or they may think fit

    (ii)   confirm increase or reduce the sum awarded by the Arbitrator and to make such order as to the payment of interest on such sum as he or they may think fit

    (iii)   confirm revoke or vary any order and/or Declaratory Award made by the Arbitrator.

(b) The Appeal Arbitrator(s) and the Council may charge reasonable fees and expenses for their services in connection with the Appeal Arbitration whether it proceeds to a hearing or not and all such fees and expenses shall be treated as part of the costs of the Appeal Arbitration.

PROVISIONS AS TO PAYMENT

13. (a) In case of Arbitration if no Notice of Appeal be received by the Council in accordance with clause 11(a) the Council shall call upon the party or parties concerned to pay the amount awarded and in the event of non-payment shall subject to the Contractor first providing to the Council a satisfactory Undertaking to pay all the costs thereof realize or enforce the security and pay therefrom to the Contractor (whose receipt shall be a good discharge to it) the amount awarded to him together with interest if any. The Contractor shall reimburse the parties concerned to such extent as the Award is less than any sums paid on account or in respect of Interim Award(s).

(b) If Notice of Appeal be received by the Council in accordance with clause 11 it shall as soon as the Award on Appeal has been published by it call upon the party or parties concerned to pay the amount awarded and in the event of non-payment shall subject to the Contractor first providing to the Council a satisfactory Undertaking to pay all the costs thereof realize or enforce the security and pay therefrom to the Contractor (whose receipt shall be a good discharge to it) the amount awarded to him together with interest if any. The Contractor shall reimburse the parties concerned to such extent as the Award on Appeal is less than any sums paid on account or in respect of the Award or Interim Award(s).

(c) If any sum shall become payable to the Contractor as remuneration for his services and/or interest and/or costs as the result of an agreement made between the Contractor and the Owners or any of them the Council in the event of non-payment shall subject to the Contractor first providing to the Council a satisfactory Undertaking to pay all the costs thereof realize or enforce the security and pay therefrom to the Contractor (whose receipt shall be a good discharge to it) the said sum.

(d) If the Award and/or Interim Award(s) and/or Award on Appeal provides or provide that the costs of the Arbitration and/or of the Appeal Arbitration or any part of such costs shall be borne by the Contractor such costs may be deducted from the amount awarded or agreed before payment is made to the Contractor unless satisfactory security is provided by the Contractor for the payment of such costs.

(e) Without prejudice to the provisions of clause 4(c) the liability of the Council shall be limited in any event to the amount of security provided to it.

GENERAL PROVISIONS

14. The Master or other person signing this Agreement on behalf of the property to be salved enters into this Agreement as agent for the vessel her cargo freight bunkers stores and any other property thereon and the respective Owners thereof and binds each (but not the one for the other or himself personally) to the due performance thereof.

15. In considering what sums of money have been expended by the Contractor in rendering the services and/or in fixing the amount of the Award and/or Interim Award(s) and/or Award on Appeal the Arbitrator or Appeal Arbitrator(s) shall to such an extent and in so far as it may be fair and just in all the circumstances give effect to the consequences of any change or changes in the relevant rates of exchange which may have occurred between the date of termination of the services and the date on which the Award and/or Interim Award(s) and/or Award on Appeal is made.

16. Any Award notice authority order or other document signed by the Chairman of Lloyd's or any person authorised by the Council for the purpose shall be deemed to have been duly made or given by the Council and shall have the same force and effect in all respects as if it had been signed by every member of the Council.

17. The Contractor may claim salvage and enforce any Award or agreement made between the Contractor and the Owners against security provided under clause 4 if any in the name and on behalf of any Sub-Contractors Servants or Agents including Masters and members of the crews of vessels employed by him or by any Sub-Contractors in the services provided that he first provides a reasonably satisfactory indemnity to the Owners against all claims by or liabilities to the said persons.

18. When there is no longer any reasonable prospect of a useful result leading to a salvage reward in accordance with Convention Article 13 the owners of the vessel shall be entitled to terminate the services of the Contractor by giving notice to the Contractor in writing.

19. No person signing this Agreement or any party on whose behalf it is signed shall at any time or in any manner whatsoever offer provide make give or promise to provide demand or take any form of inducement for entering into this Agreement.

THE CONVENTION ARTICLES

Article 1

Definitions

    (a) *Salvage operation* means any act or activity undertaken to assist a vessel or any other property in danger in navigable waters or in any other waters whatsoever
    (b) *Vessel* means any ship or craft, or any structure capable of navigation
    (c) *Property* means any property not permanently and intentionally attached to the shoreline and includes freight at risk
    (d) *Damage to the environment* means substantial physical damage to human health or to marine life or resources in coastal or inland waters or areas adjacent thereto, caused by pollution, contamination, fire, explosion or similar major incidents
    (e) *Payment* means any reward, remuneration or compensation due under this Convention

Article 8

Duties of the Salvor and of the Owner and Master

1.   The salvor shall owe a duty to the owner of the vessel or other property in danger:

    (a) to carry out the salvage operations with due care;
    (b) in performing the duty specified in subparagraph (a), to exercise due care to prevent or minimize damage to the environment;
    (c) whenever circumstances reasonably require, to seek assistance from other salvors; and
    (d) to accept the intervention of other salvors when reasonably requested to do so by the owner or master of the vessel or other property in danger; provided however that the amount of his reward shall not be prejudiced should it be found that such a request was unreasonable

2.   The owner and master of the vessel or the owner of other property in danger shall owe a duty to the salvor:
    (a) to co-operate fully with him during the course of the salvage operations;
    (b) in so doing, to exercise due care to prevent or minimize damage to the environment; and
    (c) when the vessel or other property has been brought to a place of safety, to accept redelivery when reasonably requested by the salvor to do so

Article 13

Criteria for fixing the reward

1.   The reward shall be fixed with a view to encouraging salvage operations, taking into account the following criteria without regard to the order in which they are presented below:

    (a) the salved value of the vessel and other property;
    (b) the skill and efforts of the salvors in preventing or minimizing damage to the environment;
    (c) the measure of success obtained by the salvor;
    (d) the nature and degree of the danger;
    (e) the skill and efforts of the salvors in salving the vessel, other property and life;
    (f) the time used and expenses and losses incurred by the salvors;
    (g) the risk of liability and other risks run by the salvors or their equipment;

(h) the promptness of the services rendered;

(i) the availability and use of vessels or other equipment intended for salvage operations;

(j) the state of readiness and efficiency of the salvor's equipment and the value thereof

2. Payment of a reward fixed according to paragraph 1 shall be made by all of the vessel and other property interests in proportion to their respective salved values

3. The rewards, exclusive of any interest and recoverable legal costs that may be payable thereon, shall not exceed the salved value of the vessel and other property

Article 14

Special Compensation

1. If the salvor has carried out salvage operations in respect of a vessel which by itself or its cargo threatened damage to the environment and has failed to earn a reward under Article 13 at least equivalent to the special compensation assessable in accordance with this Article, he shall be entitled to special compensation from the owner of that vessel equivalent to his expenses as herein defined

2. If, in the circumstances set out in paragraph 1, the salvor by his salvage operations has prevented or minimized damage to the environment, the special compensation payable by the owner to the salvor under paragraph 1 may be increased up to a maximum of 30% of the expenses incurred by the salvor. However, the Tribunal, if it deems it fair and just to do so and bearing in mind the relevant criteria set out in Article 13, paragraph 1, may increase such special compensation further, but in no event shall the total increase be more than 100% of the expenses incurred by the salvor

3. Salvor's expenses for the purpose of paragraphs 1 and 2 means the out-of-pocket expenses reasonably incurred by the salvor in the salvage operation and a fair rate for equipment and personnel actually and reasonably used in the salvage operation, taking into consideration the criteria set out in Article 13, paragraph 1(h), (i) and(j)

4. The total special compensation under this Article shall be paid only if and to the extent that such compensation is greater than any reward recoverable by the salvor under Article 13

5. If the salvor has been negligent and has thereby failed to prevent or minimize damage to the environment, he may be deprived of the whole or part of any special compensation due under this Article

6. Nothing in this Article shall affect any right of recourse on the part of the owner of the vessel

For and on behalf of the Contractor	For and on behalf of the Owners of property to be salved.
....	....
(To be signed either by the Contractor personally or by the Master of the salving vessel or other person whose name is inserted in line 4 of this Agreement.)	(To be signed by the Master or other person whose name is inserted in line 1 of this Agreement.)

Appendix N

Australian Maritime Safety Authority (AMSA)

N.1   Until the end of 1990, the Commonwealth of Australia's functions relating to shipping and navigation were carried out by a division of the Department of Transport and Communications. On 1 January 1991 AMSA took over responsibility for the following Commonwealth functions:

(a)   survey and certification of Australian ships;

(b)   safety standards, control of foreign ships in Australia and the safe handling and carriage of sea-borne cargo;

(c)   seafarers' qualifications;

(d)   marine aids to navigation and navigation safety;

(e)   marine search and rescue and operation of the Australian Ship Reporting System;

(f)   the Commonwealth's role in sea safety education;

(g)   the Commonwealth's role in combating marine pollution;

(h)   ship registration; and

(i)   operation of the national seamen's engagement system.

N.2   The only operational marine function not transferred to AMSA was the marine accident investigation function, which remains in the Department of Transport and Communications and which can monitor AMSA operations that impact on marine safety in the context of accident investigation.

N.3   The UK Marine Accident Investigation Branch is similarly organisationally quite separate from both MSA and COASTGUARD.

N.4   AMSA has about 480 employees. 160 work in the head office in Canberra with the remainder based at locations around the coast of Australia, mainly at the major ports.

N.5   The operating expenses of AMSA in the financial year 1992-93 were about A$63 million. Some two-thirds of its revenue – A$45 million – came from the shipping industry as user of its services. The other third – about A$18 million – was funded by the Australian Government to meet "public service obligations", mainly search and rescue and communications.

Functions, funding and UK equivalents

Navigational Services

N.6   AMSA manages a network of national aids to meet the needs of commercial shipping for efficient navigation, including 284 unattended light stations, 21 attended light stations, two light vessels and a variety of buoys, beacons and auxiliary aids.

N.7   The Marine Navigation Levy – once known as "Light Dues" – is a levy on all commercial ships visiting Australian ports or operating on the Australian coast. It is calculated on the net tonnage of the ship and the rate per ton decreases as the ship increases in size. It is collected to finance the operation of the aids to navigation system around the coast. In the two years since AMSA started, the charges on industry imposed through this levy has been reduced by 25 per cent, due primarily to the improvements in efficiency that have been achieved in this period. The revenue from this levy in 1992-93 was A$34.6 million.

N.8   **The UK equivalent is the General Lighthouse Fund which finances the three General Lighthouse Authorities. Light dues are charged on vessels calling at UK ports: the system is described in paragraph 22.11.**

Ship and Personnel Safety Services

N.9   AMSA is responsible for developing and administering regulations and safety standards applying to commercial ships in Australian waters, and for providing maritime survey services. AMSA also administers the international maritime safety Conventions and ship-related aspects of pollution prevention Conventions. AMSA staff usually represent the Commonwealth Government in IMO activities and in other relevant international bodies.

N.10   General "policing" activities, provision of policy support to the Government and preparation, review and promulgation of legislation were, until recently, funded from taxation. The Australian Government decided that the costs of these activities ought to be met by the industry that gives rise to their necessity. It has therefore phased in, over a three year period, a new levy on ships visiting Australian ports or operating on the Australian coast. Among other things, the levy funds AMSA's Port State Control and IMO activities. From July 1993, receipts from the levy – called the Regulatory Functions Levy – have totally replaced budget funding for these functions. In 1993-94 the levy is expected to raise some A$7 million.

N.11   **In the UK, all these functions are funded through taxation, except that charges are made for some Port State Control inspections in the way described in 11.34.**

Surveying

N.12   Although most major hull and load line surveys in Australia are undertaken, under AMSA authority, by the more reputable classification societies, AMSA does carry out equipment surveys on Australian registered ships and is prepared to carry out hull and load line surveys if requested. These are charged for at normal commercial rates. A number of other statutory services are similarly charged for, such as the issue of marine qualifications and the approval of ship stability criteria. The total of fees charged in 1992-93 was A$2.7 million.

N.13 The UK funds survey and certification work from fees which are designed to cover full costs but which are not fully commercial.

Marine Environment Protection Services

N.14   In cooperation with State authorities and the oil and shipping industries, AMSA plans Australia's response to the threat of marine pollution from shipping. A key element in Australia's response capability is the National Plan to Combat Pollution of the Sea by Oil. This is a cooperative effort by Federal and State/Territory Governments, with the assistance of industry, funded by an oil pollution levy on ships. AMSA is the managing agency for the National Plan.

N.15   The National Plan is funded by a levy on ships, charged quarterly on all ships carrying 10 tonnes or more of oil, including bunkers. Since its inception, the National Plan has acquired equipment at a replacement cost in excess of A$13 million to respond to oil spills from ships. It also provides an integrated national system of training to Commonwealth State/Territory, port and industry personnel. In 1992-93 the levy amounted to A$1.8 million. The levy was increased on 1 October 1993 to meet costs for a new equipment acquisition programme and other initiatives of the recent review of the National Plan. Anticipated revenue in 1993-94 is A$3.5 million.

N.16 The UK equivalent is wholly funded through taxation.

Maritime Safety Services

N.17   AMSA operates the Australian Maritime Rescue Coordination Centre (MRCC), which is responsible for coordinating maritime search and rescue over an area of some 47 million square kilometres – about one-ninth of the earth's surface. In this role it cooperates closely with international search and rescue authorities. In addition, AMSA provides safety radio services under GMDSS, including the promulgation of warnings to navigators.

N.18   The SOLAS Convention requires Governments to provide distress and safety communications to ships free of charge. The funds required to provide such a service are therefore met by the Government through taxation and paid to AMSA as specific payments under a service agreement. The cost of maritime search and rescue is also treated this way. The total sums provided for these activities in 1992-93 was A$14.7 million.

N.19 The UK similarly funds both services wholly from taxation.

Ship registration and crew records

N.20   AMSA has responsibility for ship registration (a legal title service). There are about 7,200 ships on the Australian register, of which over 4,000 are recreational vessels and about 2,000 are fishing vessels. A charge is made for the registration of a ship, and separate charges are made for subsequent transactions. Registration does not have to be renewed at regular intervals – the level of charges is set to recover the costs of administration of the register and national registration charges are not used as a method of raising general revenue. The total in 1992-93 was A\$0.5 million.

N.21   AMSA also provides, as a commercial service, certain crew employment services to the Australian maritime industry. AMSA is currently contracted to the major Australian shipowners to administer a roster system for the employment of ratings on Australian ships. AMSA also maintains sea-service records for Australian seafarers, and provides information from those records at charges that recoup costs: the total in 1992-93 was A\$1.6 million.

N.22   **The UK's Registry of Shipping and Seamen, which is part of MSA, makes charges for registering merchant ships, pleasure craft and fishing vessels. A separate charge is made for subsequent transactions; registration is renewable every five years. The level of charges is set to recover registration costs of some £0.5 million a year. The registry also maintains crew and other seafarer records. British officer certificates of competence are revalidated every five years.**

Appendix O

Interim recommendation on Fair Isle Channel

Lord Donaldson's Inquiry
Chairman: The Rt Hon The Lord Donaldson of Lymington

26-28 Old Queen Street
LONDON SW1H 9HP

The Rt Hon John MacGregor MP   27 May 1993
Secretary of State for Transport
2 Marsham Street
London SW1

Dear Secretary of State

When the Inquiry took formal evidence in Lerwick last week, we were pressed very strongly to submit an interim recommendation to you requesting immediate and permanent radar coverage of the Fair Isle Strait. It was put to us that Shetland was in a special position because of the numbers of hazardous cargoes moved around its shores, the exceptionally stormy weather and the economic dependence of the islands on the sea.

I explained at the time that I was keen to ensure that our recommendations form a coherent package, and that interim recommendations could make that difficult, as our overall views are obviously still unformed. I also explained that radar coverage is by itself of little use in wide and comparatively little trafficked waters such as the Fair Isle Strait, and that there is no evidence to suggest that radar coverage could help prevent most of the pollution which arises from marine casualties, including the grounding of the BRAER. While we have great sympathy with the desire in Shetland to see protection against the possibility of another grounding in place before next winter, we are not convinced that radar coverage of the Strait is the answer.

For these reasons I do not propose to submit such an interim recommendation.

We do however need to consider whether an extension of radar coverage or of routeing measures should be included in our final recommendations, and here we are hampered by a lack of knowledge. No one knows the density of traffic through the Strait and estimates are in their very nature little more than informed guesses. We believe it would help our Inquiry, and perhaps relieve anxieties in Shetland, if solid information could be made available.

The Defence Research Agency are already under contract to the Shetland Islands Council to visit the islands in June to establish a suitable site for radar at Fitful Head in southern Shetland, and to keep radar watch there for 48 hours, as part of a wider contract to establish suitable radar sites for the Sullom Voe port operations.

I understand that although it is not in their contract, DRA intend using their powerful optical equipment to identify individual vessels when weather conditions permit during their normal working hours. I also understand that the radar picture will be recorded 24 hours a day and that it should prove possible to deduce a considerable amount of information about shipping patterns from the size of the radar echoes and the speed and direction of vessels.

We believe that it would be useful to the Inquiry and to your Department if the coverage at Fitful Head could be extended on the same basis from 2 to 7 days, to get a clearer estimate of traffic through the Strait, and that it would be reasonable for your Department to pay the marginal costs of this extension. As the DRA will be leaving for Shetland next week, an urgent decision is required.

We have considered whether it would be useful to undertake similar surveys elsewhere around the coast. I established during our hearings in Inverness that the owners of Fair Isle, the National Trust for Scotland, would be happy to cooperate with a survey there but I understand this is impracticable for technical reasons. There may be a case for a survey from North Ronaldsay (Orkney), but such a survey might not produce useful information beyond that obtainable from Fitful Head: it would be prudent to assess that information first. There is no need for a survey in the Pentland Firth which is monitored by the harbour authority at Scapa.

There may also be a case for monitoring in the Minch and the Deep Water Route to the west of the Outer Hebrides. However, more information exists on the Minch than on the Fair Isle Strait, with a radar count of traffic in the Minch in 1983 and an identification survey of traffic in the Minch and in the Deep Water Route in 1989. The voluntary reporting system instituted by the local authorities and your Department is also beginning to provide useful information. In the circumstances we believe that it would be premature to carry out an immediate radar survey of the Minch or the DWR, though it might be useful to carry out such a survey in the light of the exercise at Fitful Head.

I am copying this letter to the Convenor of the Shetland Islands Council and to Jim Wallace MP. In view of the need for an urgent decision I am also arranging for a copy to be sent by fax to the Head of your Marine Directorate.

Yours sincerely

John Donaldson

DONALDSON OF LYMINGTON

Appendix P

Interim Recommendation on the Salvage Convention and the 1992 Protocols to the 1969 Civil Liability Convention and the 1971 Fund Convention

Lord Donaldson's Inquiry
Chairman: The Rt Hon The Lord Donaldson of Lymington

26-28 Old Queen Street
LONDON SW1H 9HP

The Rt Hon John MacGregor MP   10 June 1993
Secretary of State for Transport
2 Marsham Street
London SW1

Dear Secretary of State

One recurring theme in evidence put to the Inquiry is that the UK Government should ratify the 1992 Protocols to the 1969 Civil Liability Convention and the 1971 Fund Convention as soon as possible, and should encourage other States to do the same.

My understanding is that the Government are keen to do just this, but that you need to introduce primary legislation to Parliament. In the circumstances you might like to be aware now that the Inquiry entirely agree that the Protocols should be ratified soon. Our recommendations will include one to the effect that legislation should be enacted as quickly as possible so that the UK is in a position to persuade other States to ratify the Protocols and bring them into force.

We are even more concerned that the Government has not ratified the Salvage Convention 1989. It has been pointed out to us that a decision in the Court of Appeal in 1990 means that a Master of a vessel in difficulties cannot commit the owners of its cargo to salvage terms if he has the opportunity to consult them. This is likely to lead to a waste of valuable time in a potentially polluting incident. Ratification of the Convention would give the Master clear authority to commit the cargo owner. We believe, and will say in our report, that it is essential in the interests of reducing the chances of future pollution that the Government ratifies the Convention as quickly as possible.

Yours sincerely

John Donaldson

DONALDSON OF LYMINGTON

Appendix Q

Recommendations in the Reports by UK and Liberian Investigators into the Grounding of MV *BRAER*

Standards of Training, Certification and Watchkeeping Convention (STCW)

Q.1   The Chief Inspector of Marine Accidents, United Kingdom, recommended

> *1.   The Marine Directorate of the Department of Transport should, through the International Maritime Organization (IMO), seek to ensure that the revision and strengthening of the Standards of Training, Certification and Watchkeeping Convention (STCW), now in hand under an accelerated procedure, lays stress on the need for practical experience, training and thorough assessment of competence in seamanship in the widest sense of the term. Flag States accepting the certificates of other Administrations should take care to ensure that these matters have been properly addressed.*

The UK Government responded

> *A review of the Standards of Training, Certification and Watchkeeping Convention (STCW) is under way at the International Maritime Organization by means of an accelerated procedure using consultants to inform the debate. The review is looking specifically at means of fully defining on board competence and setting appropriate standards that will enable proper training in all aspects of seamanship in its widest sense. The Department will continue to play a full part in this review.*

The Investigating Officer, Republic of Liberia, recommended

> *3.   That IMO STW investigate the necessity and implementation of simulated training in decision making and prioritising for seafarers.*

We agree with both recommendations and welcome the UK Government's response. Our discussion of the STCW Convention is in paragraphs 8.24 - 8.26, and our discussion of the international system of validation of certificates is in paragraphs 8.27 - 8.28.

The International Safety Management (ISM) Code

Q.2   The Chief Inspector of Marine Accidents, United Kingdom, recommended

> *2.   The provisions of the International Management Code for the Safe Operation of Ships and for Pollution Prevention (the International Safety Management (ISM) Code) recently adopted by the International Maritime Organization (IMO) should be implemented by the shore management of shipping companies as a matter of urgency before they become mandatory. The International Chamber of Shipping (ICS) and the International Shipping Federation (ISF), who have published guidelines on the application of the Code, should encourage implementation by their members by every means possible.*

As we record in paragraph 8.10, **we agree** with this recommendation.

Standards of seamanship

Q.3   The Investigating Officer, Republic of Liberia, recommended

> *7.   The general practice of seamanship must continue to be emphasised, especially the stowage and securing of items on deck. Regular sounding of oil tanks to be taken especially before and after transfer of tank contents.*

We agree. We refer frequently (and especially in Chapter 8) to the need for high standards of seamanship and ship operations generally and possible means of improving standards.

Anchors

Q.4   The Chief Inspector of Marine Accidents, United Kingdom, recommended

> *3.   The Marine Directorate of the Department of Transport should undertake research on the feasibility of methods enabling the controlled and safe lowering of the anchors from the housed position into deep water to the full scope of the anchor cables and without the need for power. If any methods are considered feasible a requirement for fitting them should be pursued through the International Maritime Organization (IMO).*

The UK Government responded

> *A good deal of research, some of it part funded by the Department, into improved anchor handling equipment has already been undertaken. Research into the design of anchoring systems to stop and anchor a large ship was also undertaken following the stranding of the AMOCO CADIZ in 1979. The Department therefore proposes to establish what has been undertaken, worldwide, and whether further research on the feasibility of methods enabling the controlled and safe lowering of anchors from the housed position without the use of power needs to be undertaken.*

We broadly agree with the recommendation, subject to an assessment of the costs and benefits of any feasible systems, and accept the approach being taken by the UK Government. We discuss anchoring systems in paragraphs 7.91 - 7.96.

Fuel tank venting

Q.5   The Investigating Officer, Republic of Liberia, recommended

> *8.   Investigate whether each tank should have separate vent pipes.*

> *10.   The recommendations contained in Liberian Services Inc. Memo of 6 May 1993, "RECOMMENDATION ON FUEL TANK VENTING" ... should be considered as the basis for Liberian requirements.*

Whilst we do not disagree, we do not discuss this issue, which is specific to the *BRAER* accident investigation and which does not raise issues of broad principle.

Battery powered position fixing equipment

Q.6   The Investigating Officer, Republic of Liberia, recommended

6.   Consideration should be given to the requirement for vessels having on board battery powered GPS or SATNAV in order to be able to easily fix vessel position and drift when vessel is without electrical power.

We agree with this recommendation and believe that the UK Government should support it (paragraph 13.51).

Emergency Towing Equipment for Tankers and the Load Line Convention 1966

Q.7   The Chief Inspector of Marine Accidents, United Kingdom, recommended

4.   The Marine Directorate of the Department of Transport should, through the International Maritime Organization (IMO), seek to ensure, that the revision of Resolution A.535(13) (Provision of Emergency Towing Equipment for Tankers) currently underway also incorporates provisions for safe access to the anchors from the after superstructure of tankers. The Maritime Safety Committee of IMO should be urged to give urgent priority to the completion of the review and revision of the Resolution, with a view to making the requirements mandatory by an amendment to Chapter V of the 1974 SOLAS Convention.

The UK Government responded

The revision of IMO Resolution A.535(13) - Provision for emergency towing equipment for tankers will be finalised at the IMO Sub-Committee on Ship Design and Equipment when it meets in February. The Department has put a UK paper to the Sub-Committee asking it to incorporate provisions for safe access to the bow from the after superstructure of tankers.

The Investigating Officer, Republic of Liberia, recommended

1.   Emergency towing equipment as by IMO Resolution A.535(13) should be considered for all tankers of 20,000 DWT and above.

2.   IMO to investigate whether sufficient attention is being given to Regulation 25 of 1966 Loadline Convention with regard to safe access for the crew to, for example, the fo'c'stle of tankers.

We broadly agree with these recommendations. We discuss emergency towing attachments for tankers and the issue of safe access in paragraphs 7.91 - 7.96.

Requests for towage assistance

Q.8   The Chief Inspector of Marine Accidents, United Kingdom, recommended

5.   The Marine Directorate of the Department of Transport should ensure that HM Coastguard, on receipt of a request for towage assistance from any vessel carrying petroleum or dangerous cargo, relay and promulgate the request immediately by all means of communication. This action should be taken whether or not the vessel has declared an Urgency situation.

The UK Government responded

This recommendation is accepted and new guidelines have been issued to HM Coastguard accordingly.

The Investigating Officer, Republic of Liberia, recommended

5.   That rescue/anti-pollution organisations are made aware of tugs or similar vessels that are available in their area and their state of readiness.

We agree with these recommendations and welcome the UK Government's response. As we make clear in Chapter 20, where we discuss the role of HM Coastguard in emergencies of this nature, we are in no doubt that they should give every possible assistance, short of attempting to guide the route of a vessel from shore or acting as free agents.

Delegation of intervention powers

Q.9   The Chief Inspector of Marine Accidents, United Kingdom, recommended

6.   The Marine Directorate of the Department of Transport should take the necessary steps to allow the intervention powers of the Secretary of State for Transport under the Prevention of Oil Pollution Act 1971, which are delegated to the Director Marine Emergencies Organisation (DMEO) alone, to be delegated further. This should be two-fold. Firstly they should be delegated to the DMEO's deputy to allow for circumstances when the DMEO is not available. Secondly the DMEO, or in his absence his deputy, should be able to delegate the powers to a senior officer of the Department of Transport located in the area of the incident when local knowledge might result in a faster response to the emergency.

The UK Government responded

The recommendation that the Secretary of State's intervention powers should be delegated to the DMEO's deputy is accepted. The recommendation that the DMEO, or in his absence his deputy, should be able to delegate the powers to a senior officer of the Department located in the area of the incident is accepted in principle subject to defining the precise extent of the delegation, the circumstances in which it might be used and the training needed by those who might exercise it.

We agree with the recommendation and welcome the response which, as we record in 20.24, has been implemented. The intervention powers and the new arrangements are described in Appendix J. We discuss their use in Chapter 20.

Contingency planning for emergencies - effects of tides and weather

Q.10   The Investigating Officer, Republic of Liberia, recommended

4.   That Coastal States investigate the preparedness of organisations, similar to HM Coastguard, to anticipate actions of disabled vessels in their area with particular reference to the effect of tide and weather on the vessel.

We believe that there is more than one way of interpreting this recommendation. We expect contingency plans to take local experience into account, but are doubtful on whether further detailed studies would add significantly to useful information.

Peril at Sea and Salvage

Q.11   The Investigating Officer, Republic of Liberia, recommended

9.   *That ICS/OCIMF publication "Peril at Sea and Salvage" should be carried aboard all Liberian vessels.*

We make a similar recommendation in paragraph 20.50.

Index

507

516

Printed in the United Kingdom for HMSO
Dd 5062336   5/94   C5   65536   3398/4   Ord 284375   02/28988